Heterogeneous Catalysis in Industrial Practice

G000165645

Other McGraw-Hill Chemical Engineering Books of Interest

Heterogeneous Catalysis in Industrial Practice

Charles N. Satterfield
Professor of Chemical Engineering
Massachusetts Institute of Technology
Cambridge, Massachusetts

Second Edition

McGraw-Hill, Inc.

New York St. Louis San Francisco Auckland Bogotá
Caracas Hamburg Lisbon London Madrid
Mexico Milan Montreal New Delhi Paris
San Juan São Paulo Singapore
Sydney Tokyo Toronto

Library of Congress Cataloging-in-Publication Data

Satterfield, Charles N.
  Heterogeneous catalysis in industrial practice / Charles N.
  Satterfield.—2nd ed.
    p. cm.
  Includes bibliographical references and index.
  ISBN 0-07-054886-2
  1. Heterogeneous catalysis.   I. Title.
TP 156.C35S27   1991   90–19795
660'.2995—dc20   CIP

1 2 3 4 5 6 7 8 9 0 DOC/DOC 9 7 6 5 4 3 2 1

ISBN 0-07-054886-2

The sponsoring editor for this book was Gail F. Nalven, the editing
supervisor was Fred Dahl, and the production supervisor was Pamela
A. Pelton. This book was set in Century Schoolbook by McGraw-Hill's
Professional Publishing composition unit.

Printed and bound by R. R. Donnelley & Sons Company.

Contents

Preface

Since publication of the first edition in 1980, the underlying purpose of this book remains unchanged, but its contents have been brought up to date in a variety of ways to respond to the developments of the past decade. All the chapters have undergone scrutiny and revision, but the major changes are found in Chapter 5 on physical characterization, in Chapter 7 on acid and zeolite catalysts, in Chapter 8 on catalytic oxidation, in Chapter 9 on processing of petroleum and hydrocarbons, and in Chapter 10 on synthesis gas and associated processes. Some theoretical concepts of lesser significance have been condensed or discarded, and newer theories and possible mechanisms supported by evidence have been introduced. The resulting volume is a useful current reference for professionals with a variety of backgrounds who are concerned with some aspect of catalysis and heterogeneous catalysts.

Since 1980, applications of solid catalysts have continued to expand, spurred especially by growing concerns for the environment, by the continuing evolution of fossil fuel processing, and by the ever present goal of new and improved processes for chemical manufacture. Modern instrumental techniques have undergone rapid gains in providing an understanding of catalyst surface structure and interactions of adsorbed species with surfaces. The improved characterization of the complex structures of practical catalysts and correlation with performance has proceeded apace. This has been aided by major advances in analytical techniques, the use of automated experimental equipment, and data reduction by sophisticated computer methods. The goal of practical catalyst design on a rational and an a priori basis continues to beckon and is steadily being approached.

An author is indebted to countless individuals in ways that are frequently difficult to recognize and to acknowledge explicitly. The first edition was the outgrowth of class notes that I wrote for use in a subject in catalysis, directed primarily to seniors and first-year graduate students in chemical engineering, and further tested in intensive courses in industry. Since then I have continued to learn from the opportunity to engage in a wide variety of problems involving catalysts, both in the plant and in the laboratory. As with the first edition, I am indebted to Craig Abernethy for his careful typing and editing of the manuscript and to Claire Chanenchuk, one of my current doctoral thesis students, for providing a meticulous perspective on the contents. Again I wish to express my special gratitude to my wife Anne, for help in a variety of ways.

Charles N. Satterfield

Preface to the First Edition

Studies of solid catalysts and reactions catalyzed by solids have burgeoned in recent years, stimulated by an increasing number and variety of applications in industry. Significant contributions have come from individuals or groups whose formal academic education was in one or more of a wide variety of disciplines: these have ranged over the entire field of chemistry (including organic chemistry, inorganic chemistry, physical chemistry, chemical kinetics, and surface chemistry) to solid-state and surface physics, ceramics, physical metallurgy, and chemical reaction engineering.

One's first impression, which may be reinforced by further study, is apt to be that it is a vast and confusing field replete with an enormous quantity of perhaps significant but empirical facts intermixed with perhaps useful theories. The situation is not surprising when one reflects that heterogeneous catalysis in practice is concerned with controlling the rate and direction of a chemical reaction or group of reactions, whose basic mechanism is frequently understood only in broad outline; by means of a complex solid substance, typically rather poorly characterized, selected from one or more of the many elements of the periodic table.

In such a situation there is the need for an overview of the landscape to identify features that provide orientation. This book has been written for chemists, chemical engineers, and others who seek such an overview, and especially for those who have had little previous exposure to heterogeneous catalysis and would like an introduction to the subject. The term "industrial practice" in the title is to warn the reader that attention is devoted primarily to catalysts and reactions that are of industrial significance for large-scale operations and utilized under practicable conditions of pressure, temperature, and contact time, often processing impure reactants or mixtures. At present, theoretical concepts are the most successful in interpretation of the reactions of small molecules such as hydrogen, carbon monoxide, oxygen, and nitrogen on well-characterized surfaces. In the present volume, theory has not been neglected, but the attention devoted to various theoretical concepts is in some proportion to those that have stood the test of time and also seem to be of present practical importance or of some value for prediction for those reactions of industrial interest. Properly applied and with appreciation for their limitations, these various correlations, hypotheses, and theories can be a useful guide for effectively employing knowledge, past experience, and intuition.

This book is intended to provide a comprehensive introduction to the kinds of information that one needs to know in order to work with solid catalysts in the laboratory, pilot plant, or commercial installations. For those concerned with chemical reaction engineering it may provide some perspective on the chemical aspects that must be considered in reactor design in addition to the mathematical aspects treated in numerous texts. In this respect the present volume can be useful as a text or reference.

To some degree, the value of an introductory treatment such as this may be inversely proportional to its size, and therefore it has been attempted, at the risk of oversimplification, to reduce each topic to its essentials. It is hoped that readers may find the balance appropriate and useful for their needs. Because of their rather specialized nature, polymerization reactions, photochemical and electrochemical catalysis, and electrocatalysis have not been considered. Experience has shown that many laboratory studies of practical catalysts are vitiated by inadequate experimental procedures, and especially by lack of recognition of the possible effects of mass- and heat-transfer gradients. Some suggestions on design of experiments and warning signals to look for in analyzing data are made in the last chapter.

Chapter

1

Introduction and Basic Concepts

1.1 Introduction

The concept of catalysis as a method of controlling the rate and direction of a chemical reaction has captured the imagination of scientists and technologists since Berzelius in 1835 coordinated a number of disparate observations on chemical transformations by attributing them to a "catalytic force" and coined the term *catalysis* to refer to the "decomposition of bodies" by this force. At about the same time Mitscherlich introduced the term *contact action* for a similar group of phenomena. Ideas of what constitutes a catalyst and the mechanism of catalytic activity have since undergone continuous refinement, spurred by the enormous industrial importance of catalysts as illustrated by the variety of catalytic processes characteristic of modern petroleum refineries and of the chemical industries. Most of these processes involve solid catalysts, and an understanding of catalysis from both the theoretical and practical point of view is essential to chemists and chemical engineers.

In practice catalysis is primarily a technology that draws on many fields such as organic chemistry, surface chemistry, chemical kinetics, thermodynamics, solid-state physics, ceramics, and physical metallurgy. No unified theory of catalysis exists, and there are frequently several alternative, and not necessarily mutually exclusive, theoretical explanations for any given set of facts.

A basic concept is that a catalyzed reaction involves the transitory adsorption (almost always chemisorption) of one or more of the reactants onto the surface of the catalyst, rearrangement of the bonding, and desorption of the products. This leads to three groups of theories of catalysis:

1. The *geometrical theories* emphasize the importance of the correspondence between the geometrical configuration of the active atoms at the surface of the catalyst and the arrangement of atoms in the portion of the reacting molecule that adsorbs on the catalyst, this portion sometimes being called the *index group*. In one sense the usefulness of this approach is limited in that seldom can one change the geometrical arrangement of atoms in the catalyst surface without changing something else.

Studies of reaction rates on different crystal faces of a metal have shown that the rates may indeed change with geometry. The introduction of defects by cold rolling a sheet of metal, by grinding, or by radioactive bombardment may substantially change the rate of a reaction if the reaction temperature is sufficiently low that either the defects do not rapidly anneal or the structure does not assume a more stable configuration.

An aspect of the geometrical approach of great usefulness is the observation that reaction selectivity may be markedly altered by the number and arrangement of sites required for competing reactions, which leads to the concepts of the importance of "ensembles" or specific grouping of atoms at the catalyst surface and *structure sensitivity* as affected by particle size, alloying, and other variables (Chap. 6).

2. The *electronic theories* proceed from the fact that chemisorption involves the distortion or displacement of electron clouds, and they attempt to relate activity to the electronic properties of the catalyst. This theory may be in terms of the electronic structure of the solid as a whole, or in terms of the orbitals around individual atoms. In the charge-transfer theory of catalysis (see, e.g., Volkenstein 1963), the reaction rate is postulated to be controlled by the availability of charge carriers, electrons or holes in the catalyst. These are visualized as being nonlocalized; i.e., a sea of electrons or holes is available. Chemisorption is then related to the electronic properties of the catalyst. For example, the ease or difficulty of removal or donation of an electron to or from the lattice is considered, as predicted by applying band theory developed for metals and semiconductors.

This approach, of considerable interest in the 1950s, is now seen to be too broad and inadequate or inapplicable to most cases. More recently attention has been directed to the properties of atoms as individual entities and to the electronic effects caused by the nearest neighbors in the solid rather than by the solid as a whole. In many cases separating geometrical effects from localized electronic effects is difficult; the relative importance of the two probably varies greatly from case to case.

3. The two foregoing theories reflect a primarily physical approach in that the catalyst is regarded as essentially a static material having

the property of converting reactant to product. The *chemical approach*, on the other hand, regards the catalyst as a chemical intermediate that forms an unstable, surface, transitory complex with the reactants. This intermediate decomposes into the final products, returning the catalyst to its initial state. The rates of these processes and the structures formed are assumed to obey chemical principles. If the energy of formation of the unstable intermediate is low, the affinity between catalyst and reactants is weak and the overall rate limited by the rate of formation of the intermediate. If the energy of formation is high, the intermediate compound is stable and the rate limited by the rate of breakup of this intermediate.

This theory leads to the concept that the maximum rate is obtained when the bonds between the adsorbed complex and the catalyst surface are neither too strong nor too weak. This concept is useful but limited in that the energetics are generally unknown, more than one intermediate is frequently involved, and one is more generally concerned with selectivity rather than activity.

Each of these groups of theories has evolved with time, and the relative emphasis on each has changed. The pioneering work of Sabatier (1918) emphasized the chemical approach. In subsequent decades geometrical factors received much attention under the impact of Balandin's *multiplet hypothesis* (Balandin 1969), although geometrical factors alone cannot explain most variations of catalytic activity. In the 1950s the solid-state properties of catalysts received much attention after the vigorous development of solid-state electronic devices, such as the transistor, and the availability of ultrapure materials into which controlled trace amounts of known additives could be incorporated. However, the interpretation of catalytic effects by electronic theories has usually been ambiguous, and recent years have seen a reemphasis on the chemical viewpoint, incorporating a more sophisticated understanding of the nature and behavior of chemisorbed species and bonding, an approach that stems particularly from rapid advances in various instrumental methods. Schwab (1981) has briefly reviewed the history of these and other concepts in catalysis. An earlier book by Rideal (1968) shows the general concepts of catalysis as of the 1960s, with particular emphasis on theory and ideas on mechanism.

Both physical and chemical viewpoints may provide insight. To be able to relate catalytic activity to certain specific properties of the catalyst surface is desirable. Yet an understanding of the mechanism of action and a successful search for new and more effective catalysts may proceed predominantly through the chemical approach, which relates catalytic behavior to the vast body of knowledge concerning chemical reactions. The approaches are, of course, interrelated. The fundamental question about which little is yet known is how the surface structure of a solid catalyst causes the reactants to be adsorbed, the chemical bonds to be rearranged, and the products to be desorbed. There is no such thing as a "good" catalyst per se. A substance is or is not a good catalyst only with respect to a specific reaction.

The temperature range of practical interest in catalysis is primarily (although not exclusively) between about 20 and 500°C.* Below ambient temperatures, most catalytic reactions of practical interest go too slowly and indeed would become more costly because of the necessity of providing refrigeration or cryogenic cooling. Above approximately 500°C, achieving good selectivity is increasingly difficult unless the desired product is unusually stable.

Technologists must understand the method of thinking and framework of theory within which fundamental investigators view their studies, so as to be able to utilize theories and advances in fundamental understanding and yet not be sidetracked by trying to apply them under the wrong conditions. Practicing technologists are primarily concerned with the *effect* of the catalyst: how the rate and direction of the reaction are altered by changes in catalyst composition and by changes in feed composition, pressure, temperature, degree of recycle, and reaction time.

They are concerned with the incorporation of the catalyst into a process, how poisons may inadvertently be introduced into the catalyst system by the other portions of the process, and how this can be guarded against. The catalysts are usually highly active and of complex composition; they must be mechanically rugged, show good stability over long periods of time, and have the requisite activity and selectivity. The reactions with which technologists are concerned are determined by the economic utility of the process. Frequently a variety of catalysts give nearly the same performance, and the final selection involves an economic balance on the entire process, which includes such factors as catalyst cost, along with the frequency and difficulty of replacement and/or regeneration.

Scientific investigators, on the other hand, are concerned primarily with *mechanism*. In trying to simplify their systems for more fundamental interpretation, they frequently use catalysts of as simple a composition as possible, such as pure metal films or single pure metals

---

*Some major exceptions are ortho-to-para hydrogen conversion, which is carried out industrially at cryogenic temperatures; ammonia oxidation to form nitrogen oxides, hydrogen cyanide synthesis by the Andrussow process, partial oxidation of methanol to formaldehyde on a silver catalyst; and steam reforming of natural gas and naphthas— all of which are high-temperature reactions. Catalysts for the oxidation of such pollutants as carbon monoxide and hydrocarbons and removal of nitrogen oxides from automobile engine exhaust must also be stable and effective at high temperatures.

or compounds, even if they are relatively inactive and would not be used in practice. The problem of mechanical strength and stability over long periods of time is of lesser importance. Scientific investigators' reactants are usually highly pure and chosen either for experimental convenience or for some unusual feature of the reaction. Frequently they consist of small and simple molecules. Many of the fundamental studies that are valuable in providing insight into the causes of catalyst behavior have not been made with reactions at all, but rather have been studies either of the structure of catalyst surfaces or of the nature and properties of adsorbed species.

Every theory is based on a model, and in catalysis the model may depart to a significant extent from reality. Although the theoretical framework of the model may provide a structure for organization and correlation of facts or suggest a direction for profitable investigation, theories of catalysis at present must be used with caution in attempting to predict behavior under new conditions. These theoretical approaches can be of value to technologists provided they understand the limitations of these approaches and do not confuse theoretical, enthusiastic assertions for verified fact.

1.2 Industrial Heterogeneous Catalysts

The first heterogeneous catalytic process of industrial significance, introduced about 1875, utilized platinum to oxidize SO_2 to SO_3, which was then converted to sulfuric acid, H_2SO_4, by absorption in an aqueous solution of the acid. This came to replace the lead chamber process for manufacture of H_2SO_4, in which the same series of reactions were catalyzed by a homogeneous catalyst, nitrogen oxides, probably through the formation of nitrosylsulfuric acid, $HNOSO_4$. In this "contact process" platinum in turn was superseded by a catalyst comprising vanadium oxide and potassium sulfate on a silica carrier, which was less susceptible to poisoning; essentially this same composition is used in present-day SO_2 reactors.

Other inorganic chemical catalytic processes followed. Notable was the development about 1903 by Ostwald of the oxidation of ammonia on a platinum gauze to form nitrogen oxides for conversion to nitric acid, followed in the period from about 1908 to 1914 by the synthesis of ammonia from the elements by a process developed by Haber and Bosch utilizing a catalyst developed by Mittasch. The industrial synthesis of methanol from carbon monoxide and hydrogen appeared in about 1923, and the synthesis of hydrocarbons from carbon monoxide and hydrogen by the Fischer-Tropsch process in the 1930s. The catalytic partial oxidation of methanol to formaldehyde as an industrial process started in Germany about 1890; that of naphthalene to phthalic anhydride was commercialized in the 1920s; and that of benzene to maleic anhydride, in 1928. The partial oxidation of ethylene to ethylene oxide was commercialized by Union Carbide in 1937.

In the processing of petroleum for fuels the first catalytic process, catalytic cracking, appeared in about 1937. This first used an acid-treated clay, then later a synthetic silica-alumina catalyst, and more recently zeolite crystals incorporated in a silica-alumina matrix. Reforming, using a molybdena/alumina catalyst to increase the octane number of gasoline by cyclization of paraffins and dehydrogenation to aromatics, was introduced in the United States and Germany just prior to World War II. In the early 1950s this was superseded by a catalytic reforming process using a platinum/alumina catalyst. Catalytic hydrocracking first came into use in England and Germany prior to World War II; subsequently it became relatively uneconomic, but it was revived more recently, with the advent of new types of catalysts. Hydrodesulfurization and hydrotreating processes have grown rapidly during the past three decades and are now of major importance in petroleum processing. Table 1.1 lists these and a representative selection of the catalysts used in the principal industrial heterogeneous catalytic processes of present or recent importance, together with the type of reactor commonly utilized. In addition to the compositions listed, small amounts of other substances, "promoters," are frequently added in catalyst preparation.

Heinemann (1981) presents a brief history of industrial catalysis. A book edited by Pearce and Patterson (1981), and written by a group at Imperial Chemical Industries (ICI), gives an overall treatment of catalysis and related chemical processes. The book by Weissermel and Arpe (1978) on industrial organic chemistry covers important raw materials and intermediates including information on processes and catalysts for a number of reactions not considered in the present volume. Davis and Hettinger (1983) have edited an extensive collection of histories of catalysis research in America having industrial impact.

1.3 Definitions

1.3.1 Catalyst

The basic concept of a catalyst is a substance that in a small amount causes a large change. More precise definitions of catalysis and of what constitutes a catalyst have gradually evolved as understanding of the causes of catalytic phenomena has grown. Even today there is no universal agreement on definitions; the point of view varies somewhat depending on the investigator, for example, between the fundamental investigator and the practitioner, and among researchers con-

TABLE 1.1   Selected Heterogeneous Catalysts of Industrial Importance

Reaction	Catalyst and reactor type (continuous operation unless otherwise noted)
Dehydrogenation	
C_4H_{10} (butane) $\rightarrow$ butenes	$Cr_2O_3 \cdot Al_2O_3$ (fixed bed, cyclic)
Butenes $\rightarrow C_4H_6$ (butadiene)	Fe_2O_3 promoted with Cr_2O_3 and K_2CO_3
$C_6H_5C_2H_5 \rightarrow C_6H_5CH{=}CH_2$ (ethyl benzene $\rightarrow$ styrene)	Fe_2O_3 promoted with Cr_2O_3 and K_2CO_3 (fixed bed, in presence of steam)
CH_4 or other hydrocarbons + $H_2O \rightarrow CO + H_2$ (steam reforming)	Supported Ni (fixed bed)
$(CH_3)_2CHOH \rightarrow CH_3COCH_3 + H_2$ (isopropanol $\rightarrow$ acetone + hydrogen)	ZnO
$CH_3CH(OH)C_2H_5 \rightarrow CH_3COC_2H_5 + H_2$	ZnO
Hydrogenation	
Of edible fats and oils	Ni on a support (slurry reactor, batch)
Various hydrogenations of fine organic chemicals	Pd or Pt on carbon (slurry reactor, usually batch)
$C_6H_6 + 3H_2 \rightarrow C_6H_{12}$	Ni or noble metal on support (fixed bed or slurry reactor)
$N_2 + 3H_2 \rightarrow 2NH_3$	Fe promoted with Al_2O_3, K_2O, CaO, and MgO (adiabatic fixed beds)
$C_2H_2 \rightarrow C_2H_6$ (selective hydrogenation of C_2H_2 impurity in C_2H_4 from thermal-cracking plant)	Pd on Al_2O_3 or sulfided Ni on support (adiabatic fixed bed)
Oxidation	
$SO_2 + \frac{1}{2}O_2$ (air) $\rightarrow SO_3$	V_2O_5 plus K_2SO_4 on silica (adiabatic, fixed beds)
$2NH_3 + \frac{5}{2}O_2$ (air) $\rightarrow 2NO + 3H_2O$	90% Pt–10% Rh wire gauze, oxidizing conditions
$NH_3 + CH_4 + $ air $\rightarrow$ HCN (Andrussow process)	90% Pt–10% Rh wire gauze, under net reducing conditions
$C_{10}H_8$ or $1,2\text{-}C_6H_4(CH_3)_2 + O_2 \rightarrow C_6H_4(CO)_2O$ (naphthalene or o-xylene + air $\rightarrow$ phthalic anhydride)	V_2O_5 on titania (multitube fixed bed)
$n\text{-}C_4H_{10} + O_2 \rightarrow C_4H_2O_3$ (butane + air $\rightarrow$ maleic anhydride)	Vanadia-phosphate (multitube fixed bed or fluidized bed)
$C_2H_4 + \frac{1}{2}O_2 \rightarrow (CH_2)_2O$ (ethylene oxide)	Ag on $\alpha\text{-}Al_2O_3$, promoted with Cl and Cs (multitube fixed bed)
$CH_3OH + O_2 \rightarrow CH_2O + H_2$ and/or H_2O	Ag (adiabatic reactor) or $Fe_2(MoO_4)_3$ (multitube fixed bed)
$C_3H_6 + O_2 \rightarrow CH_2{=}CHCHO$ (acrolein) and/or $CH_2{=}CHCOOH$ (acrylic acid)	Bismuth molybdate plus other components
$C_3H_6 + NH_3 + \frac{3}{2}O_2 \rightarrow CH_2{=}CHCN + 3H_2O$	Complex metal molybdates (fluidized bed)
Complete oxidation of CO and hydrocarbons, for pollution control	Pt or Pd, or both, on monolith support
Simultaneous control of CO, hydrocarbons, and NO_x in auto exhaust	Same, plus Rh, with careful control of oxidizing/reducing conditions
Simultaneous control of NO_x and SO_x in flue gases	Vanadia on titania with addition of NH_3
$C_2H_4 + \frac{1}{2}O_2 + CH_3COOH \rightarrow CH_3COOCH{=}CH_2$ (vinyl acetate)	Pd on acid-resistant support (vapor phase, multitube fixed bed)
$C_4H_8 + \frac{1}{2}O_2 \rightarrow C_4H_6 + H_2O$	Promoted ferrite spinels

TABLE 1.1   Selected Heterogeneous Catalysts of Industrial **Importance** (*Continued*)

Reaction	Catalyst and reactor type (continuous operation unless otherwise noted)
Acid-catalyzed Reactions	
Catalytic cracking	Zeolite in $SiO_2 \cdot Al_2O_3$ matrix plus other ingredients (transport reactor)
Hydrocracking	Pd on zeolite in an amorphous matrix; NiMo on silica-alumina, various other dual-function catalysts (adiabatic fixed beds)
Paraffin isomerization	Pt on H-mordenite zeolite in alumina matrix
Catalytic reforming	Pt, Pt-Re or Pt-Sn on acidified Al_2O_3 or on zeolite in matrix (adiabatic, fixed beds, or moving bed, with interstage heating)
Polymerization	H_3PO_4 on clay (fixed bed)
Hydration, e.g., propylene to isopropyl alcohol	Mineral acid or acid-type ion-exchange resin (fixed bed)
$CH_3OH + isoC_4H_8 \rightarrow$ methyl tert. butyl ether (MTBE)	Acid-type ion-exchange resin
Reactions of Synthesis Gas	
$CO + 2H_2 \rightarrow CH_3OH$	Cu^I-ZnO promoted with Al_2O_3 (adiabatic, fixed beds with interstage cooling or multitube fixed bed)
$CO + 3H_2 \rightarrow CH_4 + H_2O$ (methanation)	Supported Ni (fixed bed)
$CO + H_2 \rightarrow$ paraffins, etc. (Fischer-Tropsch synthesis)	Fe or Co with promoters (multitube fixed bed or transport reactor)
Other	
Oxychlorination (e.g., $C_2H_4 + 2HCl + \frac{1}{2}O_2$ $C_2H_4Cl_2 + H_2O$)	$CuCl_2/Al_2O_3$ with KCl promoter
Hydrodesulfurization, hydrodenitrogenation, hydrotreating	$CoMo/Al_2O_3$ or $NiMo/Al_2O_3$, sulfided (adiabatic, fixed beds with interstage cooling)
$SO_2 + 2H_2S \rightarrow 3S + 2H_2O$ (Claus process)	Al_2O_3 (fixed beds)
$H_2O + CO \rightarrow CO_2 + H_2$ (water-gas shift)	Fe_3O_4 promoted with Cr_2O_3 (adiabatic fixed bed); for a second, lower temperature stage, Cu-ZnO on Al_2O_3; CoMo on support

cerned with heterogeneous catalysis, homogeneous catalysis, polymerization reactions, and enzymes. For present purposes, however, our definition is: *A catalyst is a substance that increases the rate of reaction toward equilibrium without being appreciably consumed in the process.* This definition is basically operational.

The fundamental concept, stemming from the chemical approach to catalysis, is that a reaction involves a cyclic process in which a site on a catalyst forms a complex with reactants, from which products are desorbed, thereby restoring the original site and continuing the cycle. This concept may lead to the idea that a catalyst is unaltered by the reaction it catalyzes, but this is misleading. A catalyst may undergo major changes in its structure and composition as a result of the mechanism of its participation in the reaction.

A pure metal catalyst, on use, frequently changes in surface roughness or crystal structure. The ratio of oxygen to metal in a metal oxide catalyst frequently changes with the temperature and composition of the contacting fluid. In both cases, however, there is no stoichiometric relationship between such changes and the overall stoichiometry of the catalyzed reaction. Many so-called polymerization catalysts or initiators are not termed *catalysts* within the foregoing definition. Thus, in the use of an organic peroxide to initiate a polymerization reaction, the ratio of peroxide consumed to the quantity of monomer reacted is indeed nonstoichiometric, but the peroxide becomes completely consumed in the process; hence it cannot be regarded as a true catalyst.

A catalyst is defined as a *substance*; the acceleration of a rate by an energy-transfer process is not regarded as catalysis by this definition. Excluded cases include excitation by thermal energy (increased temperature), by bombardment of reactants with charged or high-energy particles, by electric discharge, or by photochemical irradiation. For example, the reaction of hydrogen and oxygen is increased by irradiation with ultraviolet light and even more so if a small amount of mercury vapor is present and illumination is by a mercury vapor lamp. Here the reaction is accelerated by energy transfer to the reacting gases from mercury atoms, which in turn are activated by irradiation. As a second example, the rate of thermal decomposition of a vapor at low pressure is usually increased by the addition of a second "inert" gas, which furnishes activation energy by collisions. These various methods of accelerating the rate of a reaction are more clearly understood as aspects of the mechanisms of homogeneous gas-phase reactions rather than as catalysis.

The same substance may act as a catalyst in one set of circumstances but as a reagent in another. Thus the oxidation of a mixture of o-xylene and air to phthalic anhydride is catalyzed by V_2O_5. o-Xylene by itself may also be oxidized by contacting it alone with V_2O_5, in which case the V_2O_5 acts as a reagent and becomes stoichiometrically reduced to a lower oxide. Indeed, the ability to alternate easily between two or more oxidation states is characteristic of many oxidation catalysts. Thus insight into the reasons for their catalytic activities may come from studies using the same substance as a reagent.

A catalyst *cannot* change the ultimate equilibrium determined by thermodynamics; its role is restricted to accelerating the rate of approach to equilibrium. This point is developed later.

1.3.2 Catalyst activity

The *activity* of a catalyst refers to the rate at which it causes the reaction to proceed to chemical equilibrium. The rate may be expressed in any of several ways (Sec. 3.2). The performance of an industrial reactor is frequently given in terms of a *space-time yield* (STY), which is the quantity of product formed per unit time per unit volume of reactor.

The rate of reaction depends on pressure, temperature, concentration of reactants and products, and other variables. For comparison of the activity of different catalysts, any of several methods may be used. Four possibilities are as follows:

1. Rates may be determined at a standard condition.

2. Sometimes a single rate constant may be reported, but this implies detailed knowledge of the true kinetics and ability to apply a rate expression with but a single constant.

3. To avoid having to determine rates over a range of concentrations and temperatures for comparison, catalyst activity may be expressed as the temperature required for a given conversion at a fixed feed composition and pressure.

4. The space velocity required to achieve a specified conversion at a fixed temperature is determined for a fixed feed composition and pressure.

1.3.3   Catalyst selectivity and functionality

There are usually many chemical compositions having a free-energy intermediate between that of the reactants and that of the state of complete chemical equilibrium. The *selectivity* of a catalyst is a measure of the extent to which the catalyst accelerates the reaction to form one or more of the desired products, which are usually intermediates, instead of those formed by reaction to the overall state of lowest free energy. The selectivity usually varies with pressure, temperature, reactant composition, and extent of conversion, as well as with the nature of the catalyst. For precision one should refer to the selectivity of a catalyzed reaction under specified conditions. The selectivity is determined in the first instance by the *functionality* of the catalyst, but also in part by thermodynamic equilibrium considerations. Thus, a certain undesired product may be largely avoided if it is possible to operate under conditions in which the equilibrium concentration of the product is negligible (see Sec. 1.4).

A frequently cited example of catalyst selectivity caused by function is the conversion of ethanol. Over copper the reaction proceeds as

$$C_2H_5OH \rightarrow CH_3CHO + H_2 \qquad (1.1)$$

Over alumina it proceeds as

$$C_2H_5OH \rightarrow C_2H_4 + H_2O \qquad (1.2)$$

or

$$2C_2H_5OH \rightarrow C_2H_5OC_2H_5 + H_2O \qquad (1.3)$$

Selectivity here is associated with the fact that copper adsorbs hydrogen and is a mild hydrogenation/dehydrogenation catalyst, whereas alumina adsorbs water and can act as a dehydration catalyst.

To a first approximation, certain types of functionality can be characterized by selective chemisorption of suitable reagents. For example, many hydrogenation reactions are catalyzed by metals, and reactions such as hydrocarbon isomerization are catalyzed by solid acids. The availability of metal surfaces on a catalyst can be studied by the degree of chemisorption of hydrogen, and the availability of solid acids by the amount of adsorption of bases such as ammonia or organic amines (Sec. 7.2.1).

Many catalytic reactions, however, are affected by subtleties not readily revealed by these "titration" procedures. Consequently, one may characterize certain catalyst functionalities by the response of a well-known and relatively simple "probe" reaction. From a study with ethanol (or similarly propanol), the extent to which an olefin, rather than an aldehyde, is formed is a measure of dehydration functionality versus dehydrogenation functionality. Similarly, with an unsaturated hydrocarbon, products formed by an isomerization versus a hydrogenation path indicate the extent of functional acidity versus functional hydrogenation (see also Chap. 9). This approach of letting a reaction characterize the catalyst can be especially helpful in dealing with complex and ill-defined catalysts that are more or less multifunctional.

Some reactions involve the formation and subsequent reaction of various intermediates. Some of the reaction steps may be catalyzed by one kind of site, and others by a second kind of site. When these steps occur in series, both kinds of sites must be in proximity to one another in order for the overall reaction to occur, and usually they are both on the same catalyst particle. In some cases an intermediate can be desorbed from one kind of site into the bulk fluid and adsorbed on a second site. Then, an intimate mechanical mixture of two kinds of particles, each possessing only one kind of site, can effectively catalyze the overall reaction, although either one by itself is relatively ineffective. An example is the isomerization of an n-paraffin to an iso-paraffin on a platinum catalyst supported on an acidic base. The n-paraffin is first dehydrogenated to an n-olefin. This isomerizes to an isoolefin, which is hydrogenated to an isoparaffin. The hydrogenation and dehydrogenation steps occur on platinum; the isomerization steps, on an acid site (Sec. 9.5). This mechanism is significant in some of the reactions occurring in catalytic reforming and in catalytic hydrocracking.

A catalyst may be useful for either its activity or its selectivity or both. If a variety of products are possible, selectivity is usually the more important. Activity can usually be stepped up by raising the temperature, although frequently increased temperature shortens the life of the catalyst or increases undesirable reactions that may be catalytic or thermal or both. A higher temperature may also decrease the maximum conversion obtainable if the reaction is exothermic and is limited in extent by thermodynamic equilibrium.

If a variety of products are thermodynamically possible, increased temperature may either increase or decrease selectivity, depending on the overall kinetics and the desired product. Thus, for the general case of $A \rightarrow B \rightarrow C$, if B is the desired product, some intermediate temperature is usually optimum; if C is desired, increased temperature helps drive the reaction to completion. If B is desired, the maximum selectivity for this type of kinetics occurs at the lowest conversion. Control of catalyst selectivity is primarily a matter of minimizing the rates of undesired reactions while maximizing that of the desired reaction. This is determined not only by catalyst structure, but also by feed composition, operating conditions, degree of conversion, and reactor design and operation (Chap. 11).

Selectivity is defined as the percentage of the consumed reactant that forms the desired product. It is usually a function of degree of conversion and reaction conditions. *Yield* is an engineering or industrially used term that refers to the quantity of product formed per quantity of feedstock (reactant) consumed in the overall reactor operation. Within this operation there may be a recycle of various reactants and/or intermediates, as after separation from the product. Yield is frequently reported on a weight basis; hence a yield exceeding 100 percent (w/w) may be obtained, for example, in a partial oxidation process in which oxygen is introduced into the product molecule with high selectivity. In the fuels industry, products are conventionally sold on a volume rather than a weight basis; hence a yield exceeding 100 percent (v/v) may be obtained when the products are of lower density than the reactants.

1.3.4 Negative catalyst

A *negative catalyst* is a substance that decreases the rate of reaction. This is usually found only when the reaction proceeds by the formation and disappearance of free radicals.

The negative catalyst acts by interfering with the free-radical processes, converting radicals into less active forms, or removing them from reaction. An example is the use of lead alkyls such as tetraethyl lead to improve the antiknock properties of gasoline in an internal combustion engine. After compression, a part of the gasoline-air mixture inside the engine cylinder may spontaneously ignite before the combustion wave initiated by the spark plug reaches it, thus producing a sudden and uncontrolled pressure increase or "knock." The degradation products from the lead compound, most probably some kind of finely dispersed lead oxide and lead oxyhalides, interfere with the preignition reactions. Organic peroxides are probably formed in the early stages of hydrocarbon oxidation reactions. The role of the lead compounds may be to destroy these peroxides, which otherwise would split into free radicals and thus initiate a rapidly propagating reaction.

The mechanism of action of a negative catalyst is different from that of most positive catalysts, and a negative catalyst should be described more meaningfully as a "reaction inhibitor." As another example, oxidation inhibitors such as phenolic compounds and amines contain one or more labile hydrogen atoms and act by transferring them to an active free radical. This exchange of an active radical for a less active one causes a slowing down of the overall reaction.

1.3.5 Heterohomogeneous catalysis

A catalyst may sometimes act by generating free radicals, which desorb from the surface and initiate a chain reaction in the bulk of the reacting fluid. Examples are well documented for various liquid-phase reactions in which free radicals have been trapped or otherwise identified. For gas-phase reactions, generally temperatures above 400°C or in some cases above about 800°C are required. A recent detailed review (Driscoll et al. 1987) describes methods of direct detection of surface-generated gas-phase radicals and observations on a variety of systems.

The foregoing description is the classical form of heterohomogeneous catalysis, but a catalytic reaction and a homogeneous reaction may interact with each other in various subtle ways such that the net effect is not simply the sum of the two. Instead of a free radical being desorbed into the gas phase, a molecular intermediate may be formed on the catalyst and released. Its fate depends on the relative probability of being adsorbed and reacted on another site of the catalyst in contrast to reacting in a different manner in the gas phase. The overall behavior of the system may depend not only on the void fraction of a packed bed of catalyst and the amount of open volume downstream, but also on geometrical and other factors. In many catalytic oxidations the exit gas must be rapidly quenched to avoid over-oxidation or decomposition of the desired product, but there is limited evidence about the extents to which heterohomogeneous catalysis may contribute to partial oxidation processes under practical conditions. The subject is reviewed by Garibyan and Margolis (1989–90).

In some reactions of hydrocarbons, such as steam reforming of methane and other hydrocarbons to form synthesis gas, the extent to which carbon may deposit on the catalyst and gradually inactivate it is determined in part by the balance between homogeneous reactions leading to carbonaceous deposit precursors and the desired heterogeneous reaction. In various hydrotreating processes in the fuels industry, thermal reactions occur simultaneously with catalytic reactions, causing interactions that may be only dimly perceived. These thermal gas-phase reactions generally proceed by free-radical mechanisms, whether initiated homogeneously or heterogeneously.

1.3.6 Sites

Under reaction conditions all solid catalysts are nonuniform or heterogeneous in the sense that chemical and physical properties vary with location on the surface. Even in a pure metal, the atoms at specific locations, such as at lattice defects and at edges and corners of crystallites, have a different environment from that of atoms in a surface plane. The heterogeneity of catalyst surfaces can be demonstrated and to some extent characterized by a variety of methods. The variation of the differential heat of adsorption with coverage or the change in activation energy of adsorption with coverage may be measured, or temperature-programmed desorption studies may be used. More than one maximum in chemisorption isobars may be observed (Fig. 2.2), showing that more than one kind of chemisorption may occur. Some catalysts may be effectively poisoned by adsorption of an amount of material comprising much less than a monolayer, indicating that only a fraction of such a surface is effective for reaction (but see Sec. 6.6).

These facts and others led to the concept, introduced by H. S. Taylor (1948), that reaction takes place only on specific locations on the catalyst, termed *sites*. Those that are active for one reaction may not be so for a second reaction, but it is usually difficult to determine their identity and structure precisely. In some cases a site may be a group or cluster of neighboring atoms on the catalyst surface; sometimes it may actually be a species adsorbed onto the catalyst. The term *active center* is frequently used as a synonym for site or to refer to a group of sites. A catalyst frequently undergoes reconstruction during reaction, causing a change in the total area and nature of the surface and possibly a change in the number and nature of the sites.

For some reactions on metals, the rate is independent of the size, shape, or other physical characteristics of the metal crystallite and is proportional only to the total number of metal atoms exposed to the reactant. (This is typically about 10^{15} atoms per square centimeter.) Such reactions are termed *structure-insensitive* in contrast to *structure-sensitive* reactions whose rates and selectivities vary with the detailed structure of the surface. The terms *facile* for *structure-insensitive* and *demanding* for *structure-sensitive* are also used. The concentration of active sites on acid catalysts is usually considerably less than that on metals and is typically of the order of magnitude of about 10^{11} to 10^{13} sites per square centimeter. Note that a "site" cannot be observed as such; its characteristics are inferred indirectly from a variety of studies (see "Structure Sensitivity," Sec. 6.1.1).

In a complex overall reaction, an adsorbed entity may surface-diffuse over several neighboring sites while undergoing a series of intermediate reactions. These reactions are typically structure-sensitive. In hydrocarbon processing, some reactions apparently occur on an overlayer, such as that of hydrocarbon fragments strongly adsorbed onto a metal. These reactions are essentially structure-insensitive in that they are not markedly affected by the metal surface structure under the overlayer.

1.3.7   Turnover number

The *turnover number*, or *turnover frequency*, is the number of molecules that react per site per unit time. As a basic measure of true catalytic activity, this is a useful concept, but it is limited by the difficulty of determining the true number of active sites. In general it is easier to make this determination for metals than for nonmetal catalysts since techniques such as selective chemisorption are available to measure the exposed surface area of metals. For acid catalysts, the measurement of site concentration by poisoning or adsorption of bases may be ambiguous and may lead to erroneously high values since sites may be active for sorption but not for reaction. As with rates of reaction in general, the turnover number is a function of pressure, temperature, and composition of the reacting fluid.

1.3.8   Naming of catalysts and catalyst structures

Most catalysts are complex, and often the terms by which they are described only list the active elements present and the support, without specifying the form in which the element may exist, either in the catalyst as manufactured or under reaction conditions. In part this stems from uncertainties concerning the actual composition under reaction conditions. For example, a so-called CoMo/Al$_2$O$_3$ catalyst is commonly used for hydrodesulfurization. The solidus (slash) separates the active elements, cobalt and molybdenum, from the support, Al$_2$O$_3$. The catalyst is usually supplied in the form of the metal oxide, which is converted to a sulfide before use. Its actual structure is highly complex.

Sometimes a catalyst is described as a compound, but that compound as such may actually not be effective. For example, an early industrial catalyst for methanol synthesis was zinc oxide with which chromia was incorporated. This is sometimes described as a "zinc chromite" catalyst, but this may be misleading since true zinc chromite, Zn(Cr$_2$O$_4$), as a crystalline spinel is relatively inactive. Zinc chromite functions primarily as a textural promoter that minimizes sintering (Sec. 4.6.1). Again, the structure of the active catalyst is complex. The council of the International Union of Pure and Applied Chemistry (IUPAC) has adopted a recommended set of symbols and terminology for heterogeneous catalysis, which is published in Volume 26 of *Advances in Catalysis* (Burwell 1977).

The fact that catalysts obey all the normal principles of chemistry is to be borne in mind. The catalyst structure, both physical and chemical, can be markedly affected by the environment, and indeed this principle is frequently utilized to maintain a catalyst in a desired state. In catalytic reforming reactions, an acidified support is required, and this is usually achieved by adding a small concentration of an organic chloro-compound to the feed. In the reactor this decomposes to the corresponding acid, which adsorbs onto the catalyst support and is incorporated into it, producing acidic sites. Addition must be more or less continuous since chlorine will be slowly removed by reaction. A CoMo catalyst used for hydrotreating is more active in the sulfide than in the oxide form. In the absence of sulfur compounds in a feed stream, a small concentration of H$_2$S may be added to the reactant to maintain the catalyst in the desired structure.

The selectivity of a metal oxide catalyst for a partial oxidation reaction is frequently caused by a specific crystallographic form or a specific compound (Chap. 8). This may become converted irreversibly to a different and inactive form if the reaction mixture becomes too highly oxidizing or too reducing in character, or it may be slowly changed in composition by the reacting mixture itself.

1.3.9   Catalyst deactivation

A catalyst may lose its activity or its selectivity for a wide variety of reasons. The causes may be grouped loosely into

1. Poisoning
2. Fouling
3. Reduction of active area by sintering or migration
4. Loss of active species

A catalyst *poison* is an impurity present in the *feed stream* that re-duces catalyst activity. In a complex reaction it may affect one reac-tion step more than another; hence the selectivity toward a desired re-action may be improved by deliberately adding a poison. It adsorbs on active sites of the catalyst and, if not adsorbed too strongly, is gradu-ally desorbed when the poison is eliminated from the feed stream. The phenomenon is then temporary. If adsorption is strong, the effect is permanent.

The desorption may be enhanced by reaction with the fluid. Thus, in a hydrogenation reaction a metallic catalyst may be poisoned by ad-sorption of a sulfur compound, but desorption may be enhanced by its conversion to H_2S by reaction with H_2. If a reaction product is strongly adsorbed, the reaction may be termed *self-poisoned* or *self-inhibited* (see also Sec. 3.6). The effect of the poisoning may be that of simple blocking of sites or, more subtly, the poison may act by an electronic effect in which it alters the bond strength of an adsorbed reactant or product (Chap. 6).

In formulating an expression for rate of catalyst deactivation, to a first approximation deactivation caused by poisoning is a function of the amount of feed contacted with the catalyst, whereas that caused only by sintering is instead a function primarily of time and temper-ature. The particular active species may also be converted to another form less active or selective, as is the case with certain complex metal oxides used in partial oxidation reactions. A complex metal oxide may also decompose into other compounds, sometimes due to loss of a par-ticular element via volatilization of a compound. An example is iron molybdate, $Fe_2(MoO_4)_3$, used in a process for partially oxidizing meth-anol to formaldehyde. MoO_3 is slowly formed and volatilized from the catalyst, reducing its performance.

A somewhat amorphous catalyst may crystallize, or a compound ac-tive in one crystal habit may be converted into a less active crystalline form. A supported metal catalyst may be reduced in activity or selec-tivity by becoming alloyed with a metallic impurity or by reaction with the support; for example, a nickel/alumina catalyst may be con-verted to a nickel aluminate.

Various examples are discussed in conjunction with specific cases or groups of cases. Sintering of supported metal catalysts is discussed in Sec. 6.4. The formation of carbonaceous deposits, which may be regarded primarily as a fouling mechanism, is discussed in Sec. 6.5 and Chap. 7. An example of deliberate poisoning to enhance selectivity at the cost of reduced activity is the addition of an organochlorine compound to ethylene in the commercial process for making ethylene oxide (Sec. 8.3).

In addition to the foregoing, catalysts may also deteriorate because of slow crumbling of a support by chemical attack, by physical grinding in an agitated vessel, or for reasons that are poorly understood. Sometimes a poison lowers selectivity because it itself is a catalyst for an undesired side reaction; thus a trace of metal compound in a feed stream may lead to the deposit of elemental metal, which may catalyze hydrogenation/dehydrogenation reactions where they are not desired.

1.4   Thermodynamics and Energetics

A true heterogeneous catalyst accelerates the rate of approach to equilibrium but cannot alter that equilibrium. This is readily seen by considering a simple reversible reaction A $\rightleftharpoons$ B. The standard free-energy change is expressed as $\Delta G° = -RT \ln K = -RT \ln (a_B/a_A)$, where a_B and a_A are the activities of product and reactant, respectively. The presence of the solid catalyst cannot change $\Delta G°$ and hence does not change the ratio a_B/a_A. (If, however, reactants and products were dissolved in a homogeneous catalyst, such as a mineral acid, which in effect alters their structure, the activity ratio and the equilibrium composition could likewise change.)

In many practical cases a large number of products are possible under equilibrium conditions, but only one or a related group is desired. The selectivity of a catalyst may be related to its ability to direct one reaction essentially to equilibrium while having little or no effect on alternate pathways, so that the most stable products are not necessarily formed. Selectivity effects are intimately related to the selective chemisorption characteristics of the catalyst. In the conversion of CO and H_2 to CH_3OH, products such as paraffins, olefins, and higher alcohols are more stable thermodynamically under synthesis conditions but are scarcely formed on the usual $CuZnO/Al_2O_3$ catalyst. Paraffins and olefins, undesired in CH_3OH synthesis, are readily formed from CO and H_2 on iron or cobalt as in the Fischer-Tropsch synthesis (Sec. 10.2). Because these products are more favored thermodynamically and if the iron or cobalt catalysts are of sufficient activity, the reaction can be carried out at lower pressures and temperatures (e.g., 0.1 to 2.0 MPa, 150 to 300°C) than those required for CH_3OH synthesis. The quantities of CH_3OH then formed are insignificant because, under these milder reaction conditions, the amount that can exist under equilibrium conditions is small.

Consideration of alternate reaction pathways in order of increasing difficulty based on structure or kinetic insights may be a fruitful way of searching for an appropriate catalyst within the overall constraints set by thermodynamics. As an example, consider the isomerization of an olefin such as l-butene on an acid catalyst. A wide variety of transformations are possible. In general, cis-trans isomerization occurs most readily, and then double-bond migration. Carbon skeletal rearrangement is the most difficult. Cis-trans equilibrium without other changes can probably be achieved on a mild acid catalyst, but strong acidity is required for skeletal rearrangement. Correspondingly, if skeletal rearrangement is achieved, the easier reactions will probably all proceed essentially to equilibrium (Sec. 7.4).

Under actual process conditions, improving the performance over that allowed by thermodynamics is sometimes possible by removing a product either chemically or physically. In a dehydrogenation reaction, the concentration of hydrogen in the products may be lowered by adding oxygen to convert it to water; in other cases a product may be removed by *ab*sorption or *ad*sorption into another phase under dynamic conditions.

According to the principle of microscopic reversibility, if a catalytic reaction proceeds by a single step, then a catalyst that accelerates the rate of a forward reaction should also accelerate the rate of the reverse reaction. This can be illustrated by the reaction $A \rightleftharpoons B$. The equilibrium constant K equals k_1/k_2. Since the value of K is independent of the presence or absence of the catalyst, a catalyst that increases k_1 should also increase k_2. The same argument can be extended to a reaction occurring in a series of steps, one of which is rate-limiting, all others being in equilibrium with one another. Again, a catalyst that accelerates the rate-limiting step in the forward direction should accelerate the rate in the reverse direction.

The complications in applying this seemingly powerful generalization are twofold. First, operating conditions (pressure, temperature, and/or composition) must perforce be different when carrying out the forward reaction than the reverse, since they must lie on opposite sides of the equilibrium condition. This change in operating conditions between the two sides of the equilibrium may have a significant effect on the catalyst. Increasing the temperature may cause a rapid decrease in activity with time, such as may be caused by crystal growth. Increasing the pressure may cause a shift in the relative amounts of adsorbed species on a catalyst, thus altering the catalyst activity and/or selectivity.

Second, in practice a multiplicity of reactions frequently occur, and side reactions may be much more significant when approached from one side of equilibrium than from the other. In hydrogenation/dehydrogenation reactions involving organic compounds, a nickel catalyst is usually highly active for hydrogenation. Yet it is frequently ineffective for dehydrogenation because coke is formed on the catalyst surface by side reactions and the catalyst rapidly loses activity.

This generalization is probably of greatest use in a preliminary search for catalysts, and its greatest applicability is when few or no side products can be formed in the reaction direction of interest. Thus active catalysts for the synthesis of ammonia from the elements are also active for its decomposition.

1.4.1   Reaction pathways

Consider a gas-phase reaction that may occur either homogeneously or be catalyzed heterogeneously. The two reaction pathways occur simultaneously, but in order for the catalyzed reaction to be observed it must occur measurably faster than the homogeneous reaction. We now inquire into how the catalyst brings this about.

The rate of a single elementary step of a homogeneous reaction is proportional to a rate constant k that varies with temperature according to the Arrhenius relationship $k = Ae^{-E/RT}$, where E is the activation energy and R is the gas constant. The preexponential factor A is a constant that in collision theory is identified as a collision number for bimolecular processes and, for unimolecular processes, as a frequency factor or the probability of reaction of an activated molecule.

The ability of a catalyst to increase a reaction rate can be ascribed in a general way to its causing a reduction in the activation energy of the reaction. But even for the simplest kind of reaction, the single-step conversion of A to B, the situation is considerably more complicated than this simple statement may imply. The catalyzed reaction involves three rate processes: (1) adsorption, (2) the formation and breakup of an activated complex, and (3) desorption of products. Each of these has its own activation energy. The rate of each is also determined by the total surface area of the catalyst present (or, more precisely, by the number of active sites) and by the concentration on the catalyst surface of various adsorbed species. The idealized homogeneous reaction has a single activation energy, and its rate is a function of the gas-phase concentration.

For a reaction to be noticeably catalyzed, the various factors that determine the overall rate of the heterogeneous reaction must, in the entirety of their interactions, outweigh that of the different group of factors determining the rate of the homogeneous reaction. Generally the most important effect of the catalyst is to provide a pathway whereby the activation energy for the formation of the intermediate surface complex is considerably less than for the homogeneous reaction. Because the activation energy appears in the rate equation as an exponent, a slight change in activation energy has a marked effect on the rate.

The rate of the catalyzed reaction is proportional to the active surface area, and the rate of a homogeneous reaction is proportional to the volume of fluid. Hence, the maximum ratio of catalyzed rate to the homogeneous rate occurs with the use of high-area (porous) catalyst pellets packed in a reactor. Catalysts such as those frequently utilized in practice have areas of the order of 100 m^2/g or more. Arguments based on the absolute theory of reaction rates show that, although very seldom observed, the rate of a catalyzed reaction may proceed faster than the corresponding homogeneous reaction, even when the activation energy for the rate-limiting step on the catalyst is no less than that for the homogeneous reaction (Schlosser 1972, p. 57).

The changes in energy associated with the different steps in a simple exothermic reaction can be depicted as shown in Fig. 1.1. E_{hom} is the activation energy for the homogeneous reaction, E_{ads} for adsorption of reactants onto the catalyst, E_{cat} for the formation of the activated complex, and E_{des} for the desorption of products. λ_{ads} is the heat of adsorption of reactants, taken to be exothermic, and λ_{des} is the heat of desorption of products, taken to be endothermic. The overall energy

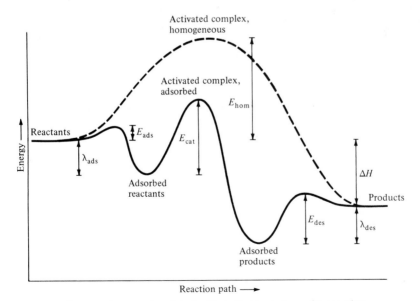

Figure 1.1   Energy changes associated with individual steps of a reaction.

change upon reaction is ΔH and is, of course, the same for the two pathways.

From experimental rate data, an *apparent activation energy* can be calculated from the slope of an Arrhenius plot of the log of an observed rate constant as a function of the reciprocal of the absolute temperature. To proceed from this to calculation of the activation energy of a surface process in the general case requires a knowledge or assumption of the mechanism of the surface reaction, identification of the rate-controlling step, and heats of adsorption and desorption, as developed in Chap. 3. This treatment also shows that there is no reason why a straight-line relationship between $\log k$ and $1/T$ should be expected to be encountered over a substantial range of temperature.

It is usually found that the apparent or effective activation energy for a catalyzed reaction is less than that for the same reaction proceeding homogeneously, both being determined from the slope of an Arrhenius plot. It is to be emphasized, however, that there is no fundamental reason why this should always be the case. Nevertheless, a consequence of this common behavior is that with increased temperature a point is usually reached beyond which the rate of a catalyzed reaction is exceeded by the rate of the homogeneous reaction.

With some endothermic reactions, high temperatures are required in order for a substantial amount of the product to be present at equilibrium, and these temperatures may be so high that no significant increase in rate is achieved by any catalyst. An example is the dehydrogenation of ethane to form ethylene and hydrogen, in which a temperature of about 725°C is required for 50-percent conversion to equilibrium at atmospheric pressure. Little increase in rate is obtained with a heterogeneous catalyst, and the process is carried out industrially as a homogeneous thermal reaction. For conversion of a higher paraffin such as butane to butene, however, a specified degree of conversion to equilibrium can be obtained at considerably lower temperatures than with ethane, and a substantial increase in rate is observed with use of a catalyst such as chromia-alumina.

1.5   Classification and Selection of Catalysts

Catalysts effective in practice range from minerals used with little or no further processing; to simple massive metals, to substances of precise and complex composition. The latter may have to be carefully prepared under closely controlled conditions, and their effectiveness in use may also require careful control of the environment in the reactor. The desired catalytic action may range from the acceleration of a simple inorganic reaction that can go in only one direction, to a highly selective organic reaction that may involve complicated interactions among many intermediate species.

The difficulty of choosing or developing a catalyst may vary greatly as indicated by a scheme of the order of increasing complexity, suggested by Roginskii (1968):

I. Selection among known catalysts
   A. For known reactions
   B. For reactions analogous to known catalytic reactions
   C. For new reactions
II. Search for new catalysts
   A. For well-known catalytic reactions
   B. For reactions analogous to those well known
   C. For reactions of new types, having no analogues among well-known reactions.

Only a few broad generalizations are offered at this point about correlations between the nature of a catalyst and the reactions it catalyzes. More specific correlations within groups of catalysts or groups of reactions are discussed later.

Solids exhibiting catalytic activity possess, in general, strong interatomic fields, such as those involved in ionic or metallic bonding. Activity is frequently associated with defects on an atomic scale. Organic covalent compounds in general are noncatalytic. A fundamental requirement is that the desired catalytic structure be stable under reaction conditions; e.g., a desired metal must remain metallic and not be converted to an inactive compound. Table 1.2 lists some of the types of reactions that are catalyzed by metals, metal oxides, and acids, and some that require both metal and acid functionality.

The metals that catalyze hydrogenation reactions do so usually because they adsorb hydrogen with dissociation and the bonding is not too strong. These are essentially the elements in group VIII [Fe, Co, Ni, and the *platinum-group metals* (pgm)] plus copper in group 1B (see Table 1.3). Both dissociated hydrogen and diatomic hydrogen may be present, but in most cases reaction occurs through a form of chemisorbed and dissociated hydrogen. Diatomic hydrogen dissociates especially readily on palladium and nickel, also on cobalt and iron. Dissociation does not occur very readily on copper, since the binding energy of hydrogen atoms on copper is relatively low. Hence, copper is a mild hydrogenating catalyst. Hydrogenation activity drops in general in the sequence Pd > Ni > Co > Fe > Cu.

The term *activation*, as applied to a reactant, is used in a very general and loose way to refer to any alteration in the chemical structure of a reactant upon adsorption that causes it to be more reactive. Thus dissociation of hydrogen (or oxygen) upon adsorption, as well as disso-

TABLE 1.2 Classification of Heterogeneous Catalysts According to Principle Functions*

	Metals		Metal oxides		Acids		Metal plus acid	
Function	Function	Examples	Function	Examples	Function	Examples	Function	Examples
Hydrogenation Hydrogenolysis†		Ni, Pd, Pt (Cu)	Partial oxidation	Complex metal molybdates	Hydration	Acid-type ion-exchange resin	Paraffin isomerization	Pt/acidified support
Oxidation		Ag, Pt		Multimetallic oxide compositions	Polymerization	H_3PO_4 on carrier	Hydrogenolysis†	Pd/zeolite
			Dehydrogenation	Fe_2O_3, ZnO, Cr_2O_3/Al_2O_3	Cracking Hydrogen transfer‡ Disproportionation§	SiO_2–Al_2O_3, zeolites in acid form		

*Some reactions are too complex to be simply classified. These include reactions of synthesis gas, the introduction of amine or nitrile groups, hydrodesulfurization and hydrodenitrogenation, and others.

†*Hydrogenolysis* is addition of hydrogen across a single bond to cause splitting into two molecules, for example, $C_2H_6 + H_2 \rightarrow 2CH_4$, also termed *hydrocracking*. It can occur on a metal by itself or, more rapidly, on a dual-function catalyst (Secs. 6.1, 9.5, 9.7 and 9.13)

‡Hydrogen transfer involves protons or hydride ions formed by rupture of a C–H bond and transferred to another molecule, for example, $C_2H_4 + C_4H_{10} \rightleftharpoons C_2H_6 + C_4H_8$.

§An example of disproportionation is

TABLE 1.3   Periodic Table of the Elements

Period	Group IA	Group IIA	Group IIIB	Group IVB	Group VB	Group VIB	Group VIIB	Group VIII			Group IB	Group IIB	Group IIIA	Group IVA	Group VA	Group VIA	Group VIIA	Group 0
1 1s	1 H																	2 He
2 2s2p	3 Li	4 Be											5 B	6 C	7 N	8 O	9 F	10 Ne
3 3s3p	11 Na	12 Mg											13 Al	14 Si	15 P	16 S	17 Cl	18 Ar
4 4s3d4p	19 K	20 Ca	21 Sc	22 Ti	23 V	24 Cr	25 Mn	26 Fe	27 Co	28 Ni	29 Cu	30 Zn	31 Ga	32 Ge	33 As	34 Se	35 Br	36 Kr
5 5s4d5p	37 Rb	38 Sr	39 Y	40 Zr	41 Nb	42 Mo	43 Tc	44 Ru	45 Rh	46 Pd	47 Ag	48 Cd	49 In	50 Sn	51 Sb	52 Te	53 I	54 Xe
6 6s(4f)5d6p	55 Cs	56 Ba	57* La	72 Hf	73 Ta	74 W	75 Re	76 Os	77 Ir	78 Pt	79 Au	80 Hg	81 Tl	82 Pb	83 Bi	84 Po	85 At	86 Rn
7 7s(5f)6d	87 Fr	88 Ra	89† Ac															

*Lanthanide series 4f	58 Ce	59 Pr	60 Nd	61 Pm	62 Sm	63 Eu	64 Gd	65 Tb	66 Dy	67 Ho	68 Er	69 Tm	70 Yb	71 Lu
†Actinide series 5f	90 Th	91 Pa	92 U	93 Np	94 Pu	95 Am	96 Cm	97 Bk	98 Cf	99 Es	100 Fm	101 Md	102 No	103 Lw

ciation of an organic molecule upon adsorption, may loosely be termed *activation*. However, hydrogen adsorption is also affected by impurities in the metal and by various species adsorbed on the surface. Thus under a particular set of circumstances, hydrogen adsorption can be low on pure copper but may be considerably enhanced by the presence of impurities, such as carbonaceous residues. Almost all these reactions are of the homolytic type (those involving noncharged intermediates). *Catalyst* activation is a different concept (Chap. 4).

Some metals also catalyze oxidations by chemisorbing oxygen, but the base metals in general cannot be used in the metallic form since they usually are converted to the oxide throughout their bulk. Only the platinum-group metals (Ru, Rh, Pd, Os, Ir, Pt) and silver and gold are sufficiently resistant. Of these, gold has little adsorptivity in general and hence has little catalytic activity; within the platinum group, osmium and iridium are very scarce. Of the others, platinum and palladium are the most important. Note, however, that the oxide form of many metallic elements, both base and noble, may be active for oxidation reactions.

Oxygen is more strongly adsorbed by metals than is hydrogen; apparently the bonds are generally too strong to be easily arranged, so higher temperatures are generally required for oxidations to occur on metals than for hydrogenations. Oxygen dissociates on copper and silver and may activate adsorbed organic species by removal of hydrogen to form a hydroxyl. Likewise, oxygen may activate adsorbed aldehydes or esters by attacking a carbon atom.

The oxide catalysts may be divided into two groups by structure. If the structure is ionic and oxygen atoms can be readily transferred to or from the lattice, the substance may be a good catalyst for partial oxidation reactions, and an oxidation-reduction "redox" (*red*uction and *ox*idation) mechanism comes into play (See 8.1). The easy movement of oxygen atoms (in some cases whether these are radicals or ions is unclear) causes the compounds to be generally nonstoichiometric, and the ratio of oxygen to metal may vary significantly with the composition of the reacting mixture. Examples are the complex molybdates containing several metals and various multimetallic oxide compositions.

The second group consists of dehydrogenation catalysts in which the oxygen is more tightly bound and the oxide must not be reducible to the metal by hydrogen at the reaction temperature. Thus the oxides suitable for partial oxidation reactions are generally not suitable for dehydrogenations. Some oxides such as chromia are intrinsically dualfunction in nature, catalyzing acid-type reactions as well as dehydrogenation reactions. Multimetallic oxide structures may also be multifunctional. Metals as such usually are not suitable for dehydrogenations because under representative reaction conditions they become rapidly deactivated by carbonaceous deposits. Note that the structure at the catalyst surface is inherently different from that of the bulk, and methods of characterizing bulk structure may be of little usefulness here.

A number of solids are acidic (Chap. 7) and can catalyze a wide variety of reactions similar to those catalyzed by strong mineral acids. These include materials in which two or more elements are tightly linked together in the structure via oxygen atoms, such as in silica-alumina and in various zeolites (crystalline aluminosilicates and related materials). Solid acids may also be formed by treating alumina so as to incorporate a halogen into its structure. Many salts such as metal sulfates and phosphates exhibit little or no acidity as prepared in the hydrated form but acquire moderate acid strength after heat treatment. The development of acidity here is associated with the gradual removal of water. Correspondingly, the extent to which water vapor is present in the reaction environment may be important. In the case of acid-catalyzed reactions, the strength and nature of the acidity (Lewis or Brönsted acids or both) are of central importance, rather than the particular elements present as such.

Paraffin isomerization and hydrocracking are examples of reactions requiring that the catalyst incorporate a metallic and an acidic function in order to accelerate each of two different intermediate steps (or groups of steps) in the overall reaction.

A number of industrially significant reactions are catalyzed by metal sulfides, but the mechanisms of action are not as well understood. Metal sulfides such as those of tungsten, of cobalt plus molybdenum, or of nickel plus molybdenum are active for hydrodesulfurization and hydrodenitrogenation (Secs. 9.9 and 9.10). Some metal sulfides are probably significantly acidic, thereby being bif· c-tional in themselves and capable of catalyzing both hydroge⁷   ɔn/ dehydrogenation reactions and acid-catalyzed reactions.

Many industrial catalysts are more complex than Table 1.1 implies. Promoters and carriers play an important role, and the trend is toward more precise tailoring of the catalyst structure, in which each ingredient and each step in preparation contributes towards better activity, selectivity, or stability.

1.6 Homogeneous Catalysis

In its widest sense, homogeneous catalysis occurs when the catalyst and the reactants are both in the same phase, either gas or liquid. In more recent years the term has come to be applied more specifically to the use of a solution of certain organo-metallic compounds in which a central metal atom is surrounded by a regular pattern of atoms or molecules, known as *ligands*, with which it is coordinated. Depending on the nature of the ligands, the metal atom may be in a low-positive, zero, or low-negative state. Several different structures may exist in equilibrium in solution simultaneously, with different reactivities, but since the catalyst is dissolved in the reacting medium, each molecule of a particular structure acts like any other. In many cases the structures, although complicated, have been well characterized, and there are systematic correlations of the structure, the nature of the ligands, and the catalytic activity of the catalyst complex.

The reactions of industrial interest are primarily hydroformylation ("oxosynthesis"), carbonylation, and addition of HCN. Homogeneous catalysts can also be effective for hydrogenations and isomerizations, but they do not appear to be used industrially for this purpose.

Several liquid-phase oxidation processes utilize a dissolved catalyst, but the mechanism is basically a free-radical process involving hydrogen abstraction and formation of a hydroperoxide, which then decomposes. For example, in the Mid-Century–Amoco process, para-xylene dissolved in acetic acid is oxidized to terephthalic acid with a mixture of Co(II), Mn(II) acetates and bromides as the catalyst. A review of the basics of homogeneous catalysis from the industrial applications point of view is given by Parshall (1980).

A useful process synthesizes CH_3COOH from CH_3OH and CO by use of a rhodium complex activated with HI, which catalyzes an insertion reaction:

$$CH_3OH + CO \rightarrow CH_3COOH \tag{1.4}$$

Operating conditions are 150 to 200°C, and pressures are 1 to 4 MPa. This supersedes an earlier process using a cobalt catalyst that required pressures of 20 to 30 MPa and a temperature of about 230°C. Closely related to the foregoing is hydroformylation in which an olefin, CO, and H_2 react to form an aldehyde, for example:

$$RCH{=}CH_2 + CO + H_2 \rightarrow RCH_2CH_2CHO \tag{1.5}$$

As with acetic acid synthesis, the first commercial processes used cobalt catalysts, but very high pressures were also required. More recent processes use a rhodium catalyst instead, which is more active, and thus much lower pressures can be utilized.

Another class of homogeneously catalyzed reactions involve a redox (*reduction* and *oxidation*) system in which intermediates alternate cyclically between two oxidation states. An example is the Wacker process for oxidizing ethylene to acetaldehyde. Reaction is carried out in an aqueous solution containing palladium(II) and copper(II) chlorides.

$PdCl_2$ reacts stoichiometrically with C_2H_4 to form Pd^0, which is reconverted to $PdCl_2$ by reaction with $CuCl_2$. The basic reactions can be represented as follows:

$$C_2H_4 + PdCl_2 + H_2O \rightarrow CH_3CHO + Pd^0 + 2HCl \tag{1.6}$$

$$2CuCl_2 + Pd^0 \rightarrow 2CuCl + PdCl_2 \tag{1.7}$$

$$C_2H_4 + 2CuCl_2 + H_2O \xrightarrow{\text{PdCl}_2} CH_3CHO + 2CuCl + 2HCl \tag{1.8}$$

$$2CuCl + 2HCl + \tfrac{1}{2} O_2 \rightarrow 2CuCl_2 + H_2O \tag{1.9}$$

The overall reaction is:

$$C_2H_4 + \tfrac{1}{2}O_2 \rightarrow CH_3CHO \tag{1.10}$$

Reaction (1.6) involves the intermediate formation of a palladium complex with chlorine and ethylene. The reactions can be carried out in a one-stage process in which all four reactions proceed simultaneously in one vessel, or the first three reactions [(1.6), (1.7), and (1.8)] can be carried out in one vessel and regeneration of $CuCl_2$ (1.9) occurs in a separate oxidation reactor.

There are no a priori guidelines to indicate in advance whether a homogeneous liquid-phase catalytic process is more or less economical than a heterogeneous vapor-phase process, where both processes produce the same product. Some factors to consider are the relative degree of selectivity in the two processes and the ease of control to avoid runaway reactions or explosions. Liquid-phase operation in a stirred vessel, with either a homogeneous or heterogeneous catalyst, provides high heat capacity, which makes temperature control easier, but corrosion problems are often more severe in the liquid phase than in the vapor phase. A homogeneous catalyst may be poisonous, and one must also consider how to separate it from the product, preferably in a form that can be readily reused.* With an expensive catalyst such as rhodium, extremely high recoveries must be achieved for an economically viable process. In many cases purity specifications also set a stringent limit on the allowable catalyst concentration in the product.

Considerable attention has been paid to possible means for eliminating the separation problem while retaining the reaction characteristics of a particular homogeneous catalyst. A porous carrier may be saturated with a solution of the homogeneous catalyst, to be used in a vapor-phase process, or the homogeneous catalyst may be attached to

---

*The fact that a heterogeneous system is inherently easier to separate than a homogeneous system was once illustrated to a lay audience by this analogy: It is easier to remove the olive from a martini than the vermouth.

a solid backbone such as a high polymer. This approach has reached commercialization in the use of immobilized enzymes adsorbed on a porous carrier for several reactions, including conversion of glucose to fructose. This subject is reviewed by Bailer (1974) and Scurrell (1978). Few gas-catalyzed reactions are used industrially, although a wide variety of such reactions are known. In the now obsolete lead chamber process for manufacture of sulfuric acid, nitrogen oxides were added to a mixture of sulfur dioxide and air. The oxidation and conversion of sulfur dioxide to sulfuric acid was catalyzed by the formation of an intermediate metastable compound, nitrosylsulfuric acid, $HNOSO_4$. Bromine catalyzes the gas-phase oxidation of hydrocarbons, the reaction being initiated by the formation of a free radical by hydrogen abstraction, the hydrogen bromide thus formed being converted back to bromine by oxidation. However, such a reaction has not been commercialized. Problems of bromine recovery and corrosion can be severe.

References

Bailer, J. C.: *Catal. Reviews*, **10**, 17 (1974).

Balandin, A. A.: *Adv. Catal.*, **19**, 1 (1969).

Burwell, R. L., Jr.: *Adv. Catal.*, **26**, 351 (1977).

Davis, B. H., and W. P. Hettinger, Jr.: *Heterogeneous Catalysis. Selected American Histories*, A.C.S. *Symp. Series No. 222*, 1983.

Driscoll, D. J., K. D. Campbell, and J. H. Lunsford: *Adv. Catal.*, **35**, 139 (1987).

Heinemann, H., in J. R. Anderson and M. Boudart (eds.): *Catalysis: Science and Technology*, vol. 1, Springer, New York, 1981, p. 1.

Parshall, G. W.: *Homogeneous Catalysis*, Wiley, New York, 1980.

Pearce, R. and W. R. Patterson (eds.): *Catalysis and Chemical Processes*, Wiley, New York, 1981.

Rideal, E. K.: *Concepts in Catalysis*, Academic Press, 1968.

Roginskii, S. Z., in A. A. Balandin et al. (eds.): *Scientific Selection of Catalysts*, English translation, Keter Pub. House., Kiryat Moshe, P.O. Box 7145, Israel, 1968.

Sabatier, P.: *Catalysis in Organic Chemistry*, 1918, English translation by E. Emmet Reid, Van Nostrand, New York, 1923.

Schlosser, E.-G.: *Heterogene Katalyse*, Verlag Chemie, Weinheim, Germany, 1972.

Schwab, G.-M., in J. R. Anderson and M. Boudart (eds.): *Catalysis: Science and Engineering*, vol. 2, Springer, New York, 1981, p. 1.

Scurrell, M. S.: *Catalysis*, vol. 2, The Chemical Society, London, 1978, p. 215.

Taylor, H. S.: *Adv. Catal.*, **1**, 1 (1948).

Volkenstein, F. F.: *The Electronic Theory of Catalysis on Semi-Conductors*, English translation, Pergamon, Elmsford, 1963.

Weissermel, K., and H.-J. Arpe: *Industrial Organic Chemistry*, English translation, Verlag Chemie, 1978.

Adsorption

Two types of adsorption phenomena have been recognized in principle for many years: physical adsorption and chemical adsorption, or chemisorption. *Physical adsorption* is caused by secondary (van der Waals) attractive forces such as dipole-dipole interaction and induced dipoles and is similar in character to condensation of vapor molecules onto a liquid of the same composition. *Chemisorption* involves chemical bonding, is similar in character to a chemical reaction, and involves transfer of electrons between adsorbent and adsorbate. Borderline cases can also clearly exist since a highly unequal sharing of electrons may not be distinguishable from a high degree of distortion of an electron cloud. Physical adsorption is of particular interest here because it provides a method of measuring the surface area of a catalyst and determining pore sizes and pore size distribution. Further, a few reactions of interest are operated at pressures and temperatures only moderately above the boiling point of the mixture of reactants and products. Although the reaction might appear to occur in the vapor phase, pore condensation caused by physical adsorption may be a significant phenomenon.

Chemisorption is of concern since almost all reactions catalyzed by a solid are believed to involve, as an intermediate step in the overall reaction, the chemisorption of one or more of the reactants. The identification and knowledge of the behavior of chemisorbed species are central to an understanding of actual catalytic mechanisms. Chemisorption can also be used as a technique of determining the surface area of one particular catalyst component, e.g., a metal, in contrast to the total area, which is determined by physical adsorption.

The evidence that chemisorption is involved in almost all solid-catalyzed reactions stems from several kinds of observations. If a solid is found to affect the reaction of a fluid, this influence must have proceeded from molecules in the fluid coming into close proximity with the surface. Presumably, adsorption of some type must have occurred for a finite time. Many catalytic reactions take place at temperatures far higher than those at which any significant physical adsorption could occur, suggesting that the adsorption must be chemical in nature. Further, there is a general correlation between catalytic activity and ability to chemisorb one or more of the reactants. Finally, the forces involved in physical adsorption are much smaller than those involved in chemical bonding: it is hard to visualize that physical adsorption could cause distortion of the force fields around a molecule of sufficient magnitude to have an appreciable effect on its reactivity.

Physical adsorption may cause an increased rate of reaction where the action is that of bringing molecules close together into a quasi-liquid layer on the surface, rather than that of forming a chemisorbed intermediate. Some of the few reactions in which the catalytic effect may be of this nature are:

$$CO + Cl_2 \rightarrow COCl_2 \text{ (phosgene)} \tag{2.1}$$

$$COCl_2 + H_2O \rightarrow 2HCl + CO_2 \tag{2.2}$$

$$2NO + O_2 \rightarrow N_2O_4 \rightleftharpoons 2NO_2 \tag{2.3}$$

For reactions (2.1) and (2.2), charcoal is a common catalyst. Reaction (2.3) at 20 to 60°C is accelerated by a silica gel catalyst.

2.1 Characterization of Type of Sorption

Chemisorption is defined as involving electronic interaction between adsorbent (the solid) and adsorbate (the fluid). The problem is how to determine experimentally the extent to which this interaction occurs in any specific situation. Some methods, principally of interest for specialized laboratory studies, may be used for directly studying electronic interaction in contrast to secondary fields:

1. Surface electric potential (work function)
2. Surface electrical conductivity
3. Collective paramagnetism (Selwood 1975) (This method requires that the adsorbent be paramagnetic and is therefore limited essentially to adsorption on nickel, cobalt, or iron, but industrial-type catalysts may be examined.)

The principal difficulties in using these techniques are the detection of the small number of adsorbed molecules relative to the size of the sample, and apparatus limitations. Aside from these methods, evidence of chemisorption is indirect and rests on a number of kinds of observations. No single one of these by itself indicates clearly in all cases whether a particular adsorption being studied is physical adsorption or chemisorption, but several taken together are usually indicative.

2.1.1   Heat effect

The magnitude of the heat effect is the most important criterion for differentiation. In physical adsorption the average heat of adsorption per mole for formation of a monolayer of adsorbed vapor usually somewhat exceeds that of liquefaction, but seldom by more than a factor of about 2. Perhaps the greatest heat effects observed with physical adsorption are with molecular sieves (zeolites) or certain forms of carbon in which passageways are little larger than the molecular size of the adsorbate and the adsorbate is surrounded by the solid on all sides.

For relatively small molecules (for example, CO, N_2, CH_4) the heat of physical adsorption is typically of the order of 10 kJ/mol. (The heat of adsorption expressed on a molar basis would be expected to increase approximately proportional to molecular weight for a homologous series, as of the paraffins.) The heats of chemisorption are frequently comparable to those of chemical reactions (80 to 200 kJ/mol) and may be as high as 600 kJ/mol. Very occasionally, however, as with hydrogen under some conditions, a chemisorption may show a heat effect comparable to that of physical adsorption. The heat of adsorption may vary considerably with surface coverage in both types of adsorption (see Sec. 2.3).

Physical adsorption is always exothermic; chemisorption is usually exothermic, but in theory it is possible for it to be endothermic, like a chemical reaction. For a spontaneous process to occur, the free energy must decrease, and from the relationship $\Delta G = \Delta H - T \Delta S$, it follows that $(\Delta H - T \Delta S) < 0$ and $\Delta H < T \Delta S$. (In other words, ΔH is a larger negative number than $T \Delta S$). If adsorption occurs without reaction on a substance whose properties are not altered by the process, a more ordered system is formed that corresponds to a decrease in the number of degrees of freedom. Therefore ΔS will be negative and ΔH also must be negative; that is, the process must be exothermic. However, deBoer has shown that if a molecule dissociates on adsorption and complete two-dimensional mobility of the adsorbate occurs, the number of degrees of freedom can increase. Hence ΔS can be positive, in which event ΔH also can be positive. In this unusual circumstance, if a diatomic molecule dissociates into two adsorbed atoms upon chemisorption, the dissociation energy of the molecule must be greater than the energy of formation of the bonds with the adsorbate.

Endothermic adsorption has been observed for several cases, e.g., when hydrogen is adsorbed onto iron contaminated with sulfide, and has been suspected in a number of others (deBoer 1956, 1957). Even when the entropy of the adsorbed species decreases because of a decrease in the number of degrees of freedom, which is the usual case, this may be more than offset by an increase in entropy of the adsorbent itself, which might expand. Cases of endothermic adsorption are nevertheless rare.

2.1.2 Rate of adsorption

Physical adsorption, like condensation, requires no activation energy and therefore can occur nearly as fast as molecules strike a surface. However, on a finely porous adsorbent, such as a zeolite or some carbons, a slow uptake of a vapor may be observed in which the rate is actually limited by the rate of diffusion of vapor into fine crevices or pores rather than by that of a sorption process as such. Many types of chemisorption exhibit an activation energy and therefore proceed at an appreciable rate only above certain minimum temperatures. Some surfaces are so active, however, that chemisorption occurs rapidly even at very low temperatures; e.g., hydrogen on tungsten metal at $-183°C$ shows little or no activation energy. Rate measurements as such are thus of limited value in distinguishing between the two types of adsorption.

2.1.3 Effect of temperature on amount adsorbed

The amount of gas physically adsorbed always decreases monotonically as temperature is increased. The amount is usually correlated with the relative pressure, P/P_0, where P is the partial pressure of the vapor in the system and P_0 is the vapor pressure that would exist above pure liquid at the same temperature. The relative pressure is analogous to the concept of relative humidity. When P/P_0 is about 0.01 or less, the amount of physical adsorption is negligible, except with solids possessing fine pores. At values of P/P_0 in the region of 0.1, the amount adsorbed corresponds to a monolayer, and as P/P_0 is increased, multilayer adsorption occurs until essentially a bulk liquid is reached at $P/P_0 = 1.0$ (see Sec. 2.2). Clearly this concept applies only for conditions below the critical.

With chemisorption a long period of time may be required for equilibrium to be established, especially at lower temperatures. The effect of temperature on the amount of material chemisorbed at equilibrium varies in a complex way with different systems. Little of general value can be said, although unlike physical adsorption, the amounts of vapor chemisorbed can be substantial at temperatures greatly above the boiling point, or, indeed, above the critical point. Frequently the amount chemisorbed is fairly constant over a certain temperature range at which the surface is saturated (Fig. 2.1, 78 kPa). At lower temperatures the amount observed to be chemisorbed is frequently less than this because the rate of adsorption is so low that saturation is not reached. Determining the true equilibrium amount chemisorbed over a substantial temperature range may be difficult. More than one kind of chemisorption can occur simultaneously, one kind being rapid and a second slow.

In some cases making a distinction between strong chemisorption and reaction with the solid may be difficult. In general, if the structural arrangement of the atoms in the bulk of the solid is not affected, the process is termed chemisorption; if the atoms in the solid are displaced or rearranged, it is termed reaction. If the adsorbate is confined to a layer not exceeding one molecule thick, this is generally termed chemisorption. In the chemisorption of oxygen onto a metal it may be difficult to limit the degree of sorption to a monolayer of oxygen, and

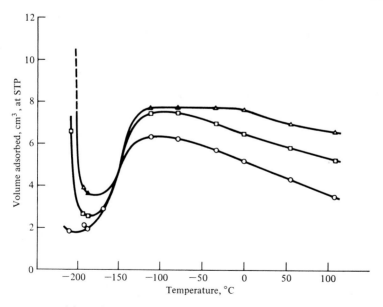

Figure 2.1   Adsorption isobars of hydrogen on nickel at 3.3 (○), 26 (□), and 78 (△) kPa. (*Benton and White 1930*)

the oxygen may readily penetrate the surface, as in the rusting of iron, sometimes termed *corrosive chemisorption.*

2.1.4 Extent of adsorption

Physical adsorption becomes multilayered at P/P_0 values above approximately 0.1 to 0.3. Chemisorption is limited to a maximum of one layer of molecules on the surface, but the maximum is frequently much less, perhaps a small fraction of a monolayer. Both physical adsorption and chemisorption can occur together, but any adsorbed layers beyond the first must presumably be physically adsorbed. A gas may be physically adsorbed initially and then more slowly form a chemisorbed species with the surface. Also, physical adsorption may occur over a chemisorbed layer. Hydrogen is readily *ab*sorbed into the interior of some metals such as nickel and palladium, and with the latter it forms two hydrides, PdH and PdH$_2$. In these cases the amount of gas sorbed can be greatly in excess of that corresponding to *ad*sorption. This behavior of Pd and Ni is one of the reasons they are good hydrogenation catalysts.

2.1.5 Reversibility

Physical adsorption is completely reversible, and equilibrium is established very rapidly unless diffusion through a finely porous structure occurs. Cycling of adsorption and desorption, as by alternately raising and lowering the pressure or temperature, can be performed repeatedly without changing the nature of the adsorbate.

Chemisorption may or may not be reversible. A chemical change in the adsorbate upon desorption is good evidence indeed that chemisorption in fact occurred. Thus oxygen chemisorbed on charcoal may be desorbed as carbon monoxide or carbon dioxide upon heating, and hydrogen adsorbed on an oxide may yield water upon heating. Ethylene adsorbed on nickel may yield other hydrocarbons on desorption. Hydrogen-deuterium exchange is also a useful diagnostic test. If HD is found in desorbed gas after H$_2$ and D$_2$ have been adsorbed onto the substrate, chemisorption must have occurred. Some chemisorbed substances are held very tenaciously. Chemisorbed oxygen on many metals, for example, can be removed only by extremely high temperature, by ion bombardment, or by reaction.

2.1.6 Specificity

Physical adsorption is relatively nonspecific. It will occur with all vapors or gases and on all surfaces, provided P/P_0 is sufficiently large. (However, this does *not* mean that the amount adsorbed at a given value of P/P_0 is independent of the nature of the adsorbate or adsorbent.) Chemisorption is highly specific: it will occur only if the adsorbate is capable of forming a chemical bond with the adsorbent. The extent of chemisorption may vary greatly with the nature of the surface and its previous treatment.

If chemisorption indeed occurs, an isobar or isotherm obtained on most catalysts will usually be complex, reflecting the heterogeneous nature of the surface. More than one type of chemisorption may be observed, and some rates may be so slow that it is questionable whether true equilibrium was reached. The sorption may be irreversible. As temperature is increased at constant pressure, more than one maxima may appear, as illustrated in Figs. 2.1 and 2.2. Data such as these may be obtained by conventional volumetric or gravimetric methods, in which the quantity of vapor transferred between the gas phase and the solid is followed as pressure or temperature is changed. Alternately, a nonadsorbing gas such as helium may be passed continuously through a sample, the gas being dosed with pulses of the adsorbate. The amount of material not adsorbed is conveniently determined by gas chromatography.

Figure 2.1 (Benton & White 1930) shows isobars for hydrogen on nickel powder at 3.3, 26, and 78 kPa pressure. The low-temperature process is ascribed to physical adsorption or to a nonactivated (i.e., a very fast) chemisorption that is weak and reversible, since the adsorbed volume decreases with increased temperature. (Since the temperature is above the critical temperature, the use of the value of relative pressure, P/P_0, to suggest degree of physical adsorption can-

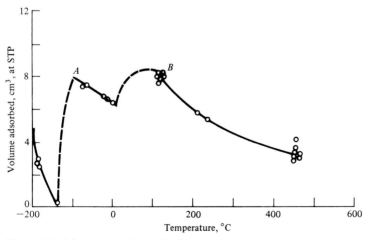

Figure 2.2 Adsorption isobar of hydrogen at atmospheric pressure on an iron catalyst used in the synthesis of ammonia, showing maxima corresponding to two types of chemisorptions. (*Emmett and Harkness 1935*)

not be applied here.) The higher-temperature process is a type of chemisorption that must be activated at least in part (i.e., the rate increases with increased temperature). Presumably, at temperatures below about $-100°C$, true equilibrium was not obtained with respect to this type of sorption. The decrease in amount adsorbed with increased temperature is consistent with that expected for a reversible exothermic process, and the plateau in the 78-kPa study suggests saturation of the surface under those conditions.

Figure 2.2 (Emmett & Harkness 1935) presents an adsorption isobar for hydrogen, at atmospheric pressure, on an iron catalyst used for ammonia synthesis. This plot shows three maxima. The low-temperature maximum is again physical adsorption or a weak chemisorption, and the maxima at A and B reflect two types of activated chemisorption. The rate of type-A sorption was inappreciable below about $-100°C$, and the rate of type-B sorption did not become appreciable until about 100°C. Strictly, Fig. 2.2 is not a true isobar in that, at least at temperatures below 100°C, true equilibrium was not obtained.

A study of hydrogen adsorption on zinc oxide is instructive, as shown in Fig. 2.3 (Taylor & Liang 1947). In the region of 111 to 154°C

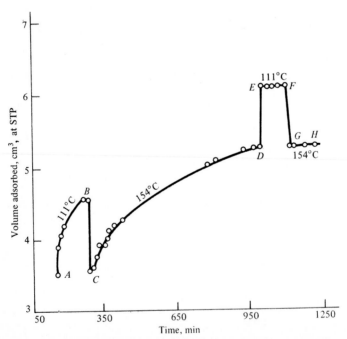

Figure 2.3 Volume of hydrogen adsorbed on zinc oxide as a function of time and temperature. (*Taylor and Liang 1947*)

the volume of hydrogen adsorbed with time was measured as temperature was alternately increased and decreased. The results indicate that two types of chemisorption were occurring simultaneously and independently of one another, suggesting that each type of sorption occurred on a different type of catalyst site. One chemisorption was extremely fast, was reversible, and decreased in amount with increased temperature; the other was slow, was irreversible, and reached a steady-state value only after many hours. The first could be ascribed to adsorption of undissociated H_2, probably on Zn atoms. The second probably comprised dissociation of H_2 onto both Zn and O atoms. Upon heating at a sufficiently high temperature, water would probably be desorbed.

2.2 Physical Adsorption Isotherms

An *adsorption isotherm* is the relationship at constant temperature between the partial pressure of the adsorbate and the amount adsorbed at equilibrium. This varies from zero at $P/P_0 = 0$ to infinity as P/P_0 reaches 1 provided that the contact angle of the condensed vapor is zero, i.e., the surface is completely wetted. If the contact angle is greater than zero, condensed vapor can form drops, and, in both theory and experiment, the condensed layer is of finite thickness at $P/P_0 = 1$. However, in practice, a slight increase in vapor pressure at $P/P_0 \approx 1$ (or slight decrease in temperature) should be sufficient to cause complete condensation to occur. If the isotherm asymptotically approaches the vertical line corresponding to $P/P_0 = 1$, this implies that the angle of contact is zero.

The shape of the isotherm may vary substantially depending on the nature of the adsorbent and the adsorbate, as illustrated by Figs. 2.4, 2.5, and 2.6. n-Pentane adsorption on three solids and on liquid water is shown in Fig. 2.4 (Kiselev & Eltekov 1957). With porous substances having pores in the general range of 2 to 50 nm (mesopores), a hysteresis loop, associated with capillary condensation, is as shown in Fig. 2.5 for argon, nitrogen, or n-butane on porous glass (Emmett & Cines 1947). Figure 2.6 shows hysteresis loops for adsorption of nitrogen on silica gel, activated carbon, and clay cracking catalyst (Ries & Johnson in Barrett et al. 1951). The lower portion of the loop is traced out on *ad*sorption, the upper portion on *de*sorption. The process is completely reproducible if the two ends of the loop are reached.

A fairly common feature is that the steep portion of the desorption branch occurs at a relative pressure that depends on the nature of the adsorbate but is almost independent of the nature of the adsorbent. (For nitrogen at its boiling point, this occurs at

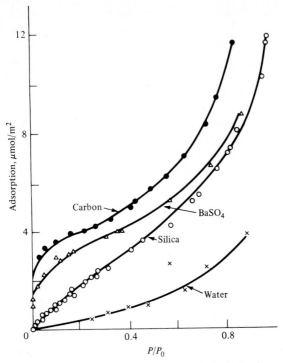

Figure 2.4 The effect of the nature of the adsorbent (marked on isotherm) on the shape of the adsorption isotherm of *n*-pentane. The adsorbent water was in liquid form. (*Kiselev and Eltekov 1957*)

$P/P_0 \sim 0.4$.) For a substance such as porous glass, in which all pores are fairly small and a narrow pore-size distribution exists, or a zeolite, the curve may reach a virtual plateau at a value of P/P_0 significantly less than 1.0. Here all the pores have become filled with condensed vapor, but the amount of vapor adsorbed on the exterior surface with increasing value of P/P_0 is small relative to that condensed in the pores (see Sec. 5.3.2).

Capillary condensation can occur in fine pores at values of $P/P_0 < 1$, since the value of P/P_0 at which this occurs is a function of the radius of curvature according to the Kelvin equation (Sec. 5.3.1). The hysteresis is caused by geometrical effects in that the surface curvature in contact with the vapor at a specified value of P/P_0 as vapor pressure is increased differs from that as the vapor pressure is decreased. This topic is addressed in Sec. 5.3 in connection with methods of determining surface area and pore-size distributions.

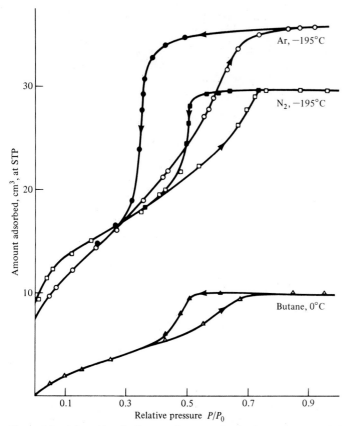

Figure 2.5 Adsorption isotherms for argon and nitrogen at −195°C and for *n*-butane at 0°C on porous glass. Open symbols, adsorption; solid symbols, desorption. (*Emmett and Cines 1947*)

2.3 Heat of Adsorption

The heat of adsorption is a significant property for characterization of the type of sorption and of the degree of heterogeneity of a surface. If truly reversible isotherms are obtainable, the differential heat of adsorption may be calculated as a function of volume of gas adsorbed, v, by cross plotting, utilizing the Clausius-Clapeyron equation:

$$\left(\frac{\partial \ln P}{\partial T}\right)_v = \frac{q}{RT^2} \tag{2.4}$$

These values of q are called *isosteric heats* of adsorption. Alternately, a calorimetric method gives an integral value of the heat of adsorption, which is the average value over the degree of surface coverage

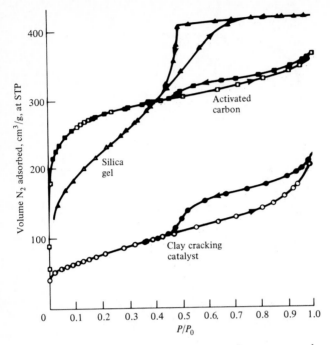

Figure 2.6 Adsorption of nitrogen at −195°C on porous substances. [*Ries and Johnson in Barrett et al. (1951)*]

studied. Differential heats of adsorption can also be determined calorimetrically by admitting small quantities of vapor at a time or by dif-
ferentiating integral data.

In general the differential heat of adsorption will decrease with increased surface coverage, although a large variety of results may be
observed. Figures 2.7 and 2.8 illustrate the kinds of information that
can be obtained (Joyner & Emmett 1948). They show differential
heats of adsorption of nitrogen on a "medium-processing" carbon black
made by the channel process, before and after graphitization, as a
function of x/x_m. x is the quantity of nitrogen adsorbed, and x_m the
quantity corresponding to a monolayer. It is evident that graphitization has made the surface much more uniform energetically. In Fig.
2.8, the slight minimum at $x/x_m \approx 0.2$ is attributed to residual surface heterogeneity; the slight maximum, to lateral interaction of
adsorbed molecules. The initial heat of adsorption on carbon is higher
before graphitization than afterwards, attributable to a few highly active centers that were removed by graphitization. Before treatment,
surface heterogeneity was so great as to overshadow any effect of lateral interaction.

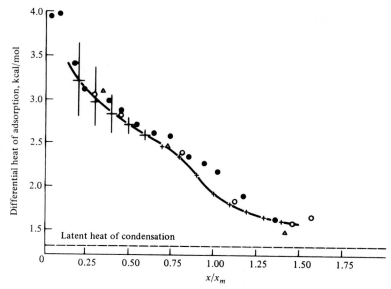

Figure 2.7   Adsorption of nitrogen on carbon black, before graphitization. The differential heat of adsorption q is plotted against x/x_m. q was determined calorimetrically at $-195°C$ ($\circ$, $\bullet$, $\triangle$), and isosterically ($+$, -194.6 to $-183.1°C$). Vertical lines indicate the maximum variation observed. (*Joyner and Emmett 1948*)

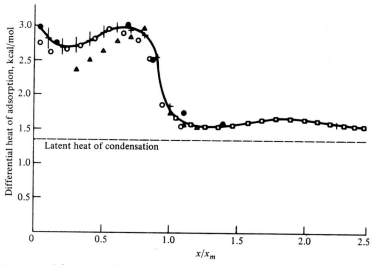

Figure 2.8   Adsorption of nitrogen on carbon black, graphitized by heating at about 3200°C. The differential heat of adsorption q is plotted against x/x_m. q was determined calorimetrically at $-195°C$ ($\circ$, $\bullet$) and also isosterically ($+$, -194.8 to $-182.8°C$; $\triangle$, -204.7 to $-194.8°C$). Vertical lines indicate maximum variation observed. (*Joyner and Emmett 1948*)

2.4   Models for Adsorption Isotherms

The derivations that follow can be applied to either physical adsorption or chemisorption, provided that equilibrium is truly reached and that the sorption process is reversible in the sense that no change in adsorbate occurs upon cycling between sorption and desorption. Theoretical derivations of isotherms may be based on kinetics, statistics, or thermodynamics.

2.4.1   Langmuir isotherm

The Langmuir adsorption isotherm is of the greatest general utility in application to catalysis because of its simplicity and because it serves as a point of departure for formulating many kinetic expressions for catalyzed reactions. A simplified version of the kinetic approach, which was originally used by Langmuir, follows. The assumptions are:

1. The adsorbed species are held onto definite points of attachment on the surface. (This implies that the maximum adsorption possible corresponds to a monolayer.) Each site can accommodate only one adsorbed species.

2. The differential energy of adsorption is independent of surface coverage. (This implies that the surface is completely uniform so that there is the same probability of adsorption on all sites. A further implication is that adsorbed molecules are localized.) Attractive or repulsive forces between adjacent adsorbed molecules are taken to be negligible, so the energy of an adsorbed species or the probability of adsorption onto an empty site are independent of whether or not an adjacent site is occupied.

Mathematical derivation.   Consider a single pure vapor A at a pressure P_A that adsorbs without dissociation onto a surface. Let the occupied fraction of sites on which adsorption is possible be θ_A. The rate of adsorption dn_A/dt is proportional to the rate of molecular collisions with unoccupied sites:

$$\left(\frac{dn_A}{dt}\right)_{ads} = k(1 - \theta_A)P_A \tag{2.5}$$

The rate of desorption is proportional to the number of molecules adsorbed.

$$\left(\frac{dn_A}{dt}\right)_{des} = k'\theta_A \tag{2.6}$$

At equilibrium, the rate of adsorption equals the rate of desorption, so that

$$k(1 - \theta_A)P_A = k'\theta_A \tag{2.7}$$

$$\theta_A = \frac{kP_A}{k' + kP_A} = \frac{K_A P_A}{1 + K_A P_A} \tag{2.8}$$

where the adsorption equilibrium constant $K_A = k/k'$. K_A can be expressed in the form $K = Ae^{+\lambda/RT}$, where λ ($= -\Delta H$) is the heat of adsorption. A large value of K implies strong bonding. The larger the value of K, the greater is the fractional surface coverage at a fixed temperature and at a fixed value of P_A, or the higher is the temperature required for a specified fractional surface coverage at fixed P_A. At low values of P_A, the fraction of the sites covered is directly proportional to P_A, but at high values of P_A, the fraction approaches unity asymptotically and becomes essentially independent of pressure.

A similar approach can be applied to derive isotherms for two or more gases competing for adsorption on the same kind of sites, for adsorption on different kinds of sites, for dissociation of gases upon adsorption, etc. Some of these cases are developed in Chap. 3 in conjunction with the formulation of correlations for kinetic data.

The Langmuir isotherm can also be derived by a thermodynamic or statistical approach, which avoids the necessity of assuming that forward and reverse rates of adsorption and desorption follow a particular postulated mechanism. A conclusion of the statistical derivation is that the assumption of no interaction between adsorbed species implies that they are immobile. This is in the sense that there is no translational motion of adsorbed species in the plane of the surface. The thermodynamic derivation assumes that adsorption is nonlocalized and arrives at the same mathematical form of the equation, but the constant K has a different theoretical interpretation. The Langmuir approach has also been applied to a heterogeneous surface. This involves assuming some distribution of energies of sites and summing up Langmuir isotherms over the total.

Few chemisorption isotherms correspond to the Langmuir equation over the whole range of surface coverage. A major objection to using the Langmuir model is that the heat of adsorption in fact generally decreases with increased surface coverage, contrary to the foregoing assumption. This is caused by one or more of the following:

1. Repulsive forces between adjacent adsorbed molecules
2. The heterogeneous character of all but the most meticulously prepared surfaces

3. The fact that more than one type of bonding may occur between the adsorbed molecules and the surface

The first two effects will cause a range of adsorption energies, and this is, in fact, commonly encountered. The initial adsorption occurs most readily on the most energetic sites, with accompanying high differential heats of adsorption, but this decreases as the less active sites become covered. In the application of the Langmuir isotherm to correlation of kinetic data, however, neglect of the variable heat of adsorption may not be serious. Molecules adsorbed on the most active sites may be held so firmly that they do not participate in the reaction, while the energy of interaction on weak sites may be too low to cause reaction to occur. Only those sites of an intermediate activity would thus actually participate in a catalytic reaction (see Chap. 3).

2.4.2 Freundlich isotherm

A classic isotherm generally associated with the name of Freundlich, and originally empirical, is:

$$\theta_A = cP_A^{1/n} \tag{2.9}$$

Here $n > 1$, and the parameters n and c usually both decrease with increasing temperature. Often this equation satisfactorily represents data over a wide range of values of θ and for systems that do not follow the Langmuir isotherm. Even for a system that does follow the Langmuir isotherm, over a moderate range of coverage intermediate between the extremes of $\theta = 0$ and $\theta = 1$, the Langmuir isotherm is nearly equivalent to θ being proportional to a fractional power of P_A. The Freundlich isotherm, by suitable adjustment of the two constants, thus can be made to fit the data almost as well.

The Freundlich isotherm can also be derived theoretically by a statistical approach in which the Langmuir adsorption isotherm is applied to a distribution of energies among the sites such that the heat of adsorption decreases logarithmically with coverage. In its empirical form the Freundlich isotherm gives no limiting value of θ, which is contrary to chemisorptions, but the statistical derivation sets a maximum value of θ that is related to the heat of adsorption. A thermodynamic derivation leads to the theoretical interpretation of n as a constant representing the mutual interaction of adsorbed species. A value of n greater than unity, the usual case, is interpreted to mean that adsorbed molecules repulse one another.

2.4.3   Temkin (Slygin-Frumkin) isotherm

The decrease in differential heat of adsorption with coverage is more likely to be linear than logarithmic, and this assumption is made in deriving the Temkin isotherm, namely,

$$q = q_0(1 - \alpha\theta) \tag{2.10}$$

Applying the Langmuir adsorption isotherm to this distribution of energies, we can show that in the middle range of coverage between $\theta = 0$ and $\theta = 1$,

$$\theta = \frac{RT}{q_0\alpha} \ln A_0 P \tag{2.11}$$

where q_0 = differential heat of adsorption at zero surface coverage, $A_0 = a_0 e^{-q_0/RT}$ (A_0 is independent of surface coverage), and a_0 and α are constants. The same mathematical expression is obtained if the decrease in q is caused either by repulsive forces on a uniform surface or from surface heterogeneity. This equation, like that of Freundlich, provides two adjustable constants, α and a_0. If q_0 is unknown, data may be correlated using A_0 and the product ($q_0\alpha$).

More details on the mathematical derivation of the various isotherms are given by Hayward and Trapnell (1964) and by Adamson (1976).

2.5   Chemisorption

The belief that chemisorption of one or more of the reactants is involved, as an intermediate step, in essentially all solid-catalyzed reactions leads to the hope that an understanding of chemisorption phenomena on catalysts would illuminate and clarify the mechanisms of catalytic action. A vast literature exists on chemisorption and the relationships between chemisorption and catalysis, but most generalizations that have emerged must be hedged with such qualifications that little can be said in summary that is helpful without being misleading. Nevertheless, several aspects of chemisorption are of particular interest in catalysis.

1. The *rates* of chemical adsorption of reactants or desorption of products, studied individually, may indicate the slow, and therefore rate-limiting, step in the catalytic reaction. They may also help characterize surface heterogeneities.

2. The *heat of chemisorption* is a measure of the strength of the bonds formed between adsorbent and adsorbate. The variation of heat of

adsorption with surface coverage is a measure of surface heterogeneity.

3. The *nature* of the actual chemisorbed species as revealed, for example, by infrared adsorption gives direct evidence of possible chemical intermediates in the reaction.

Chemisorption phenomena may also be deceptive. Many chemisorption studies have been performed on catalysts under conditions of pressure and temperature different from those used for reaction, so it is far from clear that the phenomena observed also occur as an intermediate step in the actual reaction. Frequently, two or three kinds of chemisorption have been observed between one adsorbent and one adsorbate, but it is doubtful that more than one is actually involved in the chemical reaction; other chemisorbed molecules may just "sit" on the catalyst. Chemisorption on pure metals is simpler than chemisorption on oxides, and numerous studies have been reported using pure metal films, wires, etc. However, the behavior of the same metal when supported on a carrier, as in a commercial catalyst, may be significantly different. Although conclusions from chemisorption studies are usually debatable, such studies do provide clues as to the cause of catalyst behavior.

It is frequently useful, especially in developing kinetic mechanisms, to distinguish between *nondissociative chemisorption*, in which the molecule adsorbs without fragmentation (also termed *associative chemisorption*), and *dissociative chemisorption*, in which two or more fragments are formed, all of which remain momentarily adsorbed on the surface. Hydrogen generally dissociates upon adsorption on metals, a process that can be symbolized as:

$$H\text{—}H(g) + 2* \rightarrow 2H*$$

where the asterisk represents a surface site. The initial heat of adsorption is about 80 to 100 kJ/mol for all metals.

Propylene adsorbs on certain metal oxides by dissociation, splitting off a hydrogen atom to form a π-allyl complex with the surface:

$$
\begin{array}{c}
H \\
| \\
H_2C \text{---} C \text{---} CH_2 \\
\downarrow \\
*
\end{array}
$$

Hydrogen sulfide adsorbs on a metal site without dissociation, which may be symbolized as

$$H_2S + * \longrightarrow \underset{\underset{*}{\downarrow}}{\overset{H \quad H}{\underset{\diagdown}{\diagup}}} S$$

Carbon monoxide adsorbs strongly on all group VIII metals in an undissociated form in which the carbon atom is bonded to one or two metal atoms (termed *linear* or *bridged forms*). The nature of adsorbed species, the structure of an adsorbed complex, bonding strengths, and the like are of major concern in fundamental mechanistic studies, but the subject is not pursued further here. A simple example is shown in the hydrodenitrogenation of quinoline (Sec. 9.10). The first step is either hydrogenation of the heterocyclic ring or of the benzene ring. Which occurs preferentially is determined by how the quinoline is adsorbed onto the catalyst, and this varies with reaction conditions.

The classic example of the study of chemisorption rates to indicate the slow step in a catalyzed reaction is the chemisorption of hydrogen and nitrogen on the promoted iron catalyst used for synthesis of ammonia. Three different types of hydrogen chemisorption on iron were identified by Emmett, but hydrogen chemisorption occurs rapidly at temperatures well below those used in synthesis. Nitrogen chemisorption, on the other hand, is much slower, and only at about 450°C does the rate of nitrogen adsorption during the first few seconds of exposure to the catalyst become approximately equal to the rate of synthesis of ammonia from a 3:1 H_2/N_2 mixture at the same temperature and on the same catalyst. Researchers generally agree that the rate of nitrogen adsorption is rate-limiting. For the development of a kinetic expression and deeper understanding of mechanism, however, consideration of simultaneous adsorption in the presence of both gases, the possibility of other transitory intermediates such as NH and NH_2, and the effects of varying pressure and temperature is necessary (see Sec. 10.5.2).

The fact that chemisorption and chemidesorption rates may be quite slow even at elevated reaction temperatures means that a long time lag is sometimes required for the adsorbed phase to come to equilibrium with the gas phase. This period can amount to hours or days. In a continuous-flow chemical reactor, an appreciable time may be required for a steady-state exit-gas composition to be reached when a reactant is present in the feed stream in very low concentrations. The absolute quantity of reactant entering the reactor per unit time may then be small relative to the surface area of catalyst present. Nonsteady-state methods of studying catalytic reactions in the laboratory, as by pulse-type reactors, may lead to confusing and misleading results for this and other reasons.

A perhaps extreme case occurs in practice in the use of catalysts on automobiles for control of exhaust pollutants. Traces of sulfur in the fuel are converted to sulfur oxides, some of which adsorb on the alumina-based catalyst that is commonly used. Unlike the operation of most commercial catalytic reactors, here the temperature and flow rate of gases through the catalyst bed vary erratically as the automobile is driven. The result is that sulfur oxides may be stored on and emitted from the catalyst by adsorption and desorption in a different erratic pattern.

The relative adsorptivities of different species on a catalyst can have a profound effect on activity, selectivity, poisoning, and the form of the rate expression, as developed in Chap. 3. In a mixture of two reactants, a strongly adsorbed reactant may react to the almost complete exclusion of the second if the latter is weakly adsorbed. If a product is more strongly adsorbed than a reactant, the rate of reaction may drop very markedly as degree of conversion is increased.

A few generalizations help to provide orientation, although many exceptions will arise. Within groups of hydrocarbons, the strength of adsorption typically is in the order:

$$\text{Acetylenes} > \text{diolefins} > \text{olefins} > \text{paraffins}$$

Polar substances are generally more strongly adsorbed than nonpolar substances, with the consequence that in hydrogenation reactions the product is usually less strongly adsorbed than the reactant. The opposite is frequently the case in partial oxidation reactions. Other factors being equal, the degree of adsorptivity increases with molecular weight. Adsorption can also be affected by various specific interactions. Thus, aromatic compounds may be held relatively strongly onto some metals by π bonding. On most metals, Bond (1987) finds that, in general, the strength of adsorption for some simple gases and vapors falls in the sequence:

$$O_2 > C_2H_2 > C_2H_4 > CO > H_2 > CO_2 > N_2$$

Oxygen is so strongly adsorbed that it frequently leads to a reaction in which oxygen is no longer confined to a chemisorbed surface layer. In that event the catalyst structure becomes altered or even perhaps destroyed. Similarly, metal carbides may be formed from a metal, as occurs with iron or nickel.

References

Adamson, A. W.: *Physical Chemistry of Surfaces*, 3d ed., Wiley, New York, 1976.
Barrett, E. P., L. G. Joyner, and P. P. Halenda: *J. Am. Chem. Soc.*, **73**, 373 (1951).

Benton, A. F., and T. A. White: *J. Am. Chem. Soc.*, **52**, 2325 (1930).

Bond, G. C.: *Heterogeneous Catalysis: Principles and Applications*, 2d ed., Oxford, New York, 1987.

deBoer, J. H.: *Adv. Catal.*, **8**, 17 (1956).

————: *Adv. Catal.*, **9**, 472 (1957).

Emmett, P. H., and M. Cines: *J. Phys. Chem.*, **51**, 1248 (1947).

———— and R. W. Harkness: *J. Am. Chem. Soc.*, **57**, 1631 (1935).

Hayward, D. O., and B. M. W. Trapnell: *Chemisorption*, 2d ed., Butterworth, London, 1964.

Joyner, L. G., and P. H. Emmett: *J. Am. Chem. Soc.*, **70**, 2353 (1948).

Kiselev, A. V., and Y. A. Eltekov: *International Congress Surface Activity, II*, Butterworth, London, 1957, p. 228.

Selwood, P. W.: *Chemisorption and Magnetization*, Academic, New York, 1975. (An earlier edition was published as *Adsorption and Collective Paramagnetism*, Academic, New York, 1962.)

Taylor, H. S., and S. C. Liang: *J. Am. Chem. Soc.*, **69**, 1306 (1947).

3

Rates and Kinetic Models of Catalytic Reactions

3.1 Introduction

Correlations of rate data may be sought for any of several purposes. The process engineer may wish to develop a model for a specific reaction so as to be able to predict the effect of reactor operating changes on performance. The fundamental investigator may wish to determine how the rate of a particular reaction varies as catalyst composition is systematically varied, with the aim of relating the results in a fundamental fashion to specific physical or chemical properties of the catalyst. A study of the detailed kinetics of one particular reaction has been a traditional approach to obtaining some understanding, even though indirect, of its mechanism. Regardless of the objective, the investigator desires a mathematical model to represent the data.

Consider a reaction occurring between a fluid and a porous solid catalyst. In order for reaction to occur, the reactants in the fluid must first be transported to the outer surface of the solid, and then they must diffuse through the pores of the solid to catalytically active sites. At least one of the reactant species must usually be chemisorbed onto the surface of the solid. Subsequently, reaction occurs among chemisorbed species or between a chemisorbed species and another species that is either physically adsorbed or that collides with the chemisorbed species directly from the fluid phase. After reaction, products are desorbed and diffuse out through the pores of the catalyst to the bulk fluid. Because the rates of these various steps respond in a different way to experimental variables such as pressure, temperature, bulk-fluid velocity, and chemical and physical structure of the catalyst, they can be conveniently classified as follows:

1. Mass transfer of reactants and products by counterdiffusion between the bulk fluid and the outer surface of the catalyst particle

2. Mass transfer of reactants and products by counterdiffusion through the porous structure of the catalyst

3. Adsorption of reactants onto the catalyst surface and desorption of products

4. Chemical reaction involving one or more chemisorbed species

One or more of these steps may be rate-limiting in the sense that it consumes the major portion of the chemical potential available for carrying out the process.

Quantitative methods of determining the extent to which mass-transfer effects are significantly rate-limiting (steps 1 and 2) are described elsewhere (Satterfield 1970), as well as the effect of temperature gradients that frequently accompany concentration gradients. In what follows rate of reaction is assumed to be proportional to surface area (or number of catalytically active sites) and the entire catalyst surface inside a pellet is exposed to reactant of uniform composition and temperature; i.e., effects of transfer of heat or mass to or within a porous catalyst are insignificant.

The true mechanism in all its details is not known for even the simplest catalytic reaction. The closer a model reflects actuality, of course, the more reliable it is, but an attempt to allow for the complex nature of a heterogeneous reaction may easily lead to a complicated formulation containing many parameters that must be empirically adjusted. In this event the model loses theoretical justification. If an industrial reaction proceeds by a complex and little-known mechanism, the process engineer may find it adequate to use an essentially empirical correlation. Conveniently, this is the Arrhenius expression with power functions of reactant concentrations, the exponents being arbitrary adjustable constants. In any event, the basic guiding principle should be based on a maxim enunciated by an English philosopher, William of Occam, in the fourteenth century: "Entities ought not to be multiplied except out of necessity." Since it is a mental paring device for pruning away "entities" in the sense of unnecessary hypotheses and complexities in explaining observations or experiments, it is known as *Occam's razor*. In the present context it suggests that mathematical formulations should be no more complicated than those necessary to explain the facts and to be consistent with well-established theory. The book by Boudart and Djéga-Mariadassou (1984) treats the kinetics of heterogeneous catalytic reactions on metals in terms of fundamental mechanistic arguments that provide a background for deeper understanding of some of the rate equations used in practice and possible improvement of them. A similar treatment is available in a detailed review by Temkin (1979).

3.2 Empirical Correlations

For studies of homogeneous gas-phase reactions, the rate of an elementary bimolecular reaction (one occurring at the instant of collision of two molecules, free radicals, or other species) between two species A and B is given by

$$\text{Rate,} \frac{\text{molecules reacted}}{\text{(time)(volume)}} = kC_A C_B \tag{3.1}$$

$$= Ae^{-E/RT}C_A C_B$$

Equation (3.1) is known as the *Arrhenius expression* when A, the *preexponential factor*, is taken to be independent of temperature. From collision theory, A varies as the square root of the temperature. In transition-state theory the effect of temperature on A varies somewhat with the structure of the reactant molecules and the nature of the intermediate complex formed. Since in any event the effect of temperature on A is small relative to its effect on the exponential term, one may with little error take A to be independent of temperature.

By analogy, a simple expression for the rate r of a heterogeneously catalyzed reaction between A and B is

$$\text{Rate,} \frac{\text{molecules reacted}}{\text{(time)(area)}} = k_0 e^{-E/RT} \cdot f(C_A C_B) \tag{3.2}$$

where k_0 is taken to be independent of temperature and surface area of the catalyst. The function of the concentrations which usually is easiest to use in correlating rate data, consists of simple power functions: $C_A{}^a \cdot C_B{}^b$, where a and b are empirically adjusted constants. Hence

$$-r = k_0 e^{-E/RT} C_A{}^a C_B{}^b \tag{3.3}$$

More generally, this may be expressed as

$$-r = k \prod_i C_i^{a_i} \tag{3.4}$$

where a_i is termed the order of the reaction with respect to C_i.

Equation (3.3) is an example of a *power-rate law*. For this expression to be useful, k_0 and E should indeed be functions only of the catalyst and the reacting system, and not of temperature or concentration. Likewise, the function of concentration should be independent of temperature and of composition; for example, a reaction that is first order with respect to A should follow that relationship over the range of concentrations of A that are of interest. For the most precise studies the rate should be expressed per number of active sites, termed the *turnover number* (Sec. 1.3.7). Sometimes this can be determined quantitatively, as with some supported metal catalysts, but usually the number of active sites is unknown. The rate may then be expressed per unit total area, $\bar{r}_a$; per weight or volume of catalyst, r_w or r_v; or per volume of packed reactor. For most industrial catalysts, the rate per unit weight of catalyst is most customary. The IUPAC recommendation is that r_a be termed the *areal rate of reaction*, but this usage is not currently widespread.

The term k_0 in Eq. (3.3) usually has no theoretical significance, and the exponents may be integral or fractional, positive, zero, or negative. However many catalytic reactions follow a simple relationship of this type over a sufficiently wide range of conditions as to make the correlation useful. Theoretically derived models may also reduce to power-law forms in which a and b are integers or half-integers.

Power-law kinetics can often be used to develop useful correlations, such as when a given reaction is studied on a series of catalysts, or when a series of related reactions is studied on one catalyst. As one proceeds from catalyst to catalyst, or reaction to reaction, the preexponential factor k_0 sometimes remains constant and the activation energy changes or the activation energy remains constant and the preexponential factor changes. Although such correlations may be essentially empirical, they may provide a basis for modest extrapolation of rate data, or for estimation of the rate of reaction of a substance that is a member of a homologous series for which information is available on other compounds in the group.

A more confusing series of reacting systems is also frequently found in which the concentration function in Eq. (3.2) remains constant but E and k_0 both change. When each change has the same algebraic sign (both positive or both negative), this is termed *compensation*, since the reaction rate is affected less than it would be if either E or k_0 alone varied (Sec. 3.7). Finally, the reaction rate may not fit a relationship of the form of Eq. (3.2) or Eq. (3.3). The apparent order of the reaction and the apparent activation energy may change with temperature, which requires developing a different kinetic model, such as the Langmuir-Hinshelwood formulation discussed in Sec. 3.3.1.

3.3   Formal Kinetic Models

If the rate is expressed as a simple power function, for example, of the form of Eq. (3.3), a and b may not be integers and their values, as well as the value of E, may change with temperature. In part this is because the driving force for reaction has been assumed to be a function of the concentration of reacting species in the fluid phase. A more logical driving force is the concentration of adsorbed species on the catalyst. However, in most cases neither the exact nature of these species nor their concentrations are known. In spite of this ignorance a model will clearly be somewhat closer to reality if it is possible on some rational basis to formulate rates in terms of concentration of species believed to exist on the surface. Relating these surface concentrations to those existing in the bulk phase allows the rate to be formulated in terms of readily measurable concentrations. These relationships are developed from knowledge of adsorption phenomena.

Relatively less guidance is available to indicate the actual form of the adsorbed species. In some cases calorimetric or other studies indicate that dissociation occurs on adsorption, as usually occurs with hydrogen on metals. Studies by infrared adsorption of surface species also give clues to the form of the adsorbed species. In the absence of any positive evidence to the contrary the adsorbed species is sometimes assumed to have the same molecular structure as that in the fluid phase. However, some degree of charge transfer may occur; that is, an adsorbed species may be an ion rather than a neutral molecule.

For tractability in mathematical analysis and in theoretical understanding, one step in the reaction is customarily assumed to be *rate-limiting* or *rate-controlling*. This may be the rate of adsorption of one reactant, the rate of a surface reaction between adsorbed species, or the rate of desorption of a product. All the other steps are assumed to be in equilibrium with one another. The concept of a rate-controlling step can be confusing. Since all the processes occur in series under steady-state conditions, they must all actually have the same rate, but the rate-limiting step is the one that consumes essentially all the driving force (chemical potential) available. In an electrical analogy, a current passing through several resistances in a series is the same in each resistor, but if the conductivity of one is much less than that of the others, it is the rate-limiting resistor.

The evidence identifying the rate-controlling step is frequently tentative and stems from various kinds of studies. The rates of adsorption of individual reactants onto the catalyst surface (and/or desorption of products therefrom) may be studied in the absence of reaction. Adsorption and desorption rates, as determined from studies with isotropic tracers, may be compared with the reaction rate under reaction conditions. The rate-limiting step may also be indicated by formulating the kinetic expression for the rate of reaction for each different, plausible rate-limiting step. Each formulation is then compared with experimental data, and the mathematical form that best fits the experimental facts suggests a possible mechanism for the reaction.

Frequently the same mathematical form may be derived from more than one different postulated mechanism, in which case the parameters may have considerably different theoretical interpretations. Hence, the fitting of data to a particular mathematical expression seldom, of itself, proves much concerning the true mechanism. The extent to which these approaches lead to reliable and useful conclusions varies greatly from case to case and calls for astute judgment on the part of the investigator.

In many cases the rate of reaction of one or more chemisorbed species appears to be the rate-limiting step, rather than rate of adsorption or desorption as such. The kinetic formulations based on this assumption usually bear the term *Langmuir-Hinshelwood*. The term *Langmuir-Rideal, Rideal,* or *Rideal-Eley* is applied if reaction is assumed to be between a chemisorbed species and a molecule reacting with it directly from the fluid phase or from a physically adsorbed layer.

3.3.1 Langmuir-Hinshelwood model

The assumptions underlying the Langmuir adsorption isotherm are retained (Sec. 2.4.1). Further, adsorption equilibrium is assumed to be established at all times; for example, the rate of reaction is taken to be much less than the potential rate of adsorption or desorption. The concentrations of adsorbed species are therefore determined by adsorption equilibria as given by the Langmuir isotherm. If two or more species are present, they compete with each other for adsorption on a fixed number of active sites.

Reaction is assumed to occur between adsorbed species on the catalyst. If a single reactant is decomposed, the process may be assumed to be either unimolecular or bimolecular, depending on the number of product molecules formed per reactant molecule and whether or not the products are adsorbed. A simple decomposition in which products are not adsorbed is usually taken to be unimolecular (Case 3.1). If two adsorbed product molecules are formed for each reactant molecule decomposed, it is postulated that an empty site must be adjacent to the adsorbed reactant molecule to accommodate the additional molecule formed. The reaction is then "bimolecular" in the sense that the rate is proportional to the product of the concentration of adsorbed reactants and of empty sites.

If reaction takes place between adsorbed A and adsorbed B and these species are immobile, they must be adsorbed on neighboring sites in order for reaction to occur. The mechanism may be visualized as follows, where θ_i represents the fraction of available sites on which species i is adsorbed.

$$A + B + 2* \underset{\text{adsorption}}{\overset{\longrightarrow}{\rightleftharpoons}} \quad \begin{array}{cc} A & B \\ | & | \\ -*- & -*- \end{array}$$

$$\Bigg\Downarrow\Bigg\Uparrow$$

$$\begin{array}{cc} A{-}B \\ | \quad | \\ -*{-}*{-} \end{array} \quad \text{(activated complex)}$$

$$\text{Products} + 2* \underset{\text{desorption}}{\overset{\longrightarrow}{\rightleftharpoons}} \quad -*{-}*{-}$$

The probability of reaction here is taken to be proportional to the product $\theta_A \theta_B$.

By the foregoing and analogous procedures, rate expressions can be derived for any type of postulated mechanism. The form and complexity of the expression depend on the assumptions made concerning this mechanism. A few cases are presented below:

Case 3.1: Decomposition, Products Not Adsorbed

$$A \rightarrow \text{products}$$

The reaction rate is taken to be proportional to the quantity of adsorbed A molecules. Then,

$$-r, \frac{\text{(moles)}}{\text{(time)(area)}} = k\theta_A \tag{3.5}$$

The value of θ_A is given by the Langmuir adsorption isotherm (Sec. 2.4.1):

$$\theta_A = \frac{KP_A}{1 + KP_A} \tag{3.6}$$

Combining these two equations,

$$-r = \frac{kKP_A}{1 + KP_A} \tag{3.7}$$

If the system follows this model, the reaction rate should be first order at sufficiently low values of P_A. As P_A increases, the order of reaction should gradually drop and become zero order. Similarly, the reaction rate should be first order if A is weakly adsorbed—for example, K is small—and zero order if A is strongly adsorbed. This type of behavior is indeed found for a number of decompositions.

Case 3.2: Decomposition, Products Adsorbed

$$A \rightarrow B + C$$

Assume:

1. A, B, C all may be appreciably adsorbed.
2. The reaction rate is proportional to the quantity of adsorbed A molecules.
3. No dissociation of A molecules occurs on adsorption.
4. Reverse reaction is negligible.

Again using the Langmuir adsorption isotherm, the fraction of surface covered by A, B, and C can be derived from the adsorption/desorption equilibrium to be as follows:

$$k_A[1 - \Sigma\theta]P_A = k'_A\theta_A$$

where $\Sigma\theta$ is the fraction of available sites covered with A, B, and C.

$$\theta_A = K_AP_A[1 - (\theta_A + \theta_B + \theta_C)] = K_AP_A(1 - \Sigma\theta) \qquad (3.8)$$

$$\theta_B = K_BP_B(1 - \Sigma\theta) \qquad (3.9)$$

$$\theta_C = K_CP_C(1 - \Sigma\theta) \qquad (3.10)$$

Adding Eqs. (3.8), (3.9), and (3.10),

$$\Sigma\theta = (1 - \Sigma\theta)[K_AP_A + K_BP_B + K_CP_C] \qquad (3.11)$$

Subtracting both sides of Eq. (3.11) from unity and rearranging,

$$(1 - \Sigma\theta) = \frac{1}{1 + K_AP_A + K_BP_B + K_CP_C} \qquad (3.12)$$

Two molecules are formed for each one that reacts, and both product molecules are postulated to be adsorbed. It thus seems plausible that it is necessary for an empty site to be present adjacent to the reacting molecule to accommodate one of the product molecules.

In that event

$$-r = k\theta_A(1 - \Sigma\theta) \qquad (3.13)$$

Combining Eqs. (3.8), (3.12), and (3.13) gives

$$-r = \frac{kK_AP_A}{(1 + K_AP_A + K_BP_B + K_CP_C)^2} \qquad (3.14)$$

If an inert material X is present that is significantly adsorbed, then a term K_XP_X must be added in the denominator, and Eq. (3.14) would become

$$-r = \frac{kK_AP_A}{(1 + K_AP_A + K_BP_B + K_CP_C + K_XP_X)^2} \qquad (3.15)$$

Case 3.3: Bimolecular Reaction

$$A + B \rightarrow C$$

The same assumptions as in Case 3.2 are made except that the reaction rate now is assumed to be proportional to the product of the concentration of adsorbed A and adsorbed B. The rate expression then becomes

$$-r = k\theta_A\theta_B \qquad (3.16)$$

Combining Eqs. (3.8), (3.9), (3.12), and (3.16),

$$-r = \frac{kK_AK_BP_AP_B}{(1 + K_AP_A + K_BP_B + K_CP_C)^2} \tag{3.17}$$

Case 3.4: Adsorption/Desorption with Dissociation

$$A_2 \rightleftharpoons 2A \rightarrow products$$

Assume that A dissociates upon adsorption and associates on desorption. In order for dissociation to occur, a gas molecule must plausibly impinge on the surface at a location where two sites are adjacent to one another. Up to fairly high fractional coverages, the number of pairs of adjacent sites is proportional to the square of the number of single sites. Then the rate of adsorption is given by

$$\left(\frac{dn}{dt}\right)_{ads} = kP_A(1 - \theta_A)^2 \tag{3.18}$$

where P_A is the pressure of the undissociated A. Assuming desorption involves interaction of two neighboring adsorbed atoms,

$$\left(\frac{dn}{dt}\right)_{des} = k'\theta_A^2 \tag{3.19}$$

At equilibrium, $kP_A(1 - \theta_A)^2 = k'\theta_A^2$ and

$$\theta_A = \frac{(K_AP_A)^{1/2}}{1 + (K_AP_A)^{1/2}} \tag{3.20}$$

This simple equation applies to mobile adsorbed atoms at all degrees of surface coverage or to immobile adsorbed atoms at small values of θ_A. At high coverage, some unused single sites exist in the "fully covered" region, and they are not available for chemisorbing a molecule as atoms if adsorbed atoms are immobile. The exact equation for any case depends on whether or not individual atoms are mobile and the extent of coverage.

The rate of reaction might plausibly be either first order or second order with respect to dissociated A, depending on circumstances.

If $-r = k\theta_A$, upon substituting in Eq. (3.20),

$$-r = \frac{k(K_AP_A)^{1/2}}{1 + (K_AP_A)^{1/2}} \tag{3.21}$$

Alternately,

$$-r = k\theta_A^2 = \frac{kK_AP_A}{[1 + (K_AP_A)^{1/2}]^2} \tag{3.22}$$

If two atoms of dissociated A react simultaneously with B, and product adsorption is negligible, then

$$-r = k\theta_A^2 \cdot \theta_B = \frac{kK_AP_AK_BP_B}{(1 + \sqrt{K_AP_A} + K_BP_B)^3} \tag{3.23}$$

The most common example of dissociative adsorption is encountered with hydrogen on most metals. However, hydrogenation reactions are frequently approximately first order in hydrogen rather than half order. Equation (3.23) shows that even if the hydrogen dissociates, a first-order process with respect to hydrogen (for example, A) will be observed if it is not strongly adsorbed relative to B ($K_A < K_B$). Plausibly, hydrogen atoms may add to B one at a time, one of the additions being at equilibrium and the addition of the other being the rate-limiting process. Assume, for example, that the first addition, to form adsorbed HB, is in equilibrium, and the reaction HB + H → C is the rate-limiting step. Assume further that the concentration of adsorbed HA is small, and that of adsorbed C is negligible. Then the rate expression is of the identical form of Eq. (3.23), except that a term $k'K$ replaces k. Here k' is the rate constant for the rate-limiting process and K is an equilibrium constant in terms of concentrations of surface-adsorbed species.

Case 3.5: Adsorption of Two Gases on Separate Sites

$$A + B \rightarrow products$$

In this case, A and B molecules are assumed to adsorb independently on different sites. Applying the usual assumptions,

$$\theta_A = \frac{K_AP_A}{1 + K_AP_A} \tag{3.24}$$

$$\theta_B = \frac{K_BP_B}{1 + K_BP_B} \tag{3.25}$$

If the reaction rate is proportional to the product of adsorbed A and B molecules and sites are randomly distributed,

$$-r = \frac{kK_AP_AK_BP_B}{(1 + K_AP_A)(1 + K_BP_B)} \tag{3.26}$$

This type of behavior appears to be less common than competition for the same type of site, but it may be a plausible formalism to apply where the catalyst clearly has two kinds of sites, e.g., some dual-function catalysts. The behavior of some systems suggests a mixture of independent adsorption and competitive adsorption. For example, a detailed kinetic study of the hydrodesulfurization of dibenzothiophene led to the conclusion that it and reaction products competed for one type of site while hydrogen adsorbed independently on a second type of site (Singhal et al. 1981). Poisoning experiments also suggest that in some cases two kinds of sites exist on which competitive adsorption occurs, one kind being active but easily poisoned, the second less active but more resistant to poisoning. Such a hypothesis was advanced to explain some of the effects of pyridine poisoning in the hydrodesulfurization of thiophene (Satterfield et al. 1975).

3.3.2 Apparent activation energies

If the kinetic expression is of a complex form such as Eqs. (3.14) or (3.17), the overall apparent activation energy, as determined from the effect of temperature on reaction rate at constant reactant composition, will change with temperature. An Arrhenius-type plot of ln rate versus $1/T$ will not be a straight line. For some simpler kinetic expressions, the apparent activation energy will be independent of temperature, as in Case 3.1 for low surface coverage ($K_A P_A \ll 1$). Then the kinetic expression reduces to

$$-r = k_s K_A P_A \qquad (3.27)$$

Here the experimentally observed reaction rate constant k_{exp} equals $k_s K_A$, where k_s is the reaction rate constant for the surface reaction, assumed to follow the Arrhenius expression. K_A is the adsorption equilibrium constant, which decreases exponentially with increased temperature by the factor $e^{\lambda/RT}$. Here λ is the heat of chemisorption, taken to be independent of temperature. The effect of temperature on the experimentally observed reaction rate constant for a rate expression of the type in Eq. (3.27) is given by

$$k_{exp} = A e^{-(E_s - \lambda)/RT} \qquad (3.28)$$

The apparent activation energy E_a, as calculated from a plot of ln k_{exp} versus $1/T$, equals $E_s - \lambda$. Since E_s and λ will normally both have positive values, E_a will be less than the so-called true activation energy for the surface process E_s.

In corresponding fashion consider the reaction $A \rightarrow B + C$ for the case in which C is strongly adsorbed and A and B are not. The rate expression given by Eq. (3.14) reduces to

$$-r = \frac{k K_A P_A}{(K_C P_C)^2} \qquad (3.29)$$

and the apparent activation energy is given by

$$-E_a = -E_s + \lambda_A - 2\lambda_C \qquad (3.30)$$

where λ_A is the heat of adsorption of A and λ_C is the heat of adsorption of C, both normally positive.

The apparent activation energies for some bimolecular surface reactions may similarly be formulated for specific forms of Case 3.3. Consider some examples in which product adsorption is unimportant. From Eq. (3.17),

$$-r = \frac{kK_AK_BP_AP_B}{(1 + K_AP_A + K_BP_B)^2} \qquad (3.31)$$

Case 3.3A: A and B Are Weakly Adsorbed

$$-r = kK_AK_BP_AP_B \qquad (3.32)$$

$$-E_a = -E_s + \lambda_A + \lambda_B \qquad (3.33)$$

Case 3.3B: A Weakly Adsorbed; B Strongly Adsorbed

$$-r = \frac{kK_AK_BP_AP_B}{(K_BP_B)^2} = \frac{kK_AP_A}{K_BP_B} \qquad (3.34)$$

$$-E_a = -E_s + \lambda_A - \lambda_B \qquad (3.35)$$

Case 3.3C: A and B Weakly Adsorbed; A Poison X Strongly Adsorbed

$$-r = \frac{kK_AK_BP_AP_B}{(K_XP_X)^2} \qquad (3.36)$$

$$-E_a = -E_s + \lambda_A + \lambda_B - 2\lambda_X \qquad (3.37)$$

This expression shows that adsorption of a poison increases the apparent activation energy of the reaction.

Return now to the more complex kinetic expressions when they do not reduce to power-law equations. The fact that the values of E_s and of the various λ's are usually different from one another means that the relative importance of the various terms will shift with a change in temperature. They will also, of course, shift with gas composition. If data for such a case are forced into a power function, this will shift as pressure, temperature, and composition are changed.

3.3.3 Maximum in rate with increased temperature

The rate of a catalyzed reaction may sometimes reach a maximum with increased temperature. This is observed, for example, with hydrogenation of ethylene on various catalysts and with the decomposition of hydrogen peroxide vapor on platinum. (See Fig. 11.9.) Such a temperature maximum is not consistent with a power-law rate expression. However, most of the Langmuir-Hinshelwood expressions can be made to accommodate this type of behavior by invoking plausible effects of temperature on the individual adsorption and kinetic constants. For example, consider the irreversible reaction:

$$A \rightarrow B$$

Assume B is not adsorbed (Case 3.1) and low surface coverage of A. If $\lambda > E_s$, then k_{exp} will *decrease* with increasing temperature [Eq. (3.28)]. If both A and B are adsorbed, the rate expression becomes

$$-r = \frac{kK_AP_A}{1 + K_AP_A + K_BP_B} \tag{3.38}$$

and

$$\frac{d \ln r}{d(-1/RT)} = E_s - \lambda_A + \frac{K_AP_A\lambda_A + K_BP_B\lambda_B}{(1 + K_AP_A + K_BP_B)} \tag{3.39}$$

A maximum in the rate with increased temperature can then occur if $\lambda_A > E_s$ and if the third term on the right-hand side of Eq. (3.39) is predominant at low temperatures and insignificant at high temperatures. Since K_A and K_B will both decrease with increased temperature, the latter can readily happen. A physical interpretation of the overall effect is that with increased temperature the increasing reactivity of the adsorbed intermediate complex is more than offset by a decrease in its concentration.

The explanation for such temperature maxima may also lie in the inapplicability of the assumption in the Langmuir-Hinshelwood model that the number and activity of catalytic sites is constant with temperature. Indeed, a range of energies of sites is probably almost always present, so the number of sites of requisite energy for high reactivity may well change with temperature.

3.3.4 Rideal model

From studies of the catalytic activity of platinum at 500 to 1050 K, Langmuir (1921) concluded that in the oxidation of carbon monoxide with oxygen the reaction occurred by a carbon monoxide molecule striking an adsorbed oxygen atom, even though much of the surface was covered by adsorbed carbon monoxide molecules at the lower range of these temperatures. Likewise, he concluded that the reaction of hydrogen and oxygen occurred by a similar mechanism, between a striking hydrogen molecule and an adsorbed oxygen atom.

The idea was revived in 1939 by Rideal, who proposed that a simple molecular mechanism for heterogeneous catalytic reactions was reaction between a chemisorbed radical or atom and a molecule, the latter impacting directly from the gas phase or held in a deep van der Waals layer. In either case a new chemisorbed species was formed on the surface. Specifically, Eley and Rideal (1941) concluded that the conversion of *p*-hydrogen to *o*-hydrogen on tungsten and the exchange of hydrogen and deuterium occurred between a hydrogen molecule in a loosely bound layer and a strongly bound chemisorbed hydrogen atom. [However it now appears that the para-to-ortho conversion occurs instead by adsorption of a hydrogen molecule with dissociation, a mechanism proposed by Bonhoeffer and Farkas (1931).]

Reactions of this general type are referred to variously as Langmuir-Rideal, Rideal, or Rideal-Eley mechanisms. Only a few reactions have been clearly shown to proceed in this manner. The hydrogenation of ethylene has been intensively studied (for a detailed critical review, see Horiuti and Miyahara, 1967), and the results on some catalysts such as nickel under some conditions are consistent with a Rideal mechanism. On other catalysts such as copper a Langmuir-Hinshelwood mechanism seems more probable.

To formulate the Rideal mechanism for a simple reaction between A and B to form C, retain all the other assumptions in the Langmuir-Hinshelwood model and consider reaction occurring between adsorbed molecules of B and gas-phase molecules of A. The rate is

$$-r = k\theta_B \cdot P_A \tag{3.40}$$

Performing the usual substitutions, one obtains

$$-r = \frac{kP_A K_B P_B}{1 + K_A P_A + K_B P_B + K_C P_C} \tag{3.41}$$

If the mechanism were assumed to be reaction between adsorbed A and gas-phase B, an equation of the same form is obtained, but with K_A replacing K_B.

$$-r = \frac{kP_B K_A P_A}{1 + K_A P_A + K_B P_B + K_C P_C} \tag{3.42}$$

The mechanism expressed by Eq. (3.40) could occur either with or without significant adsorption of A onto the catalyst surface (Langmuir, 1921), so further information is needed to determine whether or not the term $K_A P_A$ should be included in the denominator of Eq. (3.41).

3.3.5 Two-step kinetic models

Many real reactions probably involve the formation and disappearance of several intermediates on the surface of the catalyst, and it is evident that a mechanistically rigorous formulation can become so complex as to lose most of its utility. Boudart has addressed this problem of formulating the simplest rate equation that can significantly represent a multistep reaction. He suggests that many cases can be usefully treated by making two simplifying assumptions: (1) that one step is the rate-determining step and (2) that one surface intermediate is the dominant one, i.e., that all other species are present in relatively insignificant amounts (Boudart 1972). Under steady state all steps must occur at the same rate, but to assume details of the overall mechanism is not necessary. For a given reaction the formulation depends on the assumptions made as to the rate-determining step and the most abundant surface intermediate, and, as with other approaches, the same formal expression may be obtained from more than one set of assumptions.

Example 3.1   The approach may be illustrated by the kinetic expression found to represent initial rate data on the dehydrogenation of methylcyclohexane (M) to toluene (T) on a platinum/alumina catalyst, reported by Sinfelt et al. (1960). The rate law followed the form of Eq. (3.7), which was derived here previously by a Langmuir-Hinshelwood model assuming adsorption equilibrium and the rate-determining step to be the rate of reaction of adsorbed reactant (Case 3.1). However the rate was only slightly decreased in the presence of aromatics, which would be adsorbed preferentially to M. This and other observations suggest that instead M was adsorbed irreversibly and that the concentration of adsorbed M, θ_M was low. This also implies that hydrogen dissociates from M as it adsorbs. If it is assumed that any other surface intermediates formed by dehydrogenation before the appearance of toluene are not present in significant amounts, and that toluene desorbs irreversibly, then

$$-r = k_1 P_M(1 - \theta_T) = k_2 \theta_T \tag{3.43}$$

$$\theta_T = \frac{k_1 P_M}{k_1 P_M + k_2} \tag{3.44}$$

$$-r = \frac{k_1 P_M}{1 + (k_1/k_2)P_M} \tag{3.45}$$

This is formally the same as Eq. (3.7), but now k_1 represents the rate of adsorption of M and k_2 the rate of adsorption of toluene, rather than the ratio k_1/k_2 representing an adsorption equilibrium constant.

Which of two mechanisms is the more likely in a general case may be indicated by the magnitude of the parameters and the effect of temperature on them, that is, whether the values are more reasonable viewed as adsorption-desorption processes in contrast to an equilibrium constant. The use of isotopic tracers may also reveal the adsorption-desorption characteristics of the system and the relative rates of different steps. In this particular case, if the Langmuir-Hinshelwood mechanism indeed occurred, toluene would be expected to be more strongly adsorbed than methylcyclohexane, in which event Eq. (3.7) would not in fact express the results. Carberry (1976, p. 414) treats this example in considerable detail, illustrating how the data can be examined in terms of various models and methods of testing the reasonableness of the values of the parameters in terms of what they represent physically.

The rate-controlling step can frequently be expected to change with temperature and pressure. For example, the dehydrogenation of cyclohexane to benzene was studied on a noble metal catalyst in the presence of hydrogen-deuterium mixtures at an elevated pressure. At temperatures below 250°C, the only reaction observed was the formation of deuterated cyclohexanes, $C_6H_{12-x}D_x$. At temperatures between 250 and 300°C, some benzene was formed as well as deuterated cyclohexanes. Above 300°C no deuterated cyclohexanes were found, suggesting that the usual Langmuir-Hinshelwood mechanism occurred below 250°C, but shifted to adsorption-desorption control above 300°C. The book by Ozaki (1977) on isotopic studies of heterogeneous catalysis discusses a wide variety of specific catalytic reactions that have been investigated by use of isotopic tracers and gives extensive references. The classic example of a kinetic expression in which the rate of adsorption is the rate-determining step is the Temkin-Pyzhev equation for synthesis of ammonia from the elements (Sec. 10.5.2).

The Elovich (Roginskii-Zeldovich) equation is frequently used to express the rate of chemisorption. This is a two-parameter expression that provides for a fall in adsorption energy with increased surface coverage.

$$\frac{dn}{dt} = ae^{-\alpha\theta/RT} \tag{3.46}$$

Here a is a constant and α relates activation energy to surface coverage by the expression

$$E_a = (E_a)_0 + \alpha\theta \tag{3.47}$$

The use of the Elovich equation for deriving kinetic models is reviewed by Aharoni and Tompkins (1970).

3.3.6 Reversible reaction

By the principle of microscopic reversibility, the mechanism of the reverse reaction must be consistent with that of the forward reaction under essentially the same conditions, i.e., the molecularity of the forward and reverse reactions must be the same when they are near equilibrium.

Consider Case 3.2 and allow for the possibility of reverse reaction between B and C to produce A. The forward reaction is given by Eq. (3.14) and the reverse reaction is of the form of Eq. (3.17), thus the overall rate may be expressed as

$$-r = \frac{k_{for}K_AP_A - k_{rev} \cdot K_BP_B \cdot K_CP_C}{(1 + K_AP_A + K_BP_B + K_CP_C)^2} \tag{3.48}$$

At equilibrium the forward and reverse rates must be equal; hence

$$k_{for}K_AP_A = k_{rev}K_BP_B \cdot K_CP_C \tag{3.49}$$

Rearranging:

$$\frac{k_{for} \cdot K_A}{k_{rev} \cdot K_B K_C} = \frac{P_B \cdot P_C}{P_A} = K_{eq} \qquad (3.50)$$

The K_{eq} defined by the second equality is the usual thermodynamic equilibrium constant as applied for a homogeneous reaction. Substituting into Eq. (3.48)

$$-r = \frac{k_{for} K_A (P_A - P_B \cdot P_C/K_{eq})}{(1 + K_A P_A + K_B P_B + K_C P_C)^2} \qquad (3.51)$$

The rate becomes zero at equilibrium, as it should. Although the ratio k_{for}/k_{rev} can be visualized as an equilibrium constant for a surface reaction, it does not equal K_{eq}.

3.4   Some Uses and Limitations of Kinetic Models

Formulations of kinetic models for a large number of cases are given in various books. See, for example, Laidler (1965), Smith (1981), Carberry (1976), Rase (1977), Hill (1977), and Froment and Bischoff (1990). Hougen and Watson in a pioneering book (1947) developed expressions for a wide variety of postulated mechanisms, and rate expressions thus derived are frequently referred to by their names, especially in the chemical engineering literature. Thomas and Thomas (1967, p. 458) give a detailed listing of formulations for reactions of the types $A \rightleftharpoons P$ or $A + B \rightleftharpoons P$. The rate-controlling steps considered are adsorption, desorption, or surface reaction; and models are included in which A does or does not dissociate upon adsorption. They thus develop six possible formulations for the first type of reaction and seven for the second. Nagy, in the book by Szabó and Kalló (1976, vol. 2, pp. 480–505), lists expressions for the types $A \rightleftharpoons B$ and $A \rightarrow B$, $A \rightleftharpoons B_1 + B_2$, $A \rightarrow B_1 + B_2$, and $A_1 + A_2 \rightarrow B$, plus some suggested procedures for selecting the most appropriate formulation in light of experimental data. The various mechanisms and rate-controlling steps considered lead to six different formulations for the first type of reaction and ten for each of the others.

A useful generalized way of formulating various cases is presented by Yang and Hougen (1950). (See also Rase, 1977, p. 183.) The rate equation is expressed in the general form:

$$-r = \frac{(\text{kinetic term})(\text{potential term})}{(\text{adsorption term})^n} \qquad (3.52)$$

They present tables giving expressions for each of the three terms and for n for various adsorption or desorption processes as the rate-limiting steps, with or without dissociation, and for surface reaction as the rate-controlling step. Table 3.1 gives the expressions for the

TABLE 3.1   Terms in the Generalized Formulation of Langmuir-Hinshelwood Kinetic Models*

	Reaction			
	$A \rightleftharpoons R$	$A \rightleftharpoons R + S$	$A + B \rightleftharpoons R$	$A + B \rightleftharpoons R + S$
Kinetic term, with or without dissociation of A	$k_s K_A$	$k_s K_A$	$k_s K_A K_B$	$k_s K_A K_B$
Potential term	$P_A - P_R/K$	$P_A - P_R P_S/K$	$P_A P_B - P_R/K$	$P_A P_B - P_R P_S/K$
Value of n				
A undissociated	1	2	2	2
A dissociated	2	2	3	3

*The general form is $-r = $ (kinetic term) (potential term)/(adsorption term)^n.

Langmuir-Hinshelwood model where all reactants are taken to be adsorbed, adsorption/desorption is taken to be in equilibrium, and all species are assumed to compete for the same sites. K is the equilibrium constant for a reversible reaction, and driving force is expressed in terms of partial pressure. If deviations from ideality are significant, fugacities or activities should be used instead. The adsorption term is, in the most general case,

$$[1 + K_A P_A + K_B P_B + K_R P_R + K_S P_S + K_X P_X]^n \qquad (3.53)$$

If equilibrium adsorption of A occurs with dissociation of A, the term $K_A P_A$ in the denominator is replaced by $\sqrt{K_A P_A}$.

Some of the kinetic equations thus derived from different postulated mechanisms have the same mathematical form, but the constants have a different elementary meaning depending on the assumptions made. The fact that a mechanism is consistent with a model does not mean that it is necessarily correct. Given some experimental results, various methods may be used to select the equation best fitting the data. These depend in part on the manner in which reaction rate data were obtained, e.g., whether they are initial, differential, or integral rate data, the last being much more difficult to handle. Selection among possible equations frequently starts by determining which species (reactants and/or products) have a significant effect on the rate when their concentration is varied. The mathematical formulations thus not eliminated may then be treated in various ways. Linear regression provides the ability readily to visualize and test the data, but with modern computer capabilities nonlinear least-squares regression programs may provide a better method of weighting data. See further discussion in Froment and Bischoff (1990).

There are further tests of whether a model that correlates experimental data is consistent with the underlying assumptions made in its derivation. The apparent adsorption equilibrium constant can be expressed as:

$$-RT \ln K_p = \Delta G° = \Delta H° - T\Delta S°$$

$$K_p = e^{\Delta S°/R} \cdot e^{-\Delta H°/RT} = Ae^{\lambda/RT}$$

The heat of adsorption is thus identified as an enthalpy change and since it is almost invariably exothermic, values of K_p should decrease with increased temperature.

In principle, theoretical considerations should set some maximum and minimum realistic values of $\Delta S°$ to compare with values calculated from experimental values of K_p. Some formulations have been proposed by Boudart et al. (1967) and Knox and Dadyburjor (1981). These approaches are limited by the assumptions that must be made about the nature of the adsorbed state, and so their usefulness may be primarily for some simple and very well characterized systems.

Kittrell (1970), Hofmann (1972), and Froment (1975, 1987) in detailed reviews describe various methods of discriminating among kinetic models and of estimating the values of the parameters for a given model by linear and nonlinear methods, and they provide suggestions for statistical design of experiments to determine the best model. The book by Box et al. (1978) emphasizes methods for design of experiments as well as analysis of results and construction of models. Weller (1975) discusses some of the pros and cons of using power-law relationships in contrast to Langmuir-Hinshelwood formulations. A number of experimenters have used pulse techniques under reaction conditions to estimate the values of the adsorption parameters in kinetic expressions. However, the assumptions that have frequently been made for mathematical tractability—such as reversibility of adsorption and linear processes—and the fact that adsorption parameters are determined at low coverage severely limit the usefulness of this approach. Moreover, the behavior of a system may be considerably different under nonsteady-state than under steady-state conditions. Nevertheless, pulsing techniques can be used to compare adsorptivities and for other purposes.

There is much room for judgment concerning the degree of precision with which it is appropriate to analyze or to correlate experimental kinetic data by these various procedures. The fact that various specific models can be proposed, each leading to a specific mathematical (but not necessarily unique) formulation, tempts the experimenter to correlate data by each of a variety of mathematical expressions and then to conclude that the true kinetic mechanism is the one that leads to the mathematics that best fits the data. The utilization of this approach has sometimes led to conclusions that are more enthusiastic than realistic. Some of the more complex mechanisms, including reversible reactions, can easily lead to equations containing so many adjustable constants that the flexibility at one's disposal may allow one to obtain good fit of data to a mathematical expression while proving little concerning the actual mechanism.

Rate expressions for various specific catalytic reactions of industrial interest are discussed in separate sections later, but these must be treated with caution. Seldom is enough information available to develop a mathematical model applicable over the entire range of composition, temperature, and pressure of interest, and extrapolation beyond the range of conditions studied experimentally is hazardous. Even for the same set of experimental conditions, the form of the equation may well vary substantially with the nature of the catalyst, since this affects adsorptivity and reactivity of the various species present. In some cases the rate of reaction under industrial conditions is so fast that temperature and concentration gradients introduce great uncertainties into the validity of the data. For a well-characterized catalyst used for a fairly simple reaction, e.g., a supported metal for a simple hydrogenation, the *form* of the published kinetic model is frequently useful as the starting point for development of a mathematical model. However the numerical values may vary considerably with the detailed formulation of the catalyst and such factors as degree of loading of an active ingredient on the support.

In all the foregoing modeling, the catalyst surface structure is taken to be immutable and rates are derived in terms of adsorption-desorption processes and surface reactions. But, in a number of cases, the composition of the catalyst changes significantly with reaction conditions and this of itself alters activity and selectivity. A reaction rate expression for such systems may have little or no theoretical basis. One example is the usual industrial catalyst, based on vanadia, used for oxidation of SO_2 to SO_3. This is a complex potassium vanadia pyrosulfate, which under reaction conditions is actually a melt of varying composition on a porous support. Here, the catalytic activity may vary significantly with gas composition, highly unusual kinetic behavior may be observed, and a long period may be required for a steady-state rate to be achieved.

Another example of changing catalyst composition may be seen with the iron catalysts used to convert synthesis gas ($CO + H_2$) into hydrocarbons plus CO_2 and H_2O. In a plug flow reactor, the inlet gas is highly reducing and the catalyst consists of one or more iron carbides, plus perhaps a small amount of metallic iron. As reaction proceeds, the reacting mixture becomes more oxidizing in character, largely from the presence of H_2O formed as a product. A considerable portion of the catalyst is converted to Fe_3O_4, and catalyst activity drops substantially. The reaction rate can be expressed in the classical fashion as inhibition by adsorption of water, but more fundamentally, it is instead a decrease in activity caused by alteration of the catalyst surface structure.

Another example is illustrated by the silver catalyst used to convert methanol to formaldehyde by partial oxidation. The active catalyst structure is monatomic oxygen adsorbed onto silver. The feed gas is oxygen-lean, so in a fixed-bed reactor, as oxygen is consumed the rate drops dramatically because of a change in the catalyst surface to essentially silver alone.

Although many of the constants in the Langmuir-Hinshelwood expression are so-called adsorption equilibrium constants, it is not possible in most cases to obtain predictions of kinetic behavior using adsorption equilibrium constants obtained from a nonreacting system. One reason is that probably only a fraction of the adsorbed molecules actually participate in reaction. On intuitive grounds, molecules adsorbed on highly active sites would be expected to be so strongly held that they could not react further; instead they would act as poisons. Sites that are too unenergetic would be unable to cause any shifting of bonds. Consequently, only those sites of intermediate activity would presumably be effective.

The fact that the heat of adsorption generally decreases with surface coverage has suggested to some investigators that a more fundamental correlation of kinetic data might proceed by using the Freundlich or Temkin isotherm to relate vapor concentration to surface concentration. Nevertheless, the probability that only those sites within a fairly narrow energy range are effective in reaction suggests retention of the simpler Langmuir expressions unless compelling arguments suggest otherwise. In a recent paper Corma et al. (1988) derived rate equations based on the three types of isotherms and compared these for goodness of fit using 19 studies in the literature for which relevant kinetic data were available. In general, they calculated about the same level of fit for all three isotherm equations.

Since solid surfaces are almost invariably nonuniform, the question of how this affects kinetics has been considered at length by many investigators. Exploration of this topic is beyond the scope of the present volume, but is discussed in some detail in the book by Boudart and Djéga-Mariadassou (1984) and in the review by Temkin (1979). A recent exchange of views may also be informative (Kiperman et al. 1989; Boudart 1989). A related book by Tamaru (1978) focuses on a dynamic approach to catalysis with particular emphasis on adsorption effects.

Despite the various difficulties, the relationships suggested by the simpler Langmuir-Hinshelwood models are helpful in ordering data. They may also give a physical interpretation that can suggest how reaction conditions might be changed or the composition modified so as to improve the reactivity or selectivity of a catalyst. Inhibition of a reaction by species X is identified with a high adsorptivity of the catalyst for X. A zero-order or negative-order reaction suggests strong adsorption of one or more reactants. If the system follows the Langmuir model, such "self-inhibition" may be overcome by raising the temperature, and the increase in temperature may have a more marked effect in increasing rate than for reactions of higher order.

In principle, for a reaction of the type $A \rightarrow B + C$, the apparent activation energy is $E_a = E_s + \lambda_a$ when A is strongly adsorbed relative to other species. This drops to $E_s - \lambda$ at higher temperatures where A is not strongly adsorbed, assuming the denominator is squared in the relevant expression, as in Eq. (3.15). If the Rideal mechanism were postulated for the same reaction, the kinetic expression is given by Eq. (3.41), and the apparent activation energy E_a equals E_s at higher temperatures. Similarly, if A decomposes unimolecularly to nonadsorbed products (Case 3.1), the apparent activation energy E_a equals E_s at lower temperatures where A is strongly adsorbed, dropping to $E_s - \lambda$ as temperature is raised. The apparent activation energy can frequently be expected to drop with increased temperature.

In the development of a new process, a target consisting of some set of combinations of high value of space-time yield (STY), selectivity, and percent conversion is usually dictated by economic considerations. The highest space-time yield (quantity of product formed per unit time per unit volume of reactor) is usually associated with the lowest percent conversion (and shortest contact time), since the rate of reaction usually drops as reactant concentration drops. Sometimes increasing contact time does little to increase conversion and instead just decreases the space-time yield, even when conditions are far from equilibrium. The foregoing framework of theory suggests that this phenomenon may be caused by strong adsorption of one or more products, desired or undesired. Theory also suggests ways in which this may possibly be overcome:

1. Increased temperature may be effective, although this may cause a decrease in selectivity or in useful life of the catalyst.

2. Reformulation of the catalyst to reduce adsorptivity of the species suspected as the culprit may help.

3. Addition to the feed stream of a species that is strongly adsorbed on the catalyst and displaces the product. This may, however, decrease catalyst activity, and continuously adding an extraneous material may be costly or may contaminate the product.

Langmuir-Hinshelwood formulations also show that a ranking of catalysts in order of increasing reactivity might change with experimental conditions, even at one fixed temperature, e.g., as between a low percentage conversion and a high percentage conversion. For example, over platinum, the rate of oxidation of carbon monoxide is first order with respect to oxygen but is an inverse function of carbon monoxide concentration, whereas on base metals under some sets of circumstances the rate is proportional to carbon monoxide concentration but independent of oxygen concentration. Final test conditions must therefore be very similar to those in an application. Although in a simple homogeneous system the maximum rate of reaction occurs with a stoichiometric ratio of reactants, Langmuir-Hinshelwood formulations show that this does not necessarily occur on a heterogeneous catalyst.

Although these possible complexities need to be borne in mind, in some cases, such as rapid screening of a series of catalysts varying substantially in activity, an approximate ranking may be obtained by using as a correlation function the temperature T_R at which the conversion, for fixed feed rate, reaches some convenient value such as 50 percent. The most reactive system, then, has the lowest value of T_R. This is illustrated in Fig. 3.1, which compares the relative activity of a number of metals for the decomposition of formic acid vapor reported by Fahrenfort et al. (1960). This also shows how the Langmuir-Hinshelwood model can be used to obtain insight into the behavior of a relatively simple reaction. T_R is plotted against the heat of formation of the metal formate, taken as a measure of the heat of adsorption of formic acid on the specific metal. The maximum activity is exhibited for the metal for which formic acid presumably has an intermediate strength of adsorption, which is in consonance with the general idea that the fastest rate is achieved when the bonds between the adsorbed intermediate complex and the catalyst are neither too strong nor too weak.

The reaction on nickel was zero order and that on gold approximately first order, which again is consistent with theory since formic acid is presumably strongly adsorbed on nickel and weakly adsorbed on gold. This finding also leads to a broad generalization that, in comparing a number of catalysts for a specified reaction, the most active catalyst is that which is about half covered with the most stable adsorption complex under reaction conditions. Strictly, catalysts should be compared on the basis of equal turnover numbers, but often insufficient information is available.

The manner in which data are presented in Fig. 3.1 is frequently called a *volcano curve*, and it has been applied with varying degrees of success to a number of reactions. The concept was developed in great detail by Balandin in his multiplet theory of catalysis (1958, 1969),

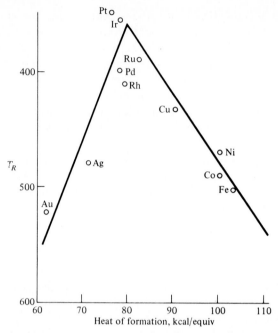

Figure 3.1 Activity of various metals for the decomposition of formic acid as a function of the heat of formation of their formates. (*Fahrenfort et al. 1960*)

but the idea has sometimes been pushed far beyond its basic limitations. A volcano curve is sometimes interpreted in terms of the semiempirical Polanyi relationship, which states that for a series of simple related reactions the change in activation energy from one to a second reaction may be proportional to the change in heat of reaction; that is,

$$E_2 - E_1 = -\alpha(q_2 - q_1) \qquad (3.54)$$

where α is a fraction between 0 and 1 (Boudart 1968, p. 167). If the heat of reaction q (positive for an exothermic step) increases by an amount Δq, the activation energy decreases by the fraction α of Δq.

As applied to catalysis, the Polanyi relationship may be used to compare the activation energy and heat of adsorption with those for breakup of the adsorbed complex for, say, a specified reaction on a series of catalysts. Weak adsorption is associated with a high activation energy for adsorption. Then the rate of adsorption is the rate-limiting process, and the surface concentration of adsorbed complex is low. Strong adsorption is associated with a low activation energy for adsorption, the rate of breakup of the adsorbed complex is the rate-limiting process, and surface concentration of the complex is high. The same approach is also applied to the Mars-van Krevelen mechanism of oxidation reactions (Sec. 8.1).

3.5   Mixtures of Reactants

On a specified catalyst, the rate of reaction of a mixture of reactants is often far different from what would be predicted by some type of additive rule from measurements on the same catalyst with the reactants taken one at a time. Moreover, the order of increasing reactivity of individual species may be greatly different in mixtures than when studied separately. This behavior can be readily understood in terms of competitive adsorption of different reactants for the same catalyst sites.

Example 3.2   Beecher et al. (1968) studied the hydrocracking of n-decane, Decalin (decahydronaphthalene), and mixtures of the two at 255°C and 3 MPa using a great excess of hydrogen on a catalyst consisting of palladium supported on a zeolite. For a specified feed rate (moles of total hydrocarbon per unit time), the conversion of Decalin alone was 21 percent and that of n-decane alone was 48 percent. With a 50:50 mixture of the two, the reaction rate of Decalin, expressed in moles per unit of time, was essentially unchanged but the amount of n-decane converted was essentially zero. This behavior suggests that the Decalin was the more strongly adsorbed, such that little of the n-decane could have access to the catalyst surface. The fact that the rate of reaction of Decalin was unchanged when its partial pressure was cut in half means that the rate was zero order with respect to Decalin, which is consistent with the hypothesis that it was strongly adsorbed.

Example 3.3   The hydrodenitrogenation of heterocyclic nitrogen compounds on $CoMo/Al_2O_3$ or $NiMo/Al_2O_3$ to convert them to NH_3 is of concern in the processing of various liquid fuels such as those derived from low-grade crude petroleum, coal, or shale oil. In studies with individual compounds, quinoline is less reactive than indole, but in real shale-oil mixtures, indole-type compounds (includes pyrroles) are less reactive than quinoline-type compounds (includes pyridines) (Koros et al. 1967).

Interaction effects are discussed in more detail in Sec. 9.14. Mixtures can show highly unusual kinetic behavior, far different from the usual textbook cases, again stemming from the relative degree of adsorptivity of individual reactant intermediates and products and the relative rate of reaction of adsorbed species. Thus, the rate of a reaction may *increase* with conversion, sometimes termed *autocatalysis*, although this term may be misleading. In the case of homogeneous free-radical reactions, autocatalysis can be readily interpreted in terms of a branched chain reaction. In heterogeneous catalysis the mechanisms involved are quite different, but the mathematical formulations for the two different types of mechanisms may be similar in form. Boudart (1968) develops the mathematical approach in considerable detail, treating "active centers" as a class, be they free radicals, surface complexes, or other active intermediates.

An increase in rate after an initial induction period can also be caused by the presence of a small amount of poison reversibly adsorbed onto a catalyst. Consider, for example, a small amount of a sulfur-compound impurity in a feedstock to be hydrogenated. Initially, the impurity is adsorbed onto the catalyst and little or no reaction is observed. However, the impurity can become hydrogenated and desorbed, whereupon the desired hydrogenation of the feed takes over and the rate of hydrogen consumption increases. Červený and Ružička (1982) review in detail a large variety of studies of competitive catalytic hydrogenation in the liquid phase.

Example 3.4 An acceleration of rate with extent of reaction is illustrated in the study by Wauquier and Jungers (1957) of the liquid-phase hydrogenation of a mixture of p-xylene (species 1) and tetralin (species 2) over a Raney nickel catalyst in a batch process. Assuming that the two species compete for one kind of site and that all active sites are occupied (since the catalyst is in contact with a liquid), the rate of reaction in terms of overall rate of uptake of hydrogen can be expressed as

$$r = \frac{k_1 K_1(A_1) + k_2 K_2(A_2)}{K_1(A_1) + K_2(A_2)} \tag{3.55}$$

If $k_1 > k_2$, the rate of reaction will increase as total reactant concentration drops wherever $k_2 K_2 > k_1 K_1$. The mechanistic interpretation is that p-xylene, once adsorbed, reacts more rapidly than does adsorbed tetralin, but the relative adsorptivity of tetralin is so great that most of the active sites are occupied by it rather than p-xylene. The increase in rate with extent of reaction must, of course, eventually reach a maximum, and a more detailed rate expression to cover the entire range of conversion should allow for this by including terms for adsorption of products. However, reactants are in general more strongly adsorbed than products in hydrogenations, so finding this accelerating effect over a wide range of conversion was not surprising.

Similar effects can occur in gas-phase, continuous packed-bed reactors. As an example, the small amount of acetylene present in ethylene produced by thermal cracking of various hydrocarbon feedstocks may be removed by selective hydrogenation. As the gas passes through the catalyst bed, first acetylene is removed with high selectivity. Then the rate of hydrogenation increases substantially, and the reaction becomes hydrogenation of ethylene, a reaction that is undesirable (Sec. 6.7.2).

In hydrogenation reactions in general, the product is often less strongly adsorbed than the reactant. Generally, olefins and aromatics are more strongly adsorbed than paraffins, and oxygenated species are usually more strongly adsorbed than hydrocarbons. The chemical nature of the solid is, of course, also important, but useful generalities are lacking.

3.6 Poisoning and Induction Periods

Many of the phenomena of poisoning and induction periods in heterogeneous catalysis can be readily understood within the foregoing framework of competitive adsorption for active sites. If a species in the reactant mixture is strongly adsorbed and is nonreactive, it is a poison and removes active sites from reaction. Sometimes, for example, in a well-stirred liquid-phase batch reactor, with successive additions of a catalyst, the rate of reaction increases more than proportionately to the amount of catalyst added. In such a case the first additions of catalyst have become largely inactivated by adsorption of impurities. Sometimes a catalyst that is spent and unsuitable for further use as such retains its adsorptive powers for impurities and may be used deliberately for this purpose. The same principle is also applied in continuous fixed-bed reactors in which a *guard catalyst* is placed in the entrance section of the reactor or in a separate vessel upstream from the reactor. The guard catalyst may be a nearly spent catalyst, possibly a lower-cost version of the main catalyst, or perhaps a bed of adsorbent.

In a liquid-phase batch reactor, an induction period may be encountered before the reaction assumes a significant rate. Excluding those cases in which free radicals are involved, the phenomenon can be caused by a poison that is strongly adsorbed but is somewhat reactive to form less strongly adsorbed products. The kinetic behavior is like that observed by Wauquier and Jungers but in an even more extreme form.

The rate of deactivation of a catalyst may vary greatly with circumstances because of the variety of phenomena that may be responsible (Sec. 1.3.9). Two limiting cases may be recognized. In one, the deactivation is caused by adsorption of a poison and the reduction in rate (as measured, for example, in a differential reactor) is a function of the quantity of poison adsorbed onto the catalyst but is independent of the time of exposure. At the other extreme are cases in which the deactivation increases with time on stream, but is relatively independent of feedstock composition, as might be caused, for example, by sintering. This rate of deactivation can sometimes be expressed adequately by a relatively simple two-parameter empirical equation of the form

$$-\frac{dk}{dt} = Ak^b \qquad (3.56)$$

in which t is the time on stream and A and b are positive constants, which, however, may vary with temperature and feed composition. Catalyst deactivation in general and the development of suitable rate expressions are reviewed by Butt (1972, 1984).

3.6.1 Rate of deactivation

Industrially, the reactor temperature is commonly increased gradually to compensate for catalyst deactivation, in order to maintain a fixed production rate. In many cases, especially operation at higher temperatures, the effect of time τ on an effective rate constant can be expressed in terms of temperature T. If the rate of reaction is kept constant by this procedure, k is constant. The decrease in k caused by deactivation is counterbalanced by the increase in k caused by increased temperature. Thus $-(dk/d\tau) = (dk/dT)$. Over a limited time-temperature interval, $\Delta T = \Delta \tau$. The rate of activity loss increases with increased temperature and frequently follows an Arrhenius expression. Then lifetime data from a single reactor or data from accelerated laboratory tests can be correlated by a plot of log $(\Delta T/\Delta \tau)$ versus reciprocal of absolute temperature. Figure 3.2 shows such a plot for a partial oxidation reaction in which data from several industrial and laboratory reactors are combined. Since the rate of deactivation increases with temperature, in the usual procedure the rate of increase of reactor temperature is also increased with time.

Shutdown may be determined by one or more of a variety of factors such as: (1) catalyst selectivity may deteriorate to an unacceptable level, (2) metallurgical limitations may be reached, (3) pressure drop may become excessive, (4) the entire unit may be shut down for a turnaround or general maintenance during which the catalyst load is replaced as a precaution to help avoid a possible future production interruption.

A more detailed mathematical treatment of time-temperature data for deactivating catalysts is given by Krishnaswamy and Kittrell (1979). See also the book by Hughes (1984).

3.7 Compensation

Consider one reaction studied on a series of catalysts or with a catalyst activated by a variety of means; or consider a series of reactions studied on one catalyst. If each of the data in the set is fitted to an Arrhenius expression, sometimes both E and A increase or both de-

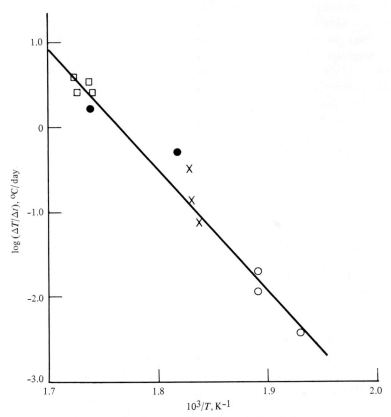

Figure 3.2 Arrhenius plot for rate of loss of catalyst activity.

crease. Consequently, k changes less than it would if only E or only A changed. A change in one is "compensated" for in whole or in part by a change in the other. The phenomenon can merely represent a false correlation (Sec. 3.7.1), or it may be a real effect. In some cases the relationship between A and E is of the form $\ln A = \alpha + \beta E$, in which case the rate constant is the same for all reactions at one particular temperature, sometimes termed the *isokinetic temperature* T_θ, or the *theta temperature*. Likewise the compensation effect is sometimes termed the *theta effect*. Above the isokinetic temperature the faster reaction has the higher activation energy; below the isokinetic temperature, the faster reaction has the lower activation energy. This is illustrated in Fig. 3.3 (Cremer 1955), which shows the decomposition of formic acid on magnesite that had previously been heated to the temperature specified in the range of 370 to 800°C.

If the isokinetic temperature occurs in the middle of the range of

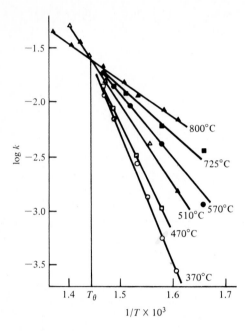

Figure 3.3   Arrhenius plots for decomposition of formic acid vapor over magnesite $(MgCO_3\text{-}MgO)$. (*Cremer and Kullich in Cremer 1955*)

temperatures covered by the measurements, the compensation effect may be simply false correlation caused by scatter of data. If the theta temperature is well below or above the range of temperatures covered by the measurements and if the variation in activation energy is large, then the correlation is significant, although the interpretation is uncertain.

From the absolute theory of reaction rates,

$$k = \frac{kT}{h} e^{\Delta S^{\ddagger}/R} \cdot e^{-\Delta H^{\ddagger}/RT} \tag{3.57}$$

where $\Delta S^{\ddagger}$ and $\Delta H^{\ddagger}$ are the differences between the values of the activated complex and those of the reactants. Compensation occurs if an increase in $\Delta H^{\ddagger}$ is associated with an increase in $\Delta S^{\ddagger}$. In homogeneous systems this plausibly may happen, since in order for reaction to occur it is necessary both that a sufficiently low energy barrier exist and that a favorable configuration be made possible, accompanied by a change in entropy. $\Delta S^{\ddagger}$ is usually a negative number, and often one finds an approximate linear relationship between $\Delta H^{\ddagger}$ and $\Delta S^{\ddagger}$.

True compensation is frequently observed for homogeneous liquid-phase reactions in a series of solvents or for a homologous series in which substituents are introduced into a reactant. The general explanation is in terms of solvent-solute interactions. Stronger bonding between solute molecules and solvent will lower the enthalpy (and increase the enthalpy change to form the intermediate complex $\Delta H^{\ddagger}$) and, by restricting freedom of vibration and rotation, will lower the entropy (and increase the entropy change $\Delta S^{\ddagger}$).

In many cases of heterogeneous catalysis, a linear relationship may likewise exist between enthalpy change and entropy change upon chemisorption over a series of catalysts, but other explanations may also be invoked. If a reaction were studied on a series of catalysts identical except for, say, calcination temperature, changing the calcination temperature might possibly alter both the number of sites (to which the preexponential factor is proportional) and the activation energy. It is also possible that molecules may surface-diffuse to the reaction site of a surrounding area, and, as the temperature is increased, the rate of surface diffusion may increase. But the rate of desorption also increases, resulting in an effective decrease in the preexponential factor with increasing temperature.

Considerable controversy has surrounded studies of the compensation effect. Processing experimental data to distinguish between statistical effects and true chemical effects can require sophisticated mathematical approaches (Krug 1980) and various interpretations of the meaning of the term *compensation* have led to many publications. Compensation in heterogeneous catalysis was earlier reviewed by Cremer (1955) and Galwey (1977). A critical review by Kral (1988) presents a detailed analysis of the situation together with extensive references.

3.7.1 False compensation

If reaction rates are measured over only a fairly small range of temperature and the activation energy is determined from an Arrhenius plot or its equivalent, the value thus determined may be subject to considerable error. Substitution into the Arrhenius expression will then yield a value of A that is likewise in error. A positive error in E results in a positive error in A, and similarly for a negative error. This results in *false compensation*. Consider reaction at two temperatures T_1 and T_2 with corresponding measured reaction rate constants k_1 and k_2. Then

$$\ln \frac{k_2}{k_1} = \frac{-E}{R}\left(\frac{1}{T_2} - \frac{1}{T_1}\right) = \frac{-E}{R}\left(\frac{T_1 - T_2}{T_1 T_2}\right) \tag{3.58}$$

If T_1 and T_2 are close together in value so that $T_1 \approx T_2 \approx T$, then

$$\frac{dk_2}{k_2} - \frac{dk_1}{k_1} = \frac{\Delta T}{RT^2} dE \tag{3.59}$$

where $\Delta T = T_2 - T_1$. The maximum error in E occurs when $dk_2 = -dk_1$. Hence

$$\delta E = \frac{2RT^2}{\Delta T} \frac{\delta k}{k} \tag{3.60}$$

The error in E is seen to be very sensitive to ΔT. For example, if k is subject to an error of ± 20 percent, at $T = 673$ K and for $\Delta T = 30°C$, the error in E may be as large as 12 kcal/mole (50 kJ/mole).

A considerable number of correlations in the literature report the effect on activation energy of such variables as changing the crystal habit of a catalyst, doping a semiconductor to change its electronic properties, etc. In some cases these effects are real, but in many instances insufficient information is published to determine whether the relationship was truly significant.

References

Aharoni, C., and F. C. Tompkins, *Adv. Catal.*, **21**, 1 (1970).

Balandin, A. A.: *Adv. Catal.*, **10**, 96 (1958); **19**, 1 (1969).

Beecher, R., A. Voorhies, Jr., and P. Eberly, Jr., *Ind. Eng. Chem., Prod. Res. Dev.*, **7**, 203 (1968).

Bonhoeffer, K. F., and A. Farkas: *Z. Phys. Chem., Abt. B*, **12**, 231 (1931).

Boudart, M., *Kinetics of Chemical Processes*, Prentice-Hall, Englewood Cliffs, N. J., 1968.

Boudart, M.: *AIChE J.*, **18**, 465 (1972).

Boudart, M.: *Ind. Eng. Chem. Res.*, **28**, 379 (1989).

Boudart, M., and G. Djéga-Mariadassou: *Kinetics of Heterogeneous Catalytic Reactions*, Princeton University Press, Princeton, N. J., 1984.

Boudart, M., D. E. Mears, and M. A. Vannice: *Ind. Chem. Belge*, **32**, special issue 281 (1967) (in English).

Box, G. E. P., W. G. Hunter, and J. S. Hunter: *Statistics for Experimenters: An Introduction to Design, Data Analysis and Model Building*, Wiley, New York, 1978.

Butt, J. B.: *Adv. Chem. Ser.*, **10**, 259 (1972); J. R. Anderson and M. Boudart (eds.): *Catalysis: Science and Technology*, vol. 6, Springer, New York, 1984, p. 1.

Carberry, J. J.: *Chemical and Catalytic Reaction Engineering*, McGraw-Hill, New York, 1976.

Červený, L., and V. Ružička: *Catal. Rev.-Sci. Eng.*, **24**, 503 (1982).

Corma, A., F. Llopis, J. B. Monton, and S. W. Weller: *Chem. Eng. Sci.*, **43**, 785 (1988).

Cremer, E.: *Adv. Catal.*, **7**, 75 (1955).

Eley, D. D., and E. K. Rideal: *Proc. R. Soc. London, Ser. A.*, **178**, 429, 452 (1941).

Fahrenfort, J., L. L. van Reyen, and W. H. M. Sachtler in J. H. deBoer (ed.): *The Mechanism of Heterogeneous Catalysis*, Elsevier, Amsterdam, 1960, p. 23.

Froment, G. F.: *AIChE J.*, **21**, 104 (1975).

Froment, G. F.: *Chem. Eng. Sci.*, **42**, 1073 (1987).

Froment, G. F., and K. B. Bischoff: *Chemical Reactor Analysis and Design*, 2d ed., Wiley, New York, 1990.

Galwey, A. K.: *Adv. Catal.*, **26**, 247 (1977).

Hill, C. G., Jr.: *An Introduction to Chemical Engineering Kinetics and Reactor Design*, Wiley, New York, 1977.

Hofmann, H.: *Adv. Chem. Ser.*, **109**, 519 (1972).

Horiuti, J., and K. Miyahara: *Hydrogenation of Ethylene on Metallic Catalysts*, U.S. Department of Commerce, National Bureau of Standards, Report NSRDS-NBS 13, 1967. (62 pp)

Hougen, O. A., and K. M. Watson: *Chemical Process Principles, part III: Kinetics and Catalysis*, Wiley, New York, 1947.

Hughes, R.: *Deactivation of Catalysts*, Academic, New York, 1984.

Kiperman, S. L., K. E. Kumbilieva, and L. A. Petrov: *Ind. Eng. Chem. Res.*, **28**, 376 (1989).

Kittrell, J. R.: *Adv. Chem. Eng.*, **8**, 97 (1970).

Knox, D., and D. B. Dadyburjor: *Chem. Eng. Commun.*, **11**, 99 (1981).

Koros, R. M., S. Bank, J. E. Hofmann, and M. I. Kay: *Prepr., Pet. Div. Am. Chem. Soc.*, **12**(4), B-165 (1967).

Kral, H.: *Chem. Eng. Technol.*, **11**, 113, 328 (1988).

Krishnaswamy, S., and J. R. Kittrell: *Ind. Eng. Chem., Process Des. Dev.*, **18**, 399 (1979).

Krug, R. R.: *Ind. Eng. Chem. Fundam.*, **19**, 50 (1980).

Laidler, K. J.: *Chemical Kinetics*, 2d ed., McGraw-Hill, New York, 1965.

Langmuir, I.: *Trans. Faraday Soc.*, **17**, 621 (1921). [See also *Trans. Faraday Soc.*, **17**, 607 (1921).]

Ozaki, A.: *Isotopic Studies of Heterogeneous Catalysis*, Kodansha, Tokyo, Academic, New York, 1977.

Rase, H. F.: *Chemical Reactor Design for Process Plants*, vol. 1: *Principles and Techniques*, Wiley, New York, 1977.

Satterfield, C. N.: *Mass Transfer in Heterogeneous Catalysis*, M.I.T. Press, Cambridge, Mass., 1970. Reprint edition, Krieger, Melbourne, Fla., 1981.

Satterfield, C. N., M. Modell, and J. F. Mayer: *AIChE J.*, **21**, 1100 (1975).

Sinfelt, J. H., H. Hurwitz, R. A. Shulman: *J. Phys. Chem.*, **64**, 1559 (1960).

Singhal, G. H., R. L. Espino, J. E. Sobel, and G. A. Huff, Jr.: *J. Catal.* **67**, 457 (1981).

Smith, J. M.: *Chemical Engineering Kinetics*, 3d ed., McGraw-Hill, New York, 1981.

Szabó, Z. G., and D. Kalló (eds.), *Contact Catalysis*, Elsevier, Amsterdam, 1976. (2 vols.)

Tamaru, K.: *Dynamic Heterogeneous Catalysis*, Academic, New York, 1978.

Temkin, M. I.: *Adv. Catal.*, **28**, 173 (1979).

Thomas, J. M., and W. J. Thomas: *Introduction to the Principles of Heterogeneous Catalysis*, Academic, New York, 1967.

Wauquier, I. P., and I. C. Jungers: *Bull. Soc. Chim. Fr.*, **10**, 1280 (1957).

Weller, S. W.: *Adv. Chem. Ser.*, **148**, 26 (1975).

Yang, K. H., and O. A. Hougen: *Chem. Eng. Prog.*, **46**, 146 (1950).

Catalyst Preparation and Manufacture

The discussion in this chapter is directed to three objectives:

1. To describe general methods of preparation for readers who desire to make their own catalysts
2. To indicate some of the methods used by and economic constraints on catalyst manufacturers as they scale up a catalyst manufacturing process
3. To provide some understanding of the properties and characteristics of industrial catalysts that may be purchased on the market

Several books and reviews give more details. A brief review by Acres et al. (1981) considers design of supported noble-metal catalysts. A book by Stiles (1983) gives detailed information on equipment and general procedures used in catalyst manufacture plus specific operating recipes for preparing a wide variety of practical catalysts. *The Catalyst Handbook* edited by Twigg (1989) has several chapters on catalyst manufacture, handling, and using catalysts in the plant, as does a book by Le Page et al. (1987, Ch. 5). The book by Stiles (1987) on catalyst supports provides a wealth of detail including numerous electron photomicrographs of support morphologies. The preparation of supported and unsupported metal catalysts in general is discussed from a scientific point of view by Anderson (1975), who also gives a number of specific procedures. A briefer discussion is given by Moss (1976). See also a review by Foger (1984) on dispersed metals on supports.

A great variety of substances exhibit catalytic activity of some type. Many of these, as studied in the laboratory in fundamental investigations, are prepared so as to have simple, uniform, or known structure, rather than high area, high activity, or good mechanical strength. Consequently, they may often represent elements, materials, or methods of preparation of little immediate industrial interest, and therefore are not discussed here. Industrial catalysts themselves comprise a wide variety of materials and are manufactured by a variety of methods. As in the manufacture of any other substance, several alternative procedures are usually available, and the process chosen represents a balance between the cost of preparation and the degree to which the ideal chemical and physical properties are achieved.

The preparation of catalysts is frequently described as an art, and a catalyst recipe may specify detailed and arcane procedures that appear to be necessary in order to achieve reproducibility and the desired properties. Even though the relationship between formulation procedures and ultimate catalyst behavior may in many cases be obscure, an understanding of some of the effects produced with typical catalyst ingredients by manipulations such as precipitation, washing, drying, heating, and so on as described in the following discussion, helps to clarify the reasons for suggested procedures and to indicate possible improved methods for preparing a specific catalyst. In all these manipulations the usual laws of chemistry apply, but are made more complicated by the complex nature of the substances of interest.

For an industrial catalyst, the chemical composition is the most overriding consideration, but other factors, primarily of a physical nature, are usually also of major importance.

Surface area. High surface area is usually desirable for high activity per unit volume or unit weight, so most catalysts are made to be porous, with internal surface areas ranging to as high as about 1000 m^2/g. However, the porous structure in the catalyst and pore size distribution may cause diffusional resistances that affect the ease of access of reactants to catalyst sites and removal of products, thereby affecting the rate and selectivity of the reaction (Chap. 11). For very fast reactions, a large-pore-size (and therefore low-area) catalyst may be desired, as for example the Ag/α-Al_2O_3 catalyst used in converting ethylene to ethylene oxide (see Fig. 8.3, Sec. 8.3). Alternately a *shell-type* catalyst may be prepared (Sec. 4.2.2).

Stability. This includes stability to heat, to poisons, to fluctuations in process conditions, and to such common components of reacting mixtures as water vapor. Many catalysts are regenerated many times before being discarded, so stability to regeneration conditions may be important

Mechanical properties. Attrition resistance, hardness, and compressive strength are of particular concern.

The desired final catalyst particle size is determined by the process in which it is to be used. For fluidized-bed reactors or slurry reactors (catalyst suspended in a liquid), particles usually range from about 20 to 300 μm in size. In fluidized beds, the lower limit is set by the difficulty of preventing excessive carryover of finely divided solid through cyclone separators in the reactors; the upper limit is set by the poorer fluidization characteristics of larger particles and possible diffusion limitations within the particles. In slurry reactors, powders that are too coarse may be difficult to suspend and may be less effective per unit mass; powders that are too fine are difficult to remove by settling or filtration. Catalyst powders for use in slurry reactors are typically similar in size to those for fluidized-bed reactors, but materials suitable for slurry reactors may be too soft and friable for use in fluidized-bed reactors.

For a typical high-area catalyst, the outside surface of a particle is a negligible portion of the total area, and in the absence of diffusional resistances, changing particle size as such has no significant effect on reactivity per unit volume. For a spherical particle, the outside surface per unit weight is given by $S/W = 6/d\rho$, where d is the diameter and ρ is the density. For a particle as fine as 20 μm and of unit density, the outside area is only 0.3 m^2/g. The enormous area present in a typical high-area catalyst can be visualized by recognizing that the quantity of such a catalyst that can easily be held in one's hand has a total surface area greater than that of a football (or soccer) field. Whether a catalyst has high or low internal area is completely unrelated to its appearance to the eye.

For use in fixed beds, catalysts generally range from about 1.5 to 10 mm in diameter and have length-to-diameter ratios of about 1 for pelleted catalysts and up to about 3 or 4 for extrudates. Figure 4.1 shows a representative commercial catalyst prepared by pelletization. In this case the sides are shiny, caused by the deformation characteristics of the powder. Solid tablets, with height/diameter ratios less than 1, are not generally used in catalysis. With the larger particle sizes, diffusion resistances may reduce the rate of reaction in the center of the particles and hence decrease the activity of the catalyst per unit mass and/or adversely affect selectivity. Hence, larger particles may frequently be pelletized as thick rings, a particle may be pierced with a number of holes, or various shapes such as one resembling a wagon-wheel* may be fabricated (see Figs. 4.2, 4.3). Extrudates may

---

*A wagon wheel usually has an odd number of spokes to distribute the stress.

Figure 4.1 High-temperature water-gas shift catalyst, iron oxide promoted with chromia; 5 × 5-mm pellets. (*Courtesy of United Catalysts Inc., Louisville, Ky.*)

 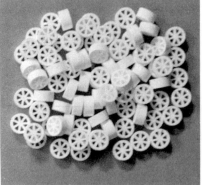

Figure 4.2 Two forms of steam-reforming catalysts. Outside diameter = 16 mm, thickness ~ 10 mm. (*Courtesy of United Catalysts Inc., Louisville, Ky.*)

Figure 4.3 Various forms of steam reforming catalysts. For the 7-hole catalyst, outside diameter = 16 mm, hole diameter = 3.5 mm, thickness = 8 to 11 mm. (*Courtesy of Haldor Topsøe A/S, Copenhagen, Denmark*)

also be made in a thick, tubular form like straight macaroni. Pellets or extrudates smaller than about 1 to 2 mm in diameter may cause excessive pressure drop through the bed. Furthermore, the cost of forming pellets or extrudates per unit weight or volume increases for smaller sizes; so an economic limitation also applies.

In a vapor-phase fixed bed there is only a moderate difference in pressure drop between solid spheres, cylinders, and multilobe catalysts having the same diameter if they are packed to provide the same void fraction (Nakai 1986). Pressure drop is very sensitive to bed void fraction and even a moderate range of particle sizes can cause a considerably greater pressure drop than that occurring with uniform packing having the same outside area per unit volume of reactor. A range of particle sizes is undesired, but, for extrudates and some other shapes of uniform size, the void fraction can be controlled within moderate limits by the method of packing.

A relatively dense packing, and consequent higher pressure drop is sometimes desired to provide a more even distribution of liquid in a trickle-bed reactor. A reactor built to withstand high temperatures and pressures is very expensive; so if diffusion limitations are negligible, as with a relatively slow reaction, it may be desired to pack as much catalyst as possible to maximize the reaction rate per unit volume. On the other hand, a very low reactor pressure drop is sometimes highly desirable, as in the dehydrogenation of ethyl benzene to form styrene (Sec. 9.17.2). For low-pressure-drop catalyst, particles may be shaped in a form to minimize close packing and hence have increased void fraction. A high void fraction may also be desired to minimize bed plugging, which may be the limiting factor in run length rather than catalyst deactivation. An example is hydroprocessing of residual fractions. Catalyst shape can also affect bed thermal conductivity, of particular importance in reactor design when heat is to be transferred through the reactor wall.

For design purposes, the Ergun equation, a semiempirical formulation, is widely used for calculating pressure drop. A review by Macdonald et al. (1979) tests various formulations of the Ergun equation against sets of data and makes recommendations. A review by

Dullien (1975) and a later book (1979) consider fluid transport through porous media from a fundamental approach.

In principle a catalyst shape could be developed for any specific application that represented the optimum combination of maximum activity and selectivity, minimum diffusion resistance, maximum resistance to pore plugging, minimum pressure drop, excellent wetting characteristics (e.g. in a trickle-bed reactor, Chap. 11), etc. Many such shapes have been patented, but the realities of cost of fabrication, requirements for mechanical strength, resistance to abrasion, and the like limit the number used commercially. For an application such as steam reforming (Sec. 10.1) a primary consideration is to manufacture a rugged material capable of withstanding very high temperatures and steam partial pressures, yet with a high bed void fraction to achieve minimum pressure drop at the high mass velocities used. Representative shapes are shown in Figs. 4.2 and 4.3.

Some extrudates have a trilobal or quadrilobal cross section, which increases the surface/volume ratio and hence helps reduce diffusional resistances (Fig. 4.4). To minimize interlocking and hence provide a more open bed and lower pressure drop, a twist to the multilobal extrudate may be achieved by suitable die design (Fig. 4.5).

In principle the overall task in catalyst manufacture is to identify the particular chemical and physical properties of the greatest importance in any specific application and then to develop means of achieving or approaching these properties by preparative methods that can be utilized economically on a large scale. In some cases, e.g., catalysts for simple reactions that do not produce by-products and that have been used industrially for a long time, the desired properties and

Figure 4.4 Extrudates of different sizes with a trilobal cross section, termed Trilobes®. Note the shadows. (*Courtesy of American Cyanamid Company*)

Figure 4.5 Twisted Trilobes®. (*Courtesy of American Cyanamid Company*)

means of achieving them may be reasonably well known. In contrast, with a reaction such as a partial oxidation of an organic compound to maximize the formation of one desired intermediate from many possible products on a multicomponent oxide catalyst, the structure of the catalyst found to be most effective may be obscure, and the method of preparation may have been developed largely by trial and error.

4.1   General Methods of Manufacture

Most catalysts are either a finely divided metal supported on a carrier such as alumina or silica, or a compound, more or less complex, either on a carrier or unsupported. Metal-sulfide catalysts are prepared first as the oxide and then treated with hydrogen sulfide or another sulfur compound in the presence of hydrogen to convert it to the sulfide. Either of two types of processes, generally termed the *precipitation method* and the *impregnation method*, is commonly used for making catalysts. The first involves in its initial stages the mixing of two or more solutions or suspensions of material, causing precipitation; this is followed by filtration, washing, drying, forming, and heating. Simple wet mixing without precipitation is occasionally used, but it may not provide the degree of intimate contact between species that is usually desired. High temperatures can subsequently be applied to provide homogeneity and compound formation by thermal diffusion and solid-state reaction, but this usually causes an undesired degree of sintering and consequent loss of surface area. Sometimes the desired degree of mixing can be achieved by kneading.

If a carrier is to be incorporated in the final catalyst, the original precipitation is usually carried out in the presence of a suspension of the finely divided support, or a compound or suspension that will eventually be converted to the support may be initially present in solution. Thus, a soluble aluminum salt may be converted to aluminum hydroxide during precipitation, and ultimately to alumina; or a supported nickel catalyst could be prepared from a solution of nickel nitrate containing a suspension of alumina, by precipitation of a nickel hydroxide with ammonium hydroxide. In general, starting with aluminum in a soluble form is probably less desirable than starting with a calcined alumina, since using a soluble aluminum salt as a reactant increases the probability of an undesirable reaction of catalyst and carrier. Silica is less reactive, and this problem may not be encountered with, e.g., a silica sol suspension such as Ludox. Binders, cements, die lubricants, thixotropic agents, etc., may also be added at this or a later stage.

The final size and shape of the catalyst particles are determined by the forming process, which may also affect pore size and pore-size distribution. Larger pores can be introduced into a catalyst by incorporating into the mixture 5 to 15 percent of wood flour, cellulose, starch, or other material that can subsequently be burned out. Final catalyst material rejected for chemical or physical reasons may in some cases by recycled without harm to product specifications by powdering it and incorporating it into the catalyst mixture. Such incorporation, however, may change the pore size distribution of the final catalyst. With a gelatinous precipitate, mechanical manipulation may have a significant effect on the ultimate pore size distribution.

After it is dried and formed, the precursor catalyst is *activated*; that is, it is converted into its active form through physical and chemical changes. This typically involves heating to cause calcination or decomposition, followed by reduction if a metallic catalyst is desired. In some cases a supported metal catalyst is pyrophoric, and reduction is carried out in the plant reactor rather than by the catalyst manufacturer to avoid hazards upon shipping and reactor loading.

Some advantages of the precipitation method are that it generally provides more uniform mixing on a molecular scale of the various catalyst ingredients, the distribution of active species through the final catalyst particle is uniform, and the ultimate sizes and shapes are not limited to the forms in which desired carriers are available. Also, more control may be available over pore size and pore size distribution. If two or more metal compounds are present, in a batch-type operation they may precipitate at different rates or in sequence rather than simultaneously, thus affecting the final structure of the solid. Both the ultimate physical and chemical structure of the catalyst are frequently very sensitive to the pH of the precipitation, in which case precipitation is carried out continuously in a well-mixed vessel with careful control of pH.

Impregnation is the easiest method of making a catalyst. A carrier, usually porous, is contacted with a solution, usually aqueous, of one or more suitable metallic compounds. The carrier is then dried, and the catalyst is activated as in the case of precipitated catalysts. The size and shape of the catalyst particles are that of the carrier. The impregnation technique requires less equipment since the filtering and forming steps are eliminated and washing may not be needed. It is the preferred process in preparing supported noble metal catalysts, for which it is usually economically desirable to spread out the metal in as finely divided a form as possible. The noble metal is usually present in the order of 1 wt % or less of the total. This makes maximum use of a very expensive ingredient; in contrast, in a precipitated catalyst some of the active ingredient may be enclosed by other material present and thus unavailable for reaction.

With catalysts consisting of supported base metals, such as cobalt and nickel, it is frequently desirable to incorporate a high percentage of the metal, up to 20 to 40 wt %, onto the support. It may be very difficult to obtain such high loadings by impregnation or even by multiple impregnations, in which case such catalysts may be prepared by a precipitation process. Although seemingly the same chemical structure may frequently be prepared by either process, the final catalysts produced by the two routes may have substantially different physical and chemical properties.

Organic solutions are sometimes found to produce better dispersion of an active ingredient or a particular desired chemical form. See formation of ethylene oxide (Sec. 8.3), and maleic anhydride (Sec. 8.6.1). In these cases, the superior performance outweighs the higher direct cost of manufacture, which will include additional safety measures required to handle more or less volatile organics and the additional expense of carrying out drying and calcinations in a safe and environmentally acceptable manner.

4.2 Precipitation Method

4.2.1 Precipitation

In a common procedure an aqueous metal salt solution is contacted with an aqueous alkali, ammonium hydroxide or ammonium carbonate, to cause the precipitation of an insoluble metal hydroxide or carbonate. These can be readily converted to oxides by heating. The starting compounds are generally chosen because of their availability and high water solubility, and in some cases to avoid introducing elements that may be deleterious in the final catalyst or that may cause difficulties in subsequent processing. For example, acids evolved from a chloride during calcining can be highly corrosive. Halogens remaining in the final catalyst may cause an undesired acidic functionality and sodium compounds may enhance sintering.

Control of air and water pollution is also an important factor. NO_x from nitrates must be removed, e.g., by scrubbing with aqueous alkali; many heavy metals are more or less toxic and cannot be simply discharged. If the final catalyst is to be a supported metal, sulfate may be undesirable, since it can be reduced to a sulfide, which is a common poison for metal catalysts. The metal nitrate salt is often preferred because it usually is highly water-soluble, generally available, and cheap, but NO_x control is required. An organic compound such as a formate or oxalate may be used, although these are more expensive and organic fragments from their decomposition on heating may adsorb on the catalyst to cause partial inactivation. Also, the average ultimate metal particle size may be considerably different if it is formed by decomposition of a compound rather than by reduction of an oxide. Sulfates and chlorides are generally water-soluble, but the anions must usually be removed by washing, and disposal of waste water may be a problem. A preferred base is usually ammonium hydroxide since it leaves no cation residue, but it may complex with some metals and keep them in solution.

If a relatively crystalline precipitate is formed, the size of the crystals may affect the ultimate particle size of a supported metal catalyst. Thus, fine crystals may be desired to produce high surface area of a supported metal catalyst, but crystals that are too fine may be difficult to filter. The size of such crystals may be controlled by a variety of techniques. In a multicomponent catalyst, crystals may be smaller if the metals are truly coprecipitated rather than precipitated in sequence. Crystal size may also be affected by temperature and by stirring, since this affects nucleation and the degree of supersaturation. *Ripening*, in which a precipitate is allowed to stand for a period, can allow for recrystallization in which small and/or amorphous particles dissolve and crystalline particles grow. This may convert a gelatinous precipitate to a more crystalline and filterable solid.

Silicic acid and a number of metal hydroxides, e.g., those of aluminum, iron, and titanium, form gelatinous colloids. This can make them extremely difficult to filter or to purify by washing. Such gels may be coagulated by electrolytes, but the process of washing to remove electrolyte impurities may cause them to redisperse into colloidal solution, termed *peptization*. Hence, a silicic acid gel may be washed with dilute hydrochloric acid, or an aluminum hydroxide gel with aqueous ammonium nitrate, to maintain an ionic environment anu hence the coagulated form. The additives can be subsequently removed by heating. Gels readily occlude ionic impurities, which may be difficult to remove by washing. The possibility of reaction between carrier and reagents should also be considered in this step. Thus, acidic solutions of reagents may react with basic carriers, and vice versa (Sec. 4.5).

4.2.2 Forming operations

The nature of the forming operations is determined by a balance among several factors, including rheological properties of the mixture, and the necessity to achieve satisfactory strength, an open-pore structure, and high activity in the ultimate catalyst, in addition to economics. Relatively hard materials, which typically have high melting points, cannot be made into pellets without suitable additives. Operations causing an increase in crushing strength usually also decrease pore volume and average pore size, and hence may cause diffusion limitations. Typically, commercial catalysts have a void fraction of about 0.5 cm^3 of voids per cubic centimeter of porous pellet.

Pelletizing. Powder is compressed in a die that shapes it into pellets or rings. A die lubricant such as stearic acid or graphite (e.g., 1 to 2 percent) is usually added to the mixture, and frequently a binder as well. The process can be used only with those powder mixtures that are free flowing and that cohere upon pressing. This is often a more expensive process than extrusion. A rotary tablet press, as used in a representative manufacturing plant, is shown in Fig. 4.6. Powder is fed through the hopper at the top and compressed by punches from both the top and bottom of the die. A row (curved) of top punches can be seen in Fig. 4.6 and ejected pellets are falling down the chute below. Usually each machine has two hoppers on opposite sides of the rotary press, so that two tablets are made in each die during one rotation. To make rings, the bottom punch is designed with a core.

An inexpensive and common binder is clay, sometimes used, for example, in making alumina supports or zeolite catalysts. However, clay has ion-exchange properties and, unless specially treated, contains sodium. At elevated reactor temperatures, sodium may migrate into the active catalyst or exchange with other alkalis in the catalyst, causing deterioration. If clay is deleterious, certain forms of colloidal or hydrated alumina may be used instead (Sec. 4.5.1).

Figure 4.6   Pelletizing operation. (*Courtesy of United Catalysts Inc., Louisville, Ky.*)

Extrusion. A thick paste is extruded through a die pierced with a large number of holes, as shown in Fig. 4.7. The spaghetti-like extrudate may be cut to size, or, more commonly, it is dried and then, by mechanical means, broken into lengths about two to four times the diameter. The product is then calcined.

Suitable rheological properties are usually obtained by incorporating methylcellulose, polyols, stearates, small amounts of clay, colloidal silica or alumina, etc. The water content may be very important in that the ultimate mechanical strength typically increases as water content is reduced, but below some critical concentration extrusion can become very difficult.

Either the extrusion or pelletizing process may produce a skin effect such that the pores at the surface are smaller than those in the interior, thus causing diffusion limitations. The gases evolved upon drying and calcining usually prevent a skin effect from being significant, but it may occur with experimental preparations that have not been calcined or if excessive temperatures cause sintering. By suitable die design, extrudates with a hole in the center, like pieces of short but straight macaroni, have been prepared and used. These structures

Figure 4.7   Extruder forming ⅟₃₂-in (0.78-mm) extrusions.
(*Courtesy of United Catalysts Inc., Louisville, Ky.*)

may be slightly misshapen in contrast to the precise shapes produced by pelletizing. This should not cause concern.

Spheres.   Fine spheres may be produced by spray-drying a slurry or a solution, as in the manufacture of catalytic-cracking catalyst in a microspheroidal form, used in fluidized beds.

Larger spheres may be formed in a continuously rotating granulator (Fig. 4.8). Fine powder and a spray of liquid are brought together in a tilted rotating pan. Granules are formed, and they roll over one another and over powder in a snowballing effect. Spheres are continuously ejected by centrifugal force once they have reached a critical size. These spheres are then screened, and undersized particles are recycled. The final catalyst prepared in this way tends to have a higher pore volume and a lower crushing strength than pellets or extrudates.

If the material has suitable rheological properties, it can be extruded and cut into short cylinders, which are then rolled or tumbled into a semispherical form. Smaller spheres can also be produced if precipitation or coagulation can be caused to occur while a liquid is falling or rising through a second immiscible liquid. The process is used to form spherical bead catalysts, which are the preferred shape for use

Figure 4.8 Sphere-forming operation. (*Courtesy of United Catalysts Inc., Louisville, Ky.*)

in a moving-bed reactor. Coagulation of a gel may be produced by dropping it into a bath of hot oil (or allowing it to rise) or by altering pH.

Shell catalysts. Sometimes the active ingredients may be deposited in the form of a skin or shell on the outside portion of a support, as with very active catalysts in which diffusion resistances are otherwise readily encountered. The support may be porous or nonporous, e.g., in the form of spheres or rings, and is coated with the active catalyst material. This is also a useful procedure when it is impractical to work with a catalyst solution. An example is V_2O_5 on titania, the preferred catalyst for partial oxidation of *o*-xylene to phthalic anhydride. The usual preparation consists of about 6 percent V_2O_5 on TiO_2 (as anatase), this in turn being coated onto ceramic rings or pellets. (Sec. 8.6.2). A V_2O_5/TiO_2 coating is applied to monolith supports in a process for control of NO_x emissions from power plants (Sec. 8.13).

Granules. A refractory catalyst support or a catalyst formed by high-temperature fusion, such as the ammonia synthesis catalyst, may be granulated simply by grinding and screening, but granulated shapes are infrequently used since fines represent an economic loss and may be difficult to reprocess. Granules also usually cause a higher pressure drop in a packed bed than do pellets of similar size, and they may dust and fragment readily. Also, flow maldistribution that can lead to hot spots or less effective contacting is more likely with granules than with more uniform packing. Grinding may also cause thermal effects that can destroy some materials, such as some zeolites.

4.2.3 Calcination

This may have several purposes. One is to eliminate extraneous material such as binders and die lubricants, as well as volatile and unstable anions and cations that have been previously introduced, but are not desired in the final catalyst. Second, a substantially elevated temperature is usually needed to increase the strength of the final pellet or extrudate by causing incipient sintering. Excessive sintering will reduce the catalyst activity by reducing surface area, and it may also cause diffusion limitations by reduction of pore size, so an optimum is desired.

If a metallic catalyst is the ultimate goal, conversion to the oxide form is frequently sought prior to reduction. If a complex catalyst is the goal, a substantially elevated firing temperature may be required to cause mixing by diffusion of individual species to form a desired compound or crystal phase. In any event, the catalyst should be heated under controlled conditions to a temperature at least as high as will be encountered in the plant reactor to remove bound water, carbon dioxide, etc. If these decompositions occur to a significant extent in the plant, they may cause structural weaknesses in pellets, leading to breakup, dusting, and so on, that may cause excessive pressure drop and premature reactor shutdown.

For small production runs, conventional batch-type multitray driers and calciners are common, but labor costs are high. For larger production runs, a continuous rotary kiln may be used. More precise temperature control is achievable with a continuous tunnel kiln. This may be heated electrically with numerous zones so that temperature rise can be programmed. Trays may be fastened onto a stainless steel mesh belt and automatically loaded and dumped, or trays may be placed and removed manually.

Upon heating pellets in a tray calciner, an exothermic reaction may develop that can lead to excessively high temperature locally, affecting the catalyst adversely. The effect can stem from an exothermic decomposition reaction, as in the thermal decomposition of an ammonium copper chromate to form a "copper chromite" catalyst or by reactions among pellet ingredients, such as that between a metal nitrate and organic admixtures such as cellulose, graphite, or stearates.

Combustion in air of these organic substances or of remaining organic solvents may also occur. The effect is most pronounced with thick layers of pellets from which heat generated internally cannot easily escape. It may be controlled by using a slower rate of heatup or using thinner layers of pellets, although it may be necessary to use layers as thin as an inch or so.

Possible reactions with the carrier during precipitation, washing, drying, and heating must also be borne in mind. The oxide or other metal compound that is the active catalyst may form a compound with the carrier or may dissolve in the carrier to form a solid solution. At the usual calcination temperatures, up to 500 to 600°C, silica does not react appreciably with most metals. γ-alumina, a commonly used carrier, can react with a divalent metal oxide to form a metal aluminate, $MeAl_2O_4$, which of itself may be relatively unreactive. The extent of its formation depends on the degree of diffusion of the metal ions into the alumina, so the structure in most cases exists only on the surface of the alumina. The process can occur with such elements as manganese, cobalt, nickel, and copper, and since the ion must be in the + 2 oxidation state, the extent of formation also depends on the firing atmosphere.

The ratio of metal oxide to alumina is also important since, with a low concentration of metal, much of it may ultimately be in the form of an aluminate but at high concentrations most of the oxide form may be retained (Lo Jacono & Schiavello 1976). Similarly, molybdenum oxide and tungsten oxide can react with alumina to form $Al_2(MoO_4)_3$ and $Al_2(WO_4)_3$, respectively. V_2O_5 can react to form $AlVO_4$, and Re_2O_7 to form $Al_2(ReO_4)_3$ [Pott & Stork 1976]. In some cases a particular surface compound may be desired as in a V_2O_5/TiO_2 catalyst used to convert o-xylene to phthalic anhydride.

The reduction of nickel aluminate incorporated with alumina to form metallic nickel may require temperatures of the order of 500°C, considerably higher than that needed for reduction of nickel oxide, and this may cause excessive sintering. The formation of a solid solution or intermediate compound with the carrier or other components present is not necessarily undesirable in forming a supported metal catalyst. Indeed, it may be deliberately sought after, at least to some degree, if the substance can be reduced to the metal at a temperature not so high that excessive sintering or other deleterious effects are encountered. Such metal crystallites may be small, well dispersed, and well stabilized by a textural promoter effect (Sec. 4.6.1).

An example is shown in a purification process for H_2 containing small amounts of carbon oxides that are removed by hydrogenation over a nickel catalyst to form CH_4. In one manufacturing process, the nickel catalyst is supported on alumina with which a small amount of a magnesium compound is included. During the calcination of $NiCO_3$, the catalyst precursor, the presence of 2 to 3 % MgO in the support retards the growth of NiO crystals, and a solid solution of NiO-MgO having crystallites considerably smaller than those of NiO is formed. The NiO-MgO solid solution is slightly more difficult to reduce than NiO, but it results in a more active catalyst with considerable sintering resistance at reaction temperature (about 315 to 365°C) (Bridger & Woodward 1976).

In general, heavy metal ions are more readily incorporated into the support when a catalyst is prepared by coprecipitation, e.g., of aluminum and nickel hydroxides, than if nickel is adsorbed by impregnation onto an alumina carrier. Although silica, in general, is more inert than alumina, silicates of nickel and other metals may be formed to some extent. Coprecipitated catalysts, with either alumina or silica, may be more difficult to reduce than the equivalent impregnated catalysts.

Supported nickel catalysts have been studied in considerable detail [see for example the review by Morikawa et al. (1969) and the discussion by Anderson (1975)]. Cobalt and iron catalysts behave similarly to nickel, although the ease of reduction decreases in the order Ni > Co > Fe.

4.2.4 Reduction to the metal

Most commonly, a metal is formed by reduction of the oxide at an elevated temperature by contact with flowing hydrogen or hydrogen diluted with nitrogen, the latter for safety reasons. A considerable excess of hydrogen may be required to sweep away the product water. If present in too high a concentration, water vapor may accelerate the sintering of an oxide, and it can also retard the rate of the reduction reaction by forming a hydroxylated surface.

Thermodynamic calculations (Anderson 1975, p. 166) show that at temperatures in the region of 570 to 770 K the reduction of the metal oxide to the metal is highly favored for all group VIII elements, plus copper, silver, gold, and rhenium. For the elements chromium, vanadium, tantalum, titanium, and manganese, the oxide form is highly favored. Tungsten and molybdenum oxides are reducible to the metallic form over a range of conditions, but the equilibrium is much less favorable than for the group VIII elements. They may also react readily with high-area alumina and silica to form compounds more difficult to reduce than the oxides. Thermodynamically, metal chlorides are slightly easier to reduce to the metal than the oxides, but the hydrogen chloride formed is highly corrosive in the presence of even small concentrations of water vapor.

Some metal compounds can be reduced by chemical reagents, such as formaldehyde, formic acid, or hydrazine, but these methods are usually more expensive. Alternately, the metal may be formed by decomposition of an organic compound, as by decomposition of nickel formate to yield deposited nickel. In this case, however, organic fragments may become absorbed onto the metallic catalyst, possibly giving rise to considerably different properties than that of a catalyst reduced in hydrogen. Moreover, the ultimate metal particle size is determined by the sintering characteristics of the metal produced, whereas in oxide reduction, particle size may be determined in part, in a rather complicated way, by the formation of metal nuclei and their growth from the oxide particles.

For minimum particle size and hence maximum surface area, with hydrogen reduction it is generally desirable to use initially as high a reduction temperature as is feasibly compatible with avoidance of significant sintering, and as low a partial pressure of water vapor as possible. This maximizes the number of metal nuclei formed (Anderson 1975, p. 171). In this initial stage hydrogen reacts with O^{2-} or OH^- ions, a process that is relatively slow. After metal nuclei are formed, the dominating mechanism in most cases changes to dissociative chemisorption of hydrogen onto the metal, from which atomic hydrogen migrates to the metal/metal-oxide interface. This mechanism is much more rapid.

In the reduction of an initially nonporous material, such as the fused magnetite catalyst used in ammonia synthesis, a much higher temperature is required than for a similar precipitated catalyst, since little area is available initially for reaction.

Sometimes reduction is carried out in situ in the plant reactor, where the large quantities of hydrogen required may be more readily available than on the catalyst manufacturers' premises. This also avoids hazards associated with handling a pyrophoric material. This is the usual procedure with the iron catalyst used for ammonia synthesis and for some nickel catalysts, such as those used for methanation. To reduce the time required for reduction in the plant reactor, the catalyst may be reduced to the metallic form by the catalyst manufacturer and then stabilized for shipment by converting a thin surface layer of the metal to the oxide by controlled oxidation. This thin oxide layer may be rapidly reduced in the plant reactor. A nickel catalyst for hydrogenation of edible oils is often coated with a hydrogenated product that is solid at room temperature but readily dissolves in the reaction mixture.

The maximum temperature for reduction obtainable in the plant reactor may not be much more than the normal reaction temperature, if that, and reduction conditions may be more difficult to control in the plant. These may be important reasons to have the reduction carried out by the catalyst manufacturer. Spent catalyst may be more pyrophoric than fresh catalyst because the absorbed organic material may spontaneously smoulder or inflame on contact with air. Such material may be doused with water or an oil with low volatility immediately upon removal.

A supported metal oxide formed by calcining a metal salt may be considerably more difficult to reduce than a nonsupported oxide, and the nature of the support may have a marked effect. This is illustrated in Figs. 4.9, 4.10 (Sieg et al. in Eischens et al. 1975), and 4.11 for nickel (Webb in Eischens et al. 1975). Reaction may occur between the oxide and the support, e.g., a nickel hydrosilicate may be formed between a nickel compound and silica. With a high degree of dispersion, much of the metal oxide may be in the form of a surface oxide on the support, which is difficult to reduce.

Figure 4.9 shows that, after calcination at 538°C, nickel oxide formed on Cabosil (a nonporous silica prepared by a flame process) is more readily reduced than nickel oxide on a silica gel. This in turn is more readily reduced than nickel oxide on alumina. The nickel content was 7 wt %, expressed as the metal, and reduction was carried out at 371°C. Figure 4.10 shows that a high calcination temperature decreases the reducibility of nickel in all cases, and for alumina it appears that the reduction would not exceed 10 percent under practical conditions. For the data in Fig. 4.11, a nickel salt on silica-alumina was first calcined at 330°C for 3 h and then reduced at 400°C for in-

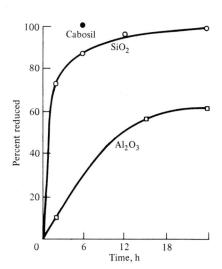

Figure 4.9 Effect of support on reducibility of nickel compound. Calcination temperature = 538°C. [*Sieg et al. in Eischens (1975)*]

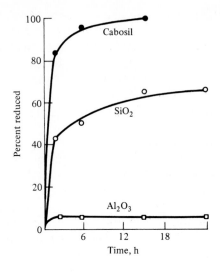

Figure 4.10 Effect of support on reducibility of nickel compound. Calcination temperature = 732°C. Compare with Fig. 4.9. [*Sieg et al. in Eischens (1975)*]

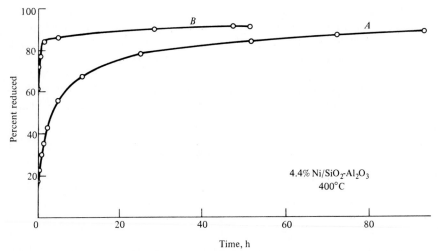

Figure 4.11 Reduction of nickel supported on silica-alumina. See text. [*Webb in Eischens (1975)*]

creasing lengths of time (curve *A*). The same sample was then reoxidized at 400°C and then rereduced at 400°C (curve *B*). Curve *B* is similar to the more rapid reduction that is observed with an unsupported catalyst and shows that there was little interaction between the support and the nickel oxide upon reoxidation (see also Sec. 6.4.1).

It is desirable to cause reduction to occur at as low a temperature as possible, to minimize sintering and maximize the surface area of the final catalyst. With hydrogen reduction, a useful procedure is to incorporate into the catalyst precursor a small amount of a compound of a second metal that is more readily reduced. Examples are copper into precipitated iron catalysts used for Fischer-Tropsch synthesis, trace amounts of platinum onto nickel, or a noble metal such as ruthenium onto cobalt.

Taking iron-copper as an example, the precursor is typically a mixture of oxides of the two metals. The copper oxide is reduced first, after which hydrogen is adsorbed onto the copper metal, presumably in a dissociated form, and diffuses onto the iron oxide, reducing it to the metal. If a base metal oxide by itself is reduced, initially the rate is low, and then it accelerates as domains of reduced metal appear onto which hydrogen can adsorb directly and then diffuse over to remaining metal oxide. See also *spillover* (Sec. 6.4.2).

The foregoing results emphasize the uncertainties that can be introduced into the study of a catalytic reaction if the supported metal element is only partly in the metallic form and partly in other combined forms that may or may not have significant catalytic activity of their own.

4.3   Impregnation

Two methods of contacting may be distinguished. The support is sometimes dipped into an excess quantity of solution, whereupon the uptake is the sum of solution occluded in the pores plus material adsorbed onto the pore surfaces. If two or more compounds are present, they are frequently adsorbed on the support surface in a ratio different from that in the solution, and solution concentrations also change with continued contacting. Additions to the solution must take these effects into account. Moreover, material may be dissolved from the support into the treating solution.

More precise control is achieved by a technique termed *dry impregnation,* or *impregnation to incipient wetness*, which is commonly used industrially. A batch of the support is tumbled and sprayed with a solution of appropriate concentration, corresponding in quantity to the total known pore volume of the support, or slightly less. This allows accurate control of the amount of the active ingredient that will be incorporated into the catalyst, but the maximum loading obtainable in a single impregnation is limited by the solubility of the reagent. The resulting catalyst is then usually dried and calcined.

In a few cases, the active ingredient may be fixed inside the catalyst by immersing the impregnated catalyst in a reagent to cause precipitation to occur.

Oxide supports such as alumina and silica are readily wet by aqueous solutions, as are most activated carbons, which have a layer of chemisorbed oxygen on them. Capillary forces then ensure that liquid is sucked into the entire porous structure. Because of capillary pressure, even pores closed at one end are nearly filled, and the solution of gas in the liquid assists the process. If the support is not readily wetted, e.g., a carbon that is highly graphitized or without chemisorbed oxygen, an organic solvent may be used or the support may be impregnated under vacuum. These procedures are somewhat more costly to use in the plant than incipient impregnation.

The time required for liquid penetration into a pore may be calculated by equating the capillary force to the viscous drag. For a wetting liquid where the contact angle is zero, the time required for liquid to penetrate a distance x into a capillary is given by $t = 4\eta x^2/\gamma d$, where η is the liquid viscosity and γ is the surface tension. Anderson (1975, p. 172) notes that for pore diameters d of 2 to 50 nm, the time required to penetrate a distance of 2 mm is typically in the range of 115 to 5 s. The distance penetrated is proportional to the square root of time and of pore diameter.

4.3.1 Distribution through pellet

Most metal reagents are adsorbed to varying degrees on most supports, but the characteristics of the process are complicated since various types of adsorption are possible. Silicas and zeolites are acidic and adsorb cations. Alumina is amphoteric. Titania is also amphoteric, but more acidic than alumina. For these adsorbents the relative adsorption of cations and anions can be controlled by adjusting pH.

Metal ions may be cation-exchanged with a surface containing hydroxyl groups or containing alkali or alkaline earth-metal ions, or they may be held by coordination. The surface structure of the carrier may also be altered by the impregnation procedure, thus changing its adsorption characteristics. The ultimate degree of dispersion of metal through the catalyst pellet is also determined by the interplay of a large number of factors whose relative importance varies with circumstances. These include the method of impregnation, the strength of adsorption, the extent to which the metal compound is present as occluded solute (that in the bulk liquid in the pores) in contrast to adsorbed species on pore walls, and the chemical reactions that occur upon heating and drying.

The situation may be further complicated by attack on the support. Silica gel is attacked at high pH, and alumina, which is amphoteric, is attacked at a pH that is either too high or too low. Indeed, during the impregnation of an alumina support with an acidic liquid, some solution of alumina may first occur, followed by precipitation as the pH increases. It may be desirable to control this effect by using a buffer.

As an example of the interplay of some of these effects, consider the preparation of a supported platinum catalyst. With chloroplatinic acid, H_2PtCl_6, a commonly used platinum reagent, platinum is present in anionic form. It is strongly adsorbed on alumina or activated carbon but not on silica gel. Its application to alumina by the incipient-wetness method leads to the deposition of a thin shell of platinum on the outer portions of the particle (this may be desirable in order to avoid diffusion limitations in a fast reaction).

To obtain a more uniform dispersion, the adsorptivity of $PtCl_6^{2-}$ ions may be reduced by adjusting pH. Alternatively, platinum could be applied to alumina as $Pt(NH_3)_4Cl_2$, in which case platinum is in the form of a cation. It is then less readily adsorbed on alumina, but more strongly adsorbed on silica gel. If a halogen-free catalyst preparation is desired, a compound such as platinum diaminodinitrite, $Pt(NH_3)_2(NO_2)_2$, may be used.

It is also possible to control the deposition by competitive adsorption, e.g., by adding a citrate to the impregnating solution. This procedure has been used to embed a catalytically active layer slightly inside a catalyst particle (Hoekstra 1968). Such a structure may be desired for prolongation of catalyst life in an application in which poisons are deposited on the outside surface of a porous catalyst support. An example is supported platinum catalysts for oxidation of pollutants in automobile engine exhaust.

In general, use of the dipping method with a great excess of solution should lead to an essentially uniform deposit of adsorbed material if sufficient time is allowed for diffusion of reagent species to the interior and if side reactions are unimportant. If adsorption is initially nonuniform and not too strong, redistribution continues even after the pellet is removed from solution, leading to a more uniform distribution.

The drying process can also affect the distribution of an active ingredient. The crystallite size of a resulting supported metal catalyst may also be altered if a considerable portion of the soluble metal is occluded rather than adsorbed. Again, the effects are complex, and little can be said of general guidance. Initially, evaporation occurs at the outer surface of the particle, but liquid evaporated from small pores will be replaced by liquid drawn from large pores by capillarity. The places where crystallization begins and the ultimate distribution of metal depend on such factors as the initial degree of saturation of the liquid, the rate of nucleation, the rate of heating, connectivity (the degree of connection of liquid paths between pores) at the time of crystallization, and the possibility of surface migration. More detailed analyses of impregnation and drying effects are given by Moss (1976) and Anderson (1975). Commercially available impregnated catalysts are usually found to have a higher concentration of metal at the outside than at the center, even when a more or less uniformly deposited catalyst is desired.

4.4 Special Preparative Methods

A number of special techniques have limited application, but they illustrate the wide variety of ways in which catalysts may be formed and utilized.

4.4.1 Massive-metal catalysts

Metal catalysts are sometimes used as massive metal, as in the form of wire screens or granules. In ammonia oxidation (Sec. 8.10) and in the Andrussow process for synthesis of hydrogen cyanide (Sec. 8.11) the catalyst is typically a number of layers of screen made of an alloy of 90% Pt and 10% Rh, typically 80 mesh and consisting of wires 0.075 mm in diameter. In one of the processes for partial oxidation of methanol to formaldehyde, metallic silver is used in the form of screens or granules (Sec. 8.4.1).

For economy it is tempting to electrolytically plate an expensive catalyst such as platinum onto a less expensive base, but in high-temperature processes such deposits may readily flake off, or structural rearrangements, upon reaction, may expose and destroy the base material. Finely divided metal powders may be compacted into desired shapes and sizes by powder metallurgy, as in the preparation of porous electrodes for fuel cells. However, sintering may occur in high-temperature operations or at lower temperatures in the presence of hydrogen or other reactants, and much higher metal dispersion can usually be obtained by use of a carrier.

4.4.2 Thermal fusion

The usual promoted iron catalyst for ammonia synthesis is made by fusion of naturally occurring magnetite, Fe_3O_4, mixed with small amounts of potassium carbonate, alumina, and other ingredients. The melt is cast, allowed to cool, crushed, and sieved into the desired particle sizes. The optimum size depends on the reactor configuration used (Sec. 10.5). Figure 4.12 shows three sizes of commercial interest. Since finely divided iron is pyrophoric, the catalyst is reduced in situ in the reactor or, if prereduced, is stabilized for shipment by forming a surface oxide layer that is then reduced in the reactor (see Sec. 4.2.4).

4.4.3 Leaching processes

The best known example of a metal catalyst prepared by leaching is Raney nickel, which is highly active for hydrogenation reactions. It is named after Murray Raney, who patented the method of preparation in 1925. Its earlier uses were reviewed by Lieber and Morritz (1953).

Figure 4.12   Topsøe ammonia-synthesis catalyst KMI. The three sizes are about 1.5 to 3 mm, 6 to 10 mm, and 12 to 21 mm. (*Courtesy of Haldor Topsøe, A/S, Copenhagen, Denmark*)

The catalyst is prepared from a nickel-aluminum alloy by leaching out much of the aluminum with caustic solution to leave behind a porous nickel catalyst. Typically a 1:1 nickel-aluminum alloy is reacted with a 20% solution of sodium hydroxide.

To achieve maximum activity and structural stability, some aluminum must be left behind, and some hydrated alumina is also formed and retained. This may act as a textural promoter (Sec. 4.6.1). The surface area of the catalyst may range up to 80 to 100 m^2/g. After deterioration from use, the catalyst may be reactivated a few times by further leaching. Raney nickel is pyrophoric, so it must be handled carefully; it is usually stored under water or under an organic solvent. Raney nickel is provided commercially in a variety of sizes, ranging from fine powders to granules.

A leaching method of making catalyst can also be applied to other metals alloyed with aluminum to make, e.g., Raney cobalt, Raney copper, etc., but these seem to be less widely used. The method may also be used to produce metal catalysts in unusual forms. Thus, in a process in which it is desired to remove heat directly from a catalyst, an aluminum alloy may be flame-sprayed directly onto a metal heat-exchange surface and the active catalyst formed by leaching.

Considerable hydrogen is evolved when Raney nickel is heated, greater than that corresponding to adsorption and solution. In the earlier literature, the high activity of Raney nickel was sometimes attributed to the existence of an unusual form of hydrogen. However, it now appears that, upon heating, the hydrogen is formed instead by reaction between bound water in the alumina and the aluminum metal.

Clay catalysts, first developed for catalytic-cracking processes, were prepared by leaching certain clays with a mineral acid such as sulfuric. An acidic structure is required for cracking activity, and this process replaces alkali and alkaline earth cations with hydrogen ions. It also increases the surface area of the catalyst and removes undesired impurities such as iron. Kaolin clay continues to be used in preparing some present-day cracking catalysts (Sec. 9.4).

4.4.4 Miscellaneous

Urushibara nickel catalysts (see Hata 1971) have sometimes been used in laboratory preparations and are somewhat similar to Raney nickel. Typically, a nickel chloride solution is treated with zinc dust to precipitate a finely divided form of metallic nickel admixed with zinc chloride. The zinc chloride is removed by treatment with acid or base. This catalyst does not seem to have been used commercially; it may deactivate too fast. An Urushibara copper catalyst can also be prepared by similar procedures.

Salts of nickel, platinum, palladium, etc., can be reduced with sodium borohydride to form active catalysts. It is not clear whether the final catalysts are essentially metallic or borides.

4.5 Catalyst Supports

The early concept of a support or a carrier was of an inert substance that provided a means of spreading out an expensive catalyst ingredient such as platinum for its most effective use, or a means of improving the mechanical strength of an inherently weak catalyst. However, the carrier may actually contribute catalytic activity, depending on the reaction and reaction conditions, and it may react to some extent with other catalyst ingredients during the manufacturing process. It can also help stabilize the catalytically active structure.

The carrier may be used as pellets or powders to be impregnated, a powdered carrier may be incorporated into a mixture to be precipitated, or the carrier may itself be precipitated from solution in the manufacturing process. Some substances such as colloidal alumina or colloidal silica may play a double role, acting as a binding agent in catalyst manufacture and as a carrier in the ultimate product. Alumina in the γ form is intrinsically weakly acidic, but such a substance may be a truly inert carrier for many reactions. In other cases it can be used by itself as a catalyst, as in dehydration of an alcohol. High-area carriers are sometimes loosely referred to as "active" carriers in contrast to low-area "inert" carriers, but this usage may be misleading.

The selection of a carrier is based on its having certain desirable characteristics. In addition to possible chemical effects, certain physical properties are important:

1. Inertness to undesired reactions
2. Desirable mechanical properties, including attrition resistance, hardness, and compressive strength
3. Stability under reaction and regeneration conditions
4. Surface area (High surface area is usually, but not always, desirable.)
5. Porosity, including average pore size and pore-size distribution (High area implies fine pores, but relatively small pores, such as < 2 nm, may become plugged in catalyst preparation, especially if high loadings are sought.)
6. Low cost

Of a wide variety of possible materials, only three combine the foregoing characteristics in an optimum way, and therefore they account for most uses. These are alumina, silica, and activated carbon; titania also has some limited uses. Of the first three, alumina is the most widely used industrially. Magnesia generally has poor strength, and zinc oxide tends to be reduced. Chromia tends to cause dehydration, and its acidity can cause undesirable reactions to occur. Zirconia, although more expensive, is stable at high temperatures, and is stable in alkaline media. For a low-area carrier, α-alumina or a magnesia-alumina silicate have been used. See also the book by Stiles (1987).

A necessary requirement for any carrier is resistance to sintering under reaction conditions. The temperature at which lattices begin to be appreciably mobile is sometimes termed the *Tammann temperature*; and that at which surface atoms become significantly mobile, the *Hüttig temperature*. For simple compounds without phase changes on heating and of low vapor pressure, the Tammann temperature is very approximately $0.5\ T_m$ and the Hüttig temperature about $0.3\ T_m$, where T_m is the melting point in absolute units. Consequently, suitable carriers must usually have fairly high melting points as a minimum. Appreciable mobility appears at about $T_m/3$ for metals, so group IB metals (Cu, Ag, Au), which have melting points in the neighborhood of 1300 K, must almost always be supported or have textural promoters incorporated with them in order for high area to be maintained. The transition metals, iron, cobalt, and nickel, with melting points of about 1800 K, will become mobile at temperatures above roughly 250 to 300°C. The platinum-group metals melt at high temperatures, but are usually supported for economy.

The foregoing are but approximate guides to behavior. Metal crystallites may grow by other mechanisms, and they may be stabilized by keeping them from contact with one another by use of textural promoters.

4.5.1 Alumina

Alumina is the most widely used support because it is inexpensive, structurally stable and because it can be prepared with a wide variety of pore sizes and pore size distributions. Commercial materials are available with surface areas in the range of 100 to 600 m^2/g and down to essentially nonporous alumina. A number of different crystalline phases can exist. In spite of detailed and extensive study, methods of control of the final structures are not completely understood, and the manufacture of aluminas for catalytic purposes still involves considerable art with respect to precipitation, aging, drying, and calcination.

Aluminas are generally prepared by dehydration of various aluminum hydroxides, but even if the hydroxide is a gel, it is readily converted to a crystalline form on aging and/or heating. The particular crystalline form obtained depends in a rather complicated way on the time–temperature–environmental history to which the hydroxide is subjected, and this may be difficult to control, especially on a large scale.

Aluminas may also contain various amounts of impurities, such as sodium and iron, as a result of the manufacturing process. For some catalyst uses these impurities are detrimental, and catalyst manufacturers or their suppliers may go to considerable pains to make a very high-purity alumina by a special process starting with high-purity aluminum metal or aluminum compounds. Such aluminas are several times more costly than aluminas prepared from bauxite (see the following) and are used mostly for catalytic reforming.

The most important aluminas for use as carriers are the transition aluminas. γ-Al_2O_3 is of greatest interest since it has a high area and is relatively stable over the temperature range of interest for most catalytic reactions. η-Al_2O_3 has been of interest in the past because it is inherently more acidic than γ, so it became a useful support in catalytic reforming. At present, however, acidity in catalytic reforming is controlled more precisely by addition of minute amounts of a chloride and water over a γ-Al_2O_3–based catalyst, and presently there are few uses of η-Al_2O_3 as such.

Both η and γ have a crystallographic form in which the oxygen at-

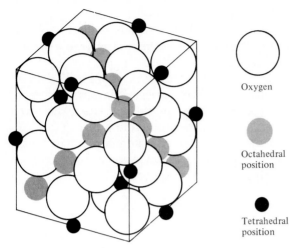

Oxygen

Octahedral
position

Tetrahedral
position

Figure 4.13 Lattice structure of spinel, $MgAl_2O_4$.
(*Ryshkewitch 1960, p. 259*)

oms are arranged similarly to that in spinel, $MgAl_2O_4$ (see Fig. 4.13), but the η form is more distorted than the γ form. All the oxygen ions in a spinel structure are equivalent, forming a close-packed cubic arrangement. The oxygen ions are much larger than the cations, and the latter fit into two kinds of gaps, octahedral (surrounded by six atoms) and tetrahedral (surrounded by four atoms), that exist between the oxygen ions in the structure. A large number of mixed oxides exist in the spinel structure, which is expressed in the general form $M^{II}M_2^{III}O_4$. Some single oxides also form this structure, for example, Mn_3O_4, Fe_3O_4, and Co_3O_4.

Crystallographically, the atomic ratio of total metal to oxygen atoms is 3:4 for a spinel but only 2:3 for alumina, which in a true spinel structure might be thought of as "Al Al_2O_4." Hence, for an alumina such as η and γ, a portion of the metal gaps are vacant and there are varying degrees of disorder. This may be one reason for the greater solubility and compound formation between heavy metal cations and γ-alumina than between heavy metal cations and silica, which occur upon heating. In particular, aluminates and spinel-type structures may be formed between γ-alumina and a catalyst supported on it. These surface compounds may have little catalytic activity. Aluminates in general are formed more readily than silicates. Aluminas react more readily with other species present during a phase change, a phenomenon that seems to be observed for solids in general and is sometimes termed the *Hedvall effect* (1956).

The surfaces of aluminas terminate as OH groups. Infrared absorption reveals the existence of at least five types of OH groups, the properties of which depend on their immediate environment. Upon heating, water is evolved, leaving behind domains of oxides and OH groups. This statistical irregularity is the source of charge distributions and hence variations in acidity (see Chap. 7).

A common manufacturing process starts with sodium aluminate produced in conjunction with the Bayer process for purification of bauxite prior to its reduction to aluminum metal. Bauxite is dissolved in sodium hydroxide to form sodium aluminate and a precipitate (so-called red mud), which contains silica and iron and is removed by filtration. The solution is then diluted with water to cause hydrolysis and precipitation of α-alumina trihydrate (gibbsite).

$$2NaAlO_2 + 4H_2O \rightarrow Al_2O_3 3H_2O + 2NaOH$$

Gibbsite can also be prepared by other procedures, but as derived from sodium aluminate it always contains at least 0.2 to 0.3% Na_2O, even after washing with dilute hydrochloric acid (Lippens & Steggerda 1970). The presence of sodium in alumina can be deleterious for many catalytic applications. At temperatures of 200 to 300°C it can slowly migrate to the surface and react with active catalyst ingredients. It can also accelerate sintering, of special importance at higher temperatures.

Transformation sequences.   Figure 4.14 (Wefers & Bell 1972) outlines the principal transformation sequences that can occur upon heating the hydrated aluminas. γ-alumina is formed from boehmite (AlOOH), also termed α-alumina monohydrate, or from pseudoboehmite (see the following). Boehmite in turn can be formed from gibbsite [α-Al(OH)$_3$] or another crystalline form of aluminum hydroxide (e.g., bayerite, or β-Al(OH)$_3$, also termed nostrandite). The set of conditions required is such as to favor a hydrothermal transformation rather than a drying/calcination type of process. This is critically related to the water vapor partial pressure at the location where the transformation takes place. The conversion to boehmite is thus favored by a moist environment, superatmospheric pressure, a rapid heating rate, and larger particle sizes. The last two operating conditions minimize the average rate of loss of water by diffusion from the particle.

At lower pressures, a ρ-alumina can be formed (also sometimes termed a rehydratable alumina), that can be converted by rehydration to pseudoboehmite. Pseudoboehmite, also termed gelatinous boehmite, has an X-ray pattern similar to that of boehmite but has a higher water content. It is a frequent choice as a precursor for manufacturing catalyst supports perhaps since, compared to boehmite, it can be converted to γ-alumina at a lower temperature (300°C versus 450°C) and

Conditions favoring transformations

Conditions	Path *a*	Path *b*
Pressure, atm	> 1	1
Atmosphere	Moist air	Dry air
Heating rate, °C/min	> 1	< 1
Particle size, μm	> 100	< 10

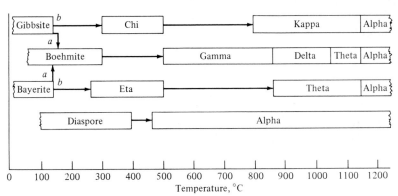

Figure 4.14   Decomposition sequence of aluminum hydroxides. (Enclosed area indicates range of occurrence. Open area indicates transition range.) (*Wefers and Bell 1972, p. 43*)

the γ-Al_2O_3 formed may be more temperature-stable (Lippens & Steggerda 1970).

Interconversions between different alumina phases can occur more or less readily during the various steps of precipitation, aging, drying, and calcination, so most commercial aluminas consist of a mixture of phases. This is usually of secondary importance, but it is not surprising that aluminas supplied by different manufacturers may be found to vary considerably in their behavior as catalyst supports, in ways that may be difficult to relate to identifiable differences.

A product consisting mainly of pseudoboehmite can also be formed in other ways (Lostaglio & Carruthers 1986). These include neutralizing sodium aluminate with acid, neutralizing an aluminum salt with NH_3, oxidizing an amalgamated aluminum with water, or hydrolyzing an aluminum alkyl. The last method produces a pure alumina with very low sodium content that is useful as a binder (e.g., Catapal, Dispal).

For many purposes, the actual form of the alumina is less important than the surface area and pore size distribution. These are determined by several factors. In the first instance, these are the particle size of crystallites in a precipitate, and their agglomeration. The latter can be affected by peptization (control of dispersion by varying pH), aging, etc. Mechanical manipulation and methods of drying and calcination all are of importance.

In some applications it may be desirable to minimize the fraction of pore volume present as very small pores, e.g., less than 1 to 2 nm or so diameter, in order to minimize accumulation of deposits that would cause a substantial drop in activity or trapping of reaction intermediates leading to undesirable overreaction. Controlled calcination or hydrothermal treatment can eliminate most fine pores without excessive loss of area. A representative "heavy alumina" used in industrial catalysis and prepared in this fashion has a surface area of about 80 m^2/g. It consists of about 80 to 90 percent theta in which 10 to 20% of large polycrystalline α is embedded with crystal sizes of ~ 0.1 to 1 μm.

Aluminas are available in a variety of sizes and shapes as determined by the forming operations. Spray-drying produces beads in the size range of 100 μm. The oil-drop technique can be used to prepare beads of a uniform diameter ranging from about 500 μm to several millimeters.

The conversion of aluminum hydroxides to active aluminas and their chemical and physical structure are reviewed in a chapter by Lippens and Steggerda (1970). These topics are more recently reviewed by Trimm and Stanislaus (1986) and, from a more industrial point of view, by Lostaglio and Carruthers (1986). More details on aluminas as supports and as catalysts are given by Poisson et al. (1987) and Oberlander (1984). Candela and Perlmutter (1986) report on a detailed study of the pore structures obtained by thermal decomposition of gibbsite.

γ-Alumina has a high surface area (typically about 250 to 350 m^2/g). Further heating to about 850°C, either in use or in regeneration, converts this to δ-alumina. Above about 1100°C this is converted to the θ form, which then goes to α-alumina with collapse of the structure and the formation of a dense, low-area material. The θ form can be stabilized by addition of rare earth oxides or other additives. The nature of various additives and impurities present as well as the environment can have a marked effect on high-temperature stability (Gauguin et al. 1975). Thermodynamically, hexagonal α-alumina is the stable form at all temperatures, and structures such as γ, η, etc., are frequently referred to as *transition aluminas*. These are not hydrated structures, and they are more or less crystalline.

For many reactions the maximum temperature reached in the reactor or upon regeneration does not exceed about 500 to 600°C. The γ-type alumina generally has good stability under these conditions. For a few uses, such as in pollution control, where oxidation reactions at very high temperatures are required, catalyst supports that are reasonably stable up to temperatures as high as 1000°C may be needed. Gauguin et al. (1975) describe some of the transformations of aluminas under these high-temperature conditions.

The aluminas formed at temperatures of about 300°C or more are not hydrated but contain small amounts of water of constitution, which is gradually evolved on heating to higher temperatures. The conversion of OH groups to water on heating leaves behind a structure with exposed aluminum atoms that behaves like a Lewis acid. In addition, a Brönsted-type acidity exists, stemming from the OH groups. The high-area aluminas of interest as supports typically exhibit an intrinsic weak acidity, which may be enhanced by traces of common impurities such as chloride, iron oxide, or sulfates, as may be found in aluminas produced by the Bayer process.

Stronger acidity may be produced by deliberately incorporating halogens such as chlorides or fluorides in the structure to catalyze reactions of various hydrocarbons as in catalytic reforming. The halide may be introduced inadvertently if a metal halogen compound such as $PdCl_2$ or H_2PtCl_6 is used in catalyst preparation. Some commercial aluminas are basic in the sense that a suspension in water exhibits a pH above 7, caused by the presence of sodium. This may be washed out to some extent, whereupon the leached alumina may behave differently as an adsorbent because of a different ultimate pH reached upon impregnation.

The thermal stability of γ-alumina may be enhanced by two different procedures. Small amounts of silica (for example, 1 to 4 wt %) may be cogelled with it in its manufacture, but this may increase its acidity (Chap. 7). It has been suggested that a viscous film of silicate is formed that isolates alumina crystallites. The thermal stability of alumina may also be enhanced by incorporating small amounts of divalent ions, such as calcium, magnesium, or barium into the alumina. These occupy tetrahedral voids in the spinel and retard the diffusion of Al^{+3} cations. They may also block cations of an active ingredient, e.g., Cu, from moving into the spinel.

A finely divided "fumed" alumina having a surface area of about 100 m^2/g is made by a flame process in which $AlCl_3$ is burned in air. The product consists of agglomerates of spheres about 20 nm in diameter, and it may have applications in catalyst formulations. Well crystallized diaspore occurs in nature and can be converted to α-alumina at much lower temperatures than those at which transition aluminas can be converted. Apparently diaspore is difficult to prepare synthetically, and this is as yet not a practicable route to α-alumina.

Colloidal aluminas. A colloidal alumina that is a suspension of α-Al_2O_3 monohydrate (boehmite) (Catapal) is prepared by hydrolysis of aluminum alcoholates or is formed as a by-product from oligimerization reactions catalyzed by aluminum compounds. It is useful as a binder and as a source of pure $\alpha\text{-Al}_2\text{O}_3$.

An alumina may be used by itself as a catalyst for dehydration of an alcohol, and alumina is a commercial catalyst in the Claus process for conversion of hydrogen sulfide to elemental sulfur (Sec. 9.9). The properties of aluminas for catalytic reactions of hydrocarbons and alcohols are reviewed by John and Scurrell (1977), with particular attention to the literature of 1970 to 1976.

4.5.2 Silica

Silica gel. This is most commonly prepared by mixing an acid with a solution of "water glass," which consists of orthosilicates (Na_4SiO_4), metasilicates (Na_2SiO_3), and related compounds. As the pH is lowered, a polymerization and condensation process takes place, which can be visualized as starting with silicic acid [Si(OH)_4]. This polymerizes with condensation of silane groups (SiOH) to form an ill-defined polymer in which the primary bonds are the siloxane type (Si-O-Si). This precipitates as a gel or as a colloid, the properties of which depend on mixing procedures, the presence of nuclei, electrolytes, temperature, aging, etc. A potassium water glass may be used in the formulation of a catalyst when some potassium is desired in the final product, but not sodium.

By proper control, a hydrogel, consisting of small micelles that are roughly spherical, is obtained. During drying, the micelles do not coalesce appreciably, particularly if the liquid is removed at a temperature and pressure above critical. Under these conditions, no interface forms that could otherwise collapse the structure by the forces of surface tension. The tiny size of the micelles and use of procedures to prevent coalescence leads to a product of high surface area. Commercial material usually has a high area, as high as about 700 m^2/g. The average pore diameter is correspondingly very low, typically in the range of 2.5 to 5 nm. (These pores are, however, considerably larger than those in zeolites and are substantially greater than the sizes of most reactant molecules of interest.) Normally no macropores are present, in contrast with many aluminas that have macropores as well as high area. Consequently, diffusion problems may be more severe with many silica gels than with available aluminas.

By varying the manufacturing and aging procedures, silica gels can be made with considerably larger pore diameter and correspondingly lower surface area, perhaps as low as about 100 m^2/g. Silica gel is generally more difficult to form than alumina. It is not as mechanically rugged, but is generally more inert. Commercial products typically contain small amounts of impurities such as sodium, calcium, iron, and alumina in the concentration range of hundreds of parts per million.

The final dry product should be referred to strictly as a xerogel or porous silica, but the term *silica gel* is in common usage. At ambient temperature the surface consists of a layer of silanol groups (SiOH) plus physically adsorbed water. Most of the water is removed upon drying in air at 150 to 200°C. Silanol groups are left on the surface, and these are progressively lost with increased temperature. Some siloxane groups

$$
\begin{array}{c}
\mathrm{O} \\
/ \quad \backslash \\
-\ \mathrm{Si}\ -\ \mathrm{Si}\ - \\
|\qquad |
\end{array}
$$

may also be present on the surface.

Colloidal silica. A variety of colloidal silicas are available as articles of commerce (for example, Ludox), containing up to 40 wt % SiO_2 in the form of spherical, nonporous particles. The colloid is stabilized by ammonium or sodium ions. It may be gelled by increasing temperature or by altering pH, and, since it is also a good binder, it is useful in formulating catalysts.

Kieselguhr. Kieselguhr (diatomaceous earth) is a naturally occurring, finely divided silica consisting of the skeletal remains of diatoms. Depending on the deposit, it typically contains small amounts of alumina and iron as part of the skeletal structure. It is inexpensive, but for use in catalysis it must usually be purified, as by acid treatment. The surface area is usually in the range of 20 to 40 m^2/g, and a rather broad range of pore sizes exists, mostly of the order of 100 nm or more.

The book by Stiles (1987) has more details on kieselguhr and other silicas, including some striking photomicrographs of individual skeletons of fossil diatoms. This type of irregular perforated structure is sometimes described as a *foraminous* material, derived from the term for the marine order to which diatoms belong. By extension, an irregular, perforated catalyst mass such as a pad of woven mesh platinum wire used for ammonia oxidation may be described as a foraminous structure.

Fumed (pyrogenic) silica. A finely divided, nonporous, and highly pure silica powder (Cabosil, Aerosil) is manufactured from high purity $SiCl_4$, which is hydrolyzed in an oxygen-hydrogen flame. HCl formed is adsorbed on the silica surface, but can be removed by subsequent high-temperature calcination. Particle sizes are about 40 to 50 nm and surface areas about 200 to 400 m^2/g. Silica gels, fumed silica, and the like are generally X-ray amorphous.

Comparison of alumina and silica carriers. The combination of useful properties of aluminas make them generally the first choice for carriers. However, active aluminas can dissolve or become soft and mushy under acidic conditions—conditions under which silica is stable. The relative inertness of silica upon calcination with other catalyst ingredients may also be a significant factor. If adsorption of products or reactants on alumina is deleterious, the nonadsorptive character of silica may be an improvement.

4.5.3 Activated carbon

An extensive literature exists on carbon since it is widely used in various forms as an adsorbent, filtering aid, and reinforcing agent in rubber, etc. Only a tiny fraction is used in catalysis.

If a carbonaceous material such as coal, lignite, wood, or petroleum pitch is heated in the absence of air, much of the substance devolatilizes, leaving behind a porous structure of carbon that usually also contains some hydrogen. This may then be activated by controlled oxidation with steam or carbon dioxide to further open up the pores and increase total surface area. The activated carbon may contain up to about 10 wt % oxygen, which may cover a large fraction of the surface as chemisorbed oxygen in the form of ketones, hydroxyls, or carboxylic acids. These can cause its adsorptive properties to be considerably different than those of a carbon heated in inert gas or under reducing conditions. The surface area can range up to about 1200 m^2/g, but much of this is then in very fine pores easily choked by deposits.

Carbon supports can obviously be used for catalytic reactions only under conditions in which the support itself is not attacked. The catalyst usually cannot be regenerated except perhaps by washing, but the active ingredient can be recovered by burning the support. Carbon supports are used primarily for noble metals and for reactions in which the strong adsorption by carbon for organic molecules may be an asset. Activated carbon may contain considerable ash (from the mineral matter in the starting material) and various metals and sulfur compounds. These can have an important and generally undesirable catalytic effect, but can be substantially removed by acid-washing.

For a catalytic support, a form of carbon essentially free of metal salts, low in sulfur, and with high surface area is preferred. Such a material may be several times more costly than a conventional activated carbon as used for removal of impurities by adsorption. An activated carbon from coal or lignite may be unacceptably soft and have an excessive impurity content. A petroleum-based coke is typically stronger than that from a coal, but it may contain some sulfur and small amounts of vanadium and nickel. These may make it unacceptable for use as a catalyst support for some applications, but acid-washing may overcome these difficulties. A wood charcoal may also be used. Carbon from coconut shells, readily available as a waste product, is relatively hard and attrition-resistant and is therefore especially useful. A high-purity support of about 500 m^2/g can be prepared by bonding carbon black with furfural and activating. For more details see a chapter by Bird in the book by Stiles (1987). Wigmans (1989) discusses industrial aspects of production and use of activated carbons.

4.5.4 Titania

Titania occurs naturally in three crystalline forms: anatase, rutile, and brookite. The last is not common. Calcination of titanium salts at moderately low temperatures forms predominantly anatase, which is converted to rutile at higher temperatures. Rutile is the thermally stable form at all temperatures, but conversion of anatase to rutile is so slow that it may be unimportant in most catalytic reactions. Anatase is the preferred form for use as a catalyst support in a vanadia-titania catalyst used for conversion of o-xylene to phthalic anhydride (Sec. 8.6.2), possibly in part because of better wetting characteristics for the vanadia. However, anatase typically has a higher surface area than rutile, which may account at least in part for its preference here and in other applications.

V_2O_5/TiO_2 is one of the best catalysts for reduction of NO with NH_3, an important process for minimizing NO_x emissions from exhaust gases from power plants (Sec. 8.13). Titania is more acidic than alumina and, unlike alumina, is not readily sulfated in the presence of sulfur oxides (SO_x). This may be of some advantage in the Claus process for conversion of H_2S to elemental sulfur by partial oxidation.

High-purity titania may be made either by an (older) precipitation process or a (newer) flame process from titanium tetrachloride. The latter product is sometimes termed *fumed titania* and consists of particles below 100 nm in size. Surface areas in the range of about 10 m^2/g to 50 m^2/g (Degussa P-25) are available. Typically, fumed titania consists of a mixture of anatase and rutile, the ratio varying somewhat with the manufacturing process. Degussa P-25 is reported to be about 85 to 90% anatase, 10 to 15% rutile. Pigment-grade titania, as prepared for use in paints, is coated, as by vapor deposition of silica or alumina, to keep the titania from being reduced by organic material.

This may make it unsuitable for use as a catalyst carrier. A pure, finely divided anatase of surface area of about 200 to 300 m²/g can be formed by hydrolysis in an aqueous solution of an organic titanium compound such as tetraisopropyl titanate (a "Tyzor").

4.5.5 Other supports

Historically, many early catalysts were supported on naturally occurring materials such as asbestos or pumice, but now these are seldom used. Several chapters in the book edited by Linsen (1970) describe active magnesia and hydrous zirconia and provide a more detailed discussion of alumina, silica, and carbon. Anderson (1975) discusses briefly the chemistry of a variety of support materials and gives extensive references to the literature. Silica-alumina and zeolites are discussed in Chap. 7. Natural clays, primarily kaolinite and montmorillonite, have been used in the past as supports and are now a commonly used binder as well as an ingredient for preparation of cracking catalysts.

Inert packing is often installed at the bottom and top of a large catalyst bed and frequently consists of several layers graded in size, large to small from the top down and small to large from the bottom up. An essentially nonporous α-alumina or a mullite-type material with a composition of about 35% Al_2O_3–65% SiO_2 is common. These may also be used for dilution of a packed catalyst bed. In laboratory work, other materials may also be used satisfactorily, e.g., acid-washed sand, ground quartz, carborundum, etc.

Figure 4.15   Representative monolith shapes. (*Courtesy of Corning, Inc.*)

An unusual support form known as a *monolith* or *honeycomb* is used in most automobile catalytic converters (Sec. 8.12), where a very low pressure drop is required to minimize power loss from the engine. This is a single block of material containing within it an array of parallel, uniform, straight, nonconnecting channels. This is manufactured by extrusion of a thick inorganic dough through a die, followed by drying and firing. The ingredients are fused into cordierite, a magnesia-alumina silicate.

A variety of cell shapes and sizes can be manufactured, and monolith blocks can likewise be fabricated in a variety of cross-sectional shapes, as shown in Figs. 4.15, 4.16, and 4.17. The cell density may vary from 200 to 400 cells per square inch. The pores in the cell walls

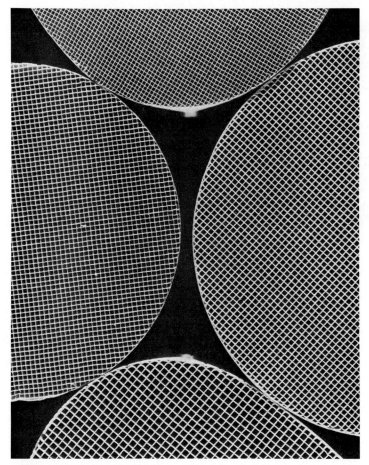

Figure 4.16 Monolith cross sections of different cell sizes. (*Courtesy of Corning, Inc.*)

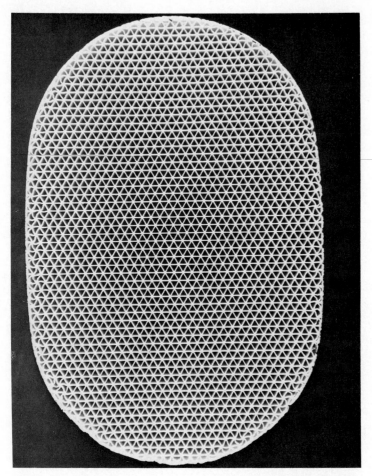

Figure 4.17 Monolith cross section with triangular cell shape. (*Courtesy of Corning, Inc.*)

are relatively large and the surface area is typically in the range of 0.1 to 1.0 m^2/g. For use in catalysis, the passageways are usually coated, as with alumina, to increase the effective surface area to the range of 20 to 50 m^2/g. Monolith supports are also commonly used for catalytic control of NO$_x$ in power plant flue gases (Sec. 8.13), but the passageways there are much larger. Somewhat similar is a ceramic α-alumina honeycomb available with several different types of internal passageways (Torvex), which can be used at temperatures up to 1500°C.

4.6 Promoters

The term *promoter* is used in a rather general sense to refer to a substance that, when added in relatively small amounts in the preparation of a catalyst, imparts better activity, selectivity, or stability. In some cases the promoter may be added to the reactant in small amounts and it acts by being adsorbed onto the catalyst. The increased performance is greater than that attributable to the promoter acting independently, which in many cases has no activity by itself for the specific reaction. The term is used to cover a wide variety of phenomena, but most promoters can be classified as textural promoters or structural promoters. A textural promoter ("stabilizer") acts by a physical effect; a structural promoter, by a chemical effect.

4.6.1 Textural promoters

A *textural promoter* is an inert substance that inhibits the sintering of microcrystals of the active catalyst by being present in the form of very fine particles. These separate the true catalyst particles from contact with one another so they do not coalesce, thus preventing or minimizing loss of active catalyst area during service. Two examples are the incorporation of a small amount of alumina in the conventional iron catalyst for the synthesis of ammonia, and the use of $ZnAl_2O_4$ in one of the formulations of a copper-based methanol synthesis catalyst.

To be effective, the textural promoter must be of somewhat smaller particle size than that of the active species, it must be well dispersed, and it must not react with or form a solid solution with the active catalyst. As a minimum, it must have a relatively high melting point. Some useful simple oxides with their melting points in degrees Celsius are as follows: Al_2O_3, 2027; SiO_2, 1700; ZrO_2, 2687; Cr_2O_3, 2435; CeO_2, 2600; MgO, 2802; TiO_2, 1855. BeO also has a high melting point but is highly poisonous; thoria is slightly radioactive and its use in catalyst formulations has been discouraged in recent years. Under reducing conditions, carbon may also be useful since it is stable to extremely high temperatures.

That a substance acts as a textural promoter can sometimes be identified in the case of a metallic catalyst by comparing the specific metal surface area (e.g., by chemisorption) of a catalyst in presence and absence of the promoter. Another method of identification is by the effective activation energy. This is unchanged by a textural promoter but may be markedly affected by a structural promoter.

In the case of mixed-oxide catalysts a particular compound, crystal form, or defect structure may be desired for maximum selectivity, or even a certain mixed phase may be required. This may be stabilized by the presence of a particular material. Frequently it is uncertain whether the promoter provides a structural or a chemical effect because of the complex nature of many of these catalysts.

4.6.2 Structural promoters

In contrast to a textural promoter, a structural promoter causes a chemical effect—it changes the chemical composition of the catalyst. In many cases the effect of the structural promoter is clear, but its mechanism of action is not. In other cases, it is not clear whether the effect of the promoter is primarily a physical or a chemical effect. Alkalis in particular show a wide variety of effects. A review by Mross (1983) categorizes at least eight modes of action. These are listed below, together with some examples. Note that more than one mode may be involved in any one case.

1. Intrinsic catalytic effect of the alkali (increase in higher alcohol content in MeOH-synthesis catalyst; increase in coke removal by reaction with steam)

2. Creation of basic sites (accelerate base-catalyzed reactions—Sec. 7.6)

3. Neutralization of acidic centers (eliminate isomerization to an undesired product, e.g., ethylene oxide to acetaldehyde, eliminate hydrocarbon cracking when undesired)

4. Modification of the adsorption properties of the catalyst surface [addition of K to NH_3-synthesis catalyst (Sec. 10.5), or to iron Fischer-Tropsch catalyst (Sec. 10.2)]

5. Auxiliary function during the preparation of the catalyst

6. Modification of the physical properties of an active component melt (vanadium pyrosulfate catalyst in SO_2 oxidation, oxychlorination catalyst)

7. Reduction of the volatility of the active component through compound formation

8. Prevention or reduction of rate of phase transformations (Fe molybdate catalyst for formaldehyde synthesis)

The effect of an alkali frequently increases with atomic weight, hence:

$$Li < Na < K < Rb < Cs$$

This is the same order as increasing basicity, which may explain the effect, at least in part. However ionic size also increases in this order, which may affect the relative rates of migration into a lattice. Since Rb and Cs are expensive, K frequently is the alkali used industrially. Other effects of an alkali can, however, be deleterious and call for rigorous exclusion. For example, small amounts of sodium can enhance undesired sintering.

Many other substances may act as promoters and by other mechanisms, for example:

1. There may be a dual-function action. The promoter may catalyze the formation of a desired intermediate. Thus, the addition of a chloride to a platinum/alumina reforming catalyst may enhance its activity and be termed "promotion," although the true mechanism is more clearly seen as an example of dual functionality.

2. The promoter may produce lattice defects or interstitial substitution. An example is the incorporation of small amounts of Li, Zn or Mo into the vanadium-phosphate catalyst used for partial oxidation of n-butane to maleic anhydride (Sec. 8.6.1).

3. The promoter may enhance the adsorption of one or more of the reactants (e.g., acrylonitrile synthesis catalysts (Sec. 8.2.1); CoMo/ Al_2O_3 and NiMo/Al_2O_3 catalysts in hydrotreating, Sec. 9.8.).

References

Acres, G. J. K., A. J. Bird, J. W. Jenkins, and F. King in *Catalysis*, vol. 4., Royal Society of Chemistry, London, 1981, p. 1.

Anderson, J. R.: *Structure of Metallic Catalysts*, Academic, New York, 1975.

Bridger, G. W., and C. Woodward in B. Delmon, P. A. Jacobs, and G. Poncelet (eds.): *Preparation of Catalysts, I*, Elsevier, Amsterdam, 1976, p. 331.

Candela, L., and D. D. Perlmutter, *AIChE J.*, **32**, 1532 (1986).

Dullien, F. A. L.: *Chem. Eng. J.*, **10**, 1 (1975).

Dullien, F. A. L.: *Porous Media: Fluid Transport and Pore Structure*, Academic, New York, 1979.

Eischens, R. P., in E. Drauglis and R. I. Jaffee (eds.): *The Physical Basis for Heterogeneous Catalysis*, Plenum, New York, 1975, p. 485.

Foger, K., in J. R. Anderson, and M. Boudart (eds.): *Catalysis: Science and Technology*, vol. 6, Springer, New York, 1984.

Gauguin, R., M. Graulier, and D. Papee: *Adv. Chem. Ser.*, **143**, 147 (1975).

Hata, K.: *New Hydrogenating Catalysts: Urushibara Catalysts*, Halsted/Wiley, New York, 1971.

Hedvall, J. A.: *Adv. Catal.*, **8**, 1 (1956).

Hoekstra, J.: U.S. Patent 3,388,077 (to U.O.P.), 1968.

John, C. S., and M. S. Scurrell: *Catalysis*, vol. I, The Chemical Society, London, 1977, p. 136.

Le Page, J. F., et al.: *Applied Heterogeneous Catalysis*, Editions Technip, Paris, 1987. Translated from the French edition of 1978, with some modifications and additions.

Lieber, E., and F. L. Morritz: *Adv. Catal.*, **5**, 417 (1953).

Linsen, B. G. (ed.): *Physical and Chemical Aspects of Adsorbents and Catalysts*, Academic, New York, 1970.

Lippens, B. C., and J. J. Steggerda in B. G. Linsen (ed.): *Physical and Chemical Aspects of Adsorbents and Catalysts*, Academic, New York, 1970, p. 171.

Lo Jacono, M., and M. Schiavello, in B. Delmon, P. A. Jacobs, and G. Poncelet (eds.): *Preparation of Catalysts, I*, Elsevier, Amsterdam, 1976, p. 473.

Lostaglio, V. J. and J. D. Carruthers: *Chem. Eng. Progress*, **82** (3), 46 (1986).

Macdonald, I. F., M. S. El-Sayed, K. Mow, and F. A. L. Dullien: *Ind. Eng. Chem., Fund.*, **18**, 199 (1979).

Morikawa, K., T. Shirasaki, and M. Okada: *Adv. Catal.*, **20**, 98 (1969).

Moss, R. L., in R. B. Anderson and P. T. Dawson (eds.): *Experimental Methods in Catalytic Research*, vol. II, Academic, New York, 1976.

Mross, W-D.: *Catal. Rev.—Sci. Eng.*, **25**, 591 (1983).

Nakai, K., S. M. Thesis, M.I.T., 1986.

Oberlander, R. K., in B. E. Leach (ed.): *Applied Industrial Catalysis*, vol. 3, Academic, New York, 1984, p. 63.

Poisson, R., J-P. Brunelle, and P. Nortier in A. B. Stiles (ed.): *Catalyst Supports and Supported Catalysts*, Butterworths, London, 1987, p. 11.

Pott, G. T., and W. H. J. Stork, in B. Delmon, P. A. Jacobs, and G. Poncelet (eds.): *Preparation of Catalysts, I*, Elsevier, Amsterdam, 1976, p. 537.

Ryshkewitch, E.: *Oxide Ceramics*, Academic, New York, 1960.

Stiles, A. B.: *Catalyst Manufacture. Laboratory and Commercial Preparations*, Dekker, New York, 1983.

Stiles, A. B., (ed.): *Catalyst Supports and Supported Catalysts*, Butterworths, London, 1987.

Trimm, D. L. and A. Stanislaus: *Appl. Catal.*, **21**, 215 (1986).

Twigg, M. V.: *Catalyst Handbook*, 2d ed., Wolfe Publishing Ltd., London, and CRC Press, Boca Raton, Fla., 1989.

Wefers, K., and G. M. Bell: *Oxides and Hydroxides of Aluminum*, Alcoa Research Labs, E. St. Louis, Ill., 1972. (A revision of "Alumina Properties," Tech. Paper No. 10.)

Wigmans, T.: *Carbon*, **27**, 13 (1989).

Physical Characterization and Examination

Most practical catalysts are highly complex materials, and a basic problem is how to correlate catalyst behavior with physical and chemical structure. Some methods of characterization are standardized or nearly so. These include determination of total surface area, void fraction, pore size distribution, and in some cases specific metal area by selective chemisorption, plus certain mechanical properties. Many analytical procedures developed for other branches of chemistry are, of course, also applicable here. Beyond these are a variety of instrumental techniques for examining and characterizing surfaces and adsorbed species. Many require expensive and elaborate apparatus and a high degree of sophistication on the part of the experimenter for interpretation of results. Several of these that are of somewhat general applicability to industrial catalysts are discussed in Sec. 5.5. Others are discussed elsewhere in conjunction with specific applications in which their usefulness can be seen by example.

Most instrumental methods of characterizing surfaces operate at very high vacuum, and the structure and behavior of surfaces and adsorbed species upon them under such conditions may be far different than in a reacting environment. This limitation must always be kept in mind. Many of the topics discussed here are treated at greater length in the book by Anderson and Pratt (1985), who also focus on specific details of experimental methods. A review by Lecloux (1981) analyzes how the texture of catalysts may be discerned by physical adsorption isotherms, mercury penetration, and particle size measurements. Characterization of porous solids is also treated in the proceedings of a recent IUPAC symposium edited by Unger et al. (1988).

5.1   Measurement of Surface Area

In comparing different catalysts or the effect of various treatments on catalytic activity, it is necessary to know the extent to which a change in activity is caused by a change in the area of a catalyst, in contrast to a change in intrinsic reactivity. Methods of measuring surface areas are of concern in many fields of science and technology and have received wide and detailed study. Direct observation by an optical or electron microscope is the most straightforward, although tedious, method of determining particle size and particle size distribution. If the solid is impervious and the shape is well established, the total surface area can then be estimated closely. But most catalysts are made to be porous in order to maximize the catalytic area per unit volume of reactor. It is this total surface area, both interior and exterior, that is of concern.

The principal method of measuring total surface area of porous structures is by adsorption of a particular molecular species from a gas or liquid onto the surface. If the conditions under which a complete adsorbed layer, averaging one molecule thick, can be established and the area covered per molecule is known, then the quantity of adsorbed material gives directly the total surface area of the sample. Sorption from the liquid phase, as of fatty acids and dyes, is of limited use in catalysis because the size of these molecules is much greater than that of many reactant molecules. Therefore, they may not have access to portions of a fine microporous structure that nevertheless may contribute to the total area of significance during reaction. The most useful measurements are by adsorption of a gas or vapor of sufficiently small molecular dimensions that interstices down to a few tenths of a nanometer are penetrated.

5.1.1   Physical adsorption isotherms

To measure total surface area, nonspecific physical adsorption is required, but even with physical adsorption the isotherm varies somewhat with the nature of the adsorbent (the solid). Most physical adsorption isotherms may be grouped into five types, as originally proposed by Brunauer, Deming, Deming, and Teller (BDDT) (Brunauer et al. 1940). More recently, the grouping has generally been termed the *Brunauer, Emmett, and Teller* (BET) *classification* (Brunauer et al. 1938). In all cases the amount of vapor adsorbed increases as its partial pressure is increased, becoming at some point equivalent to a monolayer, but then increasing to a multilayer, which eventually merges into a condensed phase as the relative pressure, P/P_0, approaches unity.

Type I is frequently called the Langmuir type. The asymptotic value was originally ascribed to a monolayer, as derived from the Langmuir equation. However, this isotherm is seldom encountered on nonporous materials. The isotherm shape is fairly commonly observed with microporous substances having relatively small external surfaces, such as certain activated carbons and zeolites. In these cases the volume of the pores is so much greater than the volume corresponding to a monolayer or a multilayer a few molecules thick that what appears to be an asymptotic value occurs at a relative pressure substantially less than unity, corresponding to complete filling of micropores rather than to monolayer adsorption (see Sec. 5.3.2).

A true Langmuir type of isotherm may be observed for reversible chemisorption.

Type II, sometimes termed the *sigmoid* or *S-shaped isotherm*, is commonly encountered on nonporous structures or macroporous materials. Point *B* occurs at a "knee" (Fig. 5.1) and is the stage at which monolayer coverage is complete and multilayer adsorption begins.

The *type III* isotherm is convex over the entire range and does not exhibit a point *B*. It is relatively rare and is typical of a system in which the forces of adsorption are relatively weak, as when the adsorbate is not wetted by the surface, e.g., water vapor on graphite.

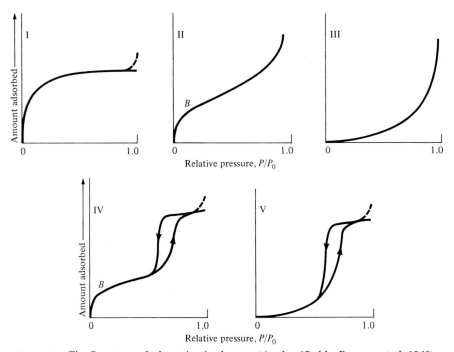

Figure 5.1   The five types of adsorption isotherms. (*As classified by Brunner et al. 1940*)

Type IV is encountered with materials having pores in the general range of 2 to 50 nm (mesopores). At low values of P/P_0 the isotherm is similar to type II, but then adsorption increases markedly at higher values of P/P_0 where pore (capillary) condensation takes place. A hysteresis effect associated with this pore condensation is usually observed (Figs. 2.5 and 2.6). Isotherms of this type are often encountered with industrial catalysts, and the capillary condensation curve may be used to determine a pore-size distribution (Sec. 5.3.1).

Type V is similar to type III, but with pore condensation taking place at higher values of P/P_0. It is also relatively rare.

A few other kinds of adsorption isotherms do not fit into the foregoing classification, but there is yet no generally accepted characterization of these. Parfitt and Sing (1976) assign *type VI* to an isotherm in which adsorption occurs in steps. Each step represents the adsorption of an additional layer, the differential heat of adsorption being fairly constant during the buildup of one layer, but then dropping abruptly as the next layer begins to be formed. (See Fig. 2.8.) This behavior is encountered only with relatively uniform surfaces such as graphite. Adamson (1976, p. 567) assigns *types VI* and *VII* to two cases in which the bulk-liquid adsorbate has a finite contact angle and hence the amount of vapor adsorbed does not approach infinity asymptotically as P/P_0 approaches unity.

Any isotherm having only a gradual curvature at low values of P/P_0 represents a case in which adsorbent-adsorbate interaction is weak. These isotherms (such as types III and V) are difficult to use for determination of surface area because second and succeeding layers build up before the first is complete.

5.1.2 Brunauer-Emmett-Teller (BET) method

The most common method of measuring surface area, and one used routinely in most catalyst studies, is that developed by Brunauer, Emmett, and Teller (1938). Early descriptions and evaluations are given by Emmett (1948, 1954). In essence, the Langmuir adsorption isotherm (Sec. 2.4.1) is extended to multilayer adsorption. As in the Langmuir approach, for the first layer the rate of evaporation is considered to be equal to the rate of condensation, and the heat of adsorption is taken to be independent of coverage. For layers beyond the first, the rate of adsorption is taken to be proportional to the fraction of the lowest layer still vacant. The rate of desorption is taken to be proportional to the amount present in that layer. (These assumptions are made largely for mathematical convenience.) The heat of adsorption for all layers except the first layer is assumed to be equal to the heat of liquefaction of the adsorbed gas. Summation over an infinite number of adsorbed layers gives the final expression as follows:

$$\frac{P}{V(P_0 - P)} = \frac{1}{V_m C} + \frac{(C - 1)P}{V_m C P_0} \tag{5.1}$$

where V = volume of gas adsorbed at pressure P
$\quad V_m$ = volume of gas adsorbed in monolayer, same units as V
$\quad P_0$ = saturation pressure of adsorbate gas at the experimental temperature
$\quad C$ = a constant related exponentially to the heats of adsorption and liquefaction of the gas

$$C = e^{(q_1 - q_L)/RT} \tag{5.2}$$

where q_1 = heat of adsorption on the first layer
$\quad q_L$ = heat of liquefaction of adsorbed gas on all other layers
$\quad R$ = the gas constant

The larger the value of C, the sharper is the curve in the region of the B point and the more accurately the surface area can be determined.

If Eq. (5.1) is obeyed, a graph of $P/V(P_0 - P)$ versus P/P_0 should give a straight line, the slope and intercept of which can be used to evaluate V_m and C. Many adsorption data show very good agreement with the BET equation (Fig. 5.2) over values of the relative pressure P/P_0 between approximately 0.05 and 0.3, and this range is usually used for surface area measurements. At higher P/P_0 values, complexities associated with the realities of multilayer adsorption and/or pore condensation cause increasing deviation. With microporous substances such as zeolites, the linear region on a BET plot occurs at much lower values of P/P_0, typically around 0.01 or less.

From Eq. (5.1), $V_m = 1/(S + I)$, where S is the slope, equal to $(C - 1)/V_m C$ and I is the intercept, equal to $1/V_m C$. This proceeds from the fact that

$$S + I = \frac{1}{V_m C}[(C - 1) + 1] = \frac{1}{V_m} \tag{5.3}$$

The surface area of the catalyst may then be calculated from V_m if the average area occupied by an adsorbed molecule is known.

Any condensible inert vapor can be used in the BET method, but for the most reliable measurements, the molecules should be small and approximately spherical. The vapor should also be easy to handle at the required temperatures; for example, P/P_0 values of 0.05 to 0.3 should be conveniently attainable. Liquid nitrogen is a readily avail-

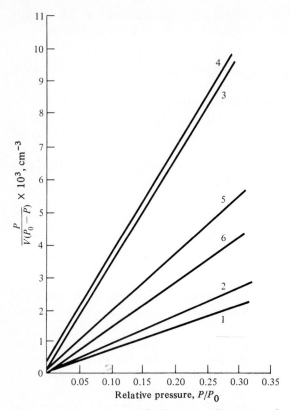

Figure 5.2 Linear plots of the Brunauer, Emmett, and Teller equation for nitrogen adsorption. Isotherms of various adsorbents. (*Brunauer et al. 1938*) Adsorption of nitrogen at 90 K on (1) unpromoted Fe catalyst #937, per 489.0 g; (2) Al_2O_3 promoted Fe catalyst #424, per 49.8 g; (3) Al_2O_3-K_2O promoted Fe catalyst #957, per 54.5 g; (4) fused Cu catalyst, per 550 g; (5) chromium oxide gel, per 1.09 g; (6) silica gel, per 0.606 g.

able coolant, and nitrogen is usually used as the adsorbate since it is relatively cheap and readily available in high purity. It yields well-defined type II curves on most surfaces, and the cross-sectional area per adsorbed molecule has been well established.

The partial pressures of nitrogen gas are in the range of 10 to 100 kPa in order to obtain values of P/P_0 in the range of 0.05 to 0.30. When the total surface area of the sample is less than a few square meters, the amounts of gas adsorbed become small relative to the total amount in the apparatus, and the accuracy of the measurements becomes poor. By using a vapor of higher boiling point as an adsorbate, measurements at the temperature of liquid nitrogen can be made at much lower pressures to achieve the desired range of P/P_0 values; so the amount of gas adsorbed on the solid is now a much larger fraction of that present and can be more precisely measured. The gas most often used is krypton, which has a vapor pressure at this temperature of about 0.4 kPa. A standard test method is ASTM D 4780-88, stated to cover the determination of surface areas in the range of 0.05 to 10 m^2/g. (In ASTM notation, '88 denotes the year of adoption or last revision.)

With any adsorbate, it is desirable to desorb water and other gases from the vessels and from the sample, typically by heating under vacuum, before making the measurements. If this is not done, slow desorption during determination of the isotherm can give misleading results. Measurements can be made either gravimetrically or volumetrically, and a variety of types of apparatus have been designed and used. In a representative static procedure, the sample is first degassed at 180 to 190°C for 10 to 15 min under vacuum. It is then cooled to liquid nitrogen temperature, and a known quantity of nitrogen gas is then admitted and allowed to equilibrate. From the equilibrium pressure and PVT relationships, the amount of nitrogen adsorbed is calculated. The procedure is repeated, yielding a series of values of the volume adsorbed corresponding to a set of increasing values of the equilibrium pressure. (See the standard test method ASTM D 4222-83.)

A "continuous" procedure may also be used. A nonadsorptive carrier gas, e.g., helium, is passed through the sample at a known rate with varying concentrations of nitrogen introduced in stages. The amount adsorbed can be determined with conventional gas chromatographic equipment or by precise monitoring of flow rates in and out of the sample.

The projected cross-sectional area of an adsorbed gas molecule A_m, can be estimated from the liquid density, but there is no assurance that the packing in a monolayer will be the same as that in the bulk. Thus, for accuracy the method has to be standardized by measurements with adsorbents whose area can be determined directly, e.g., nonporous, finely divided, uniform crystals or spheres. By this means the value for nitrogen has been established as 0.162 nm^2, which, perhaps coincidentally, equals that calculated from the bulk density.

If the constant C is sufficiently large, e.g., greater than about 50 (dimensionless), as it usually is with nitrogen adsorption, the isotherm should have a well-defined point B and the intercept is usually small relative to the slope. Hence a straight line can be drawn connecting the origin and one point obtained at a P/P_0 value of about 0.2 to 0.3 to obtain the slope for the BET equation. This is a simple, quick method requiring only one datum point, which is very useful for a surface of known properties. A standard test method is given in ASTM D 4567-86.

The use of one fixed value for the effective cross-sectional area of an adsorbed gas molecule assumes that this is unaffected by the nature of the solid. For most adsorbates on most solids the effective value of A_m varies slightly from solid to solid because the lattice parameter of the solid causes some localization of the adsorption, i.e., preferential adsorption on certain sites. Hence, a very strongly adsorbed vapor, which corresponds to a high C value, is not desired, but a weakly adsorbed vapor is likewise not desired because of the loss in accuracy in determining the amount of adsorption corresponding to a monolayer. Nitrogen is unusual in that it produces a well-defined knee on most solids, but adsorption is not excessively localized. Water vapor is not recommended for general use because it has a variety of specific interactions with oxide structures commonly encountered in catalysis and it tends to form an organized tetrahedral structure rather than a random orientation.

The theory underlying the BET model has been criticized for the fact that it postulates that adsorption can occur in the nth layer before the $(n - 1)$th layer is filled. This implies that molecules can be piled up on top of one another into a system of irregular vertical columns, whereas surface energy considerations indicate that there is probably little adsorption onto the nth layer until the $(n - 1)$th layer is largely filled. Modifications to the BET model to bring it closer to reality, however, do not change the calculated surface area appreciably from that obtained from the simple theory, probably in part because multilayer adsorption is not great over the P/P_0 range usually used for BET area measurements.

A variety of other equations can also be used [see, e.g., Gregg and Sing (1982) and Parfitt and Sing (1976)], but the BET method is common where solid catalysts are of concern. The t-method of Lippens and de Boer (Sec. 5.3.2) is also used for surface area determination of mesopores. The application of the BET method to microporous solids has been somewhat controversial, but useful empirical correlations have been developed between various methods of characterization of microporous materials by nitrogen adsorption that provide an underpinning of at least semiquantitative value even where the theory is uncertain (Raatz & Ajot 1988).

A standard test method for determining the BET surface area of catalysts based on nitrogen adsorption has been published as ASTM D 3663-84. For a catalyst containing zeolites, and hence both micropores and mesopores, a method of determining the zeolite content (or the microporous portion of the total) by nitrogen adsorption has been developed by Johnson (1978) and published as ASTM 4365. The method basically involves determining the area of mesopores by the t-plot method (Sec. 5.3.2) and subtracting this from the BET total area to obtain the zeolite area. This method was apparently developed for faujasite-type zeolites (zeolite X and Y), which have relatively large zeolite pores. Its degree of applicability to other zeolites is uncertain.

A commercially available BET instrument has been developed in the last several years (Omicron Technology) based on automated dynamic operation (Pieters & Venero 1984) that permits measurements of an extended range of pore-size distribution. The fact that it can provide isotherms to values of P/P_0 as low as 10^{-5} is of particular interest in characterization of very fine pore materials such as zeolites. Theoretical interpretation is still in its infancy, but such low-pressure isotherms characterize zeolite pore sizes and structures that cannot be differentiated by other instruments.

5.1.3 Specific area by selective chemisorption

With a supported metal catalyst it is frequently desirable to be able to determine the exposed metal area in distinction to the total surface area. This may be achieved by measuring the uptake of a gas that is chemisorbed on the metal but negligibly so on the support, under conditions that allow the coverage corresponding to a monolayer to be determined. Most useful for this purpose is hydrogen, but carbon monoxide and oxygen have also been used. Although simple in concept, the method can be complex in application. The most suitable experimental conditions vary considerably with the nature of the metal and the nature of the support. A number of factors rather specific to each system can introduce uncertainties.

As a prerequisite, it is necessary to know the chemisorption stoichiometry, that is, the number of surface atoms covered for each molecule of gas adsorbed, and the surface area occupied per metal atom. For hydrogen the stoichiometric number is almost always 2 since the hydrogen molecule usually dissociates upon adsorption and each hydrogen atom is adsorbed on one metal atom. Carbon monoxide can adsorb in either a linear form, in which it covers one metal atom (stoichiometric number of 1), or in a bridged form covering two metal atoms (stoichiometric number of 2). The number of surface atoms per unit area of metal varies slightly with the crystallographic plane, but for all metals it is about 10^{19} atoms per square meter. Specific representative values are 1.5 to 1.6×10^{19} atoms per square meter for Fe,

Co, and Ni; 1.25 to 1.33 $\times$ 10^{19} atoms per square meter for Pt, Pd, Ir, and Rh; and 1.15 $\times$ 10^{19} atoms per square meter for Ag (Anderson 1975, p. 296).

Hydrogen has been studied the most extensively, especially on platinum and nickel. It is often the first choice for other metals, except for palladium, in which it dissolves. A slow chemisorption is sometimes observed that has been ascribed to the presence of some support material or contaminant on the surface of metal particles, or possibly to the intrinsic properties of very small particles (e.g., those containing perhaps 50 atoms or less; see Chap. 6). On a carbon support or with carbon contamination, adsorbed hydrogen can surface-diffuse from metal crystallites onto the support (termed *spillover*, Sec. 6.4.2) to give erroneously high results. This does not seem to occur with oxide supports such as alumina or silica when they are clean.

The optimum temperature and pressure vary with the system and must be established experimentally. Studies must also be made with the support by itself to establish its possible contribution. High-area supports contribute excessively to hydrogen adsorption at 77 to 90 K. Preferred conditions for a dispersed platinum are about 273 to 300 K and about 0.01 to 0.3 kPa; and, for dispersed nickel, about 273 to 300 K and 20 kPa (Anderson 1975, pp. 317–322). These provide a maximum uptake on metal relative to uptake on the support.

Hydrogen chemisorption cannot be used for palladium because it is adsorbed into the bulk. Oxygen adsorption at very low pressures is a possible method, but carbon monoxide chemisorption may be more satisfactory. For nickel, hydrogen has been most commonly used, and carbon monoxide to some extent. For the iron surface area in catalysts used for ammonia synthesis, carbon monoxide adsorption has long been used. Hydrogen does not chemisorb on silver, and oxygen has been studied as a possibility.

A particular limitation to oxygen adsorption in general has been uncertainties concerning the stoichiometric number and the ease with which bulk oxidation can occur with many systems. In some cases a monolayer of oxygen can be chemisorbed under carefully controlled conditions. This can then be reduced with hydrogen, and the quantity of water formed is determined. This is termed *titration*.

Further details concerning this and other methods are given by Anderson (1975, pp. 295–323). A variety of chemisorption methods have been examined for characterization of other types of catalysts, e.g., O_2 adsorption for sulfides and NO on oxides. However, the surfaces here are more complex, and the methods are of limited applicability. Chemisorption also provides a means of determining an average particle size of a supported metal, if the quantity present is known, by assuming a particle shape (Sec. 6.2). This method can be applied over a wide range of particle sizes, including those beyond the range of the X-ray line-broadening method (Sec. 5.5.5), but chemisorption studies require a high-vacuum, high-purity system and careful experimentation and interpretation of results. ASTM D3908-88 provides a standard test procedure for determining hydrogen uptake on Pt/Al_2O_3 catalysts that may be suitable for comparing duplicate catalyst samples, but it does not consider Pt-support interactions or spillover phenomena.

5.2 Pore Volume

A direct and simple method of determining the total volume of the pores is by measuring the increase in weight when the pores are filled with a liquid of known density. The liquid should preferably be of low molecular weight so that fine pores are filled. Water or various hydrocarbons may be used satisfactorily. A simple procedure is to boil a sample of dry catalyst pellets of known weight in distilled water for 2 to 5 min to cause the water to penetrate the pores. The entire sample should then be cooled to minimize subsequent vaporization; the pellets should then be transferred to a damp cloth, rolled to remove excess water, and reweighed. This determines the total volume of pores between, approximately, 1 and 150 nm in diameter. The method is limited in accuracy by the fact that it is difficult to dry the external surface of the particles without removing liquid from the large pores, and some liquid tends to be held around the points of contact between the particles. The degree of error is probably of the order of a few percent.

More accurate results are obtained by the *mercury-helium method*. Mercury does not wet most surfaces, and therefore does not penetrate most pores at atmospheric pressure. Adsorption of helium gas is negligible at room temperature. A container of known volume V (in cubic centimeters) is filled with a known weight of pellets or powder W (in grams). After evacuation, helium is admitted, and from the gas laws the sum of the volume of the space between the pellets V' and the void volume inside the pellets V_g is calculated. The true density of the solid is

$$\rho_T = \frac{W}{V - (V' + V_g)} \tag{5.4}$$

The helium is then pumped out and the container filled with mercury at atmospheric pressure. Its volume is that of the space between the pellets V'.

The porosity or void fraction θ is the volume of voids in cubic centimeters per cubic centimeter of pellets and is given by

$$1 - \theta = \frac{V - (V' + V_g)}{V - V'} \tag{5.5}$$

The density of the pellets is given by

$$\rho_p = \frac{W}{V - V'} \, g/cm^3 \tag{5.6}$$

These measurements are often made in a mercury porosimeter (Sec. 5.3.3) in conjunction with a measurement of pore size distribution.

The total pore volume can also be determined from an adsorption measurement at a value of P/P_0 sufficiently high that all pores of interest are filled by condensed vapor (Sec. 5.3.1). For high-surface-area catalysts the amount of vapor adsorbed on the exterior of the particles is negligible compared with that condensed in the pores, so the equivalent liquid volume of the amount of vapor adsorbed is the same as the pore volume. The density is assumed to be the same as that of the liquefied vapor at its boiling point.

Operation at pressures slightly below saturation avoids condensation of liquid around the points of contact. A simple method developed by Benesi et al. (1955) achieves this by adding a small amount of nonvolatile solute to the saturating liquid to lower the vapor pressure of the latter to the desired degree, usually to 95 percent of saturation. In their early method, cetane (n-$C_{16}H_{34}$) was used as the nonvolatile solute and carbon tetrachloride as the volatile solvent, but health considerations suggest using an alternative to the latter.

Samples are dried and weighed and placed in a desiccator containing the solution in the bottom. The gain in weight combined with the known density of carbon tetrachloride, or its equivalent, gives the pore volume directly. Taking carbon tetrachloride surface tension as 0.026 N/m at 25°C, molar volume as 97.1 cm^3, and assuming zero contact angle, at P/P_0 of 0.95 all pores below 80 nm in diameter should be filled. By using various ratios of carbon tetrachloride to cetane, the partial pressure of carbon tetrachloride can be varied, and the method can be adapted to determine the total volume of pores having diameters below a specified desired value.

5.3   Pore Size Distribution

A major application of this measurement is for prediction of the effective diffusivity in a porous catalyst in conjunction with calculations of the ease of access of reactant molecules to the interior of a catalyst pellet by diffusion. Two different methods may be used: physical adsorption of a gas, which is applicable to pores less than about 60 nm in diameter, and mercury porosimetry, applicable to pores larger than about 3.5 nm. The true pore structure is of almost infinite complexity, and considerable literature exists on interpretation, in terms of pore shapes, of hysteresis loops from physical adsorption data and, to a lesser extent, from mercury porosimeter results.

The pore size distribution reported depends on the model assumed for interpretation. This is frequently taken as an array of cylindrical capillaries of different radii, randomly oriented. If the pores are fairly close in size, a useful concept is that of the average pore radius defined as $\bar{r} = 2\ V_g/S_g$, where V_g is the pore volume per gram and S_g the surface area per gram; for example, $\bar{r}$ is the radius of a cylinder having the same volume/surface ratio as the real pore. If the pores vary substantially in size, the diffusion characteristics in the structure cannot be adequately represented by an average radius, and it is necessary to determine the pore size distribution.

By the IUPAC recommended classification (Sing et al. 1985) pores larger than about 50 nm in width are termed *macropores*; those less than about 2 nm, *micropores*; and pores of intermediate size, *mesopores*. These definitions also apply to different regions of pore space. The limit between micropores and mesopores is somewhat arbitrary. From a more fundamental point of view in characterization by nitrogen adsorption, with micropores attention is directed to the primary filling of pore space in contrast to the process in mesopores of monolayer-to-multilayer adsorption followed by capillary condensation (see the following section).

5.3.1 Nitrogen adsorption

Measurements of the amount of gas adsorbed or desorbed as a function of relative pressure provide the most commonly used procedure for determining the pore size distribution of mesopores. The basic principle is that the pressure at which vapor condenses (or evaporates) is determined by the curvature of the meniscus of the condensed liquid in the pores. This is given by the Kelvin equation for the variation of vapor pressure with surface curvature in a capillary tube closed at one end.*

$$\ln \frac{P}{P_0} = \frac{-2\sigma V_m \cos \theta}{r_K RT} \tag{5.7}$$

---

*For surface curvature in two dimensions (instead of three), Eq. (5.10) applies instead of the Kelvin equation.

where P = vapor pressure of liquid over the curved surface
  P_0 = vapor pressure of liquid over a plane surface
  σ = surface tension of the liquid adsorbate
  V_m = molal volume of the liquid adsorbate
  θ = contact angle
  r_K = radius of curvature, or *Kelvin radius* (positive for a concave surface)
  R = gas constant
  T = absolute temperature

Consider a porous solid in contact with a vapor at some relative pressure P/P_0. A vapor that wets the surface, such as nitrogen, is chosen so that $\cos \theta = 1$. An adsorbed layer of thickness t is present on the walls of all unfilled capillaries. It is assumed that the radius of the meniscus in the unfilled pores is not the true physical radius r_p, but rather that this has been diminished by the thickness of the adsorbed layer and therefore $r_K = r_p - t$. The critical radius r_c is related to the relative pressure by the expression

$$r_c = \frac{-2\sigma Vm}{RT \ln (P/P_0)} + t \tag{5.8}$$

Nitrogen adsorption has been used almost universally, and the value of t as a function of P/P_0 has been calculated by a number of investigators who have worked with nonporous substances of known area. Values of t are nearly independent of the chemical nature of the adsorbent for most systems of interest at coverages greater than a monolayer.

To determine pore size distribution the following procedure is used. Consider a slight increase in pressure and let $V_r \Delta r$ be the volume of pores having radii between r_c and $r_c + \Delta r_c$ that become filled with condensate. Simultaneously, in larger pores the thickness of the adsorbed layer increases by Δt. The total volume of nitrogen found to be adsorbed, $v_r \Delta r_c$ (calculated as liquid), during this increase in pressure is the sum of the two processes. This may be expressed as

$$v_r \Delta r_c = \frac{(r_c - t)^2}{r_c^2} \cdot V_r \, \Delta r_c + \Delta t \int\limits_{r_c + \Delta r_c}^{\infty} \frac{(r_c - t)}{r_c} \frac{(2V_r \, dr_c)}{r_c} \tag{5.9}$$

The first term on the right-hand side is the volume of liquid nitrogen that has filled pores whose critical values of P/P_0 have been exceeded. The second term is the increase in volume of the adsorbed layer. The integral term is simply the surface area of all pores not filled by capillary condensation. For each increment of pressure, the

TABLE 5.1   Values of t, r_K and r_p at Different
Values of Relative Pressure, for Nitrogen at
$-195°$

p/p_0	t, Å	r_K, Å	r_p, Å
0·98	22·1	481	503
0·97	19·1	311	330
0·95	16·3	185	201
0·92	13·7	114·4	138·1
0·90	12·7	90·6	103·3
0·87	11·5	68·6	80·1
0·85	11·0	58·2	69·2
0·82	10·3	47·9	58·2
0·80	9·8	42·7	52·5
0·75	9·0	33·2	42·2
0·70	8·5	26·7	35·2
0·65	7·9	22·1	30·0
0·60	7·5	18·7	26·2
0·50	6·8	13·8	20·6
0·40	6·2	10·4	16·6
0·30	5·6	7·9	13·5

SOURCE: Gregg and Sing (1967), p. 162.

average value of t is obtained, e.g., from Table 5.1, and that of r_c and of Δr_c may be calculated from Eq. (5.8). Note that $V_r \Delta r$ is a volume term, not V_r. Table 5.1 gives as a function of P/P_0 values of t and calculated values of r_K and r_p. Methods of using Eq. (5.9) or the equivalent may be somewhat involved, but procedures are discussed in detail by Gregg and Sing (1982). Roberts (1967) also gives a method that is relatively easy to use and can be readily programmed for a computer. Gregg and Sing (1982) give a work sheet and a worked example for the Roberts method. A computational procedure is also described in ASTM D4641-88.

Originally de Boer proposed the use of a "universal t curve," but it is apparent that the correct isotherm may vary slightly with circumstances. For precise work, as in use of the t-plot method of determining surface area, the isotherm should be determined on a nonporous material as nearly identical as possible to the porous material under study. (See Sec. 5.3.2.)

The method is described in the foregoing for an adsorption curve obtained with increasing pressure, but clearly the same results should be achieved with a descending curve if the two curves coincide. The integral in the second term of Eq. (5.9) evaluated over all pores is a measure of the surface area S_{cum}, which can be compared to the BET value S_{BET}. Since the BET method is based on the amount of vapor adsorbed onto a surface at P/P_0 values in the range of 0.05 to 0.30, whereas the foregoing method involves condensation into pores at P/P_0

values primarily higher than 0.30, the two methods are essentially independent; however, S_{cum} is less reliable.

A reproducible hysteresis is usually observed, so two different values of S_{cum} are calculated depending on whether the adsorption branch or the desorption branch is used. For an incremental volume of nitrogen adsorbed, assigning it to the desorption branch identifies it with a lower value of P/P_0 than if it is assigned to the adsorption branch. Hence, from the Kelvin equation, the calculated area is, in general, greater if the desorption branch is used instead of the adsorption branch. The desorption curve may be preferred, for various reasons. Some degree of supersaturation may be needed before a pore fills with liquid, so that thermodynamic equilibrium, assumed in the Kelvin equation, would not be obtained in the adsorption branch. Also, the contact angle can be affected by surface properties, e.g., contamination, so this might change after being in contact with adsorbed vapors.

Even if the foregoing considerations do not apply, S_{BET} does not necessarily equal S_{cum} from either the adsorption or desorption curve since in either case S_{cum} depends on the true pore geometry. As an example, consider two idealized pores, a cylinder of radius r and length L and an "ink bottle" (sphere) with a neck of radius r and body of radius r', the two pores having equal volumes. Both pores empty at the same value of P/P_0 corresponding to the radius r. For equal volumes, $\pi r^2 L = (4/3)\pi r'^3$ or $L = 4r'^3/3r^2$. Let the foregoing volume be assigned to a cylinder, the usual assumption. If the true pore shape were a sphere, the calculated area would be greater than the true value if $2\pi r L > 4\pi r'^2$, or by substitution, $(2/3)r' > r$. If the inequality were reversed, the calculated area would be less than the true value. It is thus seen that S_{cum} can be either greater than or less than the BET area. The BET area is most commonly used, but comparison with other methods may help reveal details of pore structure, useful for other purposes.

The size of the largest pores that can be measured by this method is limited by the marked change of meniscus radius with pressure as the relative pressure nears unity. If pores larger than about 60 to 100 nm in diameter are also present, the pore size distribution must be limited to a value at which reasonably accurate data can be obtained, depending on the instrument and experimental procedures. Larger pores are then neglected but can be determined by mercury porosimetry. The lower limit for the N_2 adsorption method is for pores about 2 nm in diameter where the capillary condensation model no longer applies.

5.3.2   Microporosity and surface area by the *t*-plot method

Lippens and de Boer [see Broekhoff & Linsen (1970)] use a procedure that gives both surface area and micropore volume. The volume adsorbed is plotted versus t rather than the relative pressure, P/P_0, where t is determined from measurements on nonporous material identical or similar to that under study. For the plot of volume adsorbed versus t, in the absence of micropores there is usually a linear region extending through the origin, the slope of which is proportional to surface area. Figures 5.3 and 5.4 show the two methods of plotting data for N_2 adsorption on fresh (virgin) and steamed $SiO_2 \cdot Al_2O_3$ amorphous cracking catalyst (Johnson 1978) that is free of micropores. (The materials containing zeolites are discussed in the following.) When the t-plot can be extrapolated to the origin as with $SiO_2 \cdot Al_2O_3$, demonstrating the absence of micropores, the t_{area} and the BET area are nearly identical for oxide-type catalysts. Johnson, quoting data of Brunauer and co-workers, as well as his own, shows that the ratio t-area/BET-area varies slightly with the value of the constant C in the BET equation.

With a zeolite, pores are essentially filled at P/P_0 = 0.05. Adsorption at higher P/P_0 values represents that on external surfaces of the zeolites or on nonzeolitic material present. In a structure containing both micropores and mesopores, as in a cracking catalyst containing zeolite, extrapolation of a linear t-plot to t = 0 can yield the micropore

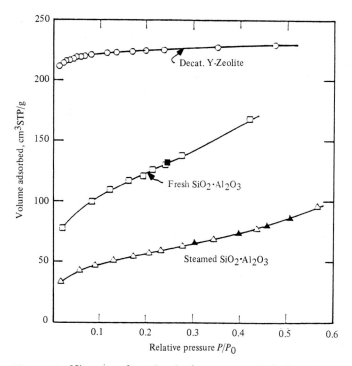

Figure 5.3 Nitrogen adsorption isotherms at $-195°C$. Desorption points are shaded. (*Johnson 1978. Reprinted with permission from the Journal of Catalysis. Copyright by Academic Press.*)

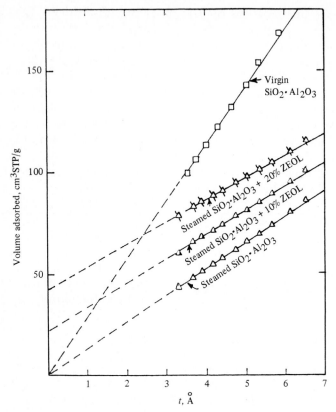

Figure 5.4 Nitrogen adsorption as a function of t. Same data as Fig. 5.3. (*Johnson 1978. Reprinted with permission from the Journal of Catalysis. Copyright by Academic Press.*)

volume. This is shown on Fig. 5.4 for steamed $SiO_2 \cdot Al_2O_3$ containing Y-zeolites. Johnson has used this procedure as a method of estimating the amount of crystalline zeolite present in a cracking catalyst and this is the basis of the ASTM method D 4365-85 used for this purpose.

A somewhat similar procedure to the t-plot method has been proposed by Sing. First, a standard isotherm is determined on a nonporous reference adsorbent with a surface structure similar to the microporous material of interest, as in the t-plot method. The amount of vapor adsorbed is then plotted against a reduced standard adsorption, α_s, in which $\alpha_s = 1$ at $P/P_0 = 0.4$. This can be used to calculate surface area and micropore volume as with the t-plot.

It is clear that in micropore filling the close proximity of the pore walls enhances adsorbent-adsorbate interactions and thus pores become filled at very low values of P/P_0. Theory is not sufficiently well established to provide a fundamental description of the process of micropore filling. The methods of Dubinin and co-workers have been frequently applied [e.g. the Dubinin-Radushkevich and Dubinin-Astakhov equations; see Gregg and Sing (1982)], but more study is needed to determine their degree of usefulness.

Procedures and suitable precautions in analyzing nitrogen adsorption isotherms have been published by Broekhoff (1979), Sing (1980) and in the IUPAC recommendations for determination of surface area and porosity (Sing et al. 1985). Lecloux (1981) critically analyzes the various methods of using physical adsorption isotherms for characterizing catalyst texture. For the mesopore range of pore sizes between 2 and 30 nm, he recommends a procedure developed by de Boer and Broekhoff and generalized by Lecloux. For more details see the book by Gregg and Sing (1982) and an extensive collection of papers comprising the proceedings of a recent IUPAC symposium (Unger et al. 1988).

Hysteresis effects. These occur almost invariably in physical adsorption on porous substances. The desorption curve always lies to the left and above the adsorption curve: i.e., at a given value of P/P_0 more vapor is condensed in the pores if a specified pressure has been approached from a higher level than from a lower level. In some cases supersaturation may be required before condensation can begin, or the contact angle may change after being in contact with adsorbed vapors, but the principal explanation lies in the complex pore geometry of typical porous materials. As one simple example, if pores consisted of cylindrically shaped capillaries open at both ends, adsorption would begin on a surface curved in only two dimensions and pores would thus become filled in the adsorption branch when P/P_0 reached the value given by

$$\ln \frac{P}{P_0} = \frac{-2\sigma V_m \cos \theta}{RT(2r_K)} \tag{5.10}$$

On the desorption branch, however, the meniscus at the pore opening is curved in three dimensions instead of two, and therefore it empties at a value of P/P_0 given by the Kelvin equation (Eq. 5.7).

Another geometry that can lead to hysteresis effects is that of an "ink bottle," in which it is visualized that many pores have necks smaller than the interior. (This is named after the old-fashioned round ink container with a narrow throat.) Condensation does not begin with increased pressure until it exceeds that corresponding to the effective radius of the interior. But after the pore is filled, pressure must be decreased to a value corresponding to the minimum radius of the neck before the pore empties. This is a simplified picture since the actual pore structure is mostly a network rather than individual closed pores. IUPAC (Sing et al. 1985) classifies four types of hysteresis loops.

In a series of interconnected pores of varying cross section, in general most of the pore volume empties at a pressure corresponding to the radius of the largest circle that can be inscribed in the throat. In predicting rates of diffusion within porous catalysts the restrictions contribute a resistance that is not offset by the enlargements, so for this purpose it is throat rather than cavity dimension that is of importance and the desorption curve may be a better measure of pore size.

The mercury penetration method, discussed in the following, also relates the quantity of mercury forced into pores to throat dimension; so results from that method might be expected to agree more closely with desorption than with adsorption curves. If an interior, interconnected porous structure has several throats in parallel, both the desorption isotherm and the mercury porosimeter method relate the interior volume to the dimension of the largest throat, which again in a qualitative sense parallels the kind of relationship governing access of diffusing molecules.

Porosity in carbon adsorbents has received extensive study and its microporous structure differs somewhat from that of inorganic materials. In recent literature, adsorption and structure was reviewed by McEnaney (1988) and a comparison of adsorption methods was published by Jaroniec et al. (1989). A summary of a workshop on carbon adsorbents was published by Marsh (1987).

5.3.3   Mercury intrusion porosimetry

This method is based on the behavior of nonwetting liquids in capillaries, again usually assuming that pores can be represented as cylinders. If the contact angle between liquid and solid, θ, is greater than 90°, the interfacial tension opposes the entrance of liquid into the pore. This can be overcome by external pressure. For a cylindrical pore, the force opposing entrance to the pore acts along the circumference and equals $-2\pi r\sigma \cos \theta$, where σ is the surface tension. The external pressure, which opposes this force, acts over the entire pore cross-sectional area and equals $\pi r^2 P$. At equilibrium the two forces are equal and

$$r = \frac{-2\sigma \cos \theta}{P} \tag{5.11}$$

The application of this principle for determination of pore size distributions was developed by Ritter and Drake (1945) and Drake (1949).

Through their work and subsequent testing by many others it has been found that the contact angle between mercury and a wide variety of catalysts is in the vicinity of 130°. Baiker and Relthaar (1982) reported that the contact angle against 20 representative catalysts varied between the extremes of 120 and 141° for an average of 129°.

For general purposes a value of 130° is usually used. Combining it with the surface tension of mercury as 0.474 N/m (474 dynes/cm) and rounding off, Eq. (5.11) reduces to

$$r = 6300/P \qquad (5.12)$$

where r is the pore radius in nanometers and P is the pressure in atmospheres. Different investigators have used slightly different values for surface tension and wetting angle, resulting in values of rP varying from 7500 to 6000. This method is sometimes referred to as the *Barrett-Joyner-Halenda (BJH) method* (Barrett et al. 1951).

In a study by Johnson (1988) of a number of $MoO_3 \cdot Al_2O_3$ catalysts by both mercury porosimetry and N_2 adsorption, the results could be brought into consonance by postulating that the apparent contact angle in Hg porosimetry varied from about 140° in the absence of MoO_3, decreasing linearly to about 120 to 125° at 30% MoO_3. ASTM test D 4284 lists contact angles for several materials as follows: titanium oxide, 141 to 160°; alkali borosilicate glass, 153°; tungsten carbide, 121°; quartz, 132 to 147°; clay minerals, 139 to 147°; aluminum oxide, 127°; zinc oxide 141°; carbon, 155°.

The pore radius into which mercury is forced is inversely proportional to the pressure, so the smallest pore sizes that can be detected by this method depend on the pressure to which mercury can be subjected in a particular apparatus. Pore diameters down to about 3.0 nm can be determined with available commercial apparatus.

At atmospheric pressure, mercury does not enter pores smaller than 6.3 μm. However, the sample is usually outgassed before the test and, if contacted with mercury at subatmospheric pressure, larger pore sizes can be determined. The first measurements can be made at about 0.012 MPa to determine pores as large as 50 μm in radius. In comparisons of the mercury porosimetry and nitrogen desorption methods for the region in which they overlap, the shapes of the curves generally agree, but there may be modest differences between the cumulative pore volume as calculated from mercury intrusion downward and that calculated from nitrogen adsorption upward (Johnson 1988; Johnson et al. 1986).

Studies by Joyner et al. (1951) showed that for a variety of charcoals, over the pore-radius range up to 30 nm the pore size-distribution curve as determined by nitrogen desorption agreed very closely with that found by the mercury porosimeter method. Indeed, a

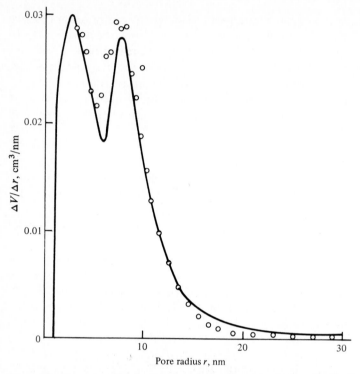

Figure 5.5 Pore size distribution in a bone char sample as calculated from a nitrogen adsorption isotherm. Experimental points were obtained on the same bone char by the mercury porosimeter method. (*Emmett 1962*)

double peak in one sample having maxima at about 2.5 and 7.5 nm was traced out by both methods (Fig. 5.5). Brown and Lard (1974) also showed good agreement between the two methods for aluminas, silicas, and related substances if the pore volume was less than about 1.2 cm^3/g. However, with a high-volume silica, the pressure of the mercury caused some of the large pore walls to collapse, forming smaller pores. This led to a spuriously low average pore radius but little change in the surface area. With an organic polymeric material, dimensional changes in structure at the temperature of liquid nitrogen may affect the results. Mercury porosimetry can also show hysteresis, as shown in a detailed study by Ternan and Fuller (1979). Lecloux (1981) gives a critical analysis of the pressure limitations on mercury porosimetry and possible sources of errors. A standardized test method is given in ASTM D 4284-88.

Davis (1984) reviews a large number of studies from which surface areas from N$_2$ adsorption and mercury penetration are compared. Other comparisons have been recently published by Milburn et al.

(1988) and Day and Fletcher (1988). Note that Hg intrusion only reflects area in pores down to those penetrated at the highest pressure obtainable with a particular instrument. For example, an instrument capable of operating at pressures up to 50,000 psia (355 MPa) does not reflect area in pores below about 3.4-nm diameter.

For relatively low-area catalysts this may not be a problem. Fig 5.6 (Le Page et al. 1987, p. 217) gives an example of determining surface area by mercury porosimetry. S corresponds to the shaded area and amounts to 6 m^2/g as calculated from the formula:

$$ S = \frac{1}{\gamma \cos \theta} \int_0^{V_{PT}} P \, dV $$

Here V_{PT} is the cumulative pore volume. This was an iron-molybdate catalyst and its area by the BET method was 5.5 m^2/g.

In applying this knowledge of pore size distribution to the prediction of diffusion rates in catalysts, the limit in accuracy is due in most cases, not to the accuracy with which the pore size distribution is known, but rather to the uncertainty concerning the proper formulation of diffusion rates in such a complex structure.

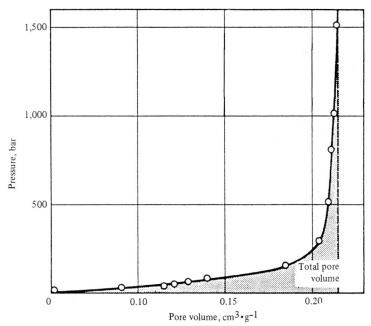

Figure 5.6 Calculation of surface area from mercury intrusion measurement. (*Le Page et al. 1987, p. 217. Reprinted with permission from Editions Technip.*)

5.3.4 Examples of pore size distributions

The pore size distribution of a carrier or a catalyst is usually presented in the form of a plot of the increment of pore volume per increment in pore size, versus pore size. Figure 5.7 gives an example for a particular alumina. The upper curve shows the adsorption isotherm; and the lower curve, the calculated pore size distribution. The upper

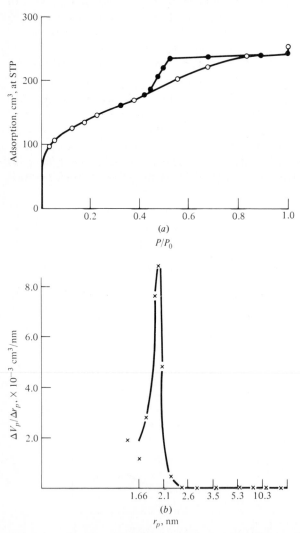

Figure 5.7 Pore size distribution from the adsorption isotherm of nitrogen at − 195°C on alumina. (a) Adsorption isotherm (○, adsorption; ●, desorption); (b) pore size distribution curve. (*Harris in Gregg and Sing 1982*)

curve at values of $P/P_0 < 0.4$ is essentially the t curve. This particular alumina had a narrow pore size distribution, most of the pores being about 2 nm in radius.

Many supports and catalysts have a more or less well-defined bimodal pore size distribution, in which the larger pores are the residual spaces between fine particles existing or formed in the catalyst preparation, and the smaller pores are developed within the particles by the calcination and reduction procedures or come about from zeolites incorporated in the catalyst. The size of the larger pores is decreased by increased pelletizing pressure, but the fine pores are essentially unaffected. An example of such a bimodal pore size distribution is shown in Fig. 5.8 for a $Fe_3O_4 \cdot Cr_2O_3$ commercial catalyst used for the water-gas shift reaction (Bohlbro 1966), obtained by splicing together nitrogen adsorption and mercury porosimeter measurements. The fine pore sizes cluster at about 3-nm radius and the macropores at about 100 nm.

Figure 5.9 shows another example of a bimodal pore size distribution obtained by splicing together nitrogen adsorption and mercury intrusion measurements. In this case, cumulative pore volume

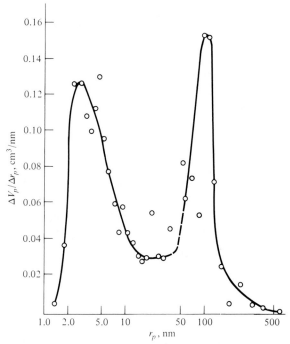

Figure 5.8 Pore size distribution for a commercial $Fe_3O_4 \cdot Cr_2O_3$ catalyst. (*Bohlbro 1966, p. 14*)

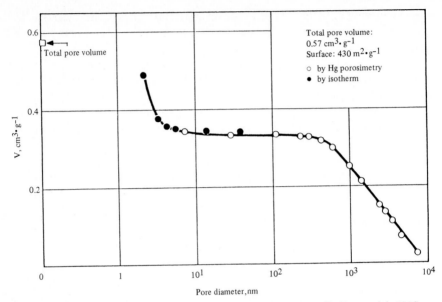

Figure 5.9 Pore size distribution of a sample of silica-alumina. (*Le Page et al. 1987, p. 217. Reprinted with permission from Editions Technip.*)

is plotted versus pore diameter for a sample of silica-alumina, and there is considerable overlap between the two methods of measurement. The figure shows the micropore distribution down to about 2.0-nm diameter and macropores in a broad micrometer range. The cumulative pore volume down to 2.0-nm diameter was 0.50 cm³/g. The total pore volume, from another measurement, was 0.57 cm³/g, indicating that pores of a size below 2.0 nm comprised a volume of 0.07 cm³/g.

In a catalyst having a bimodal pore size distribution but not containing zeolites, the fine pores are frequently in the range of 1 to 10 nm in radius and account for most of the surface area. The macropores typically are in the range of 10^2 to 10^3 nm. The latter can provide rapid mass transfer into the interstices of the mass from which the fine pores lead to the ultimate reaction sites. The pore size distribution can be varied by a variety of processing techniques. A wide distribution of pore sizes in a gelled cracking catalyst may be produced if hard microporous powders are incorporated into the gel before drying. Extruded catalysts frequently contain a network of fine pores or cracks from drying and calcining operations. In a pelleted or extruded catalyst an organic material can be incorporated into the mix and then burned out after the final particles are shaped and dried.

5.4   Mechanical Properties

The resistance to crushing (e.g., in packed beds), to attrition (e.g., in a fluidized-bed reactor), and to breakup during shipping and reactor loading are important catalyst characteristics. A considerable number of test procedures standardized by the American Society for Testing Materials (ASTM) are available for measuring these and other physical properties, and the ASTM has an active Committee on Catalysts (D32) that is concerned with development of standards for commercial purposes. The test methods are summarized by Haines (1989) and are published in volume 5.03 of the Annual Book of ASTM Standards or in succeeding editions of the ASTM Standards on Catalysts. In a test designation, e.g., D 4058-87 for abrasion resistance (see the following section), the two digits following the hyphen give the year in which the test was adopted or last revised, in this example 1987.

5.4.1   Crush tests, abrasion and attrition resistance

Procedures for crush tests are described by Bradley et al. (1989) and Brienza (1989). For bulk testing a piston is slowly forced down on a bed of catalyst and displacement is measured as a function of applied force. The flow rate of a gas through the bed is sometimes measured simultaneously to indicate the degree of increased flow resistance caused by catalyst breakup, since formation of a small amount of fines may be more deleterious to operation than a larger amount of partially fractured pellets. The increase in pressure drop with a fixed rate of gas flow or, more easily, the decrease in flow rate of a gas supplied at fixed pressure may be observed. Pellets or spheres may also be crushed individually for testing, but this is not practical for particles with irregular shapes such as extrudates or granules.

The catalyst on the bottom of a fixed bed in operation must withstand, not only the force from the catalyst above it, but also the force applied to it by the pressure drop through the bed in use, and the second may be much greater than the first. The weight of a catalyst bed is not applied completely to the catalyst at the bottom but, to a greater or lesser degree, is distributed to the reactor walls by an arch effect.

Abrasion and attrition resistance are of importance for fixed-bed catalysts to minimize breakage that may occur on handling. A representative test is to place a quantity of pellets in a rotating horizontal cylinder, 15 to 30 cm in diameter, equipped with a single flight (baffle) that raises pellets and drops them. A standardized test is available as ASTM D 4058-87. Alternately, a quantity of pellets may be dropped one at a time from a specified height, for example, 3 m, onto a hard surface. For a given catalyst composition, maximum crush and attrition resistance typically is achieved by preparing a relatively dense pellet of low porosity, but this reduces the effective diffusivity, so an optimum must be sought between this characteristic and mechanical properties.

For fluidized-bed reactors, attrition resistance of the fine catalyst is of paramount importance, and this is usually determined in an air-jet attrition test (see, e.g., Pedersen et al. (1989). Attrition and crush tests are also described by Le Page et al. (1987, Ch. 6), and in a group of papers in a volume edited by Bradley et al. (1989).

5.4.2 Particle size distribution

The average particle size and particle size distribution can markedly affect fluidization characteristics in a fluid-bed reactor and affect settling and filtering characteristics in a slurry reactor. Size fractions of a powder are commonly separated for measurement by shaking the powder through a stack of sieves of standard construction, the opening size decreasing from top to bottom. In the United States, this is the Tyler Standard Sieve Series in which the sieve is identified by the nominal number of meshes per linear inch. The finer the sieve, the finer the wire diameter used. Table 5.2 gives the sieve opening for a number of sieves commonly used. A 60- to 80-mesh powder, for example, consists of particles that pass through a screen with openings of 0.250 mm but are retained on a screen with openings of 0.177 mm. A standard test method is given in ASTM D 4513-85. Since the finer particles in a container settle toward the bottom on handling, suitable procedures for obtaining a representative sample must be used.

Measurements of the particle sizes of interest in catalysis can also

TABLE 5.2   Tyler Standard Sieve Series

Sieve size, Tyler designation	Sieve opening, mm
4	4.76
8	2.38
12	1.41
20	0.841
35	0.420
60	0.250
80	0.177
100	0.149
150	0.105
200	0.074
270	0.053
325	0.044

be made by microscopy (which is tedious) or by sedimentation. ASTM D 4438-85 describes a test method based on electronic counting and D 4464-85, a method based on laser light scattering. The range of particle sizes studied in both cases was 20 to 150 μm equivalent spherical diameter, but larger and smaller sizes can also be measured.

5.5   Selected Instrumental Methods

A great variety of instrumental methods are capable of revealing information of value to some aspect of catalysis. Methods of surface characterization are of particular importance, but many of these techniques are highly specialized and are of use mostly for fundamental research. Many methods that can be applied to plane surfaces lose much of their usefulness when confronted by porous catalysts. Spatial resolution is frequently of importance in practice and may be a primary consideration in choosing one or more optimum surface characterization methods. The following is intended to give a brief introduction to a few of the better-developed techniques that have been of particular value in working with technical catalysts.

A series of papers by Kelley (1987) and a review (Kelley, 1989) provide a useful introduction to surface analytical techniques, including several not discussed in this book except incidentally. A number of other helpful introductions have been published, as in relevant chapters in the books by Somorjai (1981) and by Campbell (1988). The book edited by Walls (1989) has chapters on various methods of surface analysis beyond those treated here, including mass spectrometry, ion-scattering spectroscopy and Rutherford backscattering spectrometry. A chapter by Bishop treats Auger electron spectroscopy; and a chapter by Christie, X-ray photoelectron spectroscopy. These are aimed at the nonspecialist to help the user determine what each technique can and cannot do. While providing the essential technical background, there is consideration of practical problem-solving methods.

5.5.1   Microscopy

Light microscopy helps to characterize materials and to define problems by revealing such features as size, shape, surface markings, occurrence of occlusions or other discontinuities, and color. It is particularly helpful to identify the characteristics of single particles and to determine particle size distribution.

Transmission electron microscopy (TEM).   The limit of resolution for a microscope is proportional to the wavelength of the illumination. For light microscopy, this is about 200 nm; an electron microscope is usually used when resolution for sizes smaller than this is required. Electrons are emitted from an electron gun, which is a heated pointed cathode (filament), and accelerated through two electrodes, the second of which is an anode. The electrons then pass through a condenser system, the specimen, and a magnetic lens system. Size or microstructure can be determined for materials in the range of about 1 nm to 30 μm.

Commercial high-resolution instruments operate at voltages up to about 200 keV and can reveal useful information on specimens less than about 100 nm thick. In general, any solid material can be studied, but if the section is too thick, and one wishes to see more than an outline, then the specimen must be sectioned or replicated. A very thin section, e.g., 30 to 40 nm thick, can be prepared by mounting the sample in an epoxy resin, cutting it slowly with a diamond knife, and floating the specimen off in a liquid. If desired, a replica can be made readily by putting a layer of polymer on a solid and depositing carbon or other material from a vapor onto the replica. A shadowing technique in which vapors are deposited from an angle provides an image looking much like a map replica.

The depth of field is typically about 150 nm, so usually the entire specimen will be in focus. Some precautions to note are:

1. The sample must be stable under vacuum.

2. The electron bombardment can cause specimen damage.

3. One must watch out for various artifacts. Impurities such as dust, etc., may be incorporated into the sample during its preparation, and the process of slicing a thin layer may cause distortion of the structure.

Transmission electron microscopy is useful for indicating the size of supported metal crystallites and changes in their size, shape, and position with catalyst use. Replicas are useful for obtaining information on pore structure. Figure 5.10 shows a thin section of an iron catalyst used for ammonia synthesis. The pores are the white, light, parallel markings and are of the order of tens of nanometers. Figure 5.11 is a thin section at higher magnification. The light areas are pore mouths; the pore cross sections appear to be quite irregular and, as in Fig. 5.10, vary considerably in size.

The development of high-resolution transmission electron microscopy (HREM) during the past decade now allows features down to 0.2 to 0.3 nm to be recognized. This has been of particular use with zeolites in which defects as well as the regular pore structure can be observed. Some representative micrographs are shown in Sec. 7.7.1.

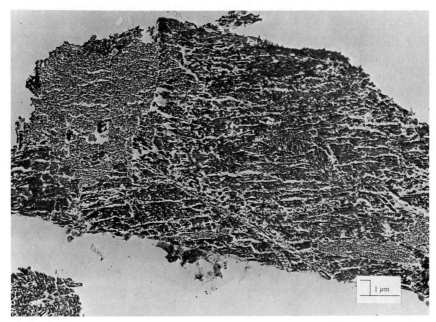

Figure 5.10   Electron micrograph of thin section of Topsøe ammonia-synthesis catalyst
KMIR. (*Nielsen 1968*)

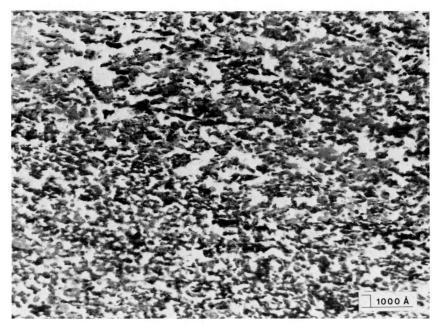

Figure 5.11   Electron micrograph of thin section of Topsøe ammonia-synthesis catalyst
KMIR. Enlargement of Fig. 5.10. (*Nielsen 1968*)

Electron bombardment effects.   The incoming electron beam gives rise to several simultaneous effects that are the basis of various methods of surface characterization. Consider an electron beam focused to a diameter of 10 nm consisting of electron energies of 50 keV, entering a sample. As shown in Fig. 5.12, electrons may be elastically scattered back out of the specimen without energy loss, or backscattered inelastically in the form of low-energy secondary electrons. If the specimen is sufficiently thin, the unscattered penetrating beam provides the image for TEM.

The incoming electron beam causes atoms to be ionized in a pear-shaped zone that, in a thick specimen, is roughly 1 μm in diameter. The energy released by deexcitation of an ionized atom may appear in different ways. Of interest here are:

1. As an X-ray photon that has a wavelength characteristic of the atomic number of the element (These are the characteristic X-rays used in electron-probe microanalysis.)

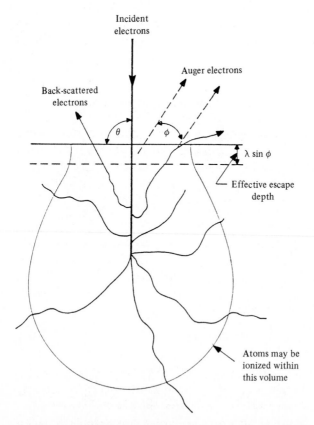

Figure 5.12   Spatial distribution of Auger electron production. (*Bishop in Walls 1989, p. 93*)

2. The formation of Auger electrons

The image in scanning electron microscopy is produced from electrons backscattered from the specimen surface, usually the secondary low-energy electrons (< 50 eV).

Scanning electron microscopy (SEM). An electron spot of about 5 nm minimum, focused on the sample, is moved over a small area by means of a set of deflecting coils. This area is displayed highly magnified on a *cathode ray tube* (CRT) by causing the currents passing through the scanning coils to pass through the corresponding deflecting coils of the cathode ray tube while the electrons emitted from the sample are collected, amplified, and used to modulate the brightness of the CRT. At the relatively poor vacuum conditions of a SEM, the surface is usually contaminated and the image contrast is determined mostly by topography. By varying the orientation of the specimen with respect to the signal detector, a light/dark effect can be produced forming a striking three-dimensional effect.

As of 1990, the resolution of representative commercial instruments allowed markings of the order of 50 nm or greater to be distinguished. Below this size, the degree of definition is determined more by the characteristics of the sample rather than by the instrument; e.g., a charge cannot be allowed to build on the sample—it distorts the image. This is a problem with all surface spectroscopies, but particularly with electron beams. Some samples are conductive, but if a sample is not, a conductive layer must be applied, or other means of charge dissipation applied. Sanders (1985) gives a detailed treatment of electron microscopy of catalysts, discussing instruments, specimens, interpretation of images, and many examples of applications to catalysts.

Scanning electron microscopy has been used particularly for examination of the topology of catalyst surfaces and the morphology of particles and crystals. Figure 8.3, of a commercial supported silver ethylene oxide catalyst, shows the irregular pore structure of the α-Al_2O_3 support and the uniform dispersion of small silver particles. Figures 8.11 and 8.13 show the growth in roughness of platinum gauzes after use in an ammonia oxidation reactor or in the Andrussow process. Figure 7.10 shows the morphologies of four different preparations of zeolite ZSM-5.

By special procedures for enclosing the specimen, it is also possible to observe dynamic events in a controlled atmosphere environment at total pressures up to a substantial fraction of an atmosphere, as shown in a series of studies by Baker (1979). By such means the mobility of small particles and the growth of carbon filaments from metal surfaces in a reducing environment (Sec. 6.5) have been observed.

Scanning transmission electron microscopy can also be applied

(STEM). In a representative procedure, the sample is powdered (e.g. 1-to 5-μm size), spread in a thin layer on a thin carbon film (e.g., 5 nm) that is transparent.

As noted in the foregoing, the incident electron beam causes the emission of Auger electrons and characteristic X-rays that can be analyzed to provide additional information about the same area of the sample on which a SEM picture is obtained. There has been much interest in instruments that combine several analytical methods. The gain from obtaining multiple information on a single specimen or from a small area on a heterogeneous sample may be purchased at some reduction in performance from that of a single-purpose instrument. One instrument may combine an electron gun and an X-ray source, and be capable of use for X-ray photoelectron spectroscopy (XPS), for Auger electron spectroscopy (AES), and for scanning electron microscopy.

5.5.2 Auger electron spectroscopy (AES)

A hole may be formed at a core electron level by bombardment with X-rays or an electron. The movement of an electron from a valence level into the hole, which increases the binding energy, converts the atom into an excited state. This energy can be dissipated by emission of a photon (fluorescent X-ray) or a second (Auger) electron. In AES, data are usually obtained in the form of intensity of electrons emitted as a function of binding energy. These electrons are typically in the energy range of 20 to 2000 eV. The Auger electron emission does not depend on how the core hole was formed in the first place, but excitation by an electron beam has the advantage that it can be precisely focused, the degree of spatial resolution varying with the instrument and the specimen. With special high-resolution Auger equipment, resolution down to about 30 nm at a depth of 1.0 nm may be possible. The focused beam consists typically of 5 to 10 keV electrons for the best signal-to-noise ratio.

The surface sensitivity of AES is determined by the escape depth of electrons λ, which is the *inelastic mean free path* (IMFP). It is determined by their energy and is affected slightly by the nature of the solid. Figure 5.13 is the so-called "universal curve" published by Seah and Dench (1979), based on analysis of a variety of data and theoretical considerations. λ is at a minimum value of about two monolayers with electron energies of about 100 eV. Quantitative analysis with AES is not straightforward since the contribution to the signal drops with depth, but accuracy to within perhaps 10 percent is achievable (the same is true of XPS).

Electron probe microanalysis (Sec. 5.5.4), which is the X-ray ana-

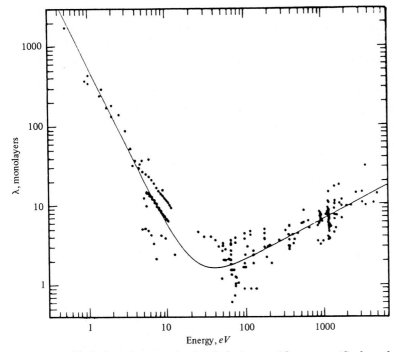

Figure 5.13   Variation of escape depth of electrons with energy. (*Seah and Dench 1979 from Bishop in Walls 1989, p. 54*)

logue of AES, can give quantitative (e.g., within 1 percent) measurements of average elemental composition within the volume excited by the electron probe. However, AES gives elemental composition on a surface and thus may indicate if a surface is clean and the extent of surface coverage by inhibitors and promoters. The degree of lateral resolution obtainable is much better than that with XPS, but it is less useful for revealing chemical information.

An important factor affecting the application of any surface spectroscopic method is the fact that most industrial catalysts are porous and material in pores 1.0 nm or so below the outside surface may be hidden.

5.5.3   X-ray photoelectron spectroscopy (XPS, ESCA)

For each core electron in an element there is a binding energy that may be visualized as the ionization energy of that electron. In XPS the specimen is irradiated by a source of essentially monochromatic X-rays under ultrahigh-vacuum conditions. These cause photoionization producing photoelectrons whose kinetic energy is primarily characteristic of the X-ray energy and the electron binding energy. A detailed series of studies by Kai Siegbahn and co-workers over a long period of time [see, e.g., Christie (1989)] showed that these binding energies at the core levels of atoms are also slightly affected by the chemical environment so as to cause a shift of up to 10 eV or more in the observed photoelectron energy. This was termed the "chemical shift" and the technique was termed by Siegbahn *electron spectroscopy for chemical analysis (ESCA)*. Basically, the distortion of valence electrons by chemical binding affects the degree of electrostatic screening of the core electrons. With conventional X-ray sources, energy resolution is usually limited to about 0.5 eV.

Core electron binding energies go up to values of 1 keV or more and the X-ray source is typically produced by bombarding an anode with a high-energy electron beam, e.g., 15 keV. The most suitable anodes are usually aluminum or magnesium, producing AlK_α X-rays (1486.6 e.v.) or MgK_α (1253.6 e.v.). X-rays are much more penetrating than electrons of the same energy. Thus, they can penetrate several microns, but the photoelectrons produced can escape only if they come from near the surface.

The escape depth λ varies with electron energy approximately as $\lambda \propto E_k^{1/2}$ for E_k values above about 50 e.v. (Fig. 5.13). The electrons are resolved for their quantity and their kinetic energy, which gives their binding energy. This is characteristic of the atomic number of the element to which the electron is bound, but of particular importance here are the chemical shifts that can give information on surface composition. XPS can be combined with ion sputtering to gradually remove surface layers and thus provide a description of composition as a function of depth.

XPS is a powerful technique that can analyze for all the elements except possibly hydrogen. The analysis is chemically nondestructive, and problems with specimen charging are much less than with electron bombardment. A possible limitation to XPS is that X-ray excitation cannot be focused very readily. The analysis area may have to be several millimeters across in order to gain sensitivity.

5.5.4 Electron microprobe analysis

A beam of energetic electrons (e.g., 15 keV) is focused onto the surface of a specimen. The inner-shell (K, L, M) ionizations of the atoms produce characteristic X-rays that are representative of the nature of the elements, and the intensity of the X-ray is proportional to concentration. Thus, an X-ray image can be produced that gives the nature and the distribution of a particular element to a high degree of resolution. The electron beam can penetrate 100 nm or more, so the composition is averaged through most of a specimen as typically prepared. The limitation of degree of resolution is not the focusing of the electron beam but rather the scatter of emitted radiation. This is about equal to 1 μm or the thickness of sample, whichever is less; consequently the resolution can be as small as a few tens of nanometers. The output may be presented in the form of a raster scan (map) or an analysis profile (line scan).

As of 1990 the electron microprobe can be used for all but the very lightest elements. It is particularly useful for obtaining a profile of the distribution of heavy metals through a catalyst particle by working with a thin slice of the material, or for detecting the buildup of poisons and their distribution through individual pellets. It may also be used as an analytical method on a ground and representative sample of a catalyst, which may be as small as 1 μm^3. Electron microprobe analysis has been applied to characterization of the promoted iron catalysts used in ammonia synthesis, to show how certain promoters dissolve in magnetite during fusion and migrate to crystallite boundaries during reduction to iron metal. Figure 8.12 (Sec. 8.10) shows its use to identify segregation of rhodium at the surface of a platinum-rhodium alloy gauze, used for the catalytic oxidation of ammonia.

An example of the power of the method is also shown by the series of X-ray images for different elements shown in Fig. 5.14. These were taken and used to determine the causes of plugging of a pilot plant reactor packed with Co-Mo·Al$_2$O$_3$ extrudates and utilized for hydrodesulfurizing a residual crude oil fraction. A section of the plugged bed was ground flat, coated with a conductive layer, and examined directly. Each X-ray map has superimposed on it an analysis profile showing the variation of concentration of the specified element along the straight line in the middle of the picture.

The plug was found to consist of a mass of catalyst extrudates embedded in a matrix of fine material acting as a binder. In Fig. 5.14, a is an optical micrograph, b is a back-scattered electron image showing the topography of the sample, and Fig. 5.14c a drawing of b showing the boundary between binder and catalyst extrudate in b and subsequent X-ray images. The binder is seen to have a high concentration of iron (d), probably present as particulates, judging from the irregularities. Nickel and vanadium are deposited from the residual feed, the vanadium preferentially at the edge of the extrudate (f), and the nickel both in the catalyst and in the binder (e). Sulfur is deposited irregularly (g). The binder contains considerable NaCl (h, i), a possible source of at least some of the plugging. Cobalt does not appear in the binder (j); therefore the plugging was not caused by ground catalyst. Molybdenum is almost uniform inside and outside the catalyst (k), and therefore must have migrated out of the catalyst. The aluminum im-

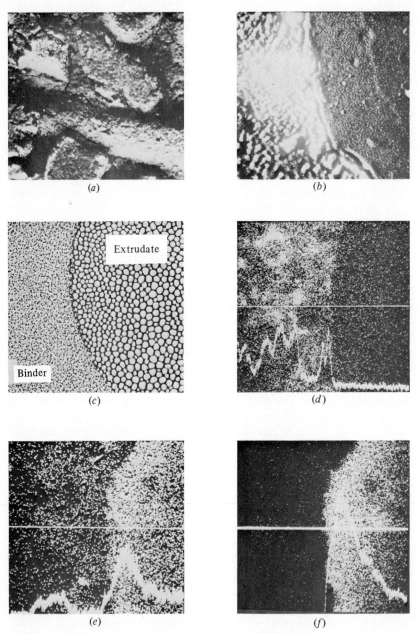

Figure 5.14   X-ray images by electron microprobe of a plugged catalyst section of a pilot plant reactor (see text). All images are of the same specimen. (a) Optical micrograph; (b) backscattered electron image; (c) drawing of (b); (d) Fe X-ray image; (e) Ni X-ray image; (f) V X-ray image. (*Work conducted by and photographs courtesy of G.W. Bailey, Exxon Research and Development Laboratories, Baton Rouge, La.*)

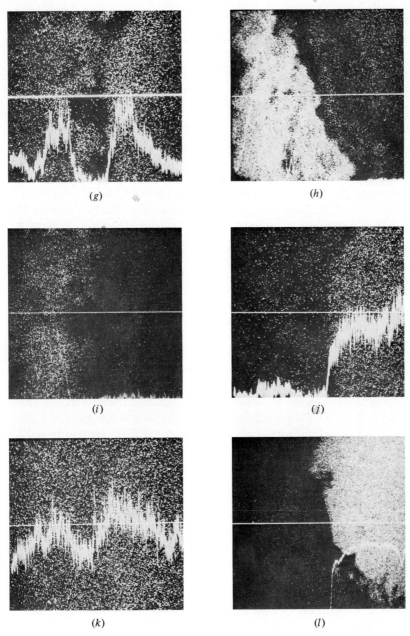

Figure 5.14   (*Continued*) X-ray images by electron microprobe of a plugged catalyst section of a pilot plant reactor (see text). All images are of the same specimen. (*g*) S X-ray image; (*h*) Na X-ray image; (*i*) Cl X-ray image; (*j*) Co X-ray image; (*k*) Mo X-ray image; (*l*) Al X-ray image. (*Work conducted by and photographs courtesy of G.W. Bailey, Exxon Research and Development Laboratories, Baton Rouge, La.*)

age (l) shows a sharp boundary at the catalyst surface, confirming the conclusion from j that the plugging was not caused by ground catalyst.

5.5.5 X-ray diffraction (XRD) crystallography

X-ray diffraction may be used to obtain information about the structure and composition of crystalline material. Common compounds can be identified using tabulations of reference patterns. The minimal limit of detection is approximately 5 percent for compounds and approximately 1 percent for elements. With calibration procedures it is possible to obtain quantitative information and thus determine the approximate amount of a particular phase in a sample. Phases for which reference patterns are not available can sometimes be identified by other X-ray procedures. A change in the cell dimensions sometimes indicates the incorporation of an isomorphous material, e.g., iron into a cobalt nickel molybdate.

XRD patterns can be of great importance in identifying specific crystal structures or crystal planes within a complex catalyst if these are responsible for a desired specificity. Indeed a patented composition of matter useful as a catalyst may be identified primarily through a stated XRD pattern combined with a composition claim. A specific example is discussed in Sec. 8.6.1.

XRD is of particular importance in characterization of zeolite catalysts (Sec. 7.7). ASTM procedure D3906-85a provides a method for determining the percentage of zeolite Y in a catalyst sample based on the intensity of a portion of the X-ray diffraction pattern of the sample relative to that of a reference zeolite Y. ASTM D3942-85 gives a standard test method for determining the unit cell dimension of a faujasite-type zeolite. This makes possible a determination of zeolite framework composition (e.g., Si/Al ratio) which cannot be done by elemental analysis when the zeolite is incorporated into a matrix.

The mean crystallite size of a material can also be determined from the broadening of an X-ray diffraction peak, measured at one-half the height. The line broadening is inversely proportional to crystallite size, and can be used to give the microcrystalline size in the range of about 5 to 50 nm, depending on the pattern, the nature of the material, its concentration, and apparatus characteristics.

Figure 5.15 shows the X-ray diffraction intensity as a function of angle, 2θ, for 2-percent Pd supported on silica, as calcined at four different temperatures. The peak becomes narrower for higher calcination temperatures, reflecting growth in crystal size. Calculated crystal diameter was 5.5 nm for calcination at 500°C and 14 nm for calcination at 800°C.

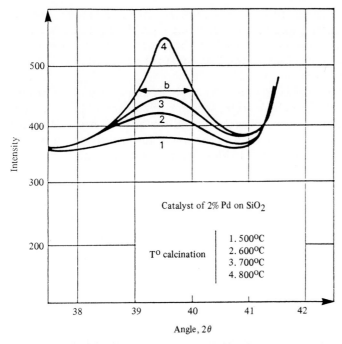

Figure 5.15 Determining the average size of palladium crystallites from the mid-height width (*b*) of X-ray diffraction lines. (*Le Page et al. 1987, p. 207. Reprinted with permission from Editions Technip.*)

Small-angle X-ray scattering (SAXS) (about 0.5° from the incident beam) may be used to give the particle size distribution in the range of about 5 to 100 nm, but special instrumentation is required that is not widely available. X-ray techniques in catalysis are reviewed by Gallezot (1984).

5.5.6 Calorimetry

Calorimetry may be employed to observe various types of chemical transformations that are accompanied by significant energy changes. For example, if a catalyst or catalyst support undergoes several irreversible phase changes at different temperatures, such as alumina does, calorimetry may indicate the maximum temperature to which the material has been subjected. With a poisoned catalyst, the disappearance of a deposit at low temperature may indicate that the poison is organic rather than inorganic. A *differential scanning calorimeter* (DSC) may be used with small samples.

5.5.7 Gravimetric methods

The change in weight of a catalyst with changing experimental conditions can be used for a variety of studies. Modern microbalance instruments can be used with catalyst samples of from a few milligrams up to gram quantities and can detect changes in weight of the order of 0.05 mg or less. Measurements can be made at temperatures up to 1000°C, which can be programmed, at constant or variable pressures, and under static or flow conditions.

Microgravimetric methods have been particularly useful for studying the rate of coking, dehydration, sorption of poisons, catalyst regeneration, etc., as a function of reaction conditions. They are also useful for catalyst characterization, e.g., of oxidation catalysts in which weight gain or loss may reveal the state of oxidation and hence stability as a function of environment.

Temperature-programmed desorption is widely used to characterize adsorbed species, particularly in combination with other studies. It can indicate how much material is adsorbed and how tightly it is bound and can provide inferences about the mechanism of desorption processes.

5.6   Reference Catalysts

Most standardized test methods as discussed in the foregoing have been developed by round-robin testing of physical properties on a set of reference materials. A number of these are now generally available as reference standards. The next level of complexity is catalytic properties together with physical characterization. An ambitious program has been carried out in Europe since 1976 of characterization in various laboratories of one sample of 6.3-percent platinum/silica manufactured by Johnson Matthey Chemicals. The catalyst is code-named EUROPT-1 and a variety of publications have appeared concerning these studies. For a recent summary see Wells (1989).

References

Adamson, A. W.: *Physical Chemistry of Surfaces*, 3d ed., Wiley, New York, 1976.
Anderson, J. R.: *Structure of Metallic Catalysts*, Academic, New York, 1975.
Anderson, J. R., and K. C. Pratt: *Introduction to Characterization and Testing of Catalysts*, Academic, New York, 1985.
Baiker, A. and A. Relthaar: *Ind. Eng. Chem., Prod. Res. Devel.*, **21**, 590 (1982).
Baker, R. T. K.: *Catal. Rev.—Sci. Eng.*: **19**, 161 (1979).
Barrett, E. P., L. G. Joyner, and P. C. Halenda: *J. Am. Chem. Soc.*, **73**, 373 (1951).
Benesi, H. A., R. V. Bonnar, and C. F. Lee: *Anal. Chem.*, **27**, 1963 (1955).
Bohlbro, H.: *An Investigation on the Kinetics of the Conversion of Carbon Monoxide with Water Vapour over Iron Oxide Based Catalysts*, Gjellerup, Copenhagen, 1966.
Bradley, S. A., M. J. Gattuso, and R. J. Bertolacini (eds.): *Characterization and Catalyst Development: An Interactive Approach*, ACS Symposium Series No. 411, 1989.
Bradley, S. A., E. Pitzer, and W. J. Koves, in S. A. Bradley, M. J. Gattuso, and R. J. Bertolacini (eds.): *Characterization and Catalyst Development: An Interactive Approach*, ACS Symposium Series No. 411, 1989, p. 398.
Brienza, P. K., in S. A. Bradley, M. J. Gattuso, and R. J. Bertolacini (eds.): *Character-*

ization and Catalyst Development: An Interactive Approach, ACS Symposium Series No. 411, 1989, p. 407.

Broekhoff, J. C. P., and B. G. Linsen, in B. G. Linsen (ed.): *Physical and Chemical Aspects of Adsorbents and Catalysts*, Academic, New York, 1970.

Broekhoff, J. C. P., in B. Delmon et al. (eds.): *Preparation of Catalysts. II*, Elsevier, New York, 1979, p. 663.

Brown, S. M., and E. W. Lard: *Powder Technol.*, **9**, 187 (1974).

Brunauer, S., L. S. Deming, W. S. Deming, and E. Teller: *J. Am. Chem. Soc.*, **62**, 1723 (1940).

Brunauer, S., P. H. Emmett, and E. Teller: *J. Am. Chem. Soc.*, **60**, 309 (1938).

Campbell, I. M.: *Catalysis at Surfaces*, Chapman and Hall, London, 1988.

Christie, A. B., in J. M. Walls (ed.): *Methods of Surface Analysis*: Cambridge University Press, N.Y., 1989, Chapter 5.

Davis, B. H.: *Appl. Catal.*, **10**, 185 (1984).

Day, M., and R. Fletcher, in K. K. Unger, J. Rouqueral, K. S. W. Sing, and H. Kral (eds.): *Characterization of Porous Solids*, Elsevier, New York, 1988, p. 491.

Drake, L. E.: *Ind. Eng. Chem.*, **41**, 780 (1949).

Emmett, P. H.: *Adv. Catal.*, **1**, 65 (1948); *Catalysis*, vol. 1, Reinhold, New York, 1954, p. 31.

Emmett, P. H.: *36th Annual Priestley Lecture*, Pennsylvania State University, University Park, 1962.

Gallezot, P., in J. R. Anderson and M. Boudart (eds.): *Catalysis: Science and Technology*, Springer-Verlag, New York, 1984, Vol. 5, p. 221.

Gregg, S. J., and K. S. W. Sing: *Adsorption, Surface Area, and Porosity*, Academic, New York, 1967, 2d. ed., 1982.

Haines, R. A., in S. A. Bradley, M. J. Gattuso, and R. J. Bertolacini (eds.): *Characterization and Catalyst Development: An Interactive Approach*, ACS Symposium Series No. 411, 1989, p. 430.

Jaroniec, M., R. Madey, J. Choma, B. McEnaney and T. J. Mays: *Carbon*, **27**, 77 (1989).

Johnson, M. F. L.: *J. Catal.*, **52**, 425 (1978).

Johnson, M. F. L., A. P. Voss, S. H. Bauer, and N-S. Chiu: *J. Catal.*, **98**, 51 (1986).

Johnson, M. F. L.: *J. Catal.*, **110**, 419 (1988).

Joyner, L. G., E. P. Barrett, and R. Skold: *J. Am. Chem. Soc.*, **73**, 3158 (1951).

Kelley, M. J.: *Chemtech*, pp. 30, 98, 170, 232, 294, 490, 632 (1987).

Kelley, M. J., in T. Inui (ed.): *Successful Design of Catalysts: Future Requirements and Development*, Elsevier, New York, 1989, p. 61.

Lecloux, A. J., in J. R. Anderson and M. Boudart (eds.): *Catalysis: Science and Technology*, vol. 2, p. 171, Springer-Verlag, New York, 1981.

Le Page, J. F. et al.: *Applied Heterogeneous Catalysis: Design, Manufacture, Use of Solid Catalysts*, Editions Technip, Paris, 1987. (Prepared by a group at the Institut Français du Pétrole. Translated from the French edition of 1978 with some modifications and additions.)

Marsh, H.: *Carbon*, **25**, 151 (1987).

McEnaney, B.: *Carbon*, **26**, 267 (1988).

Milburn, D. R., B. D. Adkins, and B. H. Davis, in K. K. Unger, J. Rouqueral, K. S. W. Sing, and H. Kral (eds.): *Characterization of Porous Solids*, Elsevier, New York, 1988, p. 501.

Nielsen, A.: *An Investigation on Promoted Iron Catalysts for the Synthesis of Ammonia*, 3d ed., Gjellerup, Copenhagen, 1968.

Parfitt, G. D., and K. S. W. Sing: *Characterization of Powder Surfaces*, Academic, New York, 1976.

Pedersen, L. A., J. A. Lowe, and C. K. Matocha, Sr., in S. A. Bradley, M. J. Gattuso, and R. J. Bertolacini (eds.): *Characterization and Catalyst Development: An Interactive Approach*, ACS Symposium Series No. 411, 1989, p. 414.

Pieters, W. J. M., and A. F. Venero, in S. Kaliaguine and A. Mahay (eds.): *Catalysis on the Energy Scene*, Elsevier, New York, 1984, p. 155.

Raatz, F., and H. Ajot, in K. K. Unger, J. Rouqueral, K. S. W. Sing, and H. Kral (eds.): *Characterization of Porous Solids*, Elsevier, Amsterdam, 1988, p. 119.

Ritter, H. L., and L. E. Drake: *Ind. Eng. Chem., Anal. Ed.*, **17**, 782, 787 (1945).

Roberts, B. F., *J. Colloid Interface Sci.*, **23**, 266 (1967).

Sanders, J. V., in J. R. Anderson and M. Boudart (eds.): *Catalysis: Science and Technology*, Springer-Verlag, New York, 1985, vol. 7, p. 51.

Seah, M. P. and W. A. Dench: *Surf. Interface Anal.*, **1**, 2 (1979).

Sing, K. S. W., in J. M. Thomas and R. M. Lambert (eds.): *Characterization of Catalysts*, Wiley, New York, 1980, p. 12.

Sing, K. S. W., D. H. Everett, R. A. W. Haul, L. Moscou, R. A. Pierotti, J. Rouqueral, and T. Siemieniewska: *Pure Appl. Chem.* (London) **57**, 603 (1985).

Somorjai, G. A.: *Chemistry in Two Dimensions: Surfaces*, Cornell University Press, Ithaca, N.Y., 1981.

Ternan, M. and O. M. Fuller: *Can. J. Chem. Eng.*, **57**, 750 (1979).

Unger, K. K., J. Rouqueral, K. S. W. Sing, and H. Kral (eds.): *Characterization of Porous Solids*, Elsevier, New York, 1988.

Walls, J. M. (ed.): *Methods of Surface Analysis*, Cambridge University Press, N. Y., 1989.

Wells, P. B.: *Faraday Discuss. Chem. Soc.*, **87**, 1 (1989).

Chapter
6

Supported Metal Catalysts

Metal catalysts are of particular interest for reactions involving hydrogen as a reactant or product. Some representative industrial hydrogenation reactions are considered in Sec. 6.7. Hydrogenolysis and catalytic reforming are discussed in Chap. 9. The use of iron for ammonia synthesis and for the Fischer-Tropsch reaction, and nickel for steam reforming and methanation is discussed in Chap. 10. In most of the applications discussed here the metal is dispersed on a support, in many cases in aggregates so small that a significant fraction of the atoms are on the surface. A central question is the extent to which the rate of a reaction per atom of exposed metal (turnover number) and, more importantly, the relative rates of parallel or sequential reactions are affected by the number and arrangement of sites on the metal. These in turn may be affected by particle size; by the use of alloys (also termed "bimetallic catalysts"); by kinks, steps, and other crystal imperfections; and by the blockage of some of the sites by deliberately added poisons or by accumulation of carbonaceous deposits. There is also a possible role of the support in influencing the properties of the metal.

Metals may also be useful for oxidation reactions. Examples are the use of supported silver for oxidation of ethylene to ethylene oxide; platinum-rhodium wire gauze for the partial oxidation of ammonia to nitric oxide or for conversion of a mixture of methane, ammonia, and air to hydrogen cyanide, and bulk silver for the partial oxidation of methanol to formaldehyde. In these cases the metals catalyze oxidations by chemisorbing oxygen. The reactions characteristically involve relatively high temperatures, so questions arise of crystal growth, migration, and the loss of active material by volatilization associated with chemisorbed oxygen and formation of metal oxides. These are discussed in Chap. 8 as well as Sec. 6.4. The discussion that follows relates primarily to uses of metals under reducing conditions. The elements that can retain their metallic form during reaction are primarily those in group VIII and group IB (see the periodic table, Table 1.3).

6.1 Metal Activity

Maximum catalytic activity is associated with rapid but not too strong chemisorption of reactants. The first transition series in group VIII consists of base metals. Their hydrogenation activity increases in the order Fe < Co < Ni. The group VIII elements of the second and third transition series are termed the platinum-group metals (pgm). Of these six elements, platinum and palladium are by far the most important in catalysis. Osmium and iridium are very rare and many osmium compounds are poisonous. Rhodium is of limited availability, but is in strong demand for automobile catalysts. It is also used as a hardening agent in alloys with platinum. Ruthenium is not widely used in catalysts, and some ruthenium oxides are poisonous. The pgm are discussed in more detail in Sec. 8.12 and in conjunction with specific oxidation processes in Chap. 8.

Group IB metals do not readily adsorb hydrogen, so copper is a very mild hydrogenation catalyst compared to, e.g., nickel. Copper is used industrially for hydration of acrylonitrile to acrylamide and for synthesis of 1,4 butynediol from acetylene and formaldehyde. Hydrogenation of the product yields 1,4 butanediol, which has a variety of uses. One of these is as an ingredient of spandex fibers, e.g., Lycra. Silver is used only as an oxidation catalyst. Gold is very unreactive.

Hydrogenation reactions are carried out with a wide variety of reactants. The most active metallic catalysts are those in group VIII. This is readily rationalized in terms of adsorption effects: The strength of adsorption on, for example, group VIB and VIIB metals is too strong; that on IB metals is too weak or nonexistent. Within group VIII, relative activity differences vary with the nature of the reaction and require a more detailed examination of the mechanism. Note that hydrogenation reactions can also occur on metal sulfides, metal oxides, and other compounds containing metallic elements, although the activity of these catalysts is generally much less than that of group VIII metals as such.

Hydrogenolysis of a hydrocarbon is the cleavage of a C—C bond accompanied by hydrogenation to form two molecules from one. Hydrogenolysis of paraffins is of great importance in petroleum processing, in which it is sometimes a desired reaction, as in commercial hydrocracking, and sometimes not. Hydrocracking as performed industrially uses a dual-function catalyst consisting of acid sites on which cracking occurs and one or more metals that provide hydrogenation functionality. Hydrocracking on the metals as such under typical industrial reaction conditions is usually unimportant. However, an excessive temperature rise in a hydrogenation reaction or dual-function-type hydrocracking can lead to excessive hydrocracking on metal sites. Being exothermic, this provides the potential for a runaway reaction.

The mechanism of hydrocracking a paraffin on a metal probably involves as the first step adsorption of the paraffin on a group of sites with dissociation of a hydrogen atom. A commonly studied model of the reaction is that of ethane and hydrogen to form methane. The relative activity of metals changes more with position in the periodic table for ethane hydrogenolysis than it does for hydrogenation. Group VIII metals are, again, the most active. In the first transition series maximum activity is shown for the third subgroup element, nickel, but in the second and third transition series it is shown for the first subgroup element, ruthenium or osmium.

The distribution of primary products from hydrogenolysis varies substantially with the nature of the metal. For paraffins on nonnoble group VIII metals (Fe, Co, Ni), cracking occurs at terminal C—C bonds, producing successive demethylation of the carbon chain with accompanying formation of methane. This is generally undesired. With the platinum-group metals, the initial cracking pattern is relatively nonselective on platinum and iridium, but terminal C—C bonds are attacked almost exclusively on palladium and rhodium.

The foregoing generalizations are developed in more detail by Sinfelt (1975) and by Dowden (1978). Maire and Garin (1984) review the mechanisms of skeletal reactions of hydrocarbons on metals. Foger (1984) reviews preparation and characterization of dispersed metal catalysts on a variety of supports.

6.1.1 Structure sensitivity

For some relatively simple reactions, especially those for which the active site is a single exposed metal atom, the activity (more specifically, turnover number) and selectivity are independent of the catalyst structure about the metal atom. These reactions are termed *structure-insensitive*, in contrast to other reactions termed *structure-sensitive*. A variety of different structure forms may be significant such as: (1) The spacing between adjacent metal atoms, as revealed by measurements on different crystallographic planes. (2) The effect of edge and corner atoms on a crystal surface in contrast to atoms in a plane, as may be revealed by systematically varying metal particle sizes, since this changes the ratio of the two (Steps, kinks, and defects on a crystal surface may also have an effect.) (3) Alloying an active metal with an inactive metal, e.g., Ni with Cu (Sec. 6.3.3), which alters the environment among the Ni atoms.

The causes of structure sensitivity or insensitivity are not always clear. However, a reaction in which the active site comprises two or more atoms (e.g., hydrocracking) or in which reaction intermediates are formed on various different sites would almost certainly be structure-sensitive.

Careful experimentation is required to show clearly whether a reaction is or is not structure-sensitive. Many reports of observing structure insensitivity do not withstand careful scrutiny. With low catalyst loadings, results may be affected by uncontrolled poisons, and there may be support effects such as partial reaction of metal with the support. Moreover, kinetics may not be measured with adequate precision.

The reactions most clearly established to be structure-insensitive are several fairly simple hydrogenations such as hydrogenation of benzene to cyclohexane on various Pd and Ni catalysts, hydrogenation of hexene to hexane on Pt/SiO_2, and cyclopropane hydrogenation and oxidation of CO to CO_2 on palladium, rhodium, and ruthenium. An example is a study of the first reaction by Aben et al. (1970). Catalysts were prepared with different crystallite sizes, and the fraction of metal atoms exposed was determined by chemisorption of hydrogen. As shown on Fig. 6.1, with both Pd and Ni catalysts the hydrogenation activity per total atoms of metal present was directly proportional to the fraction exposed.

Another example is the conversion of synthesis gas to methane:

$$CO + 3H_2 \rightarrow CH_4 + H_2O \tag{6.1}$$

Goodman and Houston (1987) report a careful study of this reaction on two different faces of Ni single crystals, a closely packed (111) face and a more open structure (100). Their results are compared on the Arrhenius plot of Fig. 6.2 with data reported by Vannice (1976) for studies of supported Ni on alumina. There is no significant variation in specific rate or activation energy as the catalyst is changed from large single crystals to small supported metal particles, and it is remarkable that this was shown to occur over five orders of magnitude change in rate.

In contrast, for hydrogenolysis of ethane,

$$C_2H_6 + H_2 \rightarrow 2CH_4 \tag{6.2}$$

significant differences in activity, expressed as a *turnover frequency* (TOF), are shown for the two Ni faces (Figure 6.3).

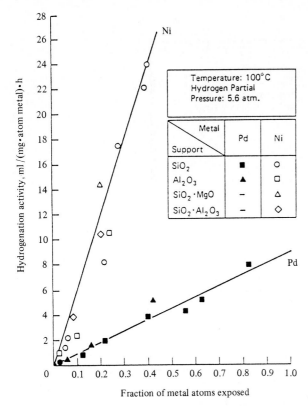

Figure 6.1   Hydrogenation activity per milligram atom of metal versus fraction of exposed metal surface atoms. (*After Aben et al. 1970. Reprinted with permission from Prentice-Hall, Englewood Cliffs, N.J.*)

6.2   Metal Dispersion (Percentage Exposed)

The extent of dispersion is defined as the ratio of the number of surface metal atoms in a catalyst to the total number present. A value of unity means that all metal atoms are exposed to reactants. The IUPAC recommendation is that the term *percentage exposed* be used instead of *dispersion*, but the former term is not widely used at present. As an example, for crystals of platinum in the shape of regular octahedra, the fraction exposed is 0.78 for an edge length of 1.4 nm, 0.49 for an edge length of 2.8 nm, and 0.30 for an edge length of 5.0 nm. A commercial platinum reforming catalyst can be made with such a high degree of dispersion that the fraction exposed can readily exceed 0.5. In contrast, even a very finely divided nonsupported platinum catalyst has a low fraction exposed. For a particle 1 μm in size, the fraction exposed is about 0.001.

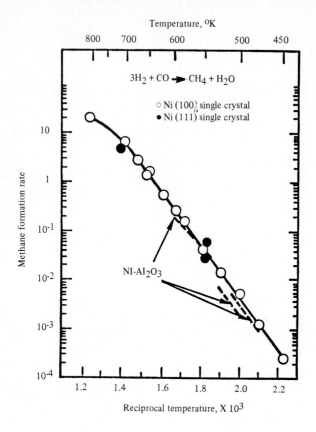

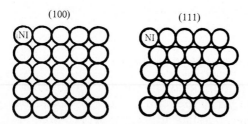

Figure 6.2   A comparison of the rate of methane synthesis over single-crystal nickel catalysts and supported Ni-Al$_2$O$_3$ catalysts at a total reactant pressure of 16 kPa. Atomic structure of a Ni(100) surface and of a Ni(111) surface are shown below. *(Goodman and Houston 1987. Reprinted with permission from* Science. *Copyright 1987 by the American Association for the Advancement of Science.)*

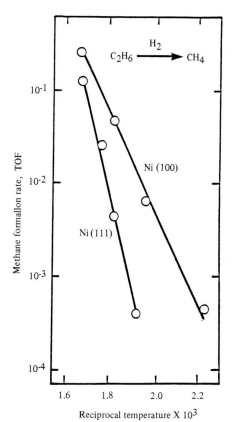

Figure 6.3 Arrhenius plots for: (i) methane formation rate (as a turnover frequency) from ethane over a Ni(100) catalyst. Total reactant pressure = 13 kPa, mol ratio of H_2 to C_2H_6 = 100; (ii) methane formation rate from ethane over a Ni(111) catalyst. Total reactant pressure = 13 kPa, mol ratio of H_2 to C_2H_6 = 100. *(Goodman and Houston 1987. Reprinted with permission from Science. Copyright 1987 by the American Association for the Advancement of Science.)*

The average fraction exposed is measured most directly by determining by selective chemisorption (Sec. 5.1.3) the number of surface atoms present and combining that information with a knowledge of the total amount of metal present. X-ray line broadening for determination of crystal size becomes too diffuse to be of much value below dimensions of about 5 nm (Sec. 5.5.5). Transmission electron microscopy may give direct measurements of particle sizes and is a useful method for comparison with results obtained by chemisorption. Some assumption concerning particle shape is necessary and a spherical or cubical shape is usually taken. However, where there is strong metal-support interaction, the metal may be spread out in the form of a layer or "raft" rather than in a compact three-dimensional form. The use of more than one method gives confidence in the reliability of conclusions. Methods of measurement are reviewed by Lemaitre et al. (1984).

Burton (1974) has shown that the structure of very small metal microclusters is different than that of macrocrystals, so that different types of surface faces are present. The lattice parameter is slightly smaller (about 3 percent less for a 1-nm particle), and the microclusters "melt" at temperatures that are low compared with those of bulk solids—typically at about one-half the normal melting point for a cluster of 55 atoms (about 1 nm). Very small particles show a dynamic fluid-like behaviour as observed directly in an electron microscope. This implies some type of "quasi-melting" of a particle in a hybrid state of solid and liquid.

Even if the same crystal habit were preserved in a tiny particle, it is evident that with particles approximately 2.5 nm or smaller, a substantial and increasingly larger fraction of the total atoms present will be on edges and corners. Hence, they will have lower coordination numbers than those in a crystal face. (For a regular octahedron of platinum atoms, the fraction of surface atoms that are on edges or corners is 0.64 for an edge length of 1.4 nm and 0.32 for an edge length of 2.8 nm. Thus it is reasonable to expect that structure-sensitive reactions would change their character as particle size is reduced in this range.)

Various theoretical calculations also provide a perspective on the foregoing. Applying molecular orbital theory to small clusters of metal atoms, one may consider how the electronic structure is predicted to vary as one proceeds from an isolated atom to a small cluster or group of atoms. Calculations show, for example, that a cluster of silver atoms approaches metal-like properties at a grouping of about 55 atoms. However, the values of such properties as the work function differ from those of the bulk metal and the cohesive energy density is only one-third that expected for bulk material (Baetzold, 1976). Ajayan and Marks (1988) apply free energy considerations resulting from various entropy contributions to predict stability ranges for various particle shapes as a function of size and temperature.

Measurements of the Curie temperature as a function of crystal size for nickel/silica show that this property varies with crystallite size over the range of about 1.0 to 10 nm. For crystallites larger than about 10 nm the magnetic properties are essentially the same as for bulk nickel (Sinfelt, 1972). (The *Curie temperature* is a transition temperature above which a ferromagnetic metal becomes paramagnetic.)

6.3 Alloy Catalysts

Studies of alloy catalysts were of considerable interest in the 1950s in conjunction with the then burgeoning electronic theories of catalysis, but then fell into disfavor. More recently they have been revived, stimulated by the industrial importance of bimetallic catalytic reforming catalysts and a more sophisticated fundamental understanding of the structure of alloys and the factors affecting the distribution of alloy components between the surface and the bulk. Of particular interest have been studies of a binary alloy of an active metal and of an essentially inert metal such as nickel-copper alloys, and, more generally, of a mixture of a group VIII metal and a group IB metal. Bimetallic catalysts are treated in detail in the monograph by Sinfelt (1983). Because of uncertainties concerning the actual structure of many "alloy catalysts," the term *bimetallic catalysts* is frequently used· instead.

6.3.1 Surface composition

The nature of the surface composition primarily determines the catalytic properties of an alloy, although there may be some long-range effects. The surface composition may be much different from that of the bulk. In nickel-copper alloys, copper is highly segregated at the surface, as shown by hydrogen chemisorption studies. Hydrogen is strongly adsorbed on nickel but not on copper. Copper is the dominant element on the surface even with copper-nickel alloys containing as little as 5 at. % copper (Sinfelt, 1975).

The surface composition of alloys can also be observed by Auger electron spectroscopy or *X-ray photoelectron spectroscopy* (XPS); but the observed electrons may escape from layers below the surface, in which event the results represent a weighted average of a layer a number of atoms deep (Sec. 5.5). Work function measurements are a good representation of the surface, as is chemisorption, but the alloy components must have substantially different work function or chemisorption characteristics for the measurements to be useful.

The degree of surface enrichment can also be a function of particle size for some alloys. Sinfelt has shown that some metallic alloy compositions (e.g., ruthenium and copper) can be obtained in the form of very small particles even when there is little miscibility of the two metals in the form of bulk alloys. The high fraction exposed in such compositions can be demonstrated by the absence of an X-ray diffraction pattern. Sinfelt uses the term *bimetallic cluster* to refer to a metallic entity containing atoms of two or more metals, highly dispersed on a support, the composition of which may or may not exist as an alloy in the bulk form. The structure of various bimetallic clusters can be inferred from probe reactions such as hydrogenolysis and dehydrogenation (Sec. 6.3.3 and Fig. 6.4) and by physical characterization using such methods as *extended X-ray absorption fine structure* (EXAFS) (Sinfelt 1983). Mössbauer spectroscopy can also be applied if one of the components is iron.

The surface composition of an alloy is determined by a number of

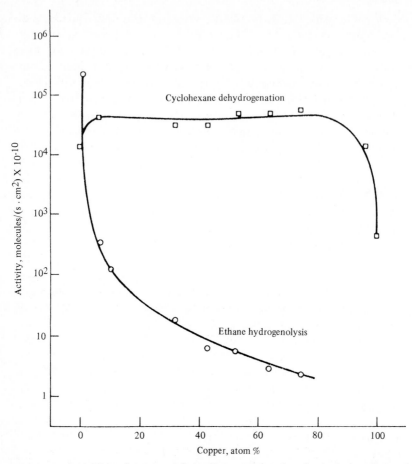

Figure 6.4 Activities of copper-nickel alloy catalysts for the hydrogenolysis of ethane to methane and the dehydrogenation of cyclohexane to benzene. Ethane hydrogenolysis activities were obtained at ethane and hydrogen pressures of 3 and 20 kPa, respectively. Cyclohexane dehydrogenation activities were obtained at cyclohexane and hydrogen pressures of 17 and 83 kPa, respectively. T = 316°C. *(Sinfelt et al. 1972. Reprinted with permission from the Journal of Catalysis. Copyright by Academic Press.)*

factors. These have been reviewed by Sachtler (1976), Sachtler and van Santen (1977), and Ponec (1975), who also discuss the effect of surface composition on selectivity. The latter is also reviewed by Clarke (1975). It is first necessary to ensure that the alloy is in its equilibrium composition, which for thin metal films requires heating for about an hour at a temperature of about $0.3\ T_m$ (the Hüttig temperature) or higher (see Sec. 4.5). (T_m is the melting point in absolute units.) If the alloy exhibits a miscibility gap, then over a particular composition range it appears that one phase—that having the lower surface energy—will envelop the other [the "cherry model" of Sachtler (1976) and Sachtler et al. (1977)].

The behavior of a catalytic reaction is determined by the composition of the outer layer and not by that of the interior (the "pit"). This kind of structure has been adduced by chemisorption studies and hydrogen isotope exchange for the system platinum-gold, which has a wide miscibility gap. As the quantity of the outer phase is lowered, the structure changes to one in which patches of the outer phase exist but do not surround the interior, and ultimately a single phase develops. Under the two-phase conditions, the surface and the interior of the outer phase may assume different compositions.

In one-phase alloys, or in the cherry model described in the foregoing, the surface tends to be enriched by the component with the lower surface energy (lower heat of sublimation), but the situation is complicated if gases in the environment can react with or be chemisorbed on the alloy. The component of the alloy with the greater affinity for the gas (e.g., higher heat of adsorption) tends to segregate at the surface. With group VIII-group IB alloys in the absence of a gas phase, the group IB metal has the lower heat of sublimation. It thus moves preferentially to the surface, as shown for example, by nickel-copper, nickel-gold, and palladium-silver. However, in the presence of oxygen, the surface of a nickel-gold system is enriched in nickel rather than gold because Ni becomes oxidized and Au does not. In the presence of carbon monoxide, the surface of palladium-silver becomes enriched with palladium instead of silver; CO is strongly adsorbed onto palladium.

Alternate oxidation and reduction of an alloy can cause separation into its components. In a platinum-rhodium alloy, Schmidt and Lee (1987) showed that this led to enriched rhodium on the surface. Platinum and rhodium are used in automobile catalysts where the expensive and scarce rhodium is active for NO_x removal, so this could be a beneficial effect, but in NH_3 oxidation it may be undesired.

6.3.2 Reactions on alloys

Some of the early work with alloy catalysts was based on the concept that an alloy might exhibit some type of averaged property of its components. More specifically, in the rigid-band electronic model of binary alloys it was assumed that a common band would be formed from the two constituents. At an alloy composition at which holes in the d band became filled, there might occur a sudden shift in catalytic properties since the adsorption characteristics of the alloy might change markedly at this point. This viewpoint is now clearly incorrect, at least for those systems most widely studied, such as nickel-copper, palladium-silver, and palladium-gold, and most probably for group VIII-group IB systems in general. This is shown by alloy spectra and a variety of reaction studies.

In these alloys the atoms do not lose their individuality, and it is more fruitful to consider the structure as a group of individual atoms, at least as a first approximation. With nickel-copper, for example, the activity is ascribed to the arrangement of nickel atoms only, and the copper is regarded as an inert diluent. This essentially geometrical concept may be modified to some extent, to consider that the nearest neighbors to a nickel atom may influence its adsorptive properties and hence catalytic behavior, i.e., there may be an electronic effect. Sachtler (1976, 1977) terms the first the *ensemble* effect and the second the *ligand* effect. In many cases it is difficult to separate the contributions of the two. The effects observed with alloy catalysts can be rationalized primarily in terms of ensemble (geometrical) effects, but it seems necessary to involve ligand effects to explain some of the changes observed in reactivity.

6.3.3 Site-number requirements (geometrical effects)

An underlying concept in catalysis for the last several decades is that some reactions require reactant adsorption on a group of sites or a "multiple site" in order to occur. Such a group of sites has been termed an *ensemble* by Kobozev and Dowden and a *multiplet* by Balandin, and the concept has been visualized and developed in a variety of ways by different investigators. In present-day terminology, these are termed *structure-sensitive* reactions. The significance is that this allows a rational approach to the tailoring of catalysts (primarily metallic catalysts) to achieve high selectivity when more than one reaction pathway may occur.

If geometrical considerations are the predominant effect, then dilution of an active metal with an inactive metal should decrease the rate of those reactions requiring the greatest number of nearby sites relative to the rate of a reaction requiring the least number of sites. That this indeed occurs has been shown notably in a series of studies by Sinfelt and coworkers (Sinfelt, 1974), and this approach has been applied in the design of industrial reforming catalysts and hydrogenation catalysts.

As an example, Fig. 6.4 shows the striking contrast between the effect of nickel-copper bulk alloy composition on the dehydrogenation of cyclohexane and on the hydrogenolysis of ethane, at 316°C. The catalyst was finely divided metal granules with surface areas of 1 to 2 m^2/g, prepared by coprecipitation of the metals as carbonates followed by calcination and reduction. As the copper concentration of the alloy is increased, the specific activity for cyclohexane dehydrogenation remains unchanged over a wide composition range, whereas that for ethane hydrogenolysis drops precipitously. (Copper moves preferentially to the surface in this system.) Other workers have likewise reported that addition of small amounts of copper to nickel greatly reduces the activity for paraffin hydrogenolysis. It is concluded that two or more adjacent nickel atoms must be required for this reaction, i.e., that it is structure-sensitive.

The dehydrogenation of cyclohexane to benzene, in contrast, is structure-insensitive and the site is probably a single nickel atom. The reasons for the decrease in rate of the latter reaction at the two extremes of the composition range are not certain, but it may be caused by a change in the rate-limiting step of the reaction. At the reaction temperature, the copper-nickel alloy system is completely miscible, but at lower temperatures a miscibility gap may occur.

Studies by Sinfelt with cyclohexane dehydrogenation on ruthenium-copper or osmium-copper at 316°C showed behavior similar to that on nickel-copper. Hydrogenolysis of cyclohexane decreased with increased copper content, but the effect was not as pronounced as that observed with hydrogenolysis of ethane.

A complicating, but significant, factor in these types of studies is that self-poisoning can occur by the accumulation of carbonaceous residues on the catalyst. This process, which is sometimes described as a polymerization of acetylenic residues or a total or deep hydrogenolysis of paraffins, plausibly involves a group of several sites. If so, it should be decreased by alloying. This appears indeed to be the case, at least for cyclohexane reactions on alloy systems. In some instances in which improved activity upon alloying has been attributed to the intrinsic properties of the alloy, the effect may have been caused, instead, primarily by a decrease in self-poisoning. This topic is addressed again in Sec. 9.5, "Catalytic Reforming," in which bimetallic catalysts are used industrially.

A number of reactions have been classified as to the number of adjacent sites that are required (Clarke, 1975). As noted in the foregoing, various reactions involving C—H bond breaking or formation seem to proceed on a single site. Those involving rupture of the carbon skeleton require two or more sites. Clarke discusses the possible mechanisms on alloys of a variety of hydrocarbon transformations such as dehydrocyclization and aromatization of paraffins, and hydrocracking.

Carbonaceous deposits may form preferentially at certain stepped regions or irregular portions of various metals such as nickel and platinum. Thus, the tendency for a catalyst to cause carbonaceous deposits may be diminished by pretreatment with a poison that is preferentially adsorbed on these types of sites. For example, a platinum catalyst may be pretreated with hydrogen sulfide to decrease its activity for hydrogenolysis (hydrocracking) and for excessive formation of carbonaceous deposits.

The formation of a small degree of carbonaceous residues may be desirable in some cases because this may cause a partial poisoning of a catalyst surface, thereby causing the preferential blocking of reactions requiring multiple sites. Thus a metal catalyst may be more selective when it is "dirty" than when it is clean. The silver catalyst used industrially for conversion of ethylene to ethylene oxide is partially poisoned with chloride to enhance its selectivity (Sec. 8.3). A number of cases have been reported in which an alloy of group VIII metals is more active than either metal by itself (Clarke 1975), but the effects are apparently not major.

Methods of preparation of alloy catalysts and reaction selectivities are outlined by Ponec (1975). A later review covers catalysis of hydrocarbon reactions by alloys (1983). Alloy catalysts and methods of characterization are also discussed by Sinfelt (1972) and Burton and Garten (1977). Some of the complications in working with alloy film catalysts are reviewed by Moss and Whalley (1972). In an earlier review Boudart (1969) analyzed information then available on structure-insensitive reactions. Structure sensitivity has also been reviewed by Cinneide and Clarke (1973). A detailed review by Moss (1981) covers aspects of the characterization and activity of supported metal and bimetallic catalysts with attention primarily to the period 1974–1980. A review by Jackson et al. (1981) discusses metal clusters and cluster catalysis. The combination of ruthenium-copper has received much study as a model bimetallic system. This is reviewed by Sinfelt (1988).

There has been little application of these geometrical or ensemble concepts to reactions on catalysts other than metals, largely because of difficulty in characterization. Magnetic methods have been applied to transition metal oxide catalysts to determine the state of dispersion, and the dispersion of chromia in chromia/alumina catalysts in particular has received considerable study. With partial oxidation reactions on oxide-type catalysts, high selectivity may be associated with a particular crystallographic phase and the degree of defects in this phase.

6.4   Sintering, Mobility, and Redispersion

To a first approximation, the rate of reaction on a metal catalyst is proportional to the total surface area effectively exposed to reactants. A nonsupported high-surface-area structure of a metal, such as may be made by compacting a metal powder, is seldom used in catalysis. The mobility of metal atoms over metal surfaces is very high, so such a compact sinters much more readily than if the individual metal particles are separated from one another by inert fine particles of a high-melting-point material, a so-called textural promoter (Sec. 4.6.1). Individual metal particles may also be spread out from one another on an inert support. Unsupported porous metals may show enhanced sintering in the presence of hydrogen, even at low temperatures. This is discussed in detail in a review by Paál (in Treacy et al., eds., 1988, p. 293). By use of a support, the fraction exposed can approach unity, much higher than that obtainable with nonsupported forms such as metal blacks or sponges. This is of particular importance with expensive materials such as the platinum-group metals.

The sintering of supported metal crystallites is a complicated phenomenon. It varies with the nature of the metal, the chemical nature and morphology of the support, and the nature of various gases that may be present, as well as temperature, pressure, and time. Several mechanisms may be involved simultaneously, such as the effect of the vapor phase, *strong metal-support interactions* (SMSI), wetting and spreading, and the effects of small amounts of impurities in the solid or the vapor. In addition, a combination of sintering and redispersion can occur. Particular attention has been devoted to platinum supported on alumina because of its technological importance. Such studies have been extended to other platinum group elements and other supports.

The principal methods of determining metal particle size distributions are chemisorption, *transmission electron microscopy* (TEM), and *X-ray diffraction* (XRD). Wanke et al. (1987) have critically reviewed these techniques and discuss their advantages and limitations. Determination of metal dispersion by H_2 and CO chemisorption is well established, but catalysts in which strong SMSI effects have occurred (Sec. 6.4.1), such as may be caused by high-temperature reduction, may show abnormally low hydrogen adsorption. [See a detailed review by Paál and Menon (1983).] With TEM, representative sampling may be a problem, but it provides a means of observing shapes and shape and size changes caused by various treatments. XRD line broadening (Sec. 5.5.5) can also be used. (See also Sec. 6.2, "Metal Dispersion.")

The various stages of sintering are shown in Fig. 6.5. Initially, the metal can be present in the form of separate atoms or in the form of a two-dimensional cluster one atom thick, in which case the fraction exposed is unity. (This is also sometimes termed a *raft* of atoms.) Generally the two-dimensional cluster is more stable than individual atoms, so individual atoms (or molecules) can surface-diffuse to form two-dimensional rafts. Larger two-dimensional clusters are more stable than smaller ones since edge atoms have a higher energy than

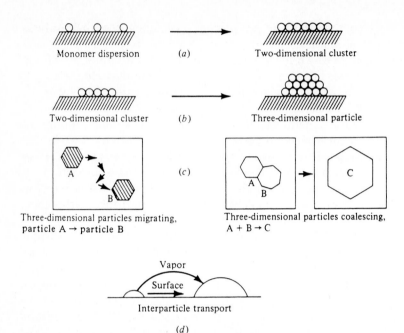

Figure 6.5 Schematic of the various stages in the formation and growth of particles from a monomer dispersion. *(Wynblatt and Gjostein 1974)*

those in the interior, so smaller two-dimensional clusters can grow to larger two-dimensional clusters by surface diffusion of atoms. This can be limited by the rate of detachment of atoms from a two-dimensional cluster or by the rate of surface diffusion.

Two-dimensional clusters can rearrange into three-dimensional particles, which will be the more stable form if metal-metal bond energies exceed metal-support energies. A larger three-dimensional particle (crystallite) is more stable than a smaller one, and growth may occur by either of two mechanisms. Atoms may detach from particle A and move to particle B, a mechanism that is sometimes termed *Ostwald ripening* by analogy to the growth of particles suspended in a gas or liquid by movement of individual atoms or molecules.

The second mechanism is the movement of individual crystallites along the surface to cause growth by coalescence, analogous to coagulation by Brownian motion, a mechanism proposed by Ruckenstein and Pulvermacher (1973) and developed by them in considerable detail. The rate-limiting process here can be that of particle migration or the process of coalescence, involving the growth of a neck between two particles and the gradual change in shape of the merged pairs into the lowest-energy configuration. For systems of interest in catalysis, the migration step rather than coalescence generally seems to be the rate-limiting process. The two mechanisms are not mutually exclusive.

The rates of these different processes are determined by a number of factors. Basically these are the values of metal-metal bond energies (and that of surface, edge, and corner atoms in contrast to those in bulk metal) relative to bond strength between metal and support. Dissociation of atoms from a crystallite occurs more readily if the atom-surface bonding is appreciable, but if this is too great, surface diffusion is slow. Some portion of the detached atoms must be mobile for surface diffusion-coalescence to occur. Individual metal atoms appear to be weakly bonded to ionic surfaces and are therefore highly mobile. The rate of detachment of metal atoms from a crystallite would seem to be slow except at very high temperatures, or unless some sort of species more strongly bonded with the surface is formed, or unless the metal is held in a reactive atmosphere.

The migration and collision of crystallites cannot be significant after the particles grow to a limiting size at which they become substantially immobile. For Pt/Al_2O_3, Wynblatt and Gjostein (1974) estimate that particle migration is rapid up to a particle radius of about 5 nm, but that particles larger than this must grow by some form of interparticle transport. This may be either surface diffusion of atoms or molecules, or vapor transport. Surface diffusion should be relatively rapid on smooth surfaces and if there is low interaction energy with the support, but supports of interest in catalysis are usually rough and often complex in composition. Hydrocarbon deposits increase adhesion, and the formation of surface compounds, e.g., a nickel aluminate, can affect surface properties. Atoms are more strongly adsorbed at various steps and dislocations on the substrate, so surface-diffusing metal atoms can nucleate and grow into crystallites at these locations, a process known as *decoration*.

In principle, whether Ostwald ripening or particle coalescence is the dominating mechanism may be determined by the change in particle size distribution with time and the effect of number of particles per unit area. The complex nature of real catalysts, however, introduces other effects that can readily overshadow prediction from this theoretical treatment. One of these is the pore structure (Wynblatt & Ahn 1975). Particles of metal dispersed into the finest pores so as to fill them, or to fill crevices within the pores, will be stabilized. This is analogous to the preferential filling of fine pores by condensation from a vapor, as predicted by the Kelvin equation (Sec. 5.3.1).

In general, stabilization should be increased with lower particle densities and with lower values of the surface diffusivity. A catalyst with a broad pore size distribution is also predicted to sinter more rapidly than one with a narrow pore-size distribution (Flynn & Wanke 1975). In an inert or reducing atmosphere, particle growth is predicted to be related inversely to the strength of the cohesive forces in a metal crystallite. For a given substrate, the stability of a number of metals of interest is found to increase in the following order. This is the same as the order of increased melting point, except for iron and palladium:

Ag < Cu < Au < Pd < Ni < Co < Pt < Rh < Ru < Ir < Os < Re

Alloying a metal with a second metal of higher melting point should also increase stability, but it may have other catalytic effects.

A useful method of correlation of sintering data is by a power-law rate function

$$\frac{-dD}{dt} = kD^n \qquad (6.3)$$

where D is the dispersion (percent exposed) and t is time. Data at different temperatures can be used to calculate an apparent activation energy for k, but this depends on the value of n used for correlation. The scatter of data makes the activation energy values reported subject to a large error.

Equation (6.3) can also be derived from some simple sintering models, but it should be regarded for most systems as an essentially empirical relationship. Wanke and Flynn cast a large number of experimental studies into this form. For several studies with Pt/Al_2O_3, they reported that higher initial dispersions generally gave higher values of n. However, values of n varied from 2 to as high as 16, and the values can also change as sintering progresses. The order in reducing atmospheres was larger than in oxygen. A high value of n means that the crystallites reached a stable size relatively quickly.

In the presence of an oxidizing atmosphere such as air, O_2, or Cl_2, the rate of sintering of metals may be markedly increased, by transport of metal oxide or oxychloride molecules through the vapor or along the surface. The vapor pressure of the platinum-group metals at most reaction temperatures of interest (up to 1000°C) is insufficient for transport of metal atoms to be a significant mechanism. In the earlier literature, an *increase* in dispersion of platinum on alumina was reported to occur in oxygen atmospheres in the temperature range of about 400 to 600°C under industrial conditions. This is highly desired for redispersion of deactivated catalysts such as reforming catalysts, and a number of procedures are listed in the patent literature.

It now appears, however, that redispersion does not occur in the presence of oxygen alone but only if small amounts of a chloride are also present in the support or the vapor phase. Traces of a chloride are invariably present in catalytic reforming because chloride compounds are deliberately added to control acidity of the alumina. During high-temperature treatment with a gas containing O_2 (< 650°C), complex chlorides or oxychlorides with platinum are formed and these become transported and adsorbed onto sites on the alumina. Upon subsequent reduction a more dispersed platinum is formed, but simultaneously some reagglomeration occurs. By proper control dispersion can be caused to outweigh agglomeration. Thus sintered platinum on alumina in the form of Pt or PtO_x particles can be converted to well-dispersed Pt.

The effect of the nature of the support on the ease of agglomeration should theoretically be related to the surface free energy of the support and Ruckenstein (1987) has developed a quantitative application of this idea. For some surfaces of interest, stability against sintering should decrease in the order:

$$MgO > Al_2O_3 > SiO_2 > TiO_2$$

Generally this order is found, but with various exceptions. The degree of reaction with the surface depends on the particular metal being supported and TiO_2 is the classic support on which SMSI effects have been reported.

Numerous reviews provide great detail on these effects. Ruckenstein (1987) reviews sintering and mobility with particular attention to quantitative theory. The role of wetting and spreading is also considered. See also a review by Ruckenstein and Sushumna (1988) which covers some of the same material, and an earlier review by Wanke et al. (1987) and by Ruckenstein and Dadyburjor (1983). Heating metal catalysts in hydrogen can bring about various permanent changes, as reviewed by Paál (1988) who also considers in detail the effect of hydrogen pressure on hydrocarbon reactions. In earlier literature the mechanisms whereby supported individual metal atoms and metal crystallites can grow are surveyed by Geus (1975). Mechanistic models are reviewed by Wanke and Flynn (1975) in conjunction with examination of a large number of sintering studies. Wynblatt and Gjostein (1974) analyze these models from a more theoretical point of view, with particular attention to the Pt/Al_2O_3 system.

6.4.1 Metal-support interactions (SMSI)

The nature of the support can affect the physical structure of a deposited metal and its chemical properties in a variety of ways. The possibility of electronic effects has been alluded to in Chap. 1. In the preparation of a supported catalyst, a surface compound is frequently first formed. The ease of its reduction can be markedly affected by the nature of the support, as illustrated by the reduction of nickel on alumina versus that on two types of silica (Sec. 4.2.4). The particle size distribution and particle shapes, as discussed in Sec. 6.4, can also be affected by the nature of the support as well as other treatments. A more specific category within this large and rather diffuse rubric is *strong metal-support interactions* (SMSI). This is a group of effects that have received considerable attention stemming in part from a series of studies at Exxon from about 1978 on, performed predominantly by Tauster and co-workers (Baker et al. 1986). Basically, group VIII metals supported on reducible oxides were found to show unusually low chemisorption of hydrogen and carbon monoxide. Attention was directed especially to noble metals on titania.

This led to a variety of catalytic reaction studies, especially reactions of CO and H_2 such as the Fischer-Tropsch synthesis and methanation, and also hydrogenolysis. A large number of adsorption and reaction studies have been reported by the Exxon group and many others, with various interpretations of the phenomena, many of them contradictory. Some of these center on postulated charge transfer between support and metal, others on alloying, still others on morphological effects such as particle size and shape and preferential exposure of a metal particle to a preferred crystal plane.

A large number of studies of metals on titania have led to a considerable consensus that some titania species migrate from the support onto the metal surface where they block sites, change crystal morphology, partially encapsulate platinum, perhaps cause electronic effects, and perhaps create new types of sites where the titania moiety and the metal meet. This overall concept has been termed the *decoration model*, and it has been extended to other oxide supports including "nonreducible" oxides. A recent book provides detailed reviews of the many ramifications of the subject, together with extensive references (Stevenson et al. 1987), as does the proceedings of a symposium (Baker et al. 1986), which includes a review by Tauster of current state of knowledge. An earlier detailed review was published by Bond and Burch (1982). Burch has also published a more recent review (1988), as have Haller and Resasco (1989).

6.4.2 Spillover

Hydrogen can adsorb with dissociation on a metal supported on an oxide and surface-diffuse, "spill over," to react at some distance from the metal. The migration may be along surface hydroxyls produced by dissociation of water, along a hydrocarbon-like surface phase, or along a carbon support. There is good evidence that the phenomenon occurs under a variety of circumstances. It can cause reduction of an oxide at a distance from a supported metal crystallite and may be a major mechanism in forming SMSI materials in which the support (e.g., titania) is reduced by hydrogen. This phenomenon may also be a significant mechanism in hydrogenation of an adsorbed hydrogen-deficient hydrocarbon and thereby reduce coke formation. The inverse effect may also occur. Dehydrogenation of a hydrocarbon may be accelerated by dissociation of hydrogen that migrates to a metal site where it recombines and is desorbed. In this mechanism the role of the metal is only to combine and desorb hydrogen; it is not involved in the initial step of the reaction. This is sometimes termed *reverse spillover* or the *porthole effect.*

Khoobiar brought attention to the phenomenon in 1964 by showing that WO_3 (yellow) could be reduced to H_xWO_3 (blue) with hydrogen at room temperature by mixing it mechanically with Pt/Al_2O_3 powder. In the absence of the Pt/Al_2O_3, temperatures above 500 K are required. Khoobiar (1987) reviews the phenomenon. Dowden (1980) gives a critical review of possible spillover mechanisms. Connor (1988) and Connor et al. (1986) summarize a large number of experiments in which results have been interpreted as possibly being caused by spillover. Bond (1983) gives a short history of the development of the concept. Hundreds of papers have been published on the subject and it is treated in a symposium volume (Pajonk et al. 1983). In some cases spillover seems to be invoked as a possible explanation for strange results, with little supporting evidence. Indeed Lilienthal (1989) has described the last symposium volume as a "wonderful collection of the bizarre."

6.4.3 Solution of metals as metal oxides

Even a noble metal element such as palladium may acquire a surface oxide when being used to hydrogenate substances containing oxygen, such as an organic hydroperoxide or a nitroaromatic compound. The oxide has a slight solubility in the liquid and hence can be transported away. In a fixed-bed reactor, palladium loss is greatest at the inlet and negligible at the outlet where reaction is complete. Indeed palladium may be deposited downstream by hydrogen reduction of the palladium dissolved upstream. A patent to Rhone-Poulenc (U.S.P. 3,694,511) applies a procedure for hydrogenation of cycloalkane hydroperoxides in a fixed-bed reactor in which direction of flow was reversed from time to time to minimize palladium loss and maintain high bed activity.

The loss of palladium in a slurry reactor is frequently ascribed to mechanical attrition, when the cause may instead be dissolution. In principle, higher hydrogen pressures may help overcome this effect, but this may be impractical. The effect does not seem to be significant with platinum but has been reported with base metals such as cobalt and copper. Solubility may be greater in strong-field liquids such as dimethyl formamide.

Mass-transfer limitations may also magnify this effect. For example, in a slurry hydrogenation reactor utilizing a finely divided palladium catalyst, a hydrogen mass-transfer limitation to the catalyst surface would lower the hydrogen concentration there. This then could cause increased disappearance of palladium by the foregoing mechanism. These effects have been quantitatively analyzed in some detail by Bird and Thompson (1980). Similarly, hydrogen mass transfer limitations within a porous catalyst pellet within which palladium is supported could cause selective removal of palladium from the core of the pellet.

6.5   Carbon Formation

Carbonaceous deposits (coke) can be formed on catalysts under a wide variety of conditions in a reducing environment. The factors involved on nonmetallic substances such as acid catalysts are substantially different from those with metals. On nonmetallic catalysts the deposit may contain considerable hydrogen, represented by an empirical formula CH_x in which x may vary between about 0.5 and 1. Carbon deposits on metals generally contain little or no hydrogen, depending in part on the reaction temperature. Many reactions can cause carbon deposits, but the process can be visualized in terms of the decomposition of CO ($2CO \rightarrow C + CO_2$), of CH_4 ($CH_4 \rightarrow C + 2H_2$), or of other gaseous reactions (e.g., $2H_2 + CO_2 \rightarrow C + 2H_2O$).

The thermodynamic equilibrium conditions under which solid carbon forms are well established. Storch et al. cover this in some detail in their classic book on Fischer-Tropsch synthesis (1951). Gruber (1975) gives a detailed treatment, as do Mills and Steffgen (1973). The analyses usually assume that carbon is present as graphite. A more active form of carbon, sometimes termed *Dent carbon*, may also be formed, especially at temperatures below about 700°C. Calculations made assuming graphitic carbon as the solid phase are conservative, in the sense that the composition zone for which graphite deposition is predicted to occur is broader than that for a more active carbon.

Even outside the composition-temperature zone in which solid carbon is thermodynamically stable, it may be present if the carbon-forming reactions are inherently faster than the carbon-removal reactions. This is a function of the nature of the reactants and of the catalyst. Thus carbon seems to deposit on iron more readily than on nickel. Carbon formation and its prevention is discussed in more detail with respect to steam reforming on a nickel catalyst in Sec. 10.1.

Carbon is often formed as filaments that grow out from the metal surface, termed *filamentous carbon*. The head of the growing filament contains a small crystal or particle of metal (or in some cases possibly a metal carbide) of about the same diameter as the filament, typically

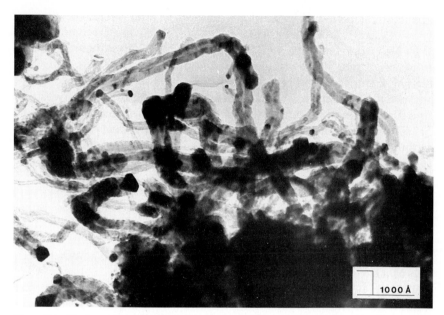

Figure 6.6 Carbon filaments formed by decomposition of methane at 500°C on a supported nickel reforming catalyst. *(Courtesy of J. Rostrup-Nielsen)*

less than about 0.5 μm. This may be seen in electron photomicrographs, such as Fig. 6.6. The metal particle at the head may disintegrate as the filament grows, and the filaments themselves may disintegrate, leaving behind a finely divided carbon containing some metal. This mechanism causes attack on the metal and disperses it through a mass of finely divided carbon, which thus may become catalytically active.

With time, the fibrous carbon structure may sinter and become more compact, whereupon it becomes less reactive; e.g., it is less easily removed by contact with steam, or the metal particle may become encapsulated by carbon. The effect has been observed on a variety of metals including iron, cobalt, nickel, and platinum, both in the form of massive metal and of supported crystallites, and with a variety of gases including carbon monoxide, methane, benzene, and acetylene.

The filament is formed by deposition of carbon on one side of the catalyst particle, followed by solution and diffusion of carbon through the particle and precipitation on the other side as a graphite-like structure. The rate-limiting step appears to be the diffusion of carbon through the particle, driven by a concentration gradient between the two sides, a temperature gradient, or perhaps both.

With iron, the effect was apparently first observed by Fischer in his early work on catalysts for the Fischer-Tropsch synthesis. It is described in some detail by Shultz et al. (1961), who refer to it as a new type of catalyst termed *carbon-expanded iron*. They report studies with a carbon steel-tube wall reactor "activated" by carbon deposition in which a quantity of carbon-expanded iron formed, having a high activity for the Fischer-Tropsch synthesis.

Carbon filament growth has since been studied by many investigators. Particularly noteworthy are a long series of reports by Baker and his coworkers, who have used electron microscopy under controlled atmosphere conditions to observe growth continuously and directly. In a review (Baker 1989) he summarizes their investigations to date and discusses proposed mechanisms, with extensive references to the literature. Bianchini and Lund (1989) discuss kinetic implications of various mechanisms, with substantial literature references. Baker and Chludzinski (1980) found that filamentous carbon growth on nickel-iron could be suppressed at temperatures below 620°C by treatment with various additives such as SiO_2, Al_2O_3, TiO_2, WO_3, Ta_2O_5 and MoO_3.

This phenomenon is a mechanism of attack on bulk metal and supported metal catalysts that can have serious consequences. Especially in a cyclic or erratic situation where carbon is alternately formed and reacted, a metal catalyst may deteriorate and the metal may be dispersed. Carbon can also be formed homogeneously in the gas phase and deposited physically onto a surface, in which case it would not be expected to contain metal.

6.6   Poisoning of Metal Catalysts

A catalyst may become deactivated for a variety of reasons (Sec. 1.3.9). In the case of metals, two of the important mechanisms are agglomeration (Sec. 4.6 and Sec. 6.4) and poisoning. The latter occurs whenever an impurity in the feed stream alters the surface composition of the metal. This may be by chemisorption; by reaction, in which the process is not confined to the surface; or by alloy formation. Obviously a large variety of possibilities exist. Some guidance comes from a general knowledge of chemical reactivities coupled with the ability to anticipate impurities likely to be introduced into the process, even in trace concentrations.

A poison that acts by chemisorption generally does so by being more strongly adsorbed than the reactant. The effect may be substantially reversible or irreversible, depending on the strength of adsorption and other factors, although many cases are intermediate. The rate of catalyst recovery after a poison has been eliminated from a feed stream may be conveniently formulated in terms of a rate of desorption.

Sulfur in a variety of chemically combined forms is a commonly encountered impurity. In the divalent form it is readily adsorbed onto metals. An adsorbed organosulfur compound may also be desorbed as hydrogen sulfide in the presence of hydrogen; i.e., the poisoned site may be freed by a hydrodesulfurization reaction. It may be helpful to think of chemisorbed poisons in terms of a possibly reversible reaction in which the poison reacts with the catalyst to form a surface compound. The surface metal layer is more reactive than the bulk, especially the surface of tiny particles and other highly disorganized surfaces. Thus a chemisorbed species such as a surface nickel sulfide can appear on metallic nickel at a partial pressure ratio P_{H_2S}/P_{H_2}, much less than that necessary for a bulk sulfide to form.

A chemisorbed poison may act by blocking an active site, which may be visualized as essentially a geometrical effect, or it may alter the adsorptivity of other species by an essentially electronic effect that may extend some distance from the chemisorbed species. If the chemisorbed material is beneficial, it may be termed a *promoter* instead of a *poison*. The situation can be confusing because an additive such as H_2S can act as an undesired poison in one situation and as a beneficial promoter in another [e.g., H_2S on nickel generally causes a drop in hydrogenation activity that may be undesired, but it may improve hydrogenation selectivity in a desired direction (see the following)].

The relative effects of poisons and promoters can sometimes be well interpreted in terms of their relative electronegativities. An interesting example is a comparison of poisoning of the methanation reaction on nickel crystallites by sulfur and phosphorus (Fig. 6.7) (Goodman and Houston 1987). Poisoning here is nonlinear with respect to coverage by adsorbed atoms (adatoms). The steep drop in activity at low sulfur coverages suggests that 10 or more nickel atoms are deactivated by one sulfur atom. With phosphorus at low coverages, each phosphorus atom inactivates only about four nearest neighbors. Since phosphorus is less electronegative than sulfur, this suggests that the poisoning here is an extended electronic effect.

Studies of this sort can be combined with surface techniques to indicate the extent of coverage of the surface by various adatoms and by carbon. An alkali element such as potassium is electropositive (it donates electrons to a metal). Consequently, it might be expected to cause effects opposite to that of sulfur. In many ways this is found to be the case. Adsorbed potassium increases the rate of CO dissociation on nickel (100), increases the carbon level, and increases the rate of formation of higher hydrocarbons. The same effect is seen on iron catalysts as used in Fischer-Tropsch synthesis. Addition of potassium up to an optimum level seems to increase the dissociation rate of CO and increases the average molecular weight of the products (Sec. 10.2).

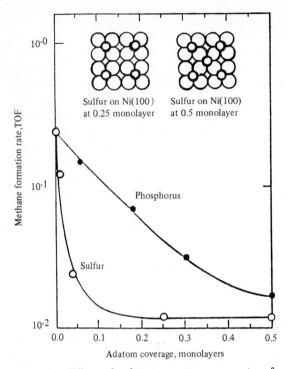

Figure 6.7 Effect of adatom coverage on rate of methanation (as a turnover frequency) over a sulfided or phosphided Ni(100) catalyst. Pressure = 16 kPa, mol ratio of H_2 to CO = 4. *(Goodman and Houston 1987. Reprinted with permission from Science. Copyright 1987 by the American Association for the Advancement of Science.)*

In NH_3 synthesis on an iron catalyst, potassium is added to enhance the rate of adsorption and dissociation of N_2. With nickel catalysts, some H_2S is sometimes provided. Nickel by itself is a very strong hydrogenation catalyst. Adsorption of H_2S weakens nickel-hydrogen bonds and allows more selective hydrogenation to take place. This principle is applied, e.g., in the removal of acetylenes from the product of thermal-cracking reactors designed primarily to make ethylene. With carefully controlled concentrations of H_2S, acetylenes can be selectively hydrogenated with minimum hydrogenation of ethylene.

The hydrogenation functionality of nickel can also be tempered by other additives such as CO or COS. If the undesired reactions are more structure-sensitive than the desired reactions, the nickel may be combined with copper. This type of catalyst may be used in treating the product from thermal cracking in which it is desirable to remove acetylenes selectively but to leave behind butadiene.

Other compounds that have an unshared pair of electrons, such as carbon monoxide, can also readily coordinate with metals to form a chemisorbed species. Carbon monoxide is of concern since the hydrogen supplied for hydrogenation is usually made from carbonaceous sources. Very low levels of carbon monoxide can have a marked poisoning effect.

For metals used as catalysts under reducing conditions (e.g., the iron catalyst used for ammonia synthesis), oxygen and water act as poisons by forming chemisorbed oxygen. Under oxidizing conditions, however, chemisorbed oxygen on metals may be required for catalytic activity, as in the silver-catalyzed oxidation of ethylene to ethylene oxide. Whether or not poisoning is reversible upon removal of the poison from the feed stream depends on the strength of the chemisorbed bond and other considerations. Even if the metallic form can be restored, catalytic activity may be diminished by the rearrangement of atoms or by the growth of crystallites, which reduces surface area.

Chloride is a commonly encountered impurity, e.g., from salt contamination or from chlorine in water. It may poison a metal by forming a surface metal chloride, or it may enhance sintering via the formation of volatile metal chlorides. Another source of poisoning is from other metals, or compounds reducible to metals under reaction conditions. These may alloy with the surface of the catalytically active metal and reduce its effectiveness. Arsenic is present in trace amounts in various feedstocks and can cause poisoning by this process. Iron is ubiquitous as a material of construction and can be a serious poison to platinum-group catalysts. Phosphorus compounds are typically serious poisons and may be introduced from additives to lubricating oils used in pumps, blowers, fans, and other machinery.

In a fixed-bed reactor, a poison, being generally strongly adsorbed, is usually deposited first on the upstream portions of the catalyst bed and on the outermost portion of the pellets. With time, the poison distributes itself progressively toward the centers of pellets and downstream in the bed. In the case of an exothermic reaction in a wall-cooled tubular reactor, the point of highest reaction rate corresponds to the maximum temperature along the tube (see, e.g., Chap. 11). This "hot spot" slowly spreads out and moves downstream with time.

Maintaining a fixed rate of production is usually desirable. Typically, the slow decrease in inherent activity is compensated for by gradually raising the reactor temperature. Operation is finally discontinued because of approaching failure of the catalyst, equipment limitations, an increasingly unacceptable selectivity, or other reasons.

6.7 Hydrogenation Reactions

A great variety of hydrogenation reactions are carried out industrially. These range from large-scale, continuous catalytic operations in petroleum refineries (Chap. 9), dealing with streams of complex composition, to small-scale batch operations in the pharmaceutical and fine chemical industry where a very precise hydrogenation step is often desired, starting with a relatively pure reactant. The most common catalyst is some form of nickel. Next is palladium, where its higher activity and/or selectivity more than compensates for its higher cost. Both these metals readily absorb hydrogen into the interstices between metal atoms. (Other metals such as iron, copper, and platinum are less adsorptive, which may explain their relatively lower catalytic hydrogenation activity.)

Hydrogen diffuses readily through palladium and, to a lesser extent, nickel. (A commercial process for separation of hydrogen from gaseous streams utilizes palladium membranes at an elevated temperature and pressure.) With palladium there is crystallographic and other evidence that, in contrast to what might be termed a solid solution, two specific hydride phases can be formed, a β phase at higher hydrogen partial pressures and an α phase at lower pressures. The two coexist under some circumstances. These two phases may have different catalytic properties.

A number of books treat catalytic hydrogenation as used for organic synthesis. See, e.g., Freifelder (1971, 1978) and Rylander (1967, 1973). A volume edited by Paál and Menon (1988) on hydrogen effects in catalysis contains 28 contributions, many of them very extensive.

Except for the fuels-processing industry, only a relatively small number of industrial hydrogenation operations are carried out on a substantial scale. A discussion of three of these follows.

6.7.1 Edible oils

Edible oils are triglycerides of fatty acids, primarily n-C_{18}, having various degrees of unsaturation. (Stearic acid is saturated; oleic acid has one C=C bond; linoleic, two C=C bonds; linolenic, three C=C bonds.) These oils are produced from a variety of natural sources throughout the world. Some of the major oils are extracted from soybeans, sunflower seeds, rapeseed, cottonseed, coconut, and palm. Oils containing highly unsaturated fatty acids are particularly susceptible to autoxidation, which affects their flavor. Consequently, it is desirable to partially hydrogenate them to improve their stability. The melting-point range is simultaneously increased. For most products, the desired softening characteristics correspond to oils that are only partially hydrogenated, so selective reaction is desired. During hydrogenation, cis-trans isomerization of the remaining double bonds and double-bond migration occur. Both of these isomerizations have an effect on the desired softening properties of the product. Growing health concerns about consumption of highly saturated fats and oils also affects the relative desirability of the various natural sources and optimum processing schemes.

The overall series of reactions is complex. This is in large part because of the varying nature of the raw materials, but also because different fatty acids in one triglyceride may behave independently. The reaction is carried out with carefully refined oils utilizing a finely divided and high-area (e.g., 50 to 100 m^2/g) nickel supported on silica and high-purity hydrogen, at temperatures in the range of 150 to 200°C and pressures of 0.1 to 0.7 MPa. All oils, even after prepurification, contain small amounts of sulfur compounds and other substances that poison the catalyst, so catalyst replacement is fairly frequent. Commercially, the nickel is frequently prereduced, stabilized in hydrogenated fat, and supplied for easy handling in the form of granules or flakes (sometimes termed *Rufert flakes*). Most processes are operated in batches in stirred autoclaves because of the variation in raw materials and desired product characteristics, but some continuous operations utilize several stirred tanks in series.

An unusual feature of the reaction is that for the desired selectivity it should be operated with a high degree of diffusional limitations with respect to hydrogen. This condition is achieved by an optimum combination of low pressure, moderate agitation, high temperature, and high catalyst loading. This results in a low concentration of dissolved hydrogen at the surface of the catalyst, which minimizes overhydrogenation. However, the reaction should *not* be pore-diffusion-limited with respect to the triglycerides, which would reduce the rate of transfer of partially hydrogenated products out of the catalyst particles. Consequently, very fine pores are undesirable. A packed column reactor utilizing larger pellets, as is sometimes proposed, would probably cause poor selectivity. Copper catalysts have also been used to a limited extent, but they are much less active than nickel, they are more sensitive to poisoning, and traces of copper in the product catalyze autoxidation reactions.

This subject has been extensively studied by Coenen over a three-decade period and is reviewed by him (Coenen 1986). In earlier papers Coenen reviewed the subject in general and Coenen et al. (1965) and van der Plank et al. (1972) discussed the mechanism of the reaction with particular emphasis on the effect of diffusion on selectivity. Grau et al. (1988) give an extensive review of catalysts, mechanisms, and reaction modeling.

6.7.2 Selective hydrogenation of unsaturated aliphatics

A variety of selective hydrogenation processes may be carried out on the effluent from the steam cracking of hydrocarbons. This process is usually designed to produce ethylene primarily, but, depending on the feedstock and operating conditions, various amounts of higher olefins, acetylenes, and butadiene are also formed. Depending on their relative concentrations, various combinations of physical separations and purification by selective hydrogenation are utilized for optimum marketability of the products.

In some cases acetylene may be economically recovered; in others, acetylenes and dienes (diolefins) may be removed by selective hydrogenation, leaving a purified olefin. The acetylenes and dienes are so much more strongly adsorbed than olefins that high selectivity with minimum hydrogenation of olefins is achievable down to very low acetylene concentrations. (Unless removed, diolefins readily polymerize to form gums and deposits.)

Steam cracking is carried out at substantially atmospheric pressure, but the product may then be compressed for fractionation, in which event hydrogenation is carried out at this pressure. Hydrogenation may be applied to a mixed product stream before fractionation or, more commonly, to individual streams after fractionation, e.g., to C_2, C_3, and C_4 streams from a naphtha cracker. In the case of a C_3 stream it is usually desired to remove acetylenes and propadiene from propylene. With a C_4 stream it may be desirable to remove acetylenic compounds selectively, leaving butadiene, which is then recovered.

If sulfur poisons are at a level below a few parts per million or if hydrogenation is to be carried out after fractionation, a supported palladium catalyst, e.g., about 0.5% Pd/Al_2O_3, is usually used. With a C_2 stream, typically the acetylene concentration can be reduced from an initial value in the region of 5000 to below 5 ppm with hydrogenation of no more than 1 percent of the ethylene, by operating at temperatures in the range of about 60 to 70°C. The acetylene is hydrogenated to ethane, not ethylene. On a palladium catalyst the selectivity of C_2H_2 hydrogenation relative to that of C_2H_4 can sometimes be improved by addition of a small amount of CO.

With a C_4 stream containing about 50% C_4H_6 and 50% C_4H_8 and 10,000–20,000 ppm of acetylenes (vinyl acetylene and ethyl acetylene) 80 to 90 percent of the acetylenes can be hydrogenated with loss of only 3 to 4 percent of the C_4H_6. Operating conditions are at about ambient temperature and 0.4 to 0.7 MPa, so the hydrocarbons are in the liquid phase, which helps keep the catalyst clean. In a similar process, methyl acetylene and allene ($H_2C{=}C{=}CH_2$) can be removed from propylene, and hydrogen treatment with a Pd/Al_2O_3 catalyst can be used in numerous ways on a variety of pyrolysis products from C_3 to gasoline (Krönig, 1970).

Potentially these reactions can run away, especially with high partial pressures of hydrogen and/or acetylenes, caused by a temperature increase that could initiate a self-accelerating exothermic hydrogenation of olefins. With ethane-propane feed, the hydrogen concentration in the product from the steam cracker may reach 30 mol %. With naphtha, a value in the range of 10 to 15 mol % is representative.

If acetylene is to be removed before substantial fractionation, a nickel catalyst is usually used, and a small amount of hydrogen sulfide or a mercaptan is added to the feed (e.g., ~1 ppm) to minimize hydrogenation of ethylene. This partial poisoning improves selectivity but lowers activity. Reaction temperatures in the neighborhood of 100 to 200°C and pressures up to 0.5 MPa are representative.

If butadiene is present and is to be recovered, the sulfur concentration can be adjusted to minimize hydrogenation of ethylene and butadiene. The sulfur reduces nickel-hydrogen bond strength and "tempers" catalytic activity by what appears to be primarily an electronic mechanism (Sec. 6.6). The palladium catalysts, being generally more active, can be used at lower temperatures, which may allow significant savings in energy.

6.7.3 Cyclohexane

About 90 percent of the cyclohexane produced is used to make adipic acid or caprolactam, intermediates to nylon 66 and nylon 6, respectively. In the United States, a relatively small amount of cyclohexane is extracted from natural gas condensate, but most is made by catalytic hydrogenation of benzene. A nickel, platinum, or palladium catalyst is generally used, in a continuous process. The benzene may be in either the vapor or liquid phase.

The temperatures and pressure depend on the catalyst used. The range of 150 to 200°C and a pressure of about 3 MPa have been quoted for a nickel/alumina catalyst and about 450°C and 30 MPa for a sulfided nickel or palladium catalyst. The reaction is highly exothermic.

$$C_6H_6 + 3H_2 \rightarrow C_6H_{12}$$

$$-\Delta H = 206 \text{ kJ/mol} \tag{6.4}$$

In one version of this process (Institut Français du Pétrole) 99+ percent conversion is obtained in the liquid phase in an autoclave reactor operated at about 200°C and autogenous pressure (2 to 3 MPa). The catalyst is finely divided Raney nickel (e.g., 50 μm average size). Product is vaporized overhead and passed through a vapor-phase fixed-bed reactor packed with Ni/Al_2O_3 for hydrogenation of remaining traces of benzene. The catalyst and process are described in more detail by Le Page et al. (1987). In another version of this process, the catalyst is formed in the autoclave by decomposing a suitable nickel compound in situ.

A commonly used procedure to control the temperature in a highly exothermic reaction carried out in a fixed-bed reactor is to cool and recycle some of the product to the inlet and mix it with fresh feed. This reduces the temperature rise down the reactor. This design is applied in a liquid-phase process for cyclohexane, in which several adiabatic beds are used in series. Cyclohexane can isomerize to form methylcyclopentane, and in these processes catalyst and reaction conditions are chosen to inhibit this reaction. Conversion is nearly 100 percent.

6.7.4 Solvent purification

Catalytic hydrogenation is used for a variety of solvent purification processes and to improve the quality of various other products. The process is sometimes termed *hydrofinishing* and may be applied to reduce aromatic or olefin content of a solvent, to remove traces of sulfur impurities, to improve color and odor, or to improve the quality of recycle streams within a plant. Nickel catalysts are commonly used for these applications. Sometimes significant deleterious hydrocracking may occur, which probably can be suppressed by addition of small amounts of copper, based on the concept of control of structure-sensitive reactions, or by proper choice of the support.

Some metal sulfides also possess catalytic activity for hydrogenation and dehydrogenation reactions. They may be more resistant than metallic catalysts to the formation of coke deposits. Thus under practical conditions a nickel sulfide catalyst may be more active than a metallic nickel catalyst for the hydrogenation of a hydrocarbon.

The catalytic activity of a metallic catalyst may be tempered by the controlled addition of a small concentration of hydrogen sulfide or other sulfur compound to the feedstock. This attenuates the initial high activity of a metallic catalyst such as nickel or platinum, which might otherwise cause rapid deactivation by coke formation via hydrogenolysis or other reactions. The long-term activity of the catalyst is thus stabilized at a higher level than it would be otherwise.

In the presence of hydrogen the degree of sulfiding is usually reversible. Aside from the effects of coke formation, sulfide catalysts (as a bulk or surface compound) are generally less active for hydrogenation than the most active metal catalysts. Hence they must usually be used at higher temperatures for practicable rates of reaction. (See also Sec. 9.8, "Molybdenum-Sulfide Catalysts.")

References

Aben, P. C., J. C. Platteeuw, and B. Southamer: *Rec. Trav. Chim.*, **89**, 449 (1970). From D. Luss in L. Lapidus and N. Amundson (eds.), *Chemical Reactor Theory*, Prentice-Hall, Englewood Cliffs, N.J., 1977, p. 213.

Ajayan, P. M. and L. D. Marks, in M. M. J. Treacy, J. M. Thomas, and J. M. White (eds.): *Microstructure and Properties of Catalysts*, Materials Research Society, Pittsburgh, Pa., 1988, p. 63.

Baetzold, R. C.: *Adv. Catal.*, **25**, 1 (1976).

Baker, R. T. K. and J. J. Chludzinski, Jr.: *J. Catal.*, **64**, 464 (1980).

Baker, R. T. K., S. J. Tauster, and J. A. Dumesic (eds.): *Strong Metal-Support Interactions, ACS Symposium Series, No. 298*, 1986.

Baker, R. T. K.: *Carbon*, **27**, 315 (1989).

Bianchini, E. C. and C. R. F. Lund: *J. Catal.*, **117**, 455 (1989).

Bird, A. J. and D. T. Thompson, in W. H. Jones, (ed.): *Catalysis in Organic Synthesis*, Academic, New York, 1980, p. 61.

Bond, G. C. and R. Burch: *Catalysis*, vol. 6, the Royal Society of Chemistry, London, 1982, p. 27.

Bond, G. C., in Pajonk, G. M., S. J. Teichner, and J. E. Germain (eds.): *Spillover of Adsorbed Species*, Elsevier, Amsterdam, 1983, p. 1.

Boudart, M.: *Adv. Catal.*, **20**, 153 (1969).

Burch, R., in Z. Paál and P. G. Menon (eds.): *Hydrogen Effects in Catalysis*, p. 347, Dekker, New York, 1988.

Burton, J. J.: *Catal. Rev.*, **9**, 209 (1974).

Burton, J. J. and R. L. Garten: *Advanced Materials in Catalysis*, Academic, New York, 1977, p. 33.

Cinneide, A. D. O. and J. K. A. Clarke: *Catal. Rev.*, **7**, 213 (1973).

Clarke, J. K. A.: *Chem. Rev.*, **75**, 291 (1975).

Coenen, J. W. E.: *Ind. Eng. Chem., Fundam.*, **25**, 43 (1986).

Coenen, J. W. E., H. Boerma, G. G. Linsen, and B. De Vries: *Proceedings of the Third International Congress on Catalysis*, North-Holland Publishing Company, Amsterdam, 1965, p. 1387.

Connor, W. C., in Z. Paál, and P. G. Menon (eds.): *Hydrogen Effects in Catalysis*, Dekker, New York, 1988, p. 311.

Connor, W. C., G. M. Pajonk, and S. J. Teichner: *Adv. Catal.*, **34**, 1 (1986).

Dowden, D. A.: *Catalysis*, vol. 2, The Chemical Society, London, 1978, Chap. 1, p. 1.

Dowden, D. A.: *Catalysis*, vol. 3, The Chemical Society, London, 1980, p. 136.

Flynn, P. C. and S. E. Wanke: *J. Catal.*, **37**, 432 (1975).

Foger, K., in J. R. Anderson and M. Boudart (eds.): *Catalysis: Science and Technology*, vol. 6, Springer, New York, 1984, p. 227.

Freifelder, M.: *Practical Catalytic Hydrogenation, Techniques and Applications*, Wiley, New York, 1971.

Geus, J. W., in G. C. Kucynski (ed.): *Sintering and Catalysis*, Plenum, New York, 1975, p. 29.

Goodman, D. W. and J. E. Houston: *Science*, **236**, April 24, 1987, p. 403.

Grau, R. J., A. E. Cassano, and M. A. Baltanás: *Cat. Rev.—Sci. Eng.*, **30**, 1 (1988).

Gruber, G.: *Adv. Chem. Ser.*, **146**, 31 (1975).

Haller, G. L. and D. E. Resasco: *Adv. Catal.*, **36**, 173 (1989).

Jackson, S. D., P. B. Wells, R. Whyman, and P. Worthington: *Catalysis*, vol. 4, Royal Society of Chemistry, London, 1981, p. 75.

Khoobiar, S., in A. B. Stiles (ed.): *Catalyst Supports and Supported Catalysts*, Butterworth, Sevenoaks, England, 1987, p. 201.

Krönig, W.: *Hydrocarbon Process.*, March 1970, p. 121.

Lemaitre, J. L., P. Govind Menon, and F. Delannay, in F. Delannay (ed.): *Characterization of Heterogeneous Catalysts*, Dekker, New York, 1984, p. 299.

Le Page, J.-F., et al.: *Applied Heterogeneous Catalysis*, Technip, Paris, 1987.

Lilienthal, D.: *Appl. Catal.*, **55**, N23 (1919).

Maire, G. L. C. and F. G. Garin, in J. R. Anderson and M. Boudart (eds.): *Catalysis: Science and Technology*, vol. 6, Springer, New York, 1984, p. 161.

Mills, G. A. and F. W. Steffgen: *Catal. Rev.*, **8**, 159 (1973).

Moss, R. L., *Catalysis*, vol. 4, Royal Society of Chemistry, London, 1981, p. 31.

Moss, R. L. and L. Whalley: *Adv. Catal.*, **22**, 115 (1972).

Paál, Z., in Z. Paál, and P. G. Menon (eds.): *Hydrogen Effects in Catalysis*, Dekker, New York, 1988.

Paál, Z. and P. G. Menon: *Catal. Rev.-Sci. Eng.*, **25**, 229 (1983).

Paál, Z. and P. G. Menon (eds.): *Hydrogen Effects in Catalysis*, Dekker, New York, 1988.

Pajonk, G. M., S. J. Teichner, and J. E. Germain (eds.): *Spillover of Adsorbed Species*, Elsevier, Amsterdam, 1983.

Ponec, V.: *Catal. Rev.-Sci. Eng.*, **11**, 41 (1975).

Ponec, V.: *Adv. Catal.*, **32**, 149 (1983).

Ruckenstein, E. and B. Pulvermacher: *AIChE J.*, **19**, 356 (1973); *J. Catal.*, **29**, 224 (1973).

Ruckenstein, E. and D. B. Dadyburjor: *Rev. Chem. Eng.*, **1**, 251 (1983).

Ruckenstein, E. and I. Sushumna, in Z. Paál and P. G. Menon (eds.): *Hydrogen Effects in Catalysis*, Dekker, New York, 1988, p. 259.

Ruckenstein, E., in S. A. Stevenson, J. A. Dumesic, R. T. K. Baker, and E. Ruckenstein (eds.): *Metal-Support Interactions in Catalysis, Sintering and Redispersion*, Van Nostrand Reinhold, New York, 1987. (The section by Ruckenstein comprises one-half of the volume.)

Rylander, P. N.: *Catalytic Hydrogenation over Platinum Metals*, Academic, New York, 1967.

Rylander, P. N.: *Organic Syntheses with Noble Metal Catalysts*, Academic, New York, 1973.

Sachtler, W. M. H.: *Catal. Rev.-Sci. Eng.*, **14**, 193 (1976).

Sachtler, W. M. H. and R. A. van Santen: *Adv. Catal.*, **26**, 69 (1977).

Schmidt, L. D., and C.-P. Lee, in E. E. Petersen and A. T. Bell (eds.): *Catalyst Deactivation*, Dekker, New York, 1987, p. 297.

Shultz, J. F., F. S. Karn, R. B. Anderson, and L. J. E. Hofer: *Fuel*, **40**, 181 (1961).

Sinfelt, J. H.: *Ann. Rev. Mater. Sci.*, **2**, 641 (1972).

Sinfelt, J. H.: *Catal. Rev.-Sci. Eng.*, **9**, 147 (1974).

Sinfelt, J. H.: *Prog. Solid State Chem.*, **10**, 55 (1975). [See also J. H. Sinfelt, *Adv. Catal.*, **23**, 91 (1973); *Catal. Rev.*, **3**, 175 (1969).]

Sinfelt, J. H.: *Bimetallic Catalysts*, Wiley, New York, 1983.

Sinfelt, J.: *Internat. Reviews in Phys. Chem.*, **7**, 281 (1988).

Sinfelt, J. H., J. L. Carter, and D. J. C. Yates: *J. Catal.*, **24**, 283 (1972).

Stevenson, S. A., J. A. Dumesic, R. T. K. Baker, and E. Ruckenstein (eds.): *Metal-Support Interactions in Catalysis, Sintering and Redispersion*, Van Nostrand Reinhold, New York, 1987.

Storch, H. H., Jr., N. Golumbic, and R. B. Anderson: *The Fischer-Tropsch and Related Syntheses*, Wiley, New York, 1951.

Treacy, M. M. J., J. M. Thomas, and J. M. White (eds.): *Microstructure and Properties of Catalysts*, Materials Research Society, Pittsburgh, Pa., 1988.

van der Plank, P., B. G. Linsen, and H. J. van den Berg: *Proceedings of the Fifth European/Second International Symposium on Chem. React. Engineering*, Elsevier, Amsterdam, 1972, p. B 6.

Vannice, M. A.: *J. Catal.*, **44**, 152 (1976).

Wanke, S. E., and P. C. Flynn: *Catal. Rev.-Sci. Eng.*, **12**, 93 (1975).

Wanke, S. E., J. A. Szymura, and T-T. Yu, in E. E. Petersen and A. T. Bell (eds.): *Catalyst Deactivation*, Dekker, New York, 1987, p. 65.

Wynblatt, P., and T. M. Ahn, in G. C. Kucynski (ed.): *Sintering and Catalysis*, Plenum, New York, 1975, p. 83.

Wynblatt, P. and N. A. Gjostein: *Prog. Solid State Chem.*, **9**, 21 (1974).

Chapter

7

Acid and Zeolite Catalysts

The concept that solid surfaces may be acidic arose from the observation that hydrocarbon reactions such as cracking that are catalyzed by acid-treated clays or silica-alumina, give rise to a much different product distribution than those obtained by thermal reaction. These solid-catalyzed reactions exhibit features similar to reactions catalyzed by mineral acids. Furthermore, it was shown that cracking catalysts could be titrated with a base and that they could be inactivated by adsorption of basic nitrogenous compounds or by inorganic basic ions.

By analogy to solution chemistry, the primary requirement for catalytic activity is postulated to be that the solid be acidic and be capable of forming carbocations by reaction with a hydrocarbon. These ions are intermediates in such reactions as cracking, polymerization, and isomerization. An acid site may be of the Brönsted type, in which it donates a proton to an unsaturated hydrocarbon, or of the Lewis type, in which it acts as an electron acceptor, removing a hydride ion from a hydrocarbon.

7.1 Source of Acidity

The structures that give rise to acidity and indeed to catalytic activity are subject to some controversy. In the case of silica-alumina or similar mixed-oxide catalysts, the source of acidity may be rationalized in terms of a theory developed largely by Linus Pauling. If an aluminum ion, which is trivalent, is substituted isomorphously for a silicon ion, which is quadrivalent, in a silica lattice comprising silica tetrahedra, the net negative charge must be stabilized by a nearby positive ion such as a proton. This positive ion can be produced by the dissociation of water, forming a hydroxyl group on the aluminum atom. The resulting structure, in which the aluminum and the silicon are both tetrahedrally coordinated, is a Brönsted acid.

If this structure is heated, water of constitution is driven off and

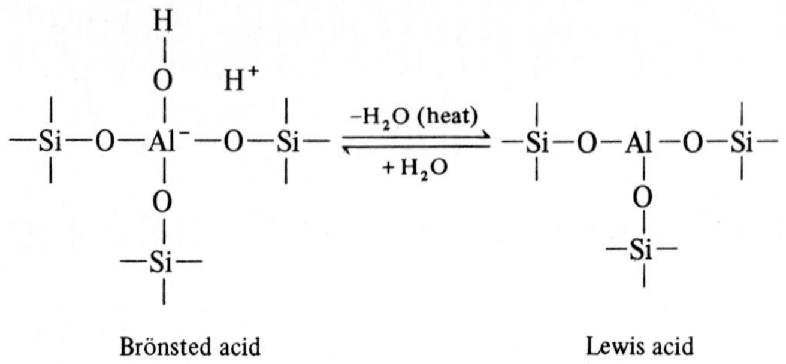

$$
\begin{array}{ccc}
\begin{array}{c}
H \\
| \\
O \quad\quad H^+ \\
| \quad\quad\quad | \\
-Si-O-Al^{-}-O-Si- \\
| \quad\quad | \quad\quad | \\
O \\
| \\
-Si- \\
|
\end{array}
&
\underset{+H_2O}{\overset{-H_2O\ (heat)}{\rightleftharpoons}}
&
\begin{array}{c}
\quad\quad | \quad\quad\quad | \\
-Si-O-Al-O-Si- \\
| \quad\quad | \quad\quad | \\
\quad\quad O \\
\quad\quad | \\
\quad\quad -Si- \\
\quad\quad |
\end{array}
\\
\text{Brönsted acid} & & \text{Lewis acid}
\end{array}
$$

Figure 7.1 Postulated structures of silica-alumina causing Brönsted and Lewis activity.

Brönsted acid sites are converted to Lewis acid sites as shown in Fig. 7.1. Some metal atoms are now three-coordinated and some four-coordinated. The reverse can also occur. The addition of water and heating can convert Lewis acid sites back to Brönsted acid sites. The aluminum atom is electrophilic and can react with hydrocarbons to form an adsorbed carbenium ion, as illustrated below for the two kinds of sites:

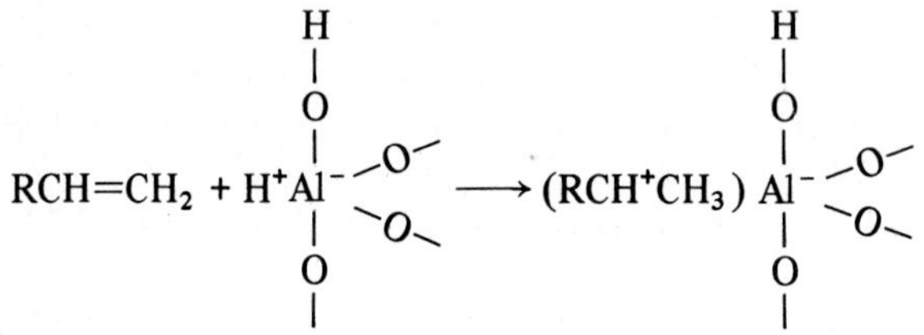

$$
RCH{=}CH_2 + H^+\!Al^{-}\!\!\begin{array}{c} \overset{|}{\underset{|}{O}} \\[-2pt] {}^{-}\!O^{-} \\ {}_{\searrow O \searrow} \end{array} \longrightarrow (RCH^+CH_3)\ Al^{-}\!\!\begin{array}{c} \overset{|}{\underset{|}{O}} \\[-2pt] {}^{-}\!O^{-} \\ {}_{\searrow O \searrow} \end{array} \tag{7.1}
$$

and

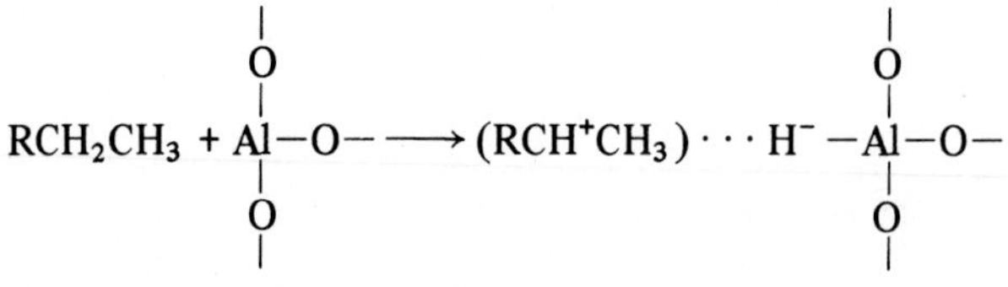

$$
RCH_2CH_3 + \overset{|}{\underset{|}{Al}}{-}O{-} \longrightarrow (RCH^+CH_3)\cdots H^{-}{-}\overset{|}{\underset{|}{Al}}{-}O{-} \tag{7.2}
$$

Similar arguments can be advanced to explain the acidity of various other mixed oxides containing metal atoms of different valence, such as $SiO_2{\cdot}MgO$, $SiO_2{\cdot}ZrO$, and $Al_2O_3{\cdot}MgO$. Even when the cations have the same valence, as in $Al_2O_3{\cdot}B_2O_3$, acidity may be observed, which can be rationalized in terms of differences in the electronegativities of the metals.

These mixed oxides typically terminate at the surface in the form of OH groups and structures in which oxygen is bridged between aluminum and silicon or between adjacent silicon atoms. A variety of configurations can exist, causing several types of Brönsted sites and Lewis sites. (The foregoing structures represent a formalism.) The focus of attention has been on Brönsted acidity because the specific process of transfer of protonic hydrogen is involved and correlations with Brönsted acidity have been more fruitful. Lewis sites are more difficult to identify and there is no unique scale to characterize them. The extent to which they may contribute to catalytic activity seems to vary greatly with the specific reaction involved. In general, Brönsted acidity appears to be of primary interest.

Silica-alumina, which is amorphous, typically has a maximum degree of acidity and activity at an Al/Si atomic ratio of less than unity. This finding can be rationalized by the concept that -Al-O-Si- type of bonds are desired but not the -Al-O-Al- type and that formation of the former is enhanced by an excess of silica in the starting composition.

Pure silica in a nonporous form such as quartz is essentially inert. Silica gel exhibits weak acidity and in some cases this may be caused by impurities. A pure alumina has acid-base characteristics (Sec. 7.6) that depend in part on the nature of heat treatments (Sec. 4.5.1) and resulting changes in structure (Sec. 7.4). Commercial aluminas are also often contaminated by foreign ions from the solutions used in their preparation. In particular, many aluminas contain small amounts of sodium that may be difficult to remove. For high-temperature stability, a very low-sodium alumina may be required. Catalysts supported on alumina may also have various impurities introduced into the alumina during catalyst preparation.

The acid strength of alumina may be deliberately increased by incorporation of halogen ions such as chloride or fluoride. The effect is to increase the acid strength, although not the total number of acid sites. Direct treatment with an aqueous mineral acid may cause partial solution or other undesirable alterations in the alumina structure. Hence the alumina may instead be contacted with an organohalogen compound in the vapor phase at an elevated temperature. This compound decomposes to provide the acid vapor in a dilute form, which is adsorbed onto the alumina.

Alternately, alumina might be impregnated with NH_4F, for example, and then calcined to incorporate up to several percent of fluoride into the structure. The halogen replaces a hydroxyl group and, having a higher electron affinity than a hydroxyl group, causes the residual hydrogen on the surface to be more acidic (Eq. 7.3). This transformation increases the activity for various acid-catalyzed reactions such as skeletal isomerization and cracking. The usual support for bifunctional reforming catalysts is alumina that has been mildly chlorided

to increase activity for skeletal isomerization (desired) without causing excessive cracking (generally undesired). Acidity is also controlled
by adjusting the partial pressure of water vapor (in the ppm range).

$$
\begin{array}{ccc}
\overset{\displaystyle H}{\underset{\displaystyle |}{}} & & \overset{\displaystyle H^+\searrow}{} \\
H^+\ \ O & & Cl \\
\diagdown\ | & & | \\
-O-Al^--O-\ \longrightarrow & & -O-Al^--O- \\
| & & | \\
O & & O \\
| & & |
\end{array}
\qquad (7.3)
$$

7.2 Determination of Acid Strength

7.2.1 Indicator methods

The acid strength of a solid may be determined by its ability to change
a neutral organic base, adsorbed on the solid, into its conjugate acid
form. This change may occur by transfer of a proton from a Brönsted
acid site to the adsorbed base, or by transfer of an electron pair from
the adsorbed molecule to a Lewis acid site, thus forming an acidic addition product. The acid strength can be expressed by the Hammett
acidity function H_0 as

$$
H_0 = pK_a + \log \frac{[B]}{[BH^+]} \qquad (7.4)
$$

or
$$
H_0 = pK_a + \log \frac{[B]}{[AB]} \qquad (7.5)
$$

where K_a is the equilibrium constant of dissociation of the acid and
$pK_a = -\log K_a$. [B] and [BH$^+$] are the concentrations of the neutral
base and of its conjugated acid, and [AB] is the concentration of the
addition product formed by adsorption of B onto a Lewis site.

Many compounds have a different color in the neutral base form
than in the conjugate acid form and are termed *color indicators*. If,
upon adsorption, such a compound assumes the color of its acid form,
at least some of the surface sites have an H_0 value less than or equal
to the pK_a value of the indicator. The lower the value of H_0, the more
acidic is the surface. Samples of a solid suspended in a ground form in
a nonaqueous, inert hydrocarbon liquid may be tested with a battery
of neutral basic indicators, each of which changes color at a different
pK_a value. This procedure gives an approximate value of the acid
strength, which typically can be measured over the range of about + 4

(very weak) to about -8 (very strong). In a formal sense, the H_0 value of a surface can be compared to an equivalent concentration of an aqueous H_2SO_4 solution, but this is not rigorous. Perhaps H_0 values (or H_R values—see the following) can be thought of best as relative quantities used to provide an acidity scale (Unger et al. 1981).

Following are some representative basic "Hammett" indicators with their pK_a value and the wt % H_2SO_4 in aqueous solution having the acid strength corresponding to the pK_a value: p-dimethylamino-azobenzene (butter yellow), $+3.3(3 \times 10^{-4}$ wt % $H_2SO_4)$; dicinnamal-acetone, $-3.0(48$ wt % $H_2SO_4)$; anthraquinone, $-8.2(90$ wt % $H_2SO_4)$ (Tanabe 1970). Other Hammett indicators are available with pK_a values as low as -16.04 (1,3,5 trinitrotoluene), but very few studies have been reported in which indicators with pK_a values lower than -8.2 have been used.

A measure of the *distribution* of acid strengths of the different sites on the catalyst may be achieved by titration with a strong base using a series of Hammett color indicators. The titrating base must be a stronger base than the indicator, and n-butylamine, $pK \sim +10$, is often used for this purpose. As the base is added it adsorbs on acid sites, the strongest ones first, and ultimately it displaces indicator molecules from the solid. When the indicator has been substantially replaced, the color changes. At this equivalence point the ratio [B]/[BH$^+$] approaches unity. If the pK_a value of the indicator is, for example, $+3.3$, then the amount of base added is equivalent to the amount of acid sites having $H_0 \leq +3.3$. By amine titration with indicators having different pK_a values, the amount of acid sites having strengths exceeding the various corresponding values of pK_a $(= H_0)$ may be determined.

There are several limitations to the method. Water must be rigorously excluded, since water itself can be readily adsorbed either physically or chemically and traces of water affect the titration method. The time required for equilibrium may be long, amounting sometimes to days. Some Hammett indicators are insufficiently adsorbed or the color change may be difficult to establish (Unger et al. 1981). Further, measurements are under conditions much different from those occurring during reaction. Also, this procedure assumes that equilibrium is attained at all times. Actually if one is dealing with a strong acid site and a strong basic amine, some amine molecules may remain more or less irreversibly attached to the first sites on which they become adsorbed or they may become adsorbed on nonacidic sites.

The method does not distinguish between Brönsted and Lewis acid sites and the two types of sites may respond in different ways to this procedure. Coordination with Lewis acid sites, for example, may be influenced by steric requirements. Nevertheless, the procedure is simple to use and it is an easy method of comparing relative acidities of a wide variety of solids.

Amine titration is of limited usefulness with zeolite catalysts. n-Butylamine can probably penetrate large pore zeolites such as zeolites X, Y, and β, but it is doubtful whether any indicator molecules can.

Another acidity function, H_R, can be developed using aryl methanol (aryl carbinol) indicators. These indicators are initially colorless and acquire color at a characteristic pK_a value. They react only with protons and, therefore, theoretically should respond only to Brönsted acidity. However, they have been much less widely used than the H_0 indicators. Equal H_R and H_0 values on the same solid do not reflect the same acid strength since they are derived from different reactions which are not well understood. Jacobs (1984) gives a table of aryl carbinol indicators that range from pK_a of $+9.36$ (very weak acidity) to -17.38 (strongest acidity).

7.2.2   Other physical methods

The amount of a gaseous base, such as ammonia or pyridine, adsorbed as a function of temperature is another, and generally superior, measure of acid strength. This technique has the advantage of allowing the study of a catalyst under conditions more nearly similar to those of reaction and can be used with zeolites. Typically, the saturated solid is gradually heated in a thermogravimetric balance and the decrease in weight with increased temperature is measured. The higher the temperature required for desorption, the stronger is the acidity of that portion of the acidic sites.

Figure 7.2 shows the amounts of each of three gaseous bases remaining on the surface of either $TiO_2 \cdot SiO_2$ (1:1 ratio) or 80% $SiO_2 \cdot$ 20% Al_2O_3 after heating to various temperatures. The amount of any one of the three bases remaining on the $TiO_2 \cdot SiO_2$ was greater than that on $SiO_2 \cdot Al_2O_3$ at all temperatures, indicating that the $TiO_2 \cdot SiO_2$ had both higher acid amount and higher acid strength than the $SiO_2 \cdot Al_2O_3$. ASTM D 4824-88 provides a standard test method for determination of catalyst acidity by ammonia chemisorption.

Infrared spectroscopic studies of species, such as ammonia or pyridine, adsorbed from the vapor phase are perhaps the most conclusive in distinguishing between Brönsted and Lewis sites, since the spectrum of, e.g., coordinately bonded pyridine is much different from that of the pyridinium ion formed by proton transfer from a Brönsted acid. See, e.g., a review of infrared spectroscopy in catalytic research by Peri (1984). However, the ratio of Lewis to Brönsted acid sites may

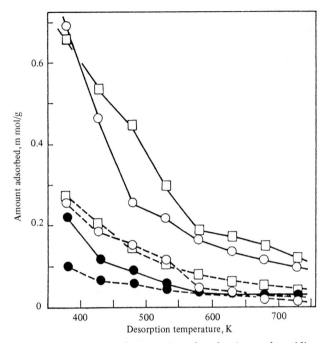

Figure 7.2 Amounts of ammonia, n-butylamine and pyridine remaining on catalyst surface after evacuating at various temperatures (—) $TiO_2 \cdot SiO_2$, (---) $SiO_2 \cdot Al_2O_3$, (□) ammonia, (○) n-butylamine, (●) pyridine. *(Tanabe 1981. Reprinted with permission from Springer-Verlag.)*

be far different under reaction conditions than those at which spectroscopic studies are made, especially if water vapor is present under one set of conditions but not the other. Acidity can also be measured by heat of adsorption of bases and temperature-programmed desorption of bases, but these methods seem to be of lesser utility.

Methods for characterizing acidity of solid catalysts and correlations of surface acidity and catalytic activity are described in reviews by Goldstein (1968), by Forni (1974), by Benesi and Winquist (1978), by Jacobs (1984), and in the book by Tanabe (1970) and Tanabe et al. (1989). A critical evaluation of color indicator methods has been published by Unger et al. (1981). Hashimoto et al. (1988) propose a method of distinguishing between Brönsted and Lewis acid sites by adsorption studies with 2-6 dimethylpyridine, postulated to poison only Brönsted acid sites, and NH_3, assumed to poison both types of sites. Acid site strength distribution was determined by color indicator methods.

7.2.3 Use of model reactions

The ultimate purpose of characterizing catalyst acidity is to correlate this parameter with reaction characteristics. Thus model ("probe") reactions should provide a better method of characterizing acid catalysts than base adsorption techniques. Guisnet (1985) has critically analyzed several possible reactions. Double-bond shift and cis-trans isomerization of olefins* (alkenes) are unsatisfactory for most acid catalysts since these reactions can occur by various mechanisms and on metals and bases in addition to acids. However, they may be useful for very weak acidic solids or acid-base substances such as alumina. Skeletal isomerization of olefins occurs on Brönsted acid sites, but not on metals or on bases; but, on highly acidic sites, a variety of secondary reactions and deactivation by coke create experimental difficulties, making skeletal isomerization an undesirable model reaction.

Cracking of cumene to form benzene and propylene is most widely used, but the cumene must be highly purified. Cumene hydroperoxide can be formed by autoxidation and the presence of as little as 0.05 percent cuts the cracking rate in half. This reaction is relatively clean, but secondary reactions can be significant under some circumstances. On weakly acidic catalysts such as alumina or an alkaline zeolite, considerable reaction can occur by a radical-type mechanism rather than an ionic mechanism. (See also Sec. 7.4.)

A number of acid-catalyzed model reactions have been studied for characterization of the pore structure of zeolites (Sec. 7.7.5). Their use in this application brings in many of the same questions of reaction mechanism that underlie the use of model reactions on nonzeolitic catalysts.

7.3 Acid Properties of Representative Solids

Table 7.1 gives the approximate range of acid strengths of a variety of solids. However, the acidic properties of most materials are substantially dependent on the method of preparation, temperature of dehydration, and possible treatment with steam.

Present-day cracking catalysts usually consist of several percent of an H-Y zeolite incorporated in a matrix consisting primarily of amor-

---

*The commonly used nomenclature in the petroleum and petrochemical industries for several classes of compounds differs from the IUPAC nomenclature. The industry nomenclature will generally be used here since that is the form usually found in the relevant literature. Some synonyms are as follows: paraffins (acyclic alkanes), olefins (alkenes), cycloalkanes (naphthenes), propylene (propene), butylenes (various butenes), cumene (isopropylbenzene).

TABLE 7.1   Approximate Acid Strength of Selected Solids

	H_0
Clays	
Original kaolinite	-3.0 to -5.6
Hydrogen kaolinite	-5.6 to -8.2
Original montmorillonite	$+1.5$ to -3.0
Hydrogen montmorillonite	-5.6 to -8.2
Oxides	
Silica-alumina	< -8.2
$Al_2O_3 \cdot B_2O_3$	< -8.2
Silica-magnesia	$+1.5$ to -3.0
ZnS heat treated (500°C)	$+6.8$ to $+3.3$
ZnO heat-treated (300°C)	$+6.8$ to $+3.3$
TiO_2 heat-treated (400°C)	$+6.8$ to $+1.5$
Mounted Acids	
1.0 mmol/g $H_3BO_3 \cdot SiO_2$	$+1.5$ to -3.0
1.0 mmol/g $H_3PO_4 \cdot SiO_2$	-5.6 to -8.2
1.0 mmol/g $H_2SO_4 \cdot SiO_2$	< -8.2
SbF_5/Al_2O_3	< -13.16
Phosphates	
Cr-phosphate	$+1.5$ to -8.2
Zr-phosphate	$+3.3$ to -3.0
NH_4-phosphate	$+1.5$ to -5.6

SOURCE: Tanabe (1970, p. 7); Jacobs (1984, p. 382).

phous silica-alumina and/or modified clays. Figure 7.3, obtained by amine titration with Hammett indicators, shows that Y zeolite has a high acid strength in the H^+ form. When exchanged with calcium or lanthanum, the amount of acidity is nearly the same, but acid strength, on average, is less.

Figure 7.4 shows the amount of acid exceeding various acid strengths for a pure alumina prepared from aluminum isopropoxide, as a function of calcination temperature. Two maxima in acidity are exhibited, at about 500°C and again at about 800°C. X-ray analysis indicated that, at 450 to 500°C, an η-alumina phase of low crystallinity was present, being converted to a highly crystalline η-alumina at 600°C. After calcination at 800°C a mixture of the η and θ phases existed, but at 1000°C the alumina was in the α form. The total amount of acidity present is comparable to that of silica-alumina and the same conclusion is reached by various other methods of characterizing alumina acidity, such as chemisorption of gaseous ammonia and of various organic bases. However, the acid strength is much lower, and the alumina does not seem to have any Brönsted-type acid sites, regardless of the calcination temperature.

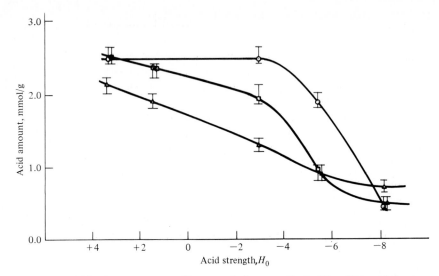

Figure 7.3 Acid amount versus acid strength for a synthetic Y zeolite, and for two cation-exchanged catalysts: the synthetic Y zeolite (H^+) ($\circ$), calcium cation-exchanged [Ca(II)($\square$)], and lanthanum cation-exchanged [La(III)($\triangle$)]. *(Ukihashi et al. in Tanabe 1970, p. 75)*

In contrast to the pure alumina characterized in Fig. 7.4, a particular commercial alumina calcined at 500°C showed an acidity of 0.287 mmol/g for $H_0 \leq +1.5$ but no acidity of strength $H_0 \leq -5.6$ (Tanabe 1970, p. 46). These and related observations showing considerable variations between the acidic properties of different aluminas, even after calcination to the same temperature, are of considerable importance in view of the widespread use of alumina as a catalyst support.

Ordinary metal sulfates or metal phosphates have no intrinsic acidity, but they acquire moderate acid strength and catalytic activity after heat treatment. With nickel sulfate, a maximum of acidity and catalytic acidity is obtained by calcination at about 375°C. The development of acidity is associated with the gradual removal of water of constitution, and maximum acidity occurs at about 0.5 mol H_2O/mol $NiSO_4$. This is an intrinsic property and is not caused by impurities. Metal sulfates are of theoretical interest in that a wide range of acid amounts and acid strengths can be obtained. Catalysis by these substances is reviewed by Takeshita et al. (1974). Acid concentrations are comparable (on an area basis) to those of other solid acidic catalysts, but the strengths are moderate relative to such acids as silica-alumina.

Superacid solid catalysts can be prepared by introducing sulfur oxides onto solids such as ZrO_2, TiO_2, Fe_2O_3, etc., and they show very high catalytic activity for a variety of reactions (Tanabe & Yamaguchi 1988). The acid strengths of $SO_4^{2-} \cdot TiO_2$ and $SO_4^{2-} \cdot ZrO_2$ as measured by the in-

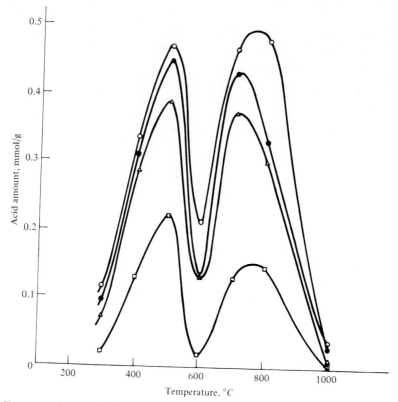

Figure 7.4 Amount of acid on Al_2O_3 at various acid strengths versus calcination temperature: acid strength $H_0 \leq 3.3$ (○), $H_0 \leq 1.5$ (●), $H_0 \leq -3.0$ (△), and $H_0 \leq -5.6$ (□). X-ray analysis: 450–500°C, η-Al_2O_3 (low crystallinity); 600°C, η-Al_2O_3 (high crystallinity); 800°C, η-Al_2O_3 + θ-Al_2O_3; 1000°C, α-Al_2O_3. *(Ito et al. in Tanabe 1970, p. 46)*

dicator method are $H_0 = -14$ and -16, respectively. As would be expected, these catalysts as such deactivate rapidly by coke formation, but this can be minimized by incorporating platinum onto the catalyst and operating in an atmosphere of H_2. A number of homogeneous superacids are known, such as antimony pentafluoride, and these can be supported on inert carriers, as discussed in the following.

Solid metal phosphates may be used to catalyze the polymerization of olefins to low-molecular-weight polymers, and they exhibit acidity comparable to that of the metal sulfates. Zinc oxide and titanium oxide exhibit only weak acidic properties, but, if prepared from the chlorides, they may exhibit fairly high acid strength, again depending on calcination conditions. Compounds such as Cr_2O_3, MoO_3, and ZnS also exhibit some acidity.

Mineral acids may be *mounted*—i.e., supported—on inert substances such as diatomaceous earth or silica gel. The order of acid strength is $H_2SO_4 > H_3PO_4 > H_3BO_3$. Mounted phosphoric acid is used to catalyze the polymerization of olefins to low-molecular-weight products, as in the conversion of a refinery stream containing C_3 and C_4 olefins to a gasoline fraction, so-called *polymer gasoline*. The process has been used since the 1930s and typically operates at about 200 to 230°C and a pressure of about 3 to 7 MPa using an acid strength of 100 to 115 percent (H_3PO_4 plus some dissolved P_2O_5, which is a viscous liquid under these conditions).* This catalyst may also be used for olefin hydration. The properties of the catalyst are markedly affected by concentration, and water may be added to the feed to maintain the acid concentration at the desired level. The process is reviewed by McMahon et al. (1963), Schaad (1955), and Villadsen and Livbjerg (1978).

7.4 Correlations between Acidity and Catalytic Activity

A variety of correlations of catalytic activity and sites of a certain range of acidity have been published. A widely used method of developing such correlations is based on the observation that the gradual poisoning of an acid catalyst, either deliberate or inadvertent, makes it inactive first for those reactions requiring the highest acid strengths, and then progressively inactive for those requiring weaker acid strengths. A typical procedure is to adsorb increasing amounts of a base such as pyridine or an alkali onto the catalyst and to correlate the extent of catalyst poisoning with catalyst activity for each of several reactions. A reaction thus eliminated is identified with the acid strengths eliminated.

Studies by Misano et al. (Tanabe 1970, p. 121) on silica-alumina poisoned by increasing amounts of pyridine showed the following list of reactions in order of increased acid strength required.

1. Dehydration of *tert*-butanol to butenes

2. Depolymerization of di-isobutylene to butenes

3. Double-bond migration and cis-trans isomerization of *n*-butenes

4. Dealkylation of *tert*-butylbenzene (cracking)

5. Skeletal isomerization of isobutylene to *n*-butenes

---

*The extent to which an acid strength exceeds 100 percent is related to the amount of water that would need to be added to form 100% H_3PO_4.

TABLE 7.2   Minimum Values of H_R Required for Selected Reactions

H_R Required	
< +4	Dehydration of alcohols
< +0.82	Cis-trans isomerization of olefins
< -6.63	Double-bond migration
	Alkylation of aromatics
	Isomerization of alkylaromatics
	Transalkylation of alkylaromatics
< -11.5	Cracking of alkylaromatics
< -11.63	Skeletal isomerization
< -16.0	Cracking of paraffins

SOURCE: Jacobs (1984).

A similar listing by Jacobs (1984) gives the minimum H_R (not H_0) values required for a variety of reactions. The list in Table 7.2 includes some additional reactions studied previously (Jacobs 1977) and data of Damon et al. (1977). The order is much the same as that of Misano et al. (Tanabe 1970). Bourdillon et al. (1990) characterized the acid strength distribution of an acid zeolite (HY) by preadsorbing pyridine on the zeolite and observing the reduction in reaction rate for each of a number of hydrocarbon reactions as a function of the temperature to which the catalyst had been heated to cause partial desorption of the pyridine.

One consequence of the foregoing effect is that, as a catalyst ages by gradual accumulation of coke deposits and poisons, the reactions requiring the highest acidity disappear first. Disproportionation (transalkylation) reactions, as of toluene to benzene and xylene, require highly acidic sites. If dimethylnaphthalene is passed over a particular acidic catalyst, considerable disproportionation occurs initially. This gradually decreases and the reaction becomes predominately isomerization, after which the entire activity dies down.

Other generalizations may be developed, based in part on the relative stability of various carbenium ions as determined from studies with mineral or liquid-phase Lewis acids. In an homologous series, reactivity increases with molecular size. Thus in the paraffin series, keeping acid strength and reaction conditions constant, with n-butane one may observe only isomerization; with n-hexane other products in addition to isomers start to appear; and with n-heptane significant cracking occurs. These and other studies show that these effects are primarily associated with acid strength rather than with surface structure.

Dealumination of certain zeolites by HCl treatment or steaming of zeolites such as Y predominantly decreases the highly acidic sites, which reduces coke formation. This treatment may not affect cracking activity until sites of a lesser acidity are reached.

Tanabe (1970) and Tanabe et al. (1989) give a more detailed discussion of correlations between acid-base properties and catalyst activity and selectivity. The early silica-alumina cracking catalysts are discussed in reviews by Oblad et al. (1951) and by Ryland et al. (1960). More recently Barthomeuf (1985) reviewed relationships between catalytic activity and various catalyst properties. Dwyer and O'Malley (1988) treat the subject from a more theoretical perspective. Dwyer (1988) evaluated Brönsted acid concepts with respect to zeolites. Reactions of hydrocarbons on bases and acid-base substances are discussed in Sec. 7.6.

7.5 Mechanism of Catalytic Cracking

The reactions occurring in catalytic cracking under industrial conditions are highly complex. A wide variety of hydrocarbons are present in the feedstock and many of the primary products undergo secondary reactions. The reaction pattern can be understood in broad outline by following suggestions by Whitmore for methods of interpreting certain hydrocarbon reactions in mineral acid solution. The theory as applied to catalytic cracking was developed by many investigators, including Greensfelder et al. (1949), Thomas (1949), and Hansford (1952). Early reviews were given by Oblad et al. (1951) and by Emmett (1965, p. 89).

The reactive intermediates are carbenium ions that can be formed in several ways. One of the simplest is via abstraction by an olefin of a proton from a Brönsted acid.

$$H_2C{=}CHR + H^+ \rightarrow CH_3CH^+R \qquad (7.6)$$

This ion can undergo a variety of reactions, including the reverse process to cause double-bond shift, as well as skeletal isomerization, cracking, and hydrogen exchange. The observed product distribution indicates that a large carbenium ion undergoes fission (cracking) at the β position, e.g.,

$$CH_3CH^+CH_2CH_2(CH_2)_nCH_3 \rightarrow CH_3CH{=}CH_2 + CH_2{}^+(CH_2)_nCH_3 \qquad (7.7)$$

The relative stability of the carbenium ions decreases in the order tert > sec > primary > ethyl > methyl. The smaller carbenium ion formed by reaction (7.7) undergoes rapid isomerization to a more stable structure. Thus various feed isomers give essentially the same product. By this mechanism no C_1 or C_2 products should appear from a paraffin reactant, and no olefin smaller than propylene can form, in general accord with the facts.

From an alkane, a carbonium ion* can be formed by proton transfer from a Brönsted acid site and subsequently undergo β-scission to form an alkane and a smaller carbenium ion, e.g.,

$$\Lambda\!\Lambda\!\Lambda \xrightarrow{\ B\ } \underset{H^+}{\Lambda\!\Lambda\!\Lambda} \longrightarrow \Lambda \;+\; \left[\Lambda\!\Lambda\right]^{+} \qquad (7.8)$$

On a Lewis site, transfer of a proton from an alkane can form a carbenium ion that then undergoes β-scission as in the foregoing, e.g.,

$$\Lambda\!\Lambda\!\Lambda \xrightarrow{\ L\ } HL \;+\; \left[\Lambda\!\Lambda\!\Lambda\right]^{+} \qquad (7.9)$$

Paraffins crack much more slowly than olefins, and the dominant path for formation of the original carbenium ion is still debatable. For a pure paraffin, the proton transfer would be the rate-limiting step if the foregoing sequence were the actual mechanism. However, in most industrial feedstocks some olefin is present, so simple protonation [Eq. (7.6)] could initiate the chain reaction, or some olefin could be formed by thermal cracking. Alternately, a slight degree of dehydrogenation of a paraffin to an olefin could be the initiating step.

Reactions subsequent to the initial cracking are also significant. Double-bond isomerization of olefins occurs so rapidly that the products are in chemical equilibrium with respect to this reaction. Hydride transfer (hydrogen exchange) may be quite rapid, and this is the principle mechanism whereby the reaction starting with a paraffin is propagated. The process can continue until all hydrocarbons formed are about C_6 or less. Hydrogen transfer is exemplified by a reaction such as

$$C_6H_{14} + C_3H_7^{\,+} \rightarrow C_6H_{13}^{\,+} + C_3H_8 \qquad (7.10)$$

---

*In more recent literature the term *carbonium ion* is reserved for a penta-coordinated structure, by analogy to "superacids" in homogeneous catalysis. What were usually termed *carbonium ions* in earlier literature are now termed *carbenium ions*, by an IUPAC decision in 1974. Strictly, a *carbenium ion* is defined as a cation in which the charged atom is carbon.

Hydrogen exchange can lead to a variety of coreaction effects. For example, in reaction (7.10) a carbenium ion of the original reactant (hexane) is formed, and simultaneously a smaller carbon skeleton can be stabilized from further cracking. Hydrogen transfer is especially rapid to tertiary olefins, converting them to the corresponding isoparaffins. Thus the ratio of isoparaffins to n-paraffins in the product from industrial catalytic cracking may exceed that calculated for thermodynamic equilibrium at the reaction temperature. The catalytic cracking mechanism overall consists of various combinations of protonation, β-scission, isomerization, hydrogen transfer, etc., and deprotonation.

Aromatics may also be formed by dimerization of olefins and cyclization of diolefins. Adsorbed aromatics and the products of polymerization and condensation reactions of olefins are the principal precursors of coke.

Haag and coworkers (1981, 1984) have identified another cracking mechanism characterized by a different distribution of products, significant formation of hydrogen, and absence of isomerization. This mechanism is postulated to occur particularly when reactants are highly constrained by a pore structure, as in a zeolite, such that a monomolecular mechanism is favored. This proceeds by a penta-coordinated carbonium ion intermediate. (See also "The constraint index," Sec. 7.7.5.) At relatively high temperatures free-radical mechanisms can also become important, and they can also be initiated on the surfaces of nonacidic zeolites such as zeolite KL.

Some reactions that are thermodynamically possible do not occur to a significant extent in the classical catalytic cracking mechanism. These include dehydrogenation of paraffins to olefins, dehydrogenation of naphthenes to aromatics, dehydrocyclization of paraffins to ring compounds, isomerization of saturated hydrocarbons (paraffins or naphthenes), decomposition of hydrocarbons to carbon and hydrogen or to methane. Essentially no dihydrogen (H_2) is formed.

Industrially, the feedstock to a catalytic-cracking reactor may consist of a mixture of paraffins, naphthenes, aromatics with alkyl side chains, and more complex molecules. Recycled feed streams may contain considerable olefins and a higher aromatic content. For hydrocarbons of the same carbon number, the order of decreasing reactivity is about as follows on silica-alumina and REXH catalysts (zeolite X exchanged with rare earths and in the hydrogen form) (Sec. 7.7.7):

1. Olefins

2. Alkylbenzenes with C_3 or larger-sized groups (Side groups are removed to form benzene and corresponding olefins.)

3. Naphthenes (rupture of ring and rather complex products)

4. Polymethyl aromatics

5. Paraffins

6. Unsubstituted aromatics (These compounds are highly stable and little or no cracking occurs.)

Catalytic cracking as an industrial process is discussed in Sec. 9.4.

7.6 Base and Acid-Base Catalysts

The strength and amount of basic sites on the surface of a catalyst can be measured by titration with benzoic acid using color indicators in a manner analogous to that used with an amine for acid catalysts, except that a different battery of color indicators is used. Adsorption of a gaseous acid can also be used, in a manner analogous to the gaseous base adsorption method used with acidic catalysts. Examples are use of carbon dioxide, nitric oxide, and possibly phenol. Many solids have acid-base properties varying from surface structures containing strong basic sites plus weak acidic sites to those with strong acidic sites plus weak basic sites. Even when a reaction is predominantly characterized by an acid site, a basic site may act by a concerted mechanism with it in a form of acid-base bifunctional catalysis. Tanabe et al. (1989) have developed a titration method of characterizing the acid-base strength distribution of a solid utilizing a common H_0 scale. This results in the term $H_{0,max}$, which is treated as a practical parameter to characterize the acid-base property. A solid with a large positive value of $H_{0,max}$ has strong basic sites and weak acidic sites. A solid with a negative value of $H_{0, max}$ has the opposite.

The basicity of a catalyst can also be characterized by the inverse ration of the rate of propylene formation r_p to that of acetone r_a in the reaction of isopropyl alcohol. Catalyst acidity is taken to be proportional to the dehydration rate to propylene. Dehydrogenation to acetone is assumed to be proportional to the product of the concentration of acid and basic sites, i.e., to proceed by a concerted mechanism. Basicity is thus taken to be proportional to r_a/r_p. This method is of interest for characterization of some complex oxidation catalysts in which product selectivity may be correlated with acid-base characteristics and which have such low surface areas that adsorption measurements are imprecise.

Alkali oxides and alkaline earth oxides exhibit strong basicity. The degree of basicity of the latter depends on such variables as temperature and method of calcination, presence of water, etc., as well as whether characterization is by a test reaction in contrast to adsorption studies. Various composite oxides and more complex structures may be of interest as base catalysts. Examples are calcium aluminate, and alkali-oxides incorporated into zeolites. Tanabe (1985) cites a number of binary metal oxides as having both basic and acidic properties: $Al_2O_3 \cdot MgO$, $MgO \cdot TiO_2$, $TiO_2 \cdot ZrO_2$, $Al_2O_3 \cdot ZnO$, and $ZrO_2 \cdot SnO_2$.

Cationic zeolites may also show acid-base characteristics. Barthomeuf (1984), drawing on her own studies and those of previous workers, states that the specific activity of basic sites in several zeolites increases in the order $Li < Na < K < Rb < Cs$.

Relatively little work has been done on reactions catalyzed by solid bases. The most effective catalysts are the alkali metals as such, notably sodium, potassium, and cesium. These catalysts are discussed in a book by Pines and Stalick (1977) and in a chapter on base-catalyzed reactions in a later book by Pines (1981). The aldol condensation of acetone to diacetone is a base-catalyzed reaction used industrially as the first step in a process to make *methyl isobutyl ketone* (MIBK). Aldol condensation has been used by Tanabe et al. (1989) as a model probe reaction to characterize basicity of a series of catalysts. The side chain alkylation of toluene with methanol appears to be highly specific to base catalysis and has been used as a model reaction by Garces et al. (1988) and Martens et al. (1988).

Guidance on base-catalyzed reactions in general can be obtained from the books by Tanabe (1970) and Tanabe et al. (1989), and reviews by Tanabe (1981, 1985, 1988). The proceedings of a symposium on catalysis by acids and bases includes a few papers on bases (Imelik et al. 1985). See also an earlier review by Ono (1980) and the book by Krylov (1970). Malinowski and Kijen'ski (1981) present a brief review on "superbasic" heterogeneous catalysts, focusing mostly on MgO systems.

An alkali zeolite such as K-Y has only a slightly greater activity for hydrocarbon cracking than an "inert" solid such as quartz. Reaction occurs by a free-radical mechanism and yields a product distribution only slightly different from that observed for the purely thermal reaction (Rabo 1981). However, if zeolite NaY is cation-exchanged with a bi- or multifunctional metal cation, to replace most of the sodium, strong acidic catalytic activity is developed. This is attributed to generation of protons by dissociation of water of hydration (Jacobs 1977).

7.7   Zeolites

Zeolites are highly crystalline, hydrated aluminosilicates that upon dehydration develop in the ideal crystal a uniform pore structure having minimum channel diameters (apertures) of from about 0.3 to 1.0 nm. The size depends primarily on the type of zeolite and secondarily

on the cations present and the nature of treatments such as calcination, leaching, and various chemical treatments. Zeolites have been of
intense interest as catalysts for some three decades because of the
high activity and unusual selectivity they provide, mostly in a variety
of acid-catalyzed reactions. In many cases, but not all, the unusual selectivity is associated with the extremely fine pore structure, which
permits only certain molecules to penetrate into the interior of the
catalyst particles, or only certain products to escape from the interior.
In some cases unusual selectivity seems to stem instead from constraints that the pore structure sets on allowable transition states,
sometimes termed *spacio-selectivity*.

The structure of a zeolite consists of a three-dimensional framework
of SiO_4 and AlO_4 tetrahedra, each of which contains a silicon or aluminum atom in the center. They are sometimes termed TO_4-
tetrahedra where T is silicon or aluminum. The oxygen atoms are
shared between adjoining tetrahedra, which can be present in various
ratios and arranged in a variety of ways. Zeolites may be represented
by the empirical formula

$$M_{2/n} \cdot Al_2O_3 \cdot xSiO_2 \cdot yH_2O \qquad (7.11)$$

or by a structural formula

$$M_{x'/n}[(AlO_2)_{x'}(SiO_2)_{y'}] \cdot wH_2O \qquad (7.12)$$

where the bracketed term is the crystallographic unit cell. The metal
cation (of valence n) is present to produce electrical neutrality since
for each aluminum tetrahedron in the lattice there is an overall
charge of -1. Access to the channels is limited by apertures consisting
of a ring of oxygen atoms of connected tetrahedra. There may be 4, 5,
6, 8, 10, or 12 oxygen atoms in the ring. In some cases an interior cavity exists of larger diameter than the aperture; in others, the channel
is of uniform diameter like a tube.

The zeolites of most interest in catalysis are those having medium
to large pore sizes, consisting of 10- or 12-ring oxygen atoms, and having relatively high Si/Al ratio. The latter may stem from the initial
synthesis method or from subsequent treatments. Zeolites of high current interest industrially include zeolite Y and mordenite, which have
a 12-ring system, and zeolite ZSM-5, which has a 10-ring system.
Some structural information on these and other zeolites of particular
interest in catalysis is given in Table 7.3.

Zeolites are often prepared in the sodium form, and this can be replaced by ion exchange with various other cations including ammonium, or by a hydrogen ion. At least 39 species of zeolite minerals
have been found in nature, and over 100 synthetic zeolites with no
known natural counterpart have been prepared (Dyer 1988). For only

TABLE 7.3   Selected Well-Characterized Zeolites of Interest in Catalysis

Number of O atoms in the larger aperture ring	Channel geometry, nm	Secondary building unit, sbu	Structure type
12			
A. Mordenite	One-dimensional tube 0.65 × 0.70 interconnecting with an 8-ring pore structure 0.29 × 0.57, one-dimensional	5-1	MOR
B. Faujasite (zeolite X,Y,LZ-210)	Three-dimensional, with 0.74 aperture, leading to 1.2 diameter cavities	D6R	FAU
C. Offretite (zeolite O, LZ-217)	0.64 one-dimensional with cavities, interconnecting with a 2-dimensional 8-ring system consisting of 0.36 × 0.49 channels. Overall, a 3-dimensional system.	S6R	OFF
D. Linde type L (in K-form)	One-dimensional, 0.71 aperture, leading to cavities of about 0.48 × 1.24 × 1.07	S6R	LTL
E. Mazzite (ZSM-4, Ω, LZ-202)	One-dimensional, nearly cylindrical channels 0.74 diameter, separated from one-dimensional 8-ring channels, 0.34 × 0.56	5-1	MAZ
F. Zeolite β (Nu-2)	Three-dimensional network (see text)		
10			
A. Zeolite ZSM-5	Two-dimensional, 0.51 × 0.55 tube interconnecting with zig-zag 0.53 × 0.56 tube	5-1	MFI
B. ZSM-11	Two-dimensional, interconnecting tubes, 0.53 × 0.54	5-1	MEL
C. Ferrierite (ZSM-35)	Two-dimensional interconnecting network of 10- and 8-ring pores, 0.54 × 0.42 and 0.48 × 0.35	5-1	FER
8			
A. Erionite	0.36 × 0.51 (tortuous), three-dimensional	S6R	ERI
B. Linde A	Three-dimensional, 0.41		

SOURCES: Various, principally Meier and Olson (1988).

a few synthetic zeolites has the complete structure been determined. The number of papers published and patents issued on zeolites has grown rapidly and, as of 1990, consists of many thousands. A guide to the literature is given at the end of this section.

Naturally occurring zeolites or their synthetic equivalents are usually described by a mineral name, e.g., mordenite. New synthetic types are usually designated by a letter or group of letters assigned by the original investigators following the term *zeolite*, for example, zeolite Y or zeolite ZSM ("Zeolite Socony-Mobil"). Type Y is structurally and topologically related to the mineral faujasite and is frequently referred to as a *faujasite-type* zeolite. The zeolites are sometimes classified into eight groups, each of which has a common *secondary building unit* (sbu). Over 40 different zeolite topologies are now known, and the International Zeolite Association assigns a three-letter code (capitalized) to each type of framework [see, e.g., the atlas authored by Meier and Olson (1988)]. Zeolite structures may be pictorially represented in several different ways (see later examples).

The atomic ratio of Si/Al in the zeolites as originally prepared substantially exceeds unity, and bonds of the type Al-O-Al are not formed. By acid treatment alumina can be selectively removed from some of the zeolites such as mordenite, which has an original SiO_2/Al_2O_3 ratio of about 10, to produce a stable structure having a much higher ratio. Other zeolites, such as some of those in the ZSM family, can be synthesized to have a high SiO_2/Al_2O_3 ratio as formed. The SiO_2/Al_2O_3 ratio of the zeolite framework can also be altered by various treatments before or after it is incorporated into a matrix to form a zeolite-based catalyst (see the following).

Many named zeolites are of uncertain structure, and in several cases early proposed structures have been found to be incorrect. Indeed, commercially there are incentives to claim new zeolites until proven to the contrary. Structural information typically comes from a combination of several methods. Single-crystal X-ray diffraction techniques have been limited by availability of suitable large crystals free of defects such as twinning and mixed phases, and the basic method is the use of X-ray powder diffraction. Additional information can be derived from electron diffraction or neutron diffraction. Possible structures can also be modeled and their diffraction patterns calculated by computer for comparison with observed patterns.

Thomas (1984, 1989) reviews the application of *high-resolution electron microscopy* (HREM) and *nuclear magnetic resonance with magic angle spinning* (MASNMR) for elucidation of zeolite structures and related substances. Steady improvement over the past decade in the resolution of HREM micrographs, down to as low as 0.2 to 0.3 nm, now makes it possible to obtain direct pictures of the pores that reveal defects as well as the regular structure (Sec. 7.7.1). Solid-state MASNMR, focusing on Si^{29} and Al^{27}, has come into use in the 1980s to reveal much information about localized structure.

The degree of sorption of a range of probe molecules of different sizes and physical properties has been extensively used to obtain information on pore volume and pore size (Sec. 7.7.3). The relative rates of reaction in a mixture of two reactants or, particularly, the nature of product distribution from a specific probe reaction can be very sensitive to slight alterations in pore configuration (Sec. 7.7.5).

Some zeolites have essentially the same structure but may be identified by different names. Some of the alternate designations for essentially similar structures are shown in Table 7.3.

Zeolites are of practical interest for various applications beyond catalysis. Zeolites have long been used for water softening, utilizing their ion-exchange capabilities, and, more recently, for drying. Utilizing a different property, the fine pore structure permits adsorption separations to be carried out on the basis of molecular size and shape, termed *molecular sieving*, as in the physical separation of *n*-paraffins from isoparaffins. The ability to alter zeolite properties by ion exchange also permits the synthesis of adsorbents of unusual selectivity, even when all molecules have free access to the interior pores of the zeolite and a molecular sieving effect as such does not occur. The ion-exchange properties also allow a high degree of flexibility in synthesizing catalysts, e.g., the ability to produce a highly dispersed metal. From the catalytic point of view, zeolites are of special interest in that they exhibit unusually high activity for various acid-catalyzed reactions such as cracking, the ability to combine a molecular-sieving property with catalysis, and unusual selectivity behavior.

In more recent years, molecular sieves have been synthesized to contain phosphorous, boron, or other elements, instead of some or all of the aluminum or silicon atoms. Classically, the term *zeolite* refers only to aluminosilicates, and the related structures may be referred to as nonaluminosilicate molecular sieves, metallosilicates, or zeotypes.

7.7.1 Pore structure

Structures may be described in terms of the kinds of pore channels present (Table 7.3.), which can exist in considerable variety. An array of parallel channels is termed a one-dimensional structure. If this array is interconnected with a second array at, for instance, right angles, the structure is two-dimensional. A third array at right angles produces a three-dimensional pore structure. In each array the pores may be of the same size and shape or, more commonly, different. The channels may be circular or elliptical, may be tubular or contain periodic cavities, may be straight or zig-zag. A two-dimensional pore structure may have a second array of pores somewhat smaller than the first, so that most molecules of interest can be accommodated only in the larger pores, making the pore structure in effect one-dimensional. The two-dimensional pore structure of ZSM-5 and ZSM-11 is such as to permit complete access from any one pore to all others in the structure, in effect making it similar to a three-dimensional pore network. With any zeolite the effective pore diameter can vary moderately with the type of cations present, the degree of hydration, and also the temperature.

The faujasite-type zeolites X and Y, zeolite β, and erionite have a network of three-dimensional intersecting channels in which the minimum free diameter is the same in each direction. Zeolites X and Y have SiO_2/Al_2O_3 ratios of about 2:3 and 3:6, respectively. These zeolites are isostructural with naturally occurring faujasite, and consist of an array of cavities having internal diameters of about 1.2 nm. Access to each cavity (also termed a *supercage*) is through six equispaced necks having a diameter of about 0.74 nm formed by a ring comprising 12 oxygen atoms. X and Y zeolites have among the largest minimum aperture restrictions of any zeolite, and the highest void fraction. Their structure may be visualized by the line drawing of Fig. 7.5. In the foreground is one of the necks, through which may be seen slight portions of three other necks. The rows of necks comprise an array of passageways perpendicular to one another in three dimensions.

Mordenite, which, as synthesized, has a SiO_2/Al_2O_3 ratio of about 10, is an example of a dual-pore system (Chen & Garwood 1986). A set of 12-ring channels are interconnected by another set of 8-ring cross

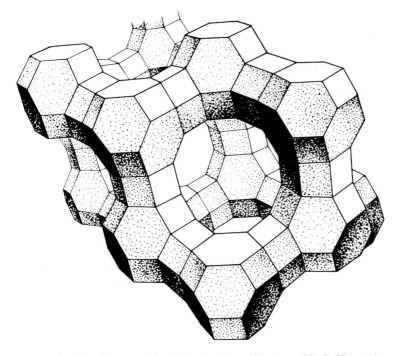

Figure 7.5   Line drawing of faujasite structure. *(Courtesy of P. B. Venuto.)*

channels. Other zeolites having interconnecting channels of either 12 and 8, or 10 and 8 rings include offretite, Linde T, gmelinite and ferrierite. In the case of mordenite, the cross channels are sufficiently small that they do not provide a means for transport of molecules between adjacent passageways, except possibly for diatomic molecules such as hydrogen and oxygen. With respect to hydrocarbons, the structure is effectively one-dimensional and may be regarded as an array of parallel, noninterconnecting channels.

In the ideal mordenite pore structure, the pores are slightly elliptical, with dimensions of about 0.70×0.67 nm. Unlike type Y, sodium mordenite can be treated directly with acid, typically aqueous HCl, which selectively leaches alumina and converts the mordenite to the H-form. Treatment also may increase channel size, up to about 0.8 to 1.0 nm diameter. SiO_2/Al_2O_3 ratios in the leached mordenite can range up to 50:1 or more, if desired, without collapse of structure.

The ZSM group of zeolites, many of which have 10 oxygen atoms in the aperture ring, are usually synthesized in the presence of a tetraalkylammonium cation or other organic compound (see the following), which is later removed by heat. The ZSM-5 zeolite is currently of more interest industrially than other ZSM zeolites. Its structure is shown in Fig. 7.6, in which the pores are shown as arrays of tubular channels (Kokotailo et al. 1978). Two pore types exist, intersecting with each other, and both formed by 10-membered oxygen rings. One pore type has straight but slightly elliptical openings (0.51×0.55 nm); the other zig-zags and has essentially circular openings (0.54×0.56 nm). Of the numerous zeolites bearing the ZSM designation for which structures have been published, only ZSM-5 and ZSM-11 have a two-dimensional pore structure. All the others for

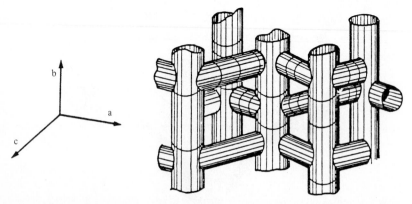

Figure 7.6   Structure of zeolite ZSM-5. Pores are shown as arrays of tubular channels. *(Kokotailo et al. 1978)*

which structures have been reported thus far have nonintersecting one-dimensional channels.

ZSM-11 is similar in structure and pore size to ZSM-5, but both sets of pores are straight. Little information has been published about chemical reactions on ZSM-11, possibly because it may be more difficult to synthesize in the requisite purity. ZSM-5 and similar medium-pore zeolites are sometimes termed *pentasils* because the framework structure (not the pore opening) consists of chains of 5-member oxygen rings as secondary building units.

ZSM-5, as synthesized, typically has a SiO_2/Al_2O_3 ratio of about 15, but it can be prepared with much higher ratios. As with other zeolites, a high SiO_2/Al_2O_3 ratio provides high temperature stability. In ZSM-5 and mordenite, each pore is of uniform dimension, unlike zeolite Y, offretite, Linde L, and others that have cavities. However, in a two-dimensional pore structure such as ZSM-5, the intersection provides an opening that in effect can provide a type of cavity. A material that is nearly pure silica, termed *silicalite*, has essentially the same structure as zeolite ZSM-5. The structures of many of the ZSM zeolites are still unknown or unpublished. It is highly probable that the Si/Al ratio in a particular zeolite varies throughout the crystal, but little information has been published.

Other 12-ring zeolites of possible interest as catalysts include zeolites O, Ω, β and L, listed in Table 7.3. Zeolite L, which has a one-dimensional pore structure, is used commercially in the Aromax cyclization process (Sec. 9.6). Zeolite β was first synthesized in 1967, but its structure was not published until 1988 (Treacy & Newsam 1988; Higgins et al. 1988). It is the only high-silica zeolite having a full three-dimensional network of 12-membered rings and is somewhat like the faujasite structure. The zeolite β seems to consist of an intergrown structure of two or three polymorphs producing random stacking faults, but sorption and reaction studies indicate a high degree of accessibility to the interior pore structure. It probably has the most complex zeolite structure yet determined.

Offretite with a small amount of erionite intergrown into it has been termed zeolite T, and is used in the Mobil Selectoforming process, replacing erionite, the original catalyst. The erionite in effect partially blocks the 12-ring pores of the offretite. Offretite possesses a structure very similar to erionite and requires carefully defined conditions if it is to be prepared in a pure form.

The SiO_2/Al_2O_3 ratio of zeolite Ω, as synthesized, is about 8, that of zeolite L is about 6. As most readily synthesized, the ratio in zeolite β is about 25. However, ratios in the broad range of about 10 to 200 can be prepared by subsequent processing.

Pore structures can be characterized by several methods that usually reveal different features and generally complement one another. These techniques include determination of crystallographic characteristics, sorption and diffusion characteristics (Sec. 7.7.4), relative rate of reaction of molecules of different sizes, and the product distribution. (Sec. 7.7.5). High-resolution transmission electron microscopy (HRTEM) is particularly helpful in revealing crystal defects such as intergrowths and faulting. Figure 7.7 is a micrograph of a sample of zeolite β, which shows extensive faulting. Figure 7.8 is a micrograph of ZSM-20. This zeolite is an intergrowth of the cubic and hexagonal modes of stacking of faujasite sheets. In contrast, the micrograph in Fig. 7.9, together with the computed image, shows the perfect structure of a particular sample of ZSM-5.

No aluminosilicate zeolites have been discovered or prepared with more than 12 oxygen atoms in the ring comprising the pore opening, although an 18-ring pore structure (VPI-5) has been reported for a molecular sieve consisting of aluminum and phosphorus (no silica) [Davis et al. 1988]. The free diameter of the pores is about 1.2 to 1.3 nm.

A number of other materials also have a fine, and more or less regular, pore structure, such as some fine-pore silicas, porous glass, montmorillonite and other clays, and porous carbons prepared by con-

Figure 7.7 [100] structure image of zeolite β. The large bright spots reveal the location of the 12-ring channels aligned along [100]. There is extensive faulting along the vertical direction. The projected framework, and multislice image simulation are superimposed for comparison. *(Courtesy of D. E. W. Vaughan.)*

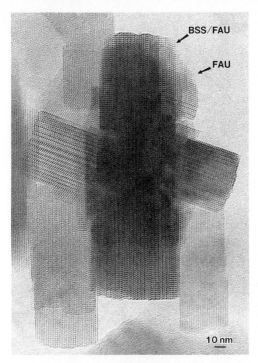

Figre 7.8 Electron micrograph of a typical ZSM-20 crystallite aggregate. Regions of both hexagonal ABB...(BSS) and cubic ABCABC...(FAU) stacking are evident. *(Vaughan et al. 1989. Courtesy of D. E. W. Vaughan.)*

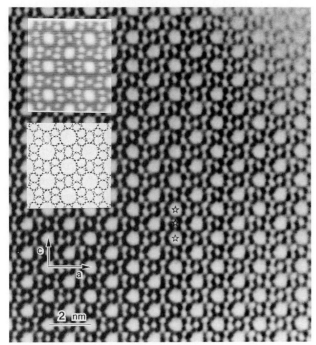

Figure 7.9 Electron micrograph of a perfect ZSM-5 structure. *(With kind permission of Prof. J. M. Thomas, Royal Institution and Dr. O. Terasaki, Tohoku University.)*

trolled pyrolysis of synthetic polymers. These materials may also exhibit molecular-sieving properties. Note that the molecular-sieving property of a zeolite is not necessarily being utilized when a particular zeolite is being used in catalysis.

7.7.2 Synthesis

Zeolites are generally synthesized by a hydrothermal process from a source of alumina (e.g., sodium aluminate or aluminum sulfate) and of silica (e.g., a silica sol, fumed silica, or sodium waterglass) and an alkali such as NaOH, and/or a quaternary ammonium compound. An inhomogeneous gel is produced which gradually crystallizes, in some cases forming more than one type of zeolite in succession. Nucleation effects can be important, and an initial induction period at near ambient temperature may be followed by crystallization temperatures that may range up to 200°C or higher. The pressure is equal to the saturated vapor pressure of the water present.

The final product depends on a complex interplay between many variables including SiO_2/Al_2O_3 ratio in the starting medium, nucleating agents, temperature, pH, water content, aging, stirring, and the presence of various inorganic and organic cations. Much remains to be learned about how the initial reaction mixture forms the precursor species and how these arrange into the final crystalline products. A key concept is that the cations present give rise to a templating action, but clearly the process is more complex than this.

Scanning electron microscopy (SEM) shows how crystal morphology and size may vary with process conditions. As an example, Fig. 7.10 (Sanders 1985) presents SEM images of four different preparations of the zeolite ZSM-5. The cabbage-like particles in Fig. 7.10b are an unwanted impurity, analcime. In Fig. 7.10a and d, the crystals are relatively large, showing stepped and smooth surfaces, respectively. The shape of the particles in Fig. 7.10c are characteristic of those with a high $SiO_2 \cdot Al_2O_3$ content and frequently consist of interpenetrating twinned crystals.

Bauer and coworkers in the early 1960s developed the use of reaction mixtures containing quaternary ammonium ions or other organic cations to direct the crystallization process (see Whyte & Dalla Betta 1982). In their work and succeeding studies, a primary motivation was to attempt to synthesize zeolites with larger apertures than X and Y. This did not occur, but instead organic species were found to modify the synthesis process in a variety of ways that led to the discovery of many new zeolites, and new methods of synthesizing zeolites with structures similar to previously known zeolites.

The mechanism of action of the organic species is still controversial.

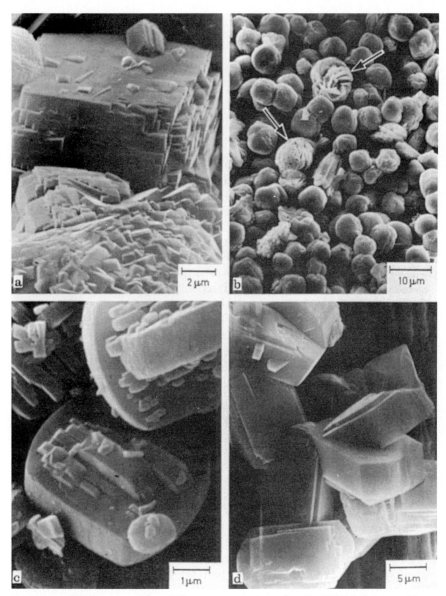

Figure 7.10   SEM images of four different preparations of zeolite ZSM-5. See text. Note different degrees of magnification. *(Sanders 1985. Courtesy of J. R. Anderson, Monash University, Melbourne, Australia.)*

It was originally thought to be primarily a templating effect, but later it was found that at least some of the zeolites could be synthesized without an organic template. Further, organic species other than quaternary ammonium compounds had directing effects not readily ascribed to their size or shape. An important result, however, was that zeolites of higher SiO_2/Al_2O_3 ratio than before could be synthesized. Previously, only structures with SiO_2/Al_2O_3 ratios of about 10 or less could be directly formed, but with organic additives, zeolites with ratios of 20 to 100 or more can be directly prepared.

After synthesis the zeolites are dried, heated to remove water of crystallization, and calcined in air, e.g., at about 550°C. Organic species are also thus removed. For most catalytic purposes, the zeolite is converted into an acidic form. For some zeolites this can be achieved by treatment with aqueous HCl without significantly altering the framework structure. For other zeolites Na^+ is replaced with NH_4^+ via an ammonium compound such as NH_4OH, NH_4Cl or NH_4NO_3. Upon heating NH_3 is driven off, leaving the zeolite in the acid form. For some reactions a hydrogenation component such as platinum or nickel is introduced by impregnation or ion exchange.

Zeolites are typically made to have a crystal size in the range of about a micrometer or less in order to minimize diffusion limitations in reaction. This very fine powder is then usually pelletized with a binder or incorporated in a gel to convert it to a usable form. The external area of the zeolite crystals is of the order of 1 percent of the internal area. The latter is typically in the region of 500 to 800 m^2/g.

Szostak (1989) gives an extensive discussion of the principles of zeolite synthesis, including comprehensive references to patents. Many detailed tables and extensive references make it a good source of guidance to the literature. An extensive appendix gives X-ray powder diffraction data for several hundred natural, patented, and reported zeolites. A book by Jacobs and Martens (1987) gives detailed synthesis methods for various high-silica zeolites, including a considerable number of specific recipes. The zeolites were identified primarily by X-ray diffraction, comparing the spectra to those in the literature. Synthesis methods are also given for some zeolites claimed in the literature and for some of still unknown structure. The proceedings of a recent symposium (Occelli & Robson, eds. 1989) contain 42 papers on zeolite synthesis. See also the earlier book by Breck (1974). The review by Whyte and Dalla Betta (1982) discusses zeolite synthesis with emphasis on use of organic reagents and treats synthesis of TMA offretite in detail as an example. (See also Sec. 7.7.10 on zeolite literature.)

7.7.3 Effective pore size

Since the pores in a zeolite are so small, the degree to which reacting molecules have access to the interior and product molecules have ease of escape under a particular set of reaction conditions assumes considerable importance. Pore sizes are frequently assigned on the basis of crystallographic measurements, but they are also affected by the nature of the cations present and by heat and other treatments. Many materials also incorporate stacking faults, impurities, or deformation of various kinds that restrict channels, or they may have been treated in various ways to open up channels. A more useful characterization in practice, especially on a relative scale, stems from measurements with a series of hydrocarbons consisting of molecules of progressively increasing size to determine the amount adsorbed (Breck 1974, p. 633).

The minimum cross-sectional diameter of the molecule is the critical dimension, and it may be estimated from bond lengths, bond angles, and van der Waals radii or from kinetic diameters, the latter being most useful for relatively spherical molecules. Table 7.4 lists

TABLE 7.4   Values of Selected Critical Molecular Diameters, nm

Compound	From structure		Kinetic diameter*
	†	‡	
C_3H_8	–	–	0.43
$n\text{-}C_4H_{10}$	–	–	0.43
iso-C_4H_{10}	0.56	–	0.50
$n\text{-}C_5H_{12}$ and all higher n-paraffins	0.49		
2,2-dimethyl propane (neopentane)	–	–	0.62
2,2,4-trimethyl pentane	0.67		
benzene	0.63	0.675	0.585
toluene	–	0.675	
cumene	0.67	0.675	
cyclohexane	0.65	0.69	0.60
m-xylene	–	0.74	0.71
p-xylene	–	0.675	
1,3,5-trimethylbenzene (mesitylene)	0.84	0.84	0.85
1,3,5-triethylbenzene	0.92	0.92	
1,3-diethylbenzene	–	0.74	
1-methylnaphthalene	–	0.79	
$(C_2F_5)_3N$	–	–	0.80
$(C_4H_9)_3N$	–	–	0.81
$(C_4F_9)_3N$	–	–	1.02

*From Lennard-Jones potential function (Breck 1974, p. 636).
†Evaluated from bond lengths, bond angles, and van der Waals radii (Pitcher 1972).
‡Moore and Katzer (1972).

critical diameters as determined by the two methods for a number of substances of interest. For a series of zeolites of the same structure but varying silica-alumina ratio, the amount of water adsorbed from a fixed partial pressure of water vapor decreases with increased SiO_2/Al_2O_3 ratio, which makes the zeolite more hydrophobic (Chen et al. 1989, p. 46).

7.7.4 Diffusion in zeolites

When the molecules in the pore are nearly the size of the passageway, the diffusing molecule is never away from the influence of the wall, and the rate of diffusion becomes relatively slow. This regime has been variously termed *restricted diffusion* or *configurational diffusion*. In contrast, *Knudsen diffusion* occurs in pores sufficiently small that the mean free path is much greater than the pore size, but sufficiently large that molecular motion occurs by free flight interrupted by momentary adsorption and desorption on the wall. Diffusion in zeolites is more complex than Knudsen diffusion or bulk diffusion, and the activation energy is usually substantially greater than that for Knudsen diffusion or bulk diffusion.

Typical reported diffusion coefficients D in zeolites range downward from about 10^{-8} cm^2/s. For comparison, representative values are in the region of 10^{-1} cm^2/s for bulk diffusion of gases and 10^{-5} cm^2/s for liquids. Values of 10^{-3} cm^2/s and less are representative for Knudsen diffusion of gases (Fig. 7.11). (Knudsen diffusion does not occur with liquids.)

The most common method of measurement is to observe the nonsteady-state rate of sorption into zeolite crystals by gravimetric or volumetric methods. The lowest values measurable are limited only by the patience of the investigator. The highest are set by the maximum rate that can be accurately followed by available experimental methods. This maximum is determined by the ratio r^2/D where r is the crystal radius.* For crystals of the order of 1 μm, this maximum corresponds to diffusivities of about 10^{-11} cm^2/s; for 10-μm crystals, to diffusivities of about 10^{-7} cm^2/s. Several experimental difficulties must be addressed to secure reliable data. Adsorption is exothermic and a local rise in temperature can shift the equilibrium and alter the diffusivity. Crystallite size and shape distribution, the existence of crystal defects, or possible surface barriers can have major effects. Chromatographic methods, in which a pulse of the adsorbate is in-

---

*The time required for a specified degree of approach to sorption equilibrium is, to a first approximation, proportional to r^2/D, provided that equilibrium is not approached too closely.

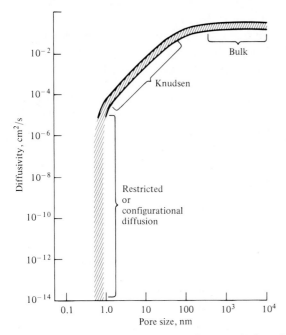

Figure 7.11   Effect of pore size on diffusivity. *(Adapted from Weisz 1973. Reprinted with permission from Chemtech. Copyright by the American Chemical Society.)*

jected into a chromatographic column, have also been used. The output signal can be processed to calculate a diffusivity.

Pulsed field gradient *nuclear magnetic resonance* (NMR) techniques can also be used to measure diffusivities, but values are usually limited to about 10^{-8} cm^2/s and greater because of apparatus limitations. Reliable studies in the region of overlap of the two methods show that the diffusivities calculated from sorption studies can be as much as three or more orders of magnitude smaller than those obtained by the NMR method, depending on the zeolite and the adsorbate. The physical situation is not precisely the same for the two types of measurement, as emphasized by Kärger and Caro (1977), Kärger (1982), and Caro et al. (1985). The NMR technique provides a self-diffusion coefficient under equilibrium conditions, whereas the adsorption or desorption method involves a measurement under a concentration gradient. However, other factors are also involved. A review of the NMR method has been published by Kärger and Pfeifer (1987).

A detailed review of diffusion in molecular sieves by Post (1990) makes available a critical analysis of the various methods and possible reasons for differences in the values reported. Sorption and diffusion in zeolites was reviewed by Palekar and Rajadhyaksha (1986) and is treated in detail in the book by Ruthven (1984) with considerable attention to theory. Diffusion in pores of roughly 1 to 5 nm diameter, in which Knudsen diffusion merges into configurational diffusion, is essentially unexplored.

Counterdiffusion is even more complex than unidirectional diffusion. In some cases counterdiffusion rates are similar to unidirectional rates; in other cases counterdiffusion rates are much slower. Some earlier scouting studies by Satterfield and Cheng (1971, 1972) and Satterfield and Katzer (1971) may give some guidance. For guidance to more recent literature and recent studies see Qureshi and Wei (1990). Diffusivities may also be significantly affected by concentration in the pore, as considered by Xiao (1990) from both an experimental and theoretical perspective.

There is an approximate correlation between zeolite pore size, critical molecular diameter of a sorbate (generally the smallest dimension for an irregularly shaped molecule) and diffusivity. Moore and Katzer (1972) quantified this by measurements of counterdiffusion of various aromatic hydrocarbons into cyclohexane-saturated zeolite NaY at 25°C. The correlation is shown in Fig. 7.12.

For a specific zeolite, the activation energy generally increases with increasing molecular size of diffusing species, within a series of similar molecules. However, adsorption phenomena and the interaction energy between diffusing molecule and pore walls are also significant variables. Gorring (1973) and others have observed a very irregular pattern of change of diffusivity with C-number of n-paraffins and also C-number distribution of cracked products. These findings seem to reflect certain geometrical relationships between the zeolite pore structure and the paraffin size (Chen et al. 1989, p. 51). As noted in the foregoing, diffusivities can also be markedly affected by slight variations in the zeolite structure, including the nature of the cations and the presence of impurities, and by the size and polarity of counterdiffusing molecules.

Counterdiffusion would seem to be inevitable in catalytic reaction if the pore structure is uniform. However, Derouane and Gabelica (1980) propose that with a zeolite such as ZSM-5, which has two types of interconnecting pores, reactant molecules might diffuse in through one type of pore, and product molecules, out through the second. This concept, which they termed *molecular traffic control*, would permit reaction without counterdiffusion. This idea appears to be difficult to test.

Polinski and Baird (1985) studied the rate of ethylbenzene isomerization to xylenes under hydrogen pressure on either H-mordenite or HY-faujasite mechanically mixed with 1.0 wt % Pt/Al_2O_3. The rate was 4 times faster on H-mordenite, which they attrib-

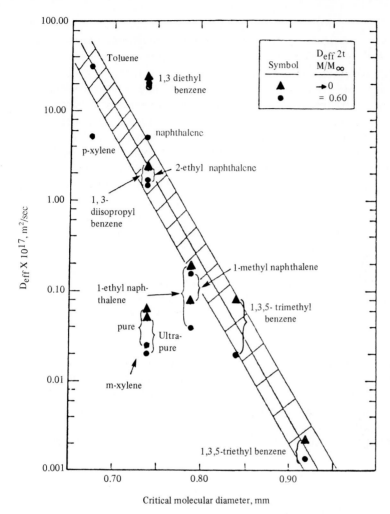

Figure 7.12   Effect of critical diameter of diffusate on apparent diffusion co-efficient. Selected aromatic hydrocarbons into NaY presaturated with cyclohexane. 25°C. *(Moore & Katzer 1972. Reprinted with permission from the AIChE Journal. Copyright, American Institute of Chemical Engineers.)*

uted to the diffusion of hydrogen product out the smaller side pores in mordenite that allowed the equilibrium to shift to the right. In a comparison of the rate of coke oxidation on three zeolites Magnoux and Guisnet (1988) found that the rate was higher on HY and H-mordenite than on H-ZSM-5. This could not be explained by the composition or location of the coke. Oxygen could freely circulate in the large cages of zeolite Y. With H-mordenite, coke was deposited at the mouths of the large pores, but it was postulated that oxygen could have access through the smaller set of channels that intersect the larger pore structure. With ZSM-5 oxygen apparently cannot diffuse through either set of channels if they are occupied by coke.

The apparent activation energy for zeolite diffusion is greater than that for bulk or Knudsen diffusion. Some of the reported values are relatively uncertain because of the limited temperature range covered and other difficulties such as deviations from Fick's law, sorption effects, and questions concerning possible differences between unidirectional and counterdiffusion and codiffusion of two species versus one in a unidirectional path. Generally, the smaller the diffusion coefficient, the higher is the activation energy. This is illustrated in Fig. 7.13 (Xiao 1990), an Arrhenius plot of vapor-phase diffusivities as a function of temperature of six C_5 and C_6 hydrocarbons measured by adsorption in ZSM-5. In this case the diffusivity values were multiplied by $\sqrt{M/T}$, but this has little effect on calculated activation energy.

As a measure of the significance of a modest change in activation energy, an increase in temperature from 25 to 310°C would increase the diffusivity by a factor of 60 with an activation energy of 21 kJ/mol or by a factor of 5000 with an activation energy of 46 kJ/mol.

Diffusion limitations may be inferred by comparing the observed activation energy to that for the same reaction under nondiffusion-limiting conditions, or by the effect of crystal particle size on reaction (Sec. 11.2), provided that uniform zeolite crystals over a range of crystal sizes are available. This is not easy to achieve. For a simple first-order reaction, the apparent activation energy with diffusion limitation is about one-half that in its absence. An approximate criterion indicating absence of significant diffusion limitation is $1/k > R^2/D$, where k is the first-order reaction rate constant, R the zeolite crystal radius, and D the diffusion coefficient for the reactant or product having the lowest diffusivity.

7.7.5 Shape-selective catalysis

The first major industrial use of a zeolite was that of zeolite Y in catalytic cracking in 1962, discussed in more detail in the following and in Sec. 9.4. This reaction was probably not diffusion-controlled, at least with respect to most of the feed. In their commercial form, zeolite catalysts usually consist of zeolites pelletized with a binder or incorporated into a gel matrix, but diffusivities are much greater in the pores of the matrix than in the zeolite pores and hence do not usually constitute a limiting rate.

Diffusion limitations inside the pores of zeolite Y may not be significant in commercial catalytic cracking using a distilled feedstock, but

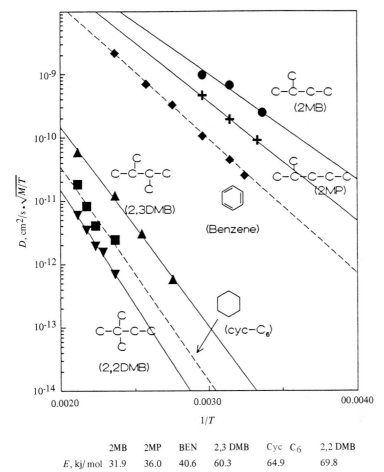

Figure 7.13 Effect of temperature on hydrocarbon diffusivity in ZSM-5. *(Xiao 1990)*

	2MB	2MP	BEN	2,3 DMB	Cyc C_6	2,2 DMB
E, kj/ mol	31.9	36.0	40.6	60.3	64.9	69.8

it depends on the amount of carbon present on the catalyst and other factors. On the basis of their size, three- and four-ring compounds may be expected to be effectively excluded from the pores of a Y-type zeolite. Usually the major activity and selectivity effects are caused by the nature and content of the zeolites present. However, the properties of the matrix and the zeolite/matrix ratio can also be adjusted, if desired, to cause some reaction to occur in the matrix in order to achieve an optimum desired process objective (Sec. 9.4).

Weisz and Frilette (1960) were apparently the first to describe shape selectivity, and they, together with Chen, Miale, and coworkers, have published extensively on a variety of applications. The pore size and shape in a zeolite may affect the selectivity of a reaction in three ways:

1. *Reactant selectivity* occurs when the aperture size of the zeolite is such that it admits only certain smaller molecules and excludes larger molecules; hence, in a mixture, effectively only the smaller molecules react.

2. *Product selectivity* occurs when bulkier product molecules cannot diffuse out, and, if formed, they are converted to smaller molecules or to carbonaceous deposits within the pore. These eventually may cause pore blockage.

3. *Spaciospecific selectivity* was first proposed by Csicsery (1970, 1971) to explain the absence of symmetrical trialkyl benzenes in the product from the disproportionation of a dialkyl benzene in H-mordenite. From this and other studies he concluded that insufficient space was available in the pores for two molecules of the dialkyl benzene to come together. This type of behavior is sometimes also termed *restricted transition-state selectivity*. Unlike reactant or product selectivity, spaciospecific selectivity should not be affected by crystal size. However, it is more difficult to establish that this mechanism is operative than when selectivity is caused by diffusion limitations.

Restricted diffusion, causing selectivity effects, is determined not only by the pore structure of perfect crystals, but also by stacking faults, disordered intergrowth of two types of closely related structures (e.g., erionite and offretite) and/or impurities in the materials, as well as by deposits inside pores and material deliberately or inadvertently deposited on pore entrances to narrow the pore mouths. Diffusion-limited shape selectivity occurs only with a particular matching of molecule sizes and pore sizes, and it is also determined by other variables such as crystal size and temperature, all contributing to a potential rate of diffusion compared with the rate of reaction. Thus, a particular zeolite may cause shape selectivity in one circumstance but not in another. Shape selectivity may also be achieved or increased by partially blocking pore mouths, and a considerable number of patents have proposed the use of compounds of antimony or phosphorous, silicones, etc. for this purpose.

The first major industrial use of a zeolite, in catalytic cracking, led to an enormous upsurge of interest in zeolites partly because, being crystalline, their structure could be studied much more effectively than that of amorphous silica-alumina, previously used. Further, their ion-exchange properties allowed methods of introducing catalytically active heavy metals in a new controlled fashion. Many papers on shape selectivity appeared from the early 1960s on. Notably, the study of Miale et al. (1966) showed marked reactant shape selectivity between n-C_6 and iso-C_6 on gmelinite, offretite, and chabazite. Robson et al. (1971) showed remarkable reactant selectivity (n-paraffin versus isoparaffin) on both natural and synthetic erionite.

The first commercial application of shape selectivity was the Mobil Selectoforming process (mid 1960s), which selectively hydrocracked n-paraffins in reformate in the presence of isoparaffins, thus improving the octane number of the liquid product. The cracking reaction formed low-molecular-weight hydrocarbon products. This process originally used natural erionite, which is usually fault-free. It is an 8-membered ring zeolite and was installed in about six refineries (Vaughan 1980). A small amount of nickel was added to minimize coke formation, but it was insufficient to hydrogenate the aromatics present. Erionite was apparently later replaced with zeolite T, which is intergrown offretite and erionite containing about 2 to 4 percent erionite. Offretite is a 12-ring zeolite and by itself does not discriminate between normal and isoparaffins. A small amount of erionite in effect causes a partial pore blocking.

In the early 1970s a closely related process, termed M-forming, was developed using zeolite ZSM-5. This zeolite has slightly larger pores than erionite so single-branched paraffins as well as benzene and toluene can penetrate the zeolite pores. Cracking was thus extended to the next lowest octane number component and part of the cracked products were alkylated onto aromatics present. Compared with Selectoforming, this increased the octane number of the liquid product and reduced loss to gas.

Straight chain paraffins ("waxes") are undesired in distillate fuels and lubricating oils because they cause undesired high viscosity at low temperature as exhibited by, e.g., a high pour point.* The waxes can be removed by shape-selective reactant hydrocracking, in processes introduced in the 1970s. The BP (British Petroleum) process uses H-mordenite with some platinum (Bennett et al. 1975). H-Ferrierite with palladium is used in a process developed by Shell. The Mobil process uses zeolite ZSM-5 without a noble metal. Mordenite has a greater tendency to coke than ZSM-5, and hence the use of a metallic component and higher hydrogen pressure is required to hydrogenate and remove coke precursors. Catalytic dewaxing processes for a number of applications are described by Chen et al. (1989, p. 175).

Zeolites or other molecular sieves are also used in processes for par-

---

*The pour point is the highest temperature at which a hydrocarbon product flows, as determined by a prescribed test.

affin isomerization (Pt-mordenite, Sec. 9.7.1), xylene isomerization (ZSM-5 or borosilicate molecular sieves, Sec. 9.7.2), hydrocracking (Zeolite Y, Sec. 9.13), and alkylation of benzene with ethylene to form ethylbenzene in route to styrene (ZSM-5 or Zeolite Y, Sec. 9.17.2). These processes are reviewed in a recent book by Chen et al. (1989). The use of ZSM-5 in the conversion of methanol to gasoline is discussed in Sec. 7.7.9. Various other processes have been announced, but not necessarily commercialized, to date. The use of molecular sieves for synthesis of organic compounds was reviewed by Hoelderich (1987, 1989).

A catalyst consisting of platinum on zeolite KL, partly exchanged with barium, has high activity and selectivity for conversion of n-hexane to benzene, and is the basis of the Chevron Aromax process. In contrast to most hydrocarbon reactions used industrially that require acid functionality and in which cyclization occurs by dual-function catalysis, this is an alkaline catalyst that operates by a monofunctional mechanism in which acid-catalyzed reactions are effectively eliminated. (See Sec. 9.6.1.) The catalyst appears to be very sensitive to traces of sulfur compounds.

A group of zeolites designated as Nu-1, Fu-1, and related zeolites have been developed by ICI, but little information is available on structure. H-Nu-1, possibly the best understood of the group, seems to have pores slightly below 0.6 nm on the basis of absorption properties (Dewing et al. 1985). Nu-2 is essentially the same as zeolite β (Briscoe et al. 1989). Reactions on synthetic ferrierites have been reported by Kibby et al. (1974), and Giannetti and Perrotta (1975). A detailed review of shape selectivity with extensive references has been published by Weitkamp et al. (1986).

A variety of nonaluminosilicate molecular sieves have been synthesized in which the tetrahedral framework contains elements other than aluminum or silicon, and considerable information has been published on reactions catalyzed by them. The Union Carbide laboratories have reported on molecular sieves containing phosphorus instead of silicon—so-called $AlPO_4$ structures—which, however, have fairly low catalytic activity. A closely related group are the SAPO structures (Pellet 1988), which apparently are mostly the $AlPO_4$ compositions plus a small amount of silica. SAPO-5 has a unique structure not analogous to any known aluminosilicate. $AlPO_4$-5 has a one-dimensional pore structure consisting of 12-membered rings about 0.73 nm in diameter. Reactions on a borosilicate similar to silicalite but with boron replacing some silica have been summarized by Kutz (1988). In general these molecular sieves have weaker acidity than the aluminosilicate zeolites.

The "constraint index." The great commercial importance of shape-selective catalysis has led to various methods of characterizing pore structure. One method of distinguishing among acidic zeolites is to compare the individual rate of reaction in a mixture of two compounds, similar chemically but of significantly different minimum molecular diameters. By measurements of the rate of cracking of n-hexane, 3-methylpentane, and 2,3-methylbutane, Chen and Garwood (1978) showed that ZSM-5 has pore openings intermediate between such small-pore zeolites as chabazite and erionite on the one hand and large-pore zeolites such as the faujasites on the other.

Frilette et al. (1981) developed a *constraint index* (C.I.) for discrimination between various acid zeolites. The C.I. is based on the ratio of the rate of cracking of n-hexane and that of 3-methylpentane in a 50:50 mixture of the two, studied at the same temperature and with a residence time to give an overall conversion between 10 percent and 60 percent. For a variety of zeolites studied at 315°C, the index varied between 1 and 12 for various intermediate-pore-size zeolites; was 0.4 to 0.6 for the large-pore zeolites mordenite, zeolite β, REY, and ZSM-4; and was 38 for erionite. The C.I. was 8.3 for ZSM-5 at 315°C, but it varied from about 11 at 290°C down to about 1 at 510°C. For other zeolites there was less effect of temperature or in some cases a reversal of the temperature dependence.

In a later study Haag and Dessau (1984) found that the nature of the products from cracking of 3-methylpentane on ZSM-5 varied substantially with temperature, and they distinguished two parallel mechanisms. At low temperatures the dominant mechanism is classical acid-catalyzed paraffin cracking by a carbenium ion chain mechanism (Sec. 7.5) leading by the primary reaction largely to C_3 and C_4 products and accompanied by isomerization. This is postulated to involve a sterically large bimolecular transition state.

In contrast, at high temperatures and at low conversions, where olefin concentrations are low, substantial H_2 is observed, as well as C_1 and C_2 products, but no isomerization. A monomolecular mechanism involving the formation first of a nonclassical penta-coordinated carbonium ion is postulated. The nonclassical mechanism was less important with Y-zeolite and amorphous silica-alumina.

For a given zeolite structure the constraint index may vary with acid site strength, the SiO_2/Al_2O_3 ratio, and crystal size. It can distinguish between large- and medium-pore zeolites, but more precise pore structure characterization requires other methods.

Instead of focusing on the relative rate of reaction of two reactants in a mixture, the procedure used in the C.I., one can focus on the nature of reaction products from one reactant. This method appears to be a more sensitive indicator of zeolite pore structure and has been developed by several researchers. Jacobs and Martens (1986, 1987) and Martens and Jacobs (1986) make a critical analysis of several test reactions including that used in the constraint index, plus m-xylene isomerization, ethylbenzene disproportionation, cracking of cyclodecane, and hydroconversion of n-decane. They proposed as particularly suitable a *refined constraint index* (C.I.^{0}) based on the ratio of 2-methylnonane to 5-methylnonane in the isomerization hydroconversion of n-decane. Their use of a bifunctional catalyst containing a small amount of a noble metal has the advantage of permitting the use of a nondeactivating reaction. This reaction seems to respond to different pore-structure characteristics than does the original constraint index. Note that the term used here may be somewhat misleading since the principle involved is quite different from that in the original constraint index as such.

A comparison of two medium-pore high-silica zeolites, ZSM-22 and ZSM-23, is interesting because although the crystallographic dimensions are almost identical (0.45 × 0.55 nm and 0.45 × 0.56 nm, respectively), the pore shapes are quite different. The constraint indexes are 8.2 and 9.1, respectively, for the two zeolites, but the modified C.I.^{0} was 14.4 and 10.8. In a similar approach Ernst et al. (1988) studied the reactions of n-decane and n-dodecane in a large excess of hydrogen over H-ZSM-22 and H-ZSM-23 loaded with 1% Pt. Their values for the C.I.^{0} based on n-decane were 8.9 and 4.0, respectively, lower on an absolute basis than the previous values, but in the same order. Considerable differences in the product distribution from n-dodecane were also observed on the two zeolites.

Weitkamp et al. (1989) discuss the use of a *spaciousness index* (S.I.), which is the yield ratio of *iso*butane to n-butane in hydrocracking a C_{10}-alkylcycloparaffin (e.g., butyl cyclohexane) over the zeolite containing a small amount of palladium or platinum. This index seems to be most useful for large-pore zeolites. These various studies show that subtle differences in pore configurations such as cross-sectional shape, tortuosity, internal cavities, puckering, etc., can significantly affect product selectivity.

7.7.6 Activity

The activation energy for cracking n-hexane has been found to be about 125 kJ/mol on each of several zeolites and on silica-alumina, under intrinsic kinetic conditions. The rate of reaction, which under a specified set of conditions requires 540°C on amorphous silica-alumina, can be achieved at 270°C or less on zeolites in the H-form

(Miale et al. 1966). Assuming that this activation energy holds over the entire temperature range and on the group of catalysts studied, this would indicate that the zeolites are of the order of 10^4 times as active as amorphous silica-alumina. In carefully prepared ZSM-5, the activity is directly proportional to the number of aluminum atoms present, and Haag et al. (1984) concluded that, on this zeolite, the activity is about 1000 times greater than the activity per Al atom for standard amorphous silica-alumina.

The reasons are still debatable. In carefully prepared zeolites, the Al atoms are all present in a tetrahedral coordination in contrast to the structure of amorphous material. Further, many of the Al atoms in amorphous silica-alumina may be buried or are otherwise unavailable. Rabo (1981) discusses mechanistic considerations that provide clues. Hydrocarbons evidently can be concentrated by the tiny pores at temperatures above their normal boiling point. The high electrostatic fields can aid the formation of hydrocarbon cations ("carbocations") and subsequent stabilization. Further, at sufficiently high Si/Al ratios the Al atoms in well-prepared zeolites are separated from one another, which would possibly give the maximum effect of an acid site not influenced by close neighbors.

A substantial number of infrared spectroscopic studies have revealed information about the extent of Brönsted and Lewis acidity as affected by various treatments such as calcination and steaming conditions. The number, strength, and type of acid sites can also be characterized by temperature-programmed desorption (the higher the temperature required to desorb NH_3, the stronger the acidity of a site), and nuclear magnetic resonance spectroscopy with magic angle spinning (MAS-NMR) provides a method of identifying the structures leading to acidity. However, a variety of kinds of acid sites can be present, and attempted correlations with catalytic activity involve many complexities. These include reaction kinetics, coking effects, and possible heat- and mass-transfer limitations.

The "alpha test." The rate of cracking of n-hexane diluted with e.g., helium, at atmospheric pressure, has been used by Mobil researchers to characterize the catalytic activity of zeolites (the "alpha test") and, similarly, the cracking of n-butane has been used at Union Carbide.

For proper interpretation of results, several conditions must be met (Miale et al. 1966): Reaction conditions must not be so severe that rapid catalyst deactivation by coke deposition occurs; temperatures must be sufficiently high (e.g., above 300°C) that adsorption effects do not interfere; and diffusion limitations must be negligible at reaction conditions. The last criterion was shown by Miale et al. to be met with several zeolites, including mordenite and faujasite treated in various ways, and with silica-alumina, but not with offretite. To compare catalysts of widely differing activities, it may be necessary to make measurements at different temperatures and assume the same activation energy. This situation held for the catalysts they studied, but the assumption would need to be reexamined for comparison of more widely differing catalysts or for different model compound reactions.

For a series of H-ZSM-5 catalysts, Olson et al. (1980) and Haag et al. (1984) showed a direct linear relationship between alumina content and n-hexane cracking activity. For a range of zeolites of differing structures and SiO_2/AlO_3 ratios, however, the relationship is more complex. Kaeding et al. (1981) compared the activities of a variety of zeolites for cracking of n-butane. Zeolites of low SiO_2/Al_2O_3 ratio (e.g., 5 to 6, represented by forms of Y, KL, and erionite) showed considerably lower activity than the more siliceous mordenite and zeolite ZSM-5. However, the data scattered considerably, and mordenite (SiO_2/Al_2O_3 of about 15) had a slightly higher activity than ZSM-5 samples with SiO_2/Al_2O_3 of about 60.

7.7.7   Catalytic cracking with zeolites

The use of zeolites in hydrocarbon cracking now accounts for over 90 percent of the total consumption of zeolite catalysts. Zeolites in the acidic form are much more active than conventional silica-alumina, but it was not so much high activity that led to their initial use, as the finding that, under suitable commercial operating conditions, a higher yield of gasoline could be achieved from gas oil. Moreover, the gasoline had a higher octane number.

For catalytic cracking, the zeolite must have sufficiently large pores to accomodate most feed molecules; have good stability to the high temperatures encountered in reaction and regeneration; and have good stability to steam, which is formed in regeneration and used as a purge between reactor and regenerator. Stability increases roughly with Si/Al ratio. Type Y, which is more hydrothermally stable and has a higher SiO_2/Al_2O_3 ratio than X (about 5 versus about 3), rapidly superseded X. The Y zeolite is synthesized in the Na form, but is then converted to the H form.

The hydrogen Y form cannot be obtained by direct treatment of NaY with acid since the structure is attacked and may disintegrate. Instead the Na^+ is replaced by NH_4^+. Not all sodium ions are identical in the crystal structure, and some are more difficult to exchange than others. Various procedures have been utilized to achieve a high degree of removal of Na^+, desired for increased temperature stability.

By thermal and hydrothermal treatment of ammonium Y, aluminum ions are removed from the zeolite framework and the ammonium ions are decomposed. The aluminum ions are mobile and a complex structural rearrangement results in the formation of a more highly siliceous H-faujasite, termed *ultrastable Y* (USY). The aluminum species remaining generally migrate to the exterior surface of the zeolite crystals, forming aluminum oxides, or some alumina may remain in the pores. This material may be acid-extracted to remove nonframework aluminum, or the aluminum extraction may be combined with a treatment with a fluorosilicate or $SiCl_4$ to replace aluminum with silicon. A considerable range of catalyst properties can be achieved by these various treatments and the final framework SiO_2/Al_2O_3 ratio can range up to as much as 20 or so if desired, although the ratio used in commercial cracking catalysts is considerably less. Nonframework alumina, which can also be generated by reaction, may add to catalyst activity, but it also increases coke formation and may decrease selectivity to gasoline.

Alternately, the NaY can be exchanged with rare earth and with NH_4^+ to form fully exchanged zeolite (REY) or partially exchanged zeolite (ReHY). The REY zeolites maximize gasoline production, and the USY-type zeolites maximize the octane rating of the gasoline formed, with REHY being intermediate. The phase-out of lead additives to gasoline increases the incentive to produce high-octane components. Hence, in the late 1980s USY catalysts have been substantially replacing REY-type catalysts.

The effect of increased octane rating is most pronounced with paraffinic feeds and stems primarily from an increased olefin content. The key is the effect of the catalyst to control the ratio of hydrogen transfer to cracking. In a highly siliceous zeolite, acid sites are more widely dispersed and this minimizes hydrogen transfer by:

$$Olefins + naphthas \rightarrow paraffins + aromatics$$

Formation of coke, which proceeds from H-deficient polyaromatics, is also reduced for the same reason. The acid sites in USY are also stronger than in rare-earth Y, which enhances cracking instead of H transfer. Activity is reduced slightly because of the smaller number of acid sites, but this can be countered by ion-exchanging small amounts of rare earths into the USY.

Incorporation of shape-selective zeolites into the final catalyst, usually in small amounts (e.g., mordenite, ZSM-5), also increases the octane number of the gasoline produced by selectively cracking normal paraffins. However, this decreases gasoline yield.

The formulation of commercial cracking catalysts is discussed in Sec. 9.4. The zeolite is usually prepared separately and then incorporated into a silica-alumina gel matrix that may contain other ingredients. This gel is spray-dried to yield microspheroidal particles averaging about 60 μm in diameter, the desired form for use in fluidized-bed reactors. The product is washed, base-exchanged to remove contaminant ions such as Na^+ and SO_4^{2-}, and dried again, as in a rotary drier.

7.7.8 Coke formation

Zeolites can become deactivated by carbonaceous deposits (coke) that cover catalytic sites and/or block pores. The coke structure varies with conditions, but consists essentially of ill-defined polyaromatic compounds. With time, and especially with increased temperature the hydrogen-carbon ratio of the coke usually decreases and the coke becomes more resistant to removal by oxidation.

To a considerable extent, coke formation on zeolites is a shape-selective process. Under comparable conditions coke deposits much more slowly on medium-pore zeolites such as H-ZSM-5 than on large pore zeolites such as H-Y. Studies by Rollman (1977), Magnoux and Guisnet and co-workers (1988) suggest that on ZSM-5 the space available at channel intersections is insufficient to accommodate polyaromatic structures in contrast to the larger cavities of H-Y. Guisnet and Magnoux (1989) review the effects of pore structure in general on coking and deactivation.

Most coke formation is initiated by reactions on acid sites and therefore is also affected by their number and degree of acidity. Unexpectedly low coke formation on high SiO_2/Al_2O_3 zeolites has been attributed to separation between acid sites, based on the theory that the formation reactions require several acid sites in close juxtaposition. Further, coke may form on external zeolite crystal surfaces versus on internal pores. A variety of techniques have been used to characterize the coke deposits and their location. Of particular interest is *scanning transmission electron microscopy* (STEM) combined with *electron energy loss spectroscopy* (EELS) (Gallezot et al. 1988). Derouane (1985) reviews the many factors that affect coking and deactivation on zeolites.

A zeolite catalyst is usually regenerated by oxidizing the coke with air or air diluted with nitrogen. This process may also be more or less shape selective. In a comparison of removal of coke laid down by cracking of n-heptane on H-Y, H-mordenite, or H-ZSM-5, Magnoux and Guisnet (1988) ascribed low oxidation rates on H-ZSM-5 to blockage of pore intersections by coke that restricted oxygen recirculation; whereas relatively high oxidation rates on H-Y were attributed to free circulation of oxygen through the supercages. On H-mordenite, coke was deposited at pore mouths of the 12-ring channels, but rapid coke removal was attributed to the ability of oxygen molecules to circulate through the second smaller pore system that intersects the larger channels. (See also Sec. 9.19.)

7.7.9 Methanol to gasoline

This is the first completely new synthetic fuel process to reach commercialization since the advent of the Fischer-Tropsch synthesis some five decades ago. It was developed by Mobil and termed by them the MTG (*methanol-to-gasoline*) process. In a preliminary step, methanol is dehydrated to dimethyl ether in equilibrium concentration. This mixture is then passed over a ZSM-5 catalyst at about 360 to 415°C and 2.0 MPa. Ethylene and/or propylene are formed first, after which a complex series of reactions takes place. The overall reaction network may be outlined as shown on Fig. 7.14.

With increased contact time, the olefins formed first undergo a variety of oligomerization (polymerization) and cracking reactions, the net result of which is a general scrambling of molecules accompanied by an overall increase in average molecular weight, e.g.,

$$C_3 + C_6 \rightarrow C_9 \Leftrightarrow C_4 + C_5$$

$$C_3 + C_4 \Leftrightarrow C_7, \text{ etc.}$$

Simultaneously, olefins of sufficient size undergo cyclization and hydrogen-transfer reactions occur whereby paraffins and aromatics are formed. No H_2 as such is produced.

If CH_3OH contacts an olefin, a higher olefin is formed by an alkylation reaction, e.g.,

$$C_3H_6 + CH_3OH \rightarrow C_4H_8 + H_2O$$

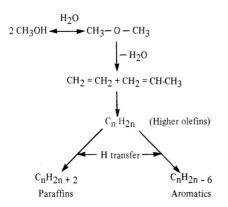

Figure 7.14 Reaction network for conversion of methanol to gasoline. *(Chang 1983)*

This rapid reaction is undesired here, and to minimize its occurrence a plug flow type of reactor is preferred, to separate CH_3OH and olefins as much as possible. Alkylation of aromatics by methanol can also occur readily and lead to formation of durene (1,2,4,5 tetramethyl benzene), which is undesired (see the following).

All these reactions are acid-catalyzed, and occur on other acidic catalysts such as silica-alumina and various other zeolites, but selectivity varies greatly. The key element of the commercial catalyst is the pore structure of ZSM-5, which has an aperture diameter of about 0.6 nm. This allows practically no aromatic hydrocarbons above C_{10} to escape from the interior. In contrast, with a 12-oxygen ring, as exists in Ω zeolite, large amounts of C_{11}-C_{12} products are formed, which are undesirable for gasoline. With erionite, with an 8-oxygen ring, little or no C_6^+ is formed, but large amounts of smaller molecules appear.

The first commercial plant using this process was constructed at Motunui, New Zealand and began operation in 1985. It has a capacity of about 14,000 barrels per day of gasoline, starting with off-shore natural gas that is converted to synthesis gas by steam reforming. Methanol synthesis uses conventional technology. Reactor design and operation is constrained by the high exothermicity of the reaction. Figure 7.15 outlines the two-step fixed-bed reactor system used in New Zealand. In the first bed, methanol (which may contain up to 20% H_2O, formed during synthesis) is converted to dimethylether in an adiabatic packed-bed reactor using an inexpensive dehydrating catalyst such as alumina, and about one-quarter of the overall heat of reaction is removed. The product is mixed with a sweep gas (mostly CH_4 by-product) at a recycle ratio of about 9 moles per mole. Thus the synthesis reactors can be operated adiabatically and the temperature rise along the bed held to an acceptable level. The catalyst gradually becomes coked and must be regenerated about once a week. Hence, five reactors in parallel are used, each operating at a different stage of the overall cycle.

Depending on operating conditions, several percent of durene (1,2,4,5 tetramethyl benzene) is formed. Durene has a melting point of 79°C and its concentration must be limited to about 2 wt % in the final product to prevent plugging in automobile carburetors. Methanol readily alkylates aromatics; thus, to minimize durene formation it must not be allowed to contact downstream products. Durene is separated by a final distillation and is sold or hydrocracked to gasoline-range product. Low-molecular-weight olefins from the reactor effluent are alkylated to gasoline. Equivalent paraffins are marketed as LPG. The existence of a nearby petroleum refinery makes it easier to integrate some of these products with normal refinery operations. The overall gasoline yield including alkylate, based on methanol, is re-

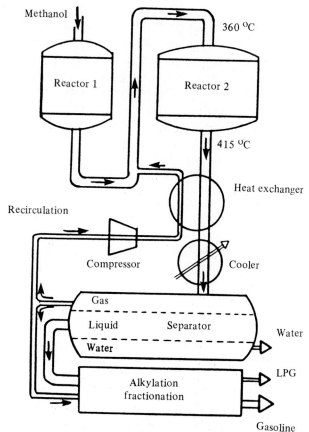

Figure 7.15 Two stage fixed-bed reactor system for synthesis of gasoline from methanol (MTG process).

portedly about 85 percent, the blended gasoline having a road octane number of about 93.

An alternate reactor design utilizes a fluidized-bed reactor, which provides good temperature control, uniform catalyst composition, and a means of continuous withdrawal of catalyst for regeneration and re-placement. A 100-barrel-per-day demonstration plant in West Germany showed that this design would also be commercially acceptable. Apparently, suitable baffling methods were developed to permit suffi-cient agitation of the catalyst to approach isothermicity in the reactor yet not cause excessive mixing of methanol and downstream reaction products.

This process (and Fischer-Tropsch synthesis from natural gas) are of interest for upgrading natural gas from sources in remote areas where there is little demand for the natural gas as such. In either case, integration of the process with a conventional petroleum refinery can make the economics somewhat more attractive. More details are available in the book by Chang (1983). Since light olefins are formed as intermediates, this process can be modified to increase total olefin selectivity (Chang 1985), but the wide distribution of olefin molecular weights is an important barrier to this becoming an industrial process.

7.7.10 Literature on zeolites

Much of the literature is in the form of patents. Papers appear in a considerable variety of sources, particularly the proceedings of the meetings of the International Zeolite Association, which are held approximately triennially, plus proceedings of other national and international conferences on zeolites. Published proceedings include volumes edited by Jacobs and van Santen (1989), Flank and Whyte (1988), Grobet et al. (1988), Murakami et al. (1987), Držaj et al. (1985), Olson and Bisio (1984), Imelik et al. (1980), and Townsend (1979). Earlier proceedings include those from conferences at the University of London in 1967 (Society of Chemical Industry 1968), followed by conferences at Worcester Polytechnic Institute, Worcester, Massachusetts in 1970 (Flanigen & Sand 1971), in Zürich in 1973 (Meier & Uytterhoeven 1973), at the University of Chicago in 1977 (Katzer 1977), and the University of Naples in 1980 (Rees 1980). Particularly useful are the review papers, plenary lectures, and keynote lectures. Individual papers vary greatly in quality, and in some cases there is considerable overlap in the contents of papers by an author or group of authors in different proceedings. See also the journal *Zeolites*.

Among recent critical reviews, Chen and Garwood (1986) discuss industrial applications of shape-selective catalysis with emphasis on the medium-pore zeolites, especially ZSM-5. A later book (Chen et al. 1989) treats the same subject with considerable new material and extensive references. In an earlier review, Haynes (1978) discusses the large-pore zeolites containing a 12-member-ring pore system. This review focuses particularly on X and Y, but also considers mordenite and L. Whyte and Dalla Betta (1982) discuss synthesis, with emphasis on use of organic reagents and ZSM-type zeolites. Palekar and Rajadhyaksha (1986) treat sorption and diffusion in zeolites. Dewing et al. (1985) review the Nu-1, FU-1, and related zeolites as developed by ICI.

In earlier reviews, the preparation and commercial utilization of zeolite cracking catalysts was covered by Magee and Blazek (1976) and Magee (1977). The earlier use of zeolites in other catalytic processes was reviewed by Bolton (1976). Minachev and Isakov (1976) reviewed metal-loaded zeolite catalysts and gave extensive references. Rudham and Stockwell (1977) reviewed in detail catalysis on faujasite-type zeolites.

The recent book by Szostak (1989) treats the principles of zeolite synthesis in detail. She includes many detailed tables of information and extensive references, especially to patents. X-ray powder diffraction data for several hundred natural, patented, and reported zeolites are given in an extensive appendix. Dyer (1988) has published a lucid introductory book on zeolites and related materials. A number of specific recipes for zeolite synthesis are given in the book by Jacobs and Martens (1987).

Earlier books include a useful, comprehensive, and detailed treatment of zeolites published by Breck (1974), which does not, however, treat catalysis. A detailed monograph edited by Rabo (1976) contains several chapters on reactions, mechanism, and technology. Jacobs (1977) critically reviewed catalytic reactions on zeolites and the relationships between activity and physical and acidic properties, focusing mainly on the literature during the period 1970 to 1976. Much of the early work on zeolites was by Barrer (1968) who reviews some aspects of their science and technology. In a later book (Barrer 1978), he treats their sorption and diffusion characteristics in detail, including that of related substances such as clays and layered silicates.

A book by Michiels and DeHerdt (1987) covers patents on synthesis, catalysis, and hydrocarbon processes based on the search files of the European Patent Office from 1975 to date of publication plus some important basic documents before 1975. A second revised edition of an atlas by Meier and Olson (1988) features stereographic drawings (designed for use with stereo glasses) of 64 topologically different zeolite structures and zeolite-like materials. It includes, for each, the structure-type codes for zeolites (3 capital letters) following the rules set up by an IUPAC Commission on zeolite nomenclature.

7.8 Other Solid Acids

A number of fine-pore solids, other than those discussed in the foregoing, show acidic properties and may be used as catalysts. These have been reviewed by Vaughan (1989). Of particular interest are *pillared interlayered clays* (PILC), which are prepared, e.g., by treatment of clay with aluminum oxychloride. This treatment provides a set of "pillars" that permanently separate the clay sheets, thus providing spaces up to 1.5 to 2.0 nm or so for the reactants to penetrate. These materials may be useful for incorporation into cracking catalysts because they can accomodate many of the larger molecules in heavy feeds that are excluded from the pores of zeolites. The structures developed thus far may be insufficiently stable for this application, but they remain of considerable interest. Pillared clays are reviewed by Occelli (1988), by Vaughan (1988a, 1988b), and in a symposium edited by Burch (1988).

Cation-exchange resins, in the form of small beads, have been used as acid catalysts for some liquid-phase reactions. The most common formulation is styrene cross-linked with divinylbenzene, which is then sulfonated (Dowex, Amberlite). The effective pore structure in these materials is very fine, however, so reactions tend to be highly diffusion-limited. This can be substantially improved by preparing a so-called *macroreticular structure*, which has a more open set of pores. An example is Amberlyst 15 (Rohm and Haas), which has pores of about 40 to 80 nm.

The use of these types of resin catalysts is limited because they begin to decompose significantly at about 90°C and are difficult to regenerate. A major industrial use is to catalyze the reaction of methanol and isobutylene to form methyl *tert*-butyl ether, widely used as a gasoline additive to improve octane number (Sec. 7.9). The structures of functionalized porous organic polymers and their uses in catalysis are reviewed by Albright (1987) and by Jakovac (1987). Fluorocarbonsulfonic acid polymers can be used at higher temperatures, but they are relatively expensive and, as currently available, have a fine pore structure (Weaver et al. 1988).

Certain forms of carbon activated under oxidizing conditions have oxygenated structures on the surface that are acidic, such as carboxylic acids. Although usually these structures are not deliberately used as acidic catalysts, they may contribute an acid-catalyzed reaction where it is not desired.

7.9   Methyl *Tert*-Butyl Ether (MTBE)

MTBE is becoming a widely used blending component in gasoline to increase octane number (Sec. 9.3), in part because it has blending characteristics similar to hydrocarbons in gasoline. It is made by reaction of methanol and isobutylene in the liquid phase, catalyzed by an acidic ion-exchange resin such as sulfonated polystyrene cross-linked with divinyl benzene (e.g., Amberlyst 15). The reaction is rapid, selective, moderately exothermic (about 37 kJ/mole at 25°C, increasing to about 45 kJ/mol at 100°C) and is equilibrium-limited. Reaction temperature is 90°C or below to increase equilibrium conversion and prolong catalyst life. Pressure is substantially above atmospheric, to keep the reaction system liquid.

Rehfinger and Hoffmann (1990) made a detailed study of the kinetics of the reaction, mostly on Amberlyst 15, as well as the thermodynamics, and they present plots of the equilibrium conversion as a function of reaction conditions. They have also determined the conditions under which macropore diffusion of methanol can become a rate-controlling step, undesired because then isobutylene dimers are formed as by-products. The conditions for significant diffusion effects are somewhat intricate because the kinetics are made complex by the strong adsorption of methanol onto the catalyst, and nonideality of the liquid reaction mixture is very significant.

Industrially, the methanol can be a commercial grade containing some water, but then some isobutyl alcohol is produced simultaneously by hydration of isobutylene. This alcohol is also a useful blending component but is slightly less valuable than MTBE. In some processes water may be first removed from the crude methanol by a simple distillation.

The hydrocarbon feed stream is typically a mixture of C_4 compounds. Butadiene, if present, is first removed to avoid any polymerization that might foul catalysts. Of the remaining C_4 compounds, only the isobutylene reacts; the remainder, including n-butylene, passes through the reactor unaffected. The C_4 stream typically contains about 50 percent isobutylene if from an ethylene cracking plant, and about 18 to 32 percent from a heavier feedstock. Most of the isobutylene produced in the United States is contained in the C_4 streams from catalytic cracking, but these streams have a much lower concentration, about 10 to 15 percent isobutylene. Isobutylene is also formed as a by-product of propylene oxide manufacture (Arco Chemical).

Several different MTBE reactor designs may be used depending on feedstock composition and other factors. With feedstocks of high isobutylene content (e.g., above about 35 percent) some type of cooling is required, e.g., by cooling and recycling some reactor effluent. With lower concentrations of isobutylene, a simple adiabatic packed-bed reactor may suffice. The feed ratio of $CH_3OH/i\text{-}C_4H_8$ is usually slightly greater than stoichiometric and 90- to 96-percent conversion is achieved in a single stage. Unreacted methanol is recycled. Several alternate processes and process economics are given by Bitar et al. (1984). Since the reaction is equilibrium-limited, an unusual process, termed catalytic distillation, may be applied. Catalytic reaction and fractionation are caused to occur simultaneously thus producing higher conversions in a single step. As of 1990 world capacity for MTBE was about 230,000 bbl/day, of which about 130,000 was in the United States. This is probably the fastest-growing chemical in the world.

Ethyl *tert*-butyl ether (ETBE) can be made from ethanol and isobutylene by a similar process. t-Butyl alcohol, produced by hydration of isobutylene with water in a similar way, has also been used as a gasoline additive, especially in a 1:1 blend with methanol. The rapid growth in use of MTBE is beginning to make it economic to isomerize n-butenes. Another source is n-butane, available from natural gas condensate, that can be isomerized to isobutane (Sec. 9.7.1), which is then dehydrogenated to isobutylene (e.g., Sec. 9.17.1).

References

Albright, R. L., in A. B. Stiles: *Catalyst Supports and Supported Catalysts*, Butterworths, Boston, 1987, p. 159.

Barrer, R. M.: *Chem. Ind.*, Sept. 7, 1968, p. 1203.

Barrer, R. M.: *Zeolites and Clay Minerals, as Sorbents and Molecular Sieves*, Academic, New York, 1978.

Barthomeuf, D., *J. Phys. Chem.*, **88**, 42 (1984).

Barthomeuf, D., in B. Imelik, C. Naccache, G. Coudurier, Y. Ben Taarit, and J. C. Vedrine, eds.: *Catalysis by Acids and Bases*, Elsevier, Amsterdam, 1985, p. 75.

Benesi, H. A., and B. H. C. Winquist: *Adv. Catal.*, **27**, 97 (1978).

Bennett, R. N., G. J. Elkes, and G. J. Wanless: *Oil Gas. J.*, **73** (1), 69 (1975).

Bitar, L. S., E. A. Hazbun, and W. J. Piel: *Hydrocarbon Process.*, October 1984, p. 63.

Bolton, A. P., in J. A. Rabo (ed.): *Zeolite Chemistry and Catalysis, ACS Monogr. No. 171*, 1976, p. 714.

Bourdillon, C., C. Gueguen, and M. Guisnet, *Appl. Catal.*, **61**, 123 (1990).

Breck, D. W., *Zeolite Molecular Sieves: Structure, Chemistry and Use*, Wiley, New York, 1974.

Briscoe, N. A., J. L. Casci, J. A. Daniels, D. W. Johnson, M. D. Shannon and A. Stewart, in P. A. Jacobs and R. A. van Santen (eds.): *Zeolites: Facts, Figures, Future*, Elsevier, Amsterdam, 1989, p. 151.

Burch, R., ed.: *Catalysis Today*, **2**, 185 (1988).

Caro, J., M. Bulow, and J. Kärger: *Chem. Eng. Sci.*, **40**, 2169 (1985).

Chang, C. D.: *Hydrocarbons from Methanol*, Dekker, New York, 1983. See also Chang, C. D.: *Catal. Rev.—Sci. Eng.*, **25**, 1 (1983).

Chang, C. D., in H. Heinemann and G. A. Somorjai (eds.): *Catal. Rev.—Sci. Eng.*, **26** (3, 4), 1985.

Chen, N. Y., and W. E. Garwood: *J. Catal.*, **52**, 453 (1978).

Chen, N. Y., and W. E. Garwood: *Catal. Rev.—Sci. Eng.*, **28**, 185 (1986).

Chen, N. Y., W. E. Garwood, and F. G. Dwyer: *Shape Selective Catalysis in Industrial Applications*, Dekker, New York, 1989.

Csicsery, S. M.: *J. Catal.*, **19**, 394 (1970). *Ibid.*, **23**, 124 (1971).

Damon, J. P., B. Delmon, and J. M. Bonnier, *J. Chem. Soc., Far. Trans.*, **1**, 372 (1977).

Davis, M. E., et al.: *Zeolites*, **8**, 362 (1988).

Derouane, E. G., and Z. Gabelica: *J. Catal.*, **65**, 486 (1980).

Derouane, E. G., in B. Imelik, C. Naccache, G. Coudurier, Y. Ben Taarit, and J. C. Vedrine (eds.): *Catalysis by Acids and Bases*, Elsevier, Amsterdam, 1985, p. 221.

Dewing, J., M. S. Spencer, and T. V. Whittam: *Catal. Rev.—Sci. Eng.*, **27**, 461 (1985).

Držaj, B., S. Hočévar, and S. Pejovnik (eds.): *Zeolites. Synthesis, Structure, Technology and Application*, Proceedings of a Symposium, Portoroz-Portorose, Elsevier, Amsterdam, 1985.

Dwyer, D., in P. J. Grobet, W. J. Mortier, E. F. Vansant, and G. Schulz-Ekloff (eds.): *Innovation in Zeolite Materials Science*, Proceedings of a Symposium, Nieuwpoort (Belgium), Elsevier, Amsterdam, 1988, p. 333.

Dwyer, D., and P. J. O'Malley, in S. Kaliaguine (ed.): *Keynotes in Energy-Related Catalysis*, Elsevier, Amsterdam, 1988, p. 5.

Dyer, A.: *An Introduction to Zeolite Molecular Sieves*, Wiley, New York, 1988.

Emmett, P. H.: *Catalysis Then and Now*, Franklin, Englewood, N.J., 1965.

Ernst, S., G. T. Kokotailo, R. Kumar and J. Weitkamp, in M. J. Phillips, and M. Ternan (eds.): *Proceedings, 9th International Congress on Catalysis*, The Chemical Institute of Canada, Ottawa, 1988, p. 388.

Flanigan, E. M. and L. B. Sand (eds.): *Molecular Sieve Zeolites, I and II, Adv. Chem. Ser. Nos. 101 and 102*, 1971.
Flank, W. H., and T. E. Whyte (eds.): *Perspectives in Molecular Sieve Science, ACS Symposium Series No. 368*, American Chemical Society, Washington, D.C., 1988.
Forni, L.: *Catal. Rev.*, **8**, 65 (1974).
Frilette, V. J., W. O. Haag, and R. M. Lago: *J. Catal.*, **67**, 218 (1981).
Gallezot, P., C. Leclerc, M. Guisnet, and P. Magnoux: *J. Catal.*, **114**, 100 (1988).
Garces, J. M., F. C. Stone, S. I. Bates, J. L. Cwinultt, and F. H. Scheidt, in P. J. Grobet, W. J. Mortier, E. F. Vansant, and G. Schulz-Ekloff (eds.): *Innovation in Zeolite Materials Science*, Proceedings of a Symposium, Nieuwpoort (Belgium), Elsevier, Amsterdam, 1988, p. 505.
Giannetti, J. P., and A. J. Perrotta: *Ind. Eng. Chem., Process Des. Devel.*, **14**, 86 (1975).
Goldstein, M. S., in R. B. Anderson (ed.): *Experimental Methods in Catalytic Research*, Academic, New York, 1968, p. 361.
Gorring, R. L.: *J. Catal.*, **31**, 13 (1973).
Greensfelder, B. S., H. H. Voge, and G. M. Good: *Ind. Eng. Chem.*, **41**, 2573 (1949).
Grobet, P. J., W. J. Mortier, E. F. Vansant, and G. Schulz-Ekloff (eds.): *Innovation in Zeolite Materials Science*, Proceedings of a Symposium, Nieuwpoort (Belgium), Elsevier, Amsterdam, 1988.
Guisnet, M., in B. Imelik, C. Naccache, G. Coudurier, Y. Ben Taarit, and J. C. Vedrine (eds.): *Catalysis by Acids and Bases*, Elsevier, Amsterdam, 1985, p. 283.
Guisnet, M., and P. Magnoux: *Appl. Catal.*, **54**, 1 (1989).
Haag, W. O., and R. M. Dessau, in DECHEMA, *Proceedings, 8th International Congress on Catalysis*, vol. II, p. 305 and vol. VI, p. 55, Verlag Chemie, Weinheim, 1984.
Haag, W. O., R. M. Lago, and P. B. Weisz: *Faraday Discussions of the Chemical Society*, **72**, 317 (1981).
Haag, W. O., R. M. Lago, and P. B. Weisz: *Nature*, **309**, 589 (1984).
Hansford, R. C.: *Adv. Catal.*, **4**, 1 (1952).
Hashimoto, K., T. Masuda, and H. Sasaki: *Ind. Eng. Chem. Res.*, **27**, 1792 (1988).
Haynes, H. W., Jr.: *Catal. Rev.—Sci. Eng.*, **17**, 273 (1978).
Higgins, J. B., R. B. La Pierre, J. L. Schlenker, A. C. Rohrman, J. D. Wood, G. T. Kerr, and W. J. Rohrbaugh: *Zeolites*, **8**, 447 (1988).
Hoelderich, W. F., in Y. Murakami, A. Iijama, and J. W. Ward (eds.): *New Developments in Zeolite Science and Technology*, Proceedings of the 7th International Zeolite Conference, Tokyo, 1986, Elsevier, Amsterdam, 1987, p. 827.
Hoelderich, W. F., in P. A. Jacobs and R. A. van Santen (eds.): *Zeolites: Facts, Figures, Future*, Elsevier, Amsterdam, 1989, p. 69.
Imelik, B., C. Naccache, Y. Ben Taarit, J. C. Vedrine, G. Coudurier, and H. Praliaud (eds.): *Catalysis by Zeolites*, Proceedings of a Symposium, CNRS Lyon, 1980, Elsevier, Amsterdam, 1980.
Imelik, B., C. Naccache, G. Coudurier, Y. Ben Taarit, and J. C. Vedrine, eds.: *Catalysis by Acids and Bases*, Elsevier, Amsterdam, 1985.
Jacobs, P. A., *Carboniogenic Activity of Zeolites*, Elsevier, New York, 1977.
Jacobs, P. A., in F. Delannay (ed.): *Characterization of Heterogeneous Catalysts*, Dekker, New York, 1984, p. 367.
Jacobs, P. A., and J. A. Martens: *Pure and Appl. Chem.*, **58**, 1329 (1986).
Jacobs, P. A., and J. A. Martens: *Synthesis of High-Silica Aluminosilicate Zeolites*, Elsevier, Amsterdam, 1987.
Jacobs, P. A., and J. A. Martens, in Y. Murakami, A. Iijama, and J. W. Ward (eds.): *New Developments in Zeolite Science and Technology*, Proceedings of the 7th International Zeolite Conference, Tokyo, 1986, Elsevier, Amsterdam, 1987, p. 23.
Jacobs, P. A. and R. A. van Santen (eds.): *Zeolites: Facts, Figures, Future*, Elsevier, Amsterdam, 1989.
Jakovac, I. J., in A. B. Stiles: *Catalyst Supports and Supported Catalysts*, Butterworths, Boston, 1987, p. 187.
Kaeding, W. W., C. Chu, L. B. Young, and S. A. Butter: *J. Catal.*, **69**, 392 (1981).
Kärger, J., and J. Caro, *J. Chem. Soc. Faraday, I*, **73**, 1363 (1977).
Kärger, J.: *AIChE J.*, **28**, 417 (1982).
Kärger, J. and H. Pfeifer: *Zeolites*, **7**, 90 (1987).

Katzer, J. R. (ed.): *Molecular Sieves, II, ACS Symp. Ser. No. 40*, 1977.
Kibby, C. L., A. J. Perrotta, and F. E. Massoth: *J. Catal.*, **35**, 256 (1974).
Kokotailo, G. T., S. L. Lawton, D. H. Olson, and W. M. Meier: *Nature*, **272**, p. 437 (March 30, 1978).
Krylov, O. V.: *Catalysis by Nonmetals*, Academic, New York, 1970.
Kutz, N. A., in W. H. Flank and T. E. Whyte (eds.): *Perspectives in Molecular Sieve Science, ACS Symposium Series No. 368*, American Chemical Society, Washington, D.C., 1988, p. 532.
McMahon, J. F., C. Bednars, and E. Solomon in J. J. McKetta (ed.): *Advances in Petroleum Chemistry and Refining*, vol. 7, Wiley, New York, 1963, p. 284.
Magee, J. S., in J. R. Katzer (ed.): *Molecular Sieves, II, ACS Symp. Ser. No. 40*, 1977, p. 650.
Magee, J. S., and J. J. Blazek in J. A. Rabo (ed.): *Zeolite Chemistry and Catalysis, ACS Monogr. No. 171*, 1976, p. 615.
Magnoux, P., and M. Guisnet: *Appl. Catal.*, **38**, 341 (1988).
Malinowski, S., and J. Kijen'ski: *Catalysis*, vol. 4, The Royal Society of Chemistry, London, 1981, p. 130.
Martens, J. A., and P. A. Jacobs: *Zeolites*, **6**, 334 (1986).
Martens, L. R., W. J. Vermeiren, D. R. Huybrechts, P. J. Grobet, and P. A. Jacobs, in M. J. Phillips and M. Ternan (eds.): *Proceedings, 9th International Congress on Catalysis*, vol. 1, The Chemical Institute of Canada, Ottawa, 1988, p. 420.
Meier, M. W., and J. B. Uytterhoeven (eds.): *Molecular Sieves, Adv. Chem. Ser. No. 121.* [Discussion and recent progress reports published as a separate volume: J. B. Uytterhoeven (ed.): *Proceedings of the Third International Conference on Molecular Sieves*, Leuven University Press, Leuven, Belgium, 1973.]
Meier, W. M., and D. H. Olson: *Atlas of Zeolite Structure Types*, 2nd ed., Butterworths, Boston, 1988.
Miale, J. N., N. Y. Chen, and P. B. Weisz: *J. Catal.*, **6**, 278 (1966).
Michiels, P., and O. C. E. DeHerdt: *Molecular Sieve Catalysts*, Pergamon, Elmsford, N.Y., 1987.
Minachev, Kh. M., and Ya. I. Isokov in J. A. Rabo (ed.): *Zeolite Chemistry and Catalysis, ACS Monogr. No. 171*, 1976, p. 552.
Moore, R. M., and J. R. Katzer: *AIChE J.*, **18**, 816 (1972).
Murakami, Y., A. Iijama, and J. W. Ward (eds.): *New Developments in Zeolite Science and Technology*, Proceedings of the 7th International Zeolite Conference, Tokyo, 1986, Elsevier, Amsterdam, 1987.
Oblad, A. G., T. H. Milliken, Jr., and G. A. Mills: *Adv. Catal.*, **3**, 199 (1951).
Occelli, M. L., in S. Kaliaguine (ed.): *Keynotes in Energy-Related Catalysis*, Elsevier, Amsterdam, 1988, p. 101.
Occelli, M. L., and H. E. Robson (eds.): *Zeolite Synthesis, ACS Symposium Series No. 398*, 1989.
Olson, D. H., and A. Bisio (eds.): *Proceedings of the Sixth International Zeolite Conference*, Butterworths, Surrey, 1984.
Olson, D. H., W. O. Haag, and R. M. Lago: *J. Catal.*, **61**, 390 (1980).
Ono, Y., in B. Imelik, C. Naccache, Y. Ben Taarit, J. C. Vedrine, G. Coudurier, and H. Praliaud (eds.): *Catalysis by Zeolites*, Proceedings of a Symposium, CNRS Lyon, 1980, Elsevier, Amsterdam, 1980, p. 19.
Palekar, M. G., and R. A. Rajadhyaksha: *Catal. Rev.—Sci. Eng.*, **28**, 371 (1986).
Pellet, R. J., P. K. Coughlin, E. S. Shamshoum, and J. A. Rabo, in W. H. Flank and T. E. Whyte (eds.): *Perspectives in Molecular Sieve Science, ACS Symposium Series No. 368*, American Chemical Society, Washington, D.C., 1988, p. 512.
Peri, J. B., in J. R. Anderson, and M. Boudart (eds.): *Catalysis: Science and Technology*, vol. 5, Springer, New York, 1984.
Pines, H.: *The Chemistry of Catalytic Hydrocarbon Conversions*, Academic, New York, 1981.
Pines, H., and W. M. Stalick: *Base-Catalyzed Reactions of Hydrocarbons and Related Compounds*, Academic, New York, 1977.
Pitcher, W. H., Jr.: Sc.D. thesis, M.I.T., Cambridge, Mass., 1972.
Polinski, L. M., and M. J. Baird: *Ind. Eng. Chem., Prod. Res. Dev.*, **24**, 540 (1985).

Post, M. F. M., in *Introduction to Zeolite Science and Practice*, to be published, Elsevier, Amsterdam, 1990.

Qureshi, W. R., and J. Wei, to be published.

Rabo, J. A. (ed.): *Zeolite Chemistry and Catalysis, ACS Monogr. No. 171*, 1976.

Rabo, J. A.: *Catal. Rev.—Sci. Eng.*, **23**, 293 (1981).

Rees, L. V. C. (ed.): *Proceedings of the Fifth International Conference on Zeolites*, Heyden, London, 1980.

Rehfinger, A., and U. Hoffmann: *Chem. Eng. Sci.*, **45**, 1605, 1619 (1990).

Robson, H. E., G. P. Hamner, and W. F. Arey, in E. M. Flanigen and L. B. Sand (eds.): *Molecular Sieve Zeolites, II, Adv. Chem. Ser., No. 102*, 1971, p. 417.

Rollman, L. D.: *J. Catal.*, **47**, 113 (1977).

Rollman, L. D., and D. E. Walsh: *J. Catal.*, **56**, 139 (1979).

Rudham, R., and A. Stockwell: *Catalysis*, vol. 1, The Chemical Society, London, 1977, p. 87.

Ruthven, D. M.: *Principles of Adsorption and Adsorption Processes*, Wiley, New York, 1984.

Ryland, L. B., M. W. Tamele, and J. N. Wilson in P. H. Emmett (ed.): *Catalysis*, vol. 7, Reinhold, New York, 1960, p. 1.

Sanders, J. V., in J. R. Anderson and M. Boudart (eds.): *Catalysis: Science and Technology*, Springer, New York, 1985, vol. 7, p. 51.

Satterfield, C. N., and C. S. Cheng: *AIChE Symp. Ser. No. 117*, **67**, 43 (1971).

Satterfield, C. N., and C. S. Cheng: *AIChE J.*, **18**, 720 (1972).

Satterfield, C. N., and J. R. Katzer, in E. M. Flanigen and L. B. Sand (eds.): *Molecular Sieve Zeolites, Adv. Chem. Ser., No. 102*, 1971, p. 193.

Schaad, R. E., in B. T. Brooks et al. (eds.): *The Chemistry of Petroleum Hydrocarbons*, vol. 3, Reinhold, New York, 1955, p. 221.

Society of Chemical Industry (London): *Molecular Sieves*, 1968.

Szostak, R., *Molecular Sieves. Principles of Synthesis and Identification*, Van Nostrand Reinhold, New York, 1989.

Takeshita, T., R. Ohnishi, and K. Tanabe: *Catal. Rev.*, **8**, 29 (1974).

Tanabe, K.: *Solid Acids and Bases*, Academic, New York, 1970.

Tanabe, K., in B. Imelik, C. Naccache, G. Coudurier, Y. Ben Taarit, and J. C. Vedrine, eds.: *Catalysis by Acids and Bases*, Elsevier, Amsterdam, 1985, p. 1.

Tanabe, K., in J. R. Anderson and M. Boudart, eds.: *Catalysis: Science and Technology*, vol. 2, Springer, New York, 1981, p. 231.

Tanabe, K., in M. J. Phillips, and M. Ternan (eds.): *Proceedings, 9th International Congress on Catalysis*, vol. 5, The Chemical Institute of Canada, Ottawa, 1988, p. 85.

Tanabe, K., M. Misono, Y. Ono, and H. Hattori, *New Solid Acids and Bases: Their Catalytic Properties*, Elsevier, Amsterdam, 1989.

Tanabe, K., and T. Yamaguchi, in T. Inui (ed.): *Successful Design of Catalysts*, Elsevier, Amsterdam, 1988, p. 99.

Tanabe, K., G. Zhang, and H. Hattori: *Appl. Catal.*, **48**, 63 (1989).

Thomas, C. L.: *Ind. Eng. Chem.*, **41**, 2564 (1949).

Thomas, J. M., in DECHEMA, *Proceedings, 8th International Congress on Catalysis*, vol. 1, Verlag Chemie, Weinheim, 1984, p. 31.

Thomas, J. M., in P. A. Jacobs, and R. A. van Santen (eds.): *Zeolites: Facts, Figures, Future*, Elsevier, Amsterdam, 1989, p. 3.

Townsend, R. P. (ed.): *The Properties and Applications of Zeolites*, Proceedings of a Conference, City University, London, 1979. The Chemical Society, London, 1980, Special Publication No. 33.

Treacy, M. M. J., and J. M. Newsam: *Nature*, **232**, 249 (1988).

Unger, K. K., U. R. Kittelmann, and W. K. Kreis: *J. Chem. Tech. Biotech.*, **31**, 435 (1981).

Vaughan, D. E. W., in R. P. Townsend (ed.): *The Properties and Applications of Zeolites*, Proceedings of a Conference, City University, London. The Chemical Society, London, 1980, Special Publication No. 33, p. 294.

Vaughan, D. E. W., *Catalysis Today*, **2**, 187 (1988).

Vaughan, D. E. W., in W. H. Flank and T. E. Whyte, Jr. (eds.): *Perspectives in Molecular Sieve Science, ACS Symposium Series No. 368*, American Chemical Society, Washington, D.C., 1988, p. 308.

Vaughan, D. E. W., in P. A. Jacobs, and R. A. van Santen (eds.): *Zeolites: Facts, Figures, Future*, Elsevier, Amsterdam, 1989, p. 95.

Vaughan, D. E. W., M. M. J. Treacy, J. M. Newsam, K. G. Strohmaier, and W. J. Mortier, in M. L. Occelli and H. E. Robson (eds.): *Zeolite Synthesis, ACS Symposium Series No. 398*, 1989, p. 544.

Villadsen, J., and H. Livbjerg: *Catal. Rev.—Sci. Eng.*, **17**, 203 (1978).

Weaver, J. D., E. L. Tasset, and W. E. Fry, in J. W. Ward (ed.): *Catalysis 1987*, Elsevier, Amsterdam, 1988, p. 483.

Weisz, P. B.: *Chemtech*, **3**, 498 (1973).

Weisz, P. B., and V. J. Frilette: *J. Phys. Chem.*, **64**, 382 (1960).

Weitkamp, J., S. Ernst, H. Dauns, and E. Gallei: *Chem.—Ing.-Tech.*, **58**, 623 (1986).

Weitkamp, J., S. Ernst, and C. Y. Chen, in P. A. Jacobs and R. A. van Santen (eds.): *Zeolites: Facts, Figures, Future*, Elsevier, Amsterdam, 1989, p. 1115.

Whyte, T. E., Jr., and R. A. Dalla Betta: *Catal. Rev.—Sci. Eng.*, **24**, 567 (1982).

Xiao, J., Ph.D. thesis, M.I.T., 1990.

Catalytic Oxidation

Partial oxidation processes using air or oxygen are used to manufacture a variety of chemicals, and complete catalytic oxidation is a widely used method for elimination of organic pollutants in gaseous streams. In the manufacture of organic chemicals, oxygen may be incorporated into the final product, as in the oxidation of propylene to acrolein, or o-xylene to phthalic anhydride; or the reaction may be an oxidative dehydrogenation in which the oxygen does not appear in the desired product, as in the conversion of butylene to butadiene. The desired reaction may or may not involve C—C bond scission. Closely related are *ammoxidation* reactions (also termed *oxidative ammonolysis*) in which a mixture of air and ammonia is reacted catalytically with an organic compound to form a nitrile, as in the ammoxidation of propylene to acrylonitrile. With the advent of more active and selective catalysts, direct oxidation processes have gradually replaced earlier processes that utilized such oxidizing agents as nitrogen dioxide, chromic acid, and hypochlorous acid.

Catalytic oxidation processes for manufacture of organic chemicals have several features in common.

1. They are highly exothermic. Heat- and mass-transfer effects may be very important, so multitube heat-exchange reactors or fluidized beds are usually used. An important element of reactor design is to prevent catalyst deactivation by excessive temperature or runaway reaction.

2. Certain composition regions may be explosive. The ratio of organic compound to air (or oxygen) in the feed stream may be selected in large part to avoid these regions. For the same reason, air may be introduced at multiple points. Operation may be either "fuel-rich" or "fuel-lean."

3. The desired product must be sufficiently stable relative to the reactant, under reaction conditions, that it can be removed from product gases in an economic yield, usually involving rapid quenching, before it decomposes or undergoes further reaction. Most of the compounds currently made industrially have ring structures that are highly stable, e.g., phthalic anhydride, maleic anhydride, and ethylene oxide; or a conjugated structure that imparts stability, such as $C{=}C{-}C{=}C$, $C{=}C{-}C{\equiv}N$, and $C{=}C{-}C{=}O$. In contrast, although there have been many attempts to develop a process for the direct heterogeneous oxidation of methane to formaldehyde, no economic method has been invented since the product is much less stable than the reactant.

Sometimes relatively good selectivity to a desired product can be achieved at low-percent conversions. In that case the product is typically removed from the reactor exit gas and the remaining stream is recycled, perhaps after purification, and mixed with fresh feed, and the mixture is fed to the reactor inlet.

Effective catalysts for oxidation reactions fall into two categories:

1. Transition metal oxides in which oxygen is readily transferred to and from the structure: Most but not all of the industrial catalysts of this type are mixed oxides containing two or more cations, and the compounds are nonstoichiometric. Examples are an iron-molybdate catalyst for oxidizing methanol to formaldehyde, complex bismuth molybdates for oxidizing propylene to acrolein or ammoxidation of propylene to acrylonitrile, and catalysts containing vanadium oxide for converting benzene or n-butane to maleic anhydride and naphthalene or o-xylene to phthalic anhydride.

2. Metals onto which oxygen is chemisorbed: Examples are ethylene to ethylene oxide on a supported silver catalyst, ammonia oxidation to nitric oxide on platinum gauze, and methanol to formaldehyde on silver granules.

Practical oxide catalysts may be much more difficult to characterize than other types of catalysts. In the case of a supported oxide catalyst, methods for determining active area in contrast to total area—analogous to the use of selective chemisorption for supported metal catalysts or base titration to estimate the number of acid sites on an acidic catalyst—are much more rudimentary. Many of the oxide catalysts may be more or less amorphous, and even when an X-ray pattern can be observed, the contribution of the crystalline phase to total catalytic properties may be far from clear. Some useful catalyst compositions may contain as many as four or five metal elements, each of which must be present for optimum performance, but their role remains obscure. Defects in a crystal structure appear to play a role, but the extent to which they exist under reaction conditions is speculative.

For some comprehensive discussions of mechanisms of oxidation catalysis see, for example, reviews by Bielan'ski and Haber (1979), Haber (1981), Boreskov (1982), Bond (1989), and the book by Kiselev and Krylov (1989). See also the papers in a Faraday Discussions (1989).

In a few cases, at reaction temperatures the catalyst appears to be a liquid held in the pores of a support rather than a solid. This occurs under at least some reaction conditions for the vanadium oxide-potassium sulfate catalyst used for oxidation of sulfur dioxide to sulfur trioxide (Sec. 8.9), and also for some metal chloride catalysts used in oxychlorination (Sec. 8.8).

8.1 Redox Mechanism

The behavior of most oxidation catalysts can be interpreted within the framework of a redox mechanism (*red*uction-*ox*idation). This postulates that the catalytic reaction comprises two steps:

1. Reaction between catalyst in an oxidized form, Cat-O, and the hydrocarbon R, in which the oxide becomes reduced: Cat-O + R → RO + Cat.

2. The reduced catalyst, Cat, becomes oxidized again by oxygen from the gas phase: $2Cat + O_2 \rightarrow 2Cat-O$. Under steady-state conditions, the rates of the two steps must be the same.

Within this framework more specific models were developed by Mars and van Krevelen (1954) to explain the kinetic behavior of the partial oxidation of several aromatic hydrocarbons. The rate was noted to be independent of the nature of the hydrocarbon or its partial pressure over a substantial range of concentration.

Strictly, their derivation makes no assumption about the form of the oxygen in the catalyst; that is, it can be either chemisorbed or lattice oxygen. However lattice oxygen systems seem to follow this model in a general way, whereas some chemisorbed oxygen systems exhibit kinetic behavior that may be more clearly understood in terms of the Langmuir-Hinshelwood or Rideal models. In the case of lattice oxygen, the active species is presumably the O^{2-} ion.

For the hydrocarbon oxidation studies, to develop a simple mathematical model Mars and van Krevelen assumed that the rate of oxidation of the reactant is proportional to the fraction of active sites in the oxidized state and to the hydrocarbon partial pressure. The rate of reoxidation of the catalyst is taken to be proportional to the fraction of sites on the catalyst in the reduced (or empty) state and to $P_{O_2}^{\ n}$. Then under steady state conditions

$$r = kP_{HC}(1 - \theta) = \left(\frac{k^*}{\beta}\right) P_{O_2}^{\ n} \theta \qquad (8.1)$$

where, in present nomenclature,

P_{HC} = partial pressure of hydrocarbon
  k = reaction rate constant for oxidation of hydrocarbon
  k^* = reaction rate constant for surface reoxidation
  β = moles O_2 consumed per mole of hydrocarbon reacted
  θ = fraction of active sites in reduced state

$$\theta = \frac{kP_{HC}}{kP_{HC} + (k^*/\beta)\, P_{O_2}^{\ n}} \qquad (8.2)$$

Substituting Eq. (8.2) into the second equality of Eq. (8.1) gives

$$r = \frac{1}{(\beta/k^*P_{O_2}^{\ n}) + (1/kP_{HC})} \qquad (8.3)$$

Their data for the hydrocarbon oxidation reactions were best fitted by $n = 1$.

Equation (8.3) leads to several conclusions. If the potential rate of oxidation of the hydrocarbon by the catalyst exceeds that of reoxidation of the catalyst, then

$$kP_{HC} >> \frac{k^*P_{O_2}^{\ n}}{\beta} \qquad (8.4)$$

and Eq. (8.3) reduces to

$$r = \left(\frac{k^*}{\beta}\right) P_{O_2}^{\ n} \qquad (8.5)$$

The overall observed reaction rate should then be equal to the potential rate of oxidation of the catalyst surface and therefore should be independent of hydrocarbon partial pressure (i.e., zero order). In this simplified model, the rate constant k^* at a fixed temperature should be independent of the nature of the hydrocarbon. Mars and van Krevelen indeed found this to be true for several aromatic substances on a catalyst consisting of 9 wt % V_2O_5, 2.9 wt % MoO_3, and 0.03 wt % P_2O_5 on a corundum carrier.

In a later study of oxidation of o-xylene to phthalic anhydride on a V_2O_5/SiC catalyst (Calderbank & Caldwell 1972), the reoxidation was likewise reported to be the rate-limiting step, with an activation energy of about 167 kJ/mol. The activation energy for the hydrocarbon oxidation step was estimated at about 113 kJ/mol. Thus, at relatively higher temperatures, the inequality of Eq. (8.4) could conceivably be reversed, whereupon the reaction would become independent of oxygen pressure and proportional to hydrocarbon partial pressure.

For other oxidation reactions this reversed inequality is indeed found $(k^*/\beta >> k$ for $n = 1)$. An example is the ammoxidation of propylene to acrylonitrile on the bismuth-molybdate or antimony-uranium oxide catalysts used industrially. Here the rate-limiting process is the reaction of hydrocarbon with the catalyst rather than reoxidation of the catalyst. A further consequence is that for these cases only a slight excess of oxygen should be needed to keep the catalyst in a high oxidation state.

The concept of a redox system can also be applied to a single "mixed valence" compound in which a catalytically active element can exist in more than one oxidation state. For example, in vanadium phosphate, a catalyst for conversion of n-butane to maleic anhydride, V atoms can exist in different crystallographic sites, and a redox mechanism could operate without structural change.

If one considers a broad range of oxide catalysts, it might be expected that, for a specified reaction, the maximum rate would be encountered at some intermediate degree of heat of reaction for reoxidation of the catalyst, Q_0. That is, a plot of reaction rate versus Q_0 would show a volcano curve analogous to that found for some reactions on metals. This concept has been developed by many investigators and was reviewed by Germain (1972) and Haber (1975). However, application in a meaningful fashion to practical catalysts has been difficult. A more useful concept is that of oxygen mobility.

Oxygen mobility can be expressed in several ways, such as by the heat of dissociation of the first oxygen from the oxide to the next lower oxidation state, by the rate of exchange of isotopic oxygen between the bulk-gas phase and oxygen in the catalyst, or by the partial pressure of oxygen above the oxide at a specified temperature. Pulsing reactor studies (Sec. 11.8) also provide a means of obtaining clues and also some indication of the ease with which oxygen can diffuse in and out of layers below the catalyst surface.

Sachtler et al. (1970) and Sachtler and deBoer (1965) have suggested that maximum selectivity is associated with an optimum degree of oxygen mobility and this seems to be borne out in studies in which catalyst compositions have been systematically altered and correlated with selectivity data. For an optimum combination of activity and selectivity, there should be a matching between the difficulty of oxidizing the reactant and the ease of removal of oxygen from the catalyst. Tightly bound oxygen should result in a low-activity catalyst. Highly mobile oxygen should result in a high-activity catalyst, but one that is nonselective.

In at least several cases, maximum activity of an oxidation catalyst is observed when the catalyst is in a somewhat reduced state rather than completely oxidized. This behavior was shown, e.g., by Sleight and Linn (1976) for oxidation of butene over various lead-bismuth-molybdate catalysts. With vanadium oxide, maximum activity or selectivity has been reported for the composition V_2O_4 or compositions intermediate between V_2O_4 and V_2O_5 (see Sec. 8.6).

The concept of selectivity as affected by adsorption of an intermediate has been generalized by Germain (1972) in what he terms a *rake mechanism*. Considering a species such as propylene, successive abstraction of H atoms leads to a "rake" of adsorbed species:

$$C_3H_6 \rightarrow C_3H_5 \rightarrow C_3H_4 \rightarrow C_3H_3$$

The third can be desorbed as acrolein in oxidation and the fourth as acrylonitrile in ammoxidation (Sec. 8.2). The usefulness of this concept is that it suggests the possibility of improving reaction selectivity by modifying catalyst composition so as to enhance the desorption of a desired intermediate. Another example of a rake mechanism is that discussed by Bond (1989) for the partial oxidation of o-xylene to phthalic anhydride.

With oxide catalysts, chemisorbed surface oxygen as well as lattice oxygen may play a role. It seems plausible that in some cases chemisorbed oxygen would lead to a different set of products than lattice oxygen and both mechanisms could be significant. Haber (1975) advances the hypothesis that surface-adsorbed oxygen may, in general, lead to products of complete oxidation and that lattice oxygen is needed for partially oxidized products, but more study is needed to test this proposal, or indeed whether surface-chemisorbed oxygen plays any role.

Most of the metal oxides of interest are nonstoichiometric, and the oxygen-metal ratio in the solid varies with temperature, oxygen partial pressure, and the environment. Hence, reaction conditions can affect the state of oxidation of the catalyst and this in turn can affect activity and selectivity.

V_2O_x can be readily reduced down to a composition with x nearly as low as 3 and yet be rapidly reoxidized to V_2O_5. This has led to the suggestion that vanadium oxide, or other solids capable of rapid and reversible oxidation-reduction, could be used as an oxygen carrier in a recirculation process to cause a partial oxidation reaction in one vessel, the carrier being transported to and reoxidized in a second vessel with air. This has the merit of allowing different (and possibly superior) solid compositions than that corresponding to the steady-state condition in the presence of a reactant-oxygen mixture and, thus, the possibility of synthesizing products that would be too reactive in the presence of oxygen. Product would not be diluted with N_2, thus lowering separation costs.

One disadvantage is the large quantity of solid that would need to be moved back and forth between reactor and regenerator relative to the quantity of product formed. A second is the necessity of developing a solid composition that, in addition to having the requisite chemical properties, would also be resistant to mechanical attrition and repetitive cycling between different temperatures and gas compositions. Isolation of the fluids from one another in the reactor and regenerator is also vital, so inadvertent mixing, which might lead to an explosion, cannot occur. A recirculation system of this sort has been used satisfactorily for decades in the usual catalytic cracking process in petroleum reforming. (Here catalyst becomes rapidly deactivated by coking, and it is circulated to a regenerator, where coke is removed by combustion in air.) As of 1990, a recirculation process to manufacture maleic anhydride by partial oxidation of butane was under study in a du Pont pilot plant [see Contractor et al. (1988) and Sec. 8.6.1].

If reaction selectivity is of less importance, the oxidation state of the substance may likewise be less important, and the ease of movement of oxygen to and from subsurface layers becomes a more prominent desideratum. This in turn suggests applying the foregoing concept by periodic operation of a fixed-bed reactor, in which are fed in sequence air (or oxygen), inert gas, reactant, inert gas, air, etc., with suitable means for isolating the exit streams.

Many commercial oxidation catalysts have highly complex structures, and in some cases selectivity is dependent on details of catalyst composition that may be understood only in part. Some insight into these factors may be obtained by considering specific cases that are industrially important and that have undergone intense scrutiny from a fundamental scientific viewpoint. Instructive examples are the epoxidation of ethylene to form ethylene oxide on silver (Sec. 8.3) and the partial oxidation of n-butane to maleic anhydride on a vanadium-phosphate catalyst (8.6.1).

8.2 Oxidation and Ammoxidation of Propylene

8.2.1 Acrylonitrile

The manufacture of acrylonitrile by the ammoxidation of propylene has become the dominant industrial process, based primarily on the discovery of a series of complex metal-oxide catalysts by Idol and co-workers at the Standard Oil Co. of Ohio (Sohio), now a part of British Petroleum (BP). The process, which first became commercial in about 1960, utilizes a fluidized-bed reactor, as do closely related processes by Montedison and Nitto. Ammonia, air, and propylene are supplied to the reactor at a pressure of about 2 atm and in nearly stoichiometric ratios, according to the equation

$$NH_3 + C_3H_6 + \tfrac{3}{2} O_2 \rightarrow CH_2\!=\!CHCN + 3H_2O \qquad (8.6)$$

$$-\Delta H = -515 \text{ kJ/mol}$$

The reactor temperature is in the range of 400 to 500°C, and the residence time is a few seconds. Several by-products are also formed, in particular hydrogen cyanide and acetonitrile, which may be recovered as by-products, and carbon oxides. With some catalyst compositions and under proper operating conditions, essentially all the ammonia and propylene are consumed. With other catalysts, a small amount of ammonia remains in the product gas, which may be recovered or scrubbed with sulfuric acid to convert it to ammonium sulfate before the acrylonitrile is separated. Heat released by the reaction is recovered as steam by cooling coils immersed in the reactor.

The same reaction is carried out in a multitube fixed-bed reactor in a process developed by British Petroleum (Distillers)/Ugine, which uses a catalyst containing the mixed oxides of antimony and tin, and possibly also some iron. This process is not now widely practiced.

The first of the commercial ammoxidation catalysts for the Sohio fluid-bed process was a bismuth phosphomolybdate, superseded by an antimony oxide-uranium oxide composition or (in Japan) an antimony oxide-iron oxide composition. These catalysts may also contain small amounts of other elements. In 1972 a third-generation catalyst was announced by Sohio. The patents and publications indicate that it has a complex composition such as $M_8^{II}Fe_3^{III}Bi^{III}(MoO_4)_{12}O_{12}$. M represents various amounts of Ni^{2+} and Co^{2+} (Gates et al. 1979). This catalyst produces more acrylonitrile and less by-product acetonitrile than its predecessors, and may be operated for essentially complete consumption of reactants on a once-through basis. All these catalysts are supported on silica for attrition resistance in the fluidized-bed reactor. The Montedison catalyst consists of tellurium, cerium, and molybdenum oxides on silica, and operating conditions are similar to those used with the Sohio catalyst, but apparently a small amount of ammonia passes through unreacted.

Reaction mechanism.   Bismuth molybdate and other molybdate catalysts have been among the most intensively studied mixed-oxide compositions. The reactions of propylene have also been intensively studied because of the industrial importance of manufacture of acrylonitrile and acrolein. The overall features of the oxidation and ammoxidation reactions are now reasonably well established.

The proposed reaction mechanisms are based on a variety of studies including utilization of isotopic tracers, various catalyst structural characterizations, and kinetic analyses. In essence, a complex overall redox mechanism is involved. The first step in either the oxidation or ammoxidation of propylene is dissociative adsorption with abstraction of a hydrogen atom to form an adsorbed symmetric allyl radical, C_3H_5. The catalysts effective for ammoxidation are also usually effective for formation of acrolein in the presence of oxygen but in the absence of ammonia (Sec. 8.2.2).

In the presence of ammonia, acrolein in some cases may be found in small amounts as an isolable intermediate. Presumably a surface intermediate is formed that can be either desorbed as acrolein or converted to acrylonitrile, perhaps via an imine-like structure as an intermediate step. Alternatively, this or another surface intermediate is converted to carbon oxides. The manner in which ammonia is incorporated into the product is speculative. A plausible mechanism would involve dissociation to form NH_2 or NH, although there is little direct evidence. These steps are shown in Fig. 8.1.

The first reaction, formation of adsorbed allyl, is the rate-limiting step under most circumstances. The selectivity for acrylonitrile probably centers largely about the fate of an adsorbed intermediate closely related in structure to acrolein. If oxygen is too mobile or accessible in the lattice structure, the intermediate is converted to carbon monoxide and carbon dioxide instead of acrylonitrile. With bismuth-molybdate catalysts, the first abstraction of a hydrogen atom to form the symmetric allyl seems to involve an oxygen atom associated with bismuth; the second abstraction requires a chemically different form of oxygen associated with the presence of molybdenum. This is an oxygen atom possibly bonded to both bismuth and molybdenum. The insertion of oxygen involves oxygen atoms from only molybdenum.

Reoxidation of the catalyst occurs by adsorption and dissociation of

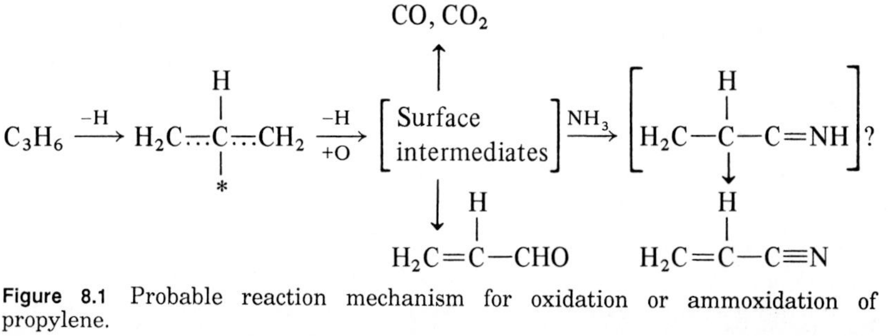

Figure 8.1 Probable reaction mechanism for oxidation or ammoxidation of propylene.

oxygen on anion vacancies associated with molybdenum. Anion vacancies on the bismuth are apparently reoxidized by transfer of oxygen from oxidized molybdenum and not directly from the gas phase. Oxygen is highly mobile in these catalysts and is readily transferred through the bulk of the catalyst. In addition to the heterogeneous catalytic reaction, some homogeneous gas-phase reaction also appears to occur, initiated by species desorbed from the surface, possibly allyl radicals (Driscoll et al. 1987).

All catalysts showing high activity and selectivity in the ammoxidation reaction consist of a complex oxide structure incorporating two or more metals. These structures have quite different properties in oxidation or ammoxidation than do the single oxides. For oxidation of propylene, Bi_2O_3 alone has low activity and causes essentially complete oxidation. MoO_3 alone shows good selectivity but has even lower activity than Bi_2O_3. In the uranium-antimony mixed-oxide system, the active and selective phase for formation of acrolein or acrylonitrile is USb_3O_{10}. Sb_2O_4 by itself is inactive, and UO_3 by itself strongly catalyzes combustion to CO_2 and CO.

The principal structure identified by X-ray in the third-generation Sohio catalyst appears to be cobalt-nickel molybdate (Gates et al. 1979), but what portion of the total this represents or in what form the other elements are present is not clear. These various molybdates can be prepared with an excess of molybdenum trioxide. Iron molybdate, used industrially for oxidative dehydrogenation of methanol to formaldehyde (Sec. 8.4.2), has a maximum selectivity for that reaction when it contains some excess molybdenum trioxide. The detailed structures of these multicomponent ammoxidation catalysts are complex, may vary considerably between the core and outer layers, and as yet are not well understood. With all these complex molybdate catalysts there is a gradual loss upon aging of MoO_3 and a change in the phases present, causing a slow drop in selectivity.

A variety of multicomponent molybdates such as those containing cobalt, iron, bismuth, tellurium, or other heavy metals have been characterized, and attempts have been made to relate structure to activity and selectivity for a variety of partial oxidation reactions (Higgins & Hayden 1977). Such patterns that have been proposed are as yet subject to debate. $CoMoO_4$ can exist in two forms, α and β, the α form being the stable form above 420°C. However, the α form can be stabilized for an indefinite period at lower temperatures on some supports or by suitable additions. The two forms clearly have quite different catalytic properties. Another poorly understood variable of importance for partial oxidation in general is the acidity of the catalyst. Grasselli et al. (1990) review the use of complex oxide catalysts containing tellurium for ammoxidation of propylene and possible application to other partial oxidation reactions.

The choice of catalyst for an industrial process rests on a complex interplay of various factors. These include aging characteristics, stability to fluctuations in process conditions, and maximum achievable selectivity. The fact that the reaction to form acrylonitrile is zero order with respect to oxygen (also zero order with respect to ammonia) and first order with respect to propylene indicates that the rate of reoxidation of the catalyst is rapid and not a rate-limiting process. The mechanism in Fig. 8.1 suggests that maximum selectivity may be achieved with the catalyst in a relatively reduced state. However, an excessive degree of reduction can lead to a change in structure and loss of the active phase. Moreover, if a metallic phase were to appear, it might cause undesired decomposition of ammonia to the elements. One of the functions of some of the minor components added may be to stabilize the desired phase to fluctuations in temperature and gas composition. That such a wide variety of multicomponent catalysts can produce nearly the same selectivity in oxidation and ammoxidation of propylene is remarkable.

The details of alternate mechanisms for propylene oxidation and ammoxidation are discussed more fully by Sleight and Linn (1976), Hucknall (1974), and Gates et al. (1979). Gates and coworkers also describe in considerable detail the bulk structures of various binary oxides that appear to be of catalytic importance and of related single metal oxides. However, little is known of the surface structures of these materials and how they may differ from the bulk. Higgins and Hayden (1977) review in detail the literature on mixed-oxide catalysts and selective hydrocarbon oxidation reactions for the period of 1973 to mid-1976. Grasselli and Burrington (1981) review selective oxidation and ammoxidation of propylene with emphasis on mechanism. In a later review Snyder and Hill (1989) present in detail the evidence for the mechanism of partial oxidation of propylene over bismuth-molybdate catalysts.

The various methods of preparing acrylonitrile, including earlier manufacturing processes such as the reaction of acetylene and hydrogen cyanide, are described by Dalin et al. (1971). Some 1400 patents and literature references are cited. The book edited by Hancock (1973) also provides considerable information. A paper by Kolchin (1973) summarizes the performance characteristics of a large number of catalyst compositions and contains numerous references. The catalytic ammoxidation of propane has received extensive study since propane is a lower-cost raw material than propylene, but no commercial process is known to have been put into operation as of 1990.

About 40 percent of the acrylonitrile produced in the United States in 1990 was used for manufacture of acrylic fibers. The second largest use is for incorporation into copolymers such as acrylonitrile-butadiene-styrene. Acrylonitrile is also hydrodimerized electrolytically (e.g., Monsanto process) to adiponitrile for manufacture of Nylon 66. In the form of an aqueous solution acrylonitrile is also hydrolyzed industrially to acrylamide using a supported metallic copper catalyst.

8.2.2 Acrolein and acrylic acid

Propylene is partially oxidized with either air or oxygen by the reaction:

$$CH_3CH{=}CH_2 + O_2 \rightarrow CH_2{=}CHCHO + H_2O \qquad (8.7)$$

$$-\Delta H = 341 \text{ kJ/mol}$$

A major process is that of Sohio, introduced in the early 1960s, which utilizes a complex multicomponent catalyst consisting basically of a bismuth molybdate plus various amounts of several other metals, very similar to catalysts used in synthesis of acrylonitrile. This supersedes an earlier catalyst consisting of a supported cuprous oxide (Shell). Propylene, air, and steam are reacted in a fixed-bed reactor at 200 to 300 kPa pressure and about 320 to 370°C. Acetaldehyde and acrylic acid are produced as by-products. About an 85-percent yield is obtained at about 20-percent conversion.

Acrylic acid is made by several similar processes. In the Distillers process used in Great Britain by Border Chemicals and in the United States by Union Carbide, a mixture of propylene, air, and steam in the ratio 1:5:4 is oxidized to acrylic acid and acrolein in a multitube reactor at slightly above atmospheric pressure. With a conversion of 22 percent of feed per pass, 12 percent is acrylic acid and 10 percent is acrolein (Hahn 1970, p. 207). Patents disclose a complex antimony-tin-vanadium mixed-oxide composition for this reaction. Acrolein can be recovered from the first reactor, or the exit stream from the first can be further oxidized to form more acrylic acid in a second reactor, probably with a different catalyst and different operating conditions. The conversion of acrolein to acrylic acid can be written:

$$2CH_2{=}CHCHO + O_2 \rightarrow 2\ CH_2{=}CHCOOH \qquad (8.8)$$

$$-\Delta H = 254 \text{ kJ/mol}$$

In a process for acrylic acid production licensed by Sohio, a two-reactor, fixed-bed system is used at 200 to 300 kPa and about 290 to 400°C with different catalysts in the two reactors. In the Toyo Soda process reaction, temperatures of 330 to 370°C are reported for the first reactor and 260 to 300°C for the second; an overall yield of acrylic acid from propylene of about 67 percent is reported. In all these processes some acetic acid is produced as a by-product. One catalyst used industrially for the conversion to acrylic acid is a complex unsupported oxide containing cobalt, molybdenum, and manganese.

The primary use of acrolein is as an intermediate to acrylic acid, which is then converted to various esters such as methyl and ethyl acrylates, typically by liquid-phase reaction using an ion-exchange-resin catalyst.

A closely related reaction is the partial oxidation of isobutylene to methacrolein, which can be converted to methacrylic acid. A number of complex metal-oxide catalyst compositions have been patented for the formation of methacrolein, but little information is available about the possible commercialization of this route.

8.2.3 Other ammoxidation processes

A substantial literature exists on ammoxidation reactions of aromatic compounds to form nitriles. An industrial process, first commercialized in Japan about 1968 to 1970 (Mitsubishi/Badger), converts *m*-xylene to isophthalonitrile in a fluid-bed reactor. A similar process is operated by Showa Denko. Small amounts of benzonitrile and *m*-tolunitrile are also formed, as well as carbon dioxide, carbon monoxide, and hydrogen cyanide. By similar reactions, heterocyclic compounds such as an alkyl pyridine may be converted to the corresponding nitrile. A nitrile in turn can be hydrolyzed to the corresponding carboxylic acid or hydrogenated to the corresponding amine. Klink et al. (1976) give some information on the development and use of a catalytic process for ammoxidation of a methylthiazole to the corresponding cyanothiazole.

8.3 Ethylene to Ethylene Oxide

Ethylene can be oxidized to ethylene oxide with high selectivity over supported silver catalysts, and this direct oxidation process now accounts for essentially all ethylene oxide produced industrially. Sometimes termed the Lefort process, it was first developed by Union Carbide, who started the world's first plant in 1937. A major improvement in selectivity was found in 1942 to be achieved by the addition of traces of chlorides (Law & Chitwood 1942). In the 1950s a direct oxidation process was also developed by Scientific Design Co., and a process using substantially pure oxygen instead of air was developed by Shell Development Co. Both of these have also been widely used. Most of the ethylene oxide produced is hydrolyzed to ethylene glycol, which is used as an antifreeze in automobile cooling systems and as one of the two monomers in polyethylene-terephthalate (polyester) fibers and polymers. Some is also converted to alcohol ethoxylates, which are used as detergents and surfactants.

The optimum reaction temperature is about 260 to 280°C when air oxidation is utilized, and about 230°C with oxygen. The contact time is about 1 s. Pressure is 1 to 3 MPa. Industrial reactors are shell-and-tube type as shown in Fig. 8.2. This kind of reactor is also used for various other partial oxidation syntheses (e.g., phthalic anhydride, maleic anhydride) and other exothermic reactions such as Lurgi-design methanol synthesis. For partial oxidation reactions, a representative reactor contains from 7000 to 10,000 tubes 2.5 to 5.0 cm in diameter encased in a shell up to 15 ft in diameter and up to 30 ft in height. Gas flow may be either upward or downward and heat is removed by an organic liquid that is directed back and forth across the tubes by baffles to provide good temperature control. The heat is then recovered as steam. For other designs and for other reactions, heat

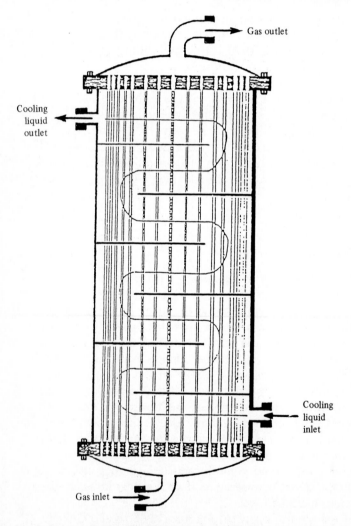

Figure 8.2   Representative shell-and-tube-type reactor.

may be removed by a boiling coolant system, e.g., water, in which coolant temperature can be controlled within limits by adjusting pressure. If reaction temperature is so high that the organic coolant would be unstable, a molten salt eutectic mixture is used.

For the desired high selectivity in ethylene oxide synthesis, the conversion is held to about 10 to 15 percent. Highest selectivity is achieved with lowest conversion, but this increases recycle costs. Activity, selectivity and aging characteristics of a catalyst, specific plant design, and operating rate relative to capacity all affect optimum conversion. Using industrial grade oxygen, the feed composition consisting of fresh feed mixed with recycled gas is typically about 20 vol % ethylene, 6 to 8% oxygen, about 6% CO_2, 4 to 5% Ar, remainder nitrogen.

With the use of air, after removal of ethylene oxide from the exit gas by scrubbing with water under pressure, a portion of the exit stream is recycled. The remainder is sent to a second reactor, which is used as a way of scavenging remaining ethylene and purging nitrogen and other inert gases from the system. Carbon dioxide inhibits the reaction, and its concentration in the mixed feed to the first reactor is controlled by absorbing it from a portion of the recycle stream with an absorbent such as a potassium carbonate solution. With nearly pure oxygen, the second reactor is unnecessary, and usually only one reactor is used; in this case unabsorbed gases are recycled and again a portion of the recycle stream is treated for carbon dioxide removal. The amount of carbon dioxide removed is determined by an economic balance between cost of removal and its effect on lowering capacity.

Use of pure oxygen allows a higher reactor productivity (production rate per unit volume of catalyst) and less costly recycle of ethylene. These factors may more than compensate for the higher cost of pure oxygen. Usually the oxygen-based process is preferred in large plants, and some air-based plants have been converted to use oxygen.

Several features of the reaction are unique. No other metal is at all comparable to silver in selectivity, and this epoxidation reaction is unique to ethylene. Propylene or butylene do not undergo analogous reactions on silver or any other known heterogeneous catalyst. Possibly they are adsorbed in the form of a π-bonded allyl that is readily oxidized to carbon oxides and water.

In order to obtain maximum selectivity, the catalyst must have a trace of cesium added and be partially poisoned by continuously adding a chlorinated compound such as ethylene dichloride to the feed. Both of these treatments, however, reduce activity. The optimum concentration of adsorbed chloride corresponds to a coverage of 30 to 40 percent of the silver surface and is achieved by a few parts per million of the organochloro compound in the feed. The chloride is not retained, so continuous addition is necessary.

A variety of silver catalyst preparations have been used industrially. In more recent years these have constituted about 10 to 15 wt % silver supported on low area (< 1 m^2/g) α-alumina, presumably to provide large pores and avoid the diffusion-limiting regime that would reduce selectivity.

A typical earlier preparation involved impregnation with aqueous silver nitrate followed by reduction by hydrogen. These catalysts provided selectivities under optimum commercial conditions of about 65 percent. A subsequent major improvement in selectivity was achieved by the discovery of Nielsen and La Rochelle (1976, 1977) that by adding small, carefully prescribed amounts of a cesium salt to an impregnating solution, a substantial further improvement in selectivity was achievable. In their preparation, silver oxalate is dissolved in a mixture of ethylene diamine and ethanolamine as the impregnating solution. These compounds act as dissolving, dispersing, and reducing agents. After drying and calcining, the silver in the resulting catalyst is present in uniform, finely divided spherical particles that enhance performance. The cesium must be combined with the use of chloride for maximum selectivity.

Potassium, in carefully specified concentrations, also enhances selectivity but less so than cesium. Rubidium has an effectiveness intermediate between potassium and cesium, but is not used industrially because it is nearly as costly as cesium. Silver may be somewhat mobile under reaction conditions and the average particle size increases moderately with time on stream. With present-day catalysts, selectivities in commercial reactors are about 78 to 80 percent.

Figure 8.3 is a SEM picture of a commercial ethylene oxide catalyst. This shows the irregular pore structure of the α-Al$_2$O$_3$, of the order of 1 μm in size. The silver particles are much smaller, and are uniformly dispersed on the alumina. The overall kinetics are of the type:

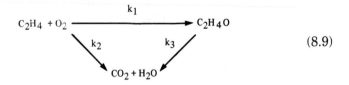

$$\tag{8.9}$$

The heats of reaction, per mole of ethylene, are $-\Delta H_1 = 146$ kJ/mol and $-\Delta H_2 = 1320$ kJ/mol. The mechanism of the epoxidation reaction has been studied extensively, but much is still in dispute. The arguments center around the various forms in which oxygen is chemisorbed onto the silver, the ways in which ethylene reacts with these species and with silver atoms, and the role of chloride and of cesium.

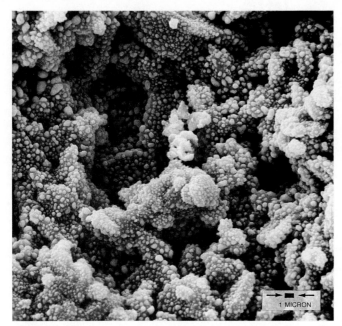

Figure 8.3   Scanning electron micrograph of an ethylene oxide catalyst.

The oxygen complexes adsorbed on silver have been characterized by a wide variety of studies, including calorimetric studies, infrared spectroscopy, isotopic exchange, electron diffraction, and kinetic studies of adsorption rates. The interpretation has been ambiguous in many cases because of the marked effects of traces of impurities on the silver. A reaction mechanism commonly advanced is that proposed by Kilty and Sachtler (1974), which is also discussed by Carrá and Forzatti (1977). Basically, *diatomic* oxygen is proposed to be adsorbed onto a single silver atom and then ethylene is strongly adsorbed onto the oxygen. (The molecular oxygen may be somewhat ionic.) The ethylene-oxygen complex splits at the O—O bond to form ethylene oxide, leaving an adsorbed oxygen atom.

$$
\begin{array}{ccccc}
& & \overset{\text{H}\quad\text{H}}{\underset{|\quad|}{\text{H}-\text{C}-\text{C}-\text{H}}} & & \overset{\text{H}\quad\text{H}}{\underset{|\quad|}{\text{H}-\text{C}-\text{C}-\text{H}}} \\
\text{H}_2\text{C}=\text{CH}_2 & & \diagdown\!\diagup & & \diagdown\!\diagup \\
+ & \longrightarrow & \text{O}^+ & \longrightarrow & \text{O} \\
\text{O} & & | & & + \\
| & & \text{O}^- & & \text{O} \\
\text{O} & & | & & | \\
| & & \text{Ag} & & \text{Ag} \\
\text{Ag} & & & &
\end{array}
\qquad (8.10)
$$

The first step may therefore be written as

$$O_2 + Ag \rightarrow O_2^-(ads) + Ag^+ \qquad (8.11)$$

Oxygen is postulated also to be dissociatively adsorbed to form monoatomic oxygen by interaction with a cluster of four adjacent silver atoms.

$$O_2 + 4Ag(adj) \rightarrow 2O^{2-}(ads) + 4Ag^+(adj) \qquad (8.12)$$

Adsorbed oxygen ions (or atoms) are postulated to lead to carbon monoxide and carbon dioxide. This undesired reaction is inhibited by adsorption of chlorine atoms when the surface is about one-quarter covered with chloride.

Maximum selectivity is thus achieved if further reaction of ethylene oxide is negligible, reaction (8.12) is blocked by adsorbed chloride, and other reactions forming monoatomic oxygen are negligible. However, by the foregoing mechanism, the maximum selectivity achievable cannot be 100 percent, since some of the ethylene must be consumed to reduce the silver with adsorbed oxygen atoms formed in reaction (8.10) back to metallic silver. The minimum quantity of ethylene required for this step would occur if the products were carbon dioxide and water, and the corresponding maximum selectivity achievable would be 6/7 or 85.6 percent. This mechanism has received considerable attention because reported selectivities have been lower than this value. A few reports of higher selectivities have not been confirmed in the published literature.

A substantial number of more recent studies suggest an alternate mechanism in which ethylene reacts with adsorbed atomic oxygen, rather than with diatomic oxygen, to form the epoxide. This would mean that the selectivity is not inherently limited to 6/7. The uniqueness of silver is then attributed to its ability to adsorb oxygen with dissociation, and the atomic oxygen that is effective is that which is weakly bonded. This allows the oxygen atom to form the epoxide directly by reaction with ethylene.

Little fundamental work has been published on catalysts promoted with alkali and chloride, so the mechanisms occurring under actual industrial reaction conditions still remain uncertain. The arguments for the monoatomic oxygen mechanism are set forth in detail in a review by van Santen and Kuipers (1987). At least two types of adsorbed oxygen atoms on silver exist with different bonding strengths, and only the weakly bonded oxygen atoms are postulated to form the epoxide. The bond strength of O atoms bonded to silver atoms sharing Cl atoms is weakened. From studies by van Santen (1988) the role of alkali is hypothesized to be the stabilization of a silver oxychloride anion which is the ethylene epoxidation agent.

Ethylene oxide is easily isomerized to acetaldehyde, which is readily oxidized on silver or the support.

$$H_2C \underset{O}{-} CH_2 \longrightarrow CH_3CHO \tag{8.13}$$

The isomerization reaction is catalyzed by even mild acid functionality, so a neutral catalyst support is required, $\alpha\text{-}Al_2O_3$ being widely used. Other materials relatively inert in other oxidation reactions may still produce more side-products than $\alpha\text{-}Al_2O_3$. Small amounts of $\gamma\text{-}Al_2O_3$, which can be inherently mildly acidic, tend to accelerate this side reaction. Addition of calcium or barium can be used to neutralize acidity. The commercial product from the reactors may typically contain about 0.1% CH_3CHO and about 0.1% $HCHO$, the latter formed directly from ethylene. The product is purified by distillation.

Earlier reviews on ethylene oxide synthesis are given by Kiguchi et al. (1976), Gans and Ozero (1976), and by Voge and Adams (1967). Berty (1983) briefly reviews processes as well as the synthesis in general. In another review Sajkowski and Boudart (1987) concluded that the reaction as carried out in the absence of inhibitors and promoters is structure-insensitive. Technology is reviewed by Zomerdijk and Hall (1981).

Propylene oxide cannot be manufactured by a process analogous to that used for ethylene oxide. Instead, a process developed by Halcon and Arco Chemical and operated by Arco can proceed in either of two ways. In one, liquid-phase ethylbenzene is oxidized with air to form the hydroperoxide. This reacts with propylene in the liquid phase to form propylene oxide and phenylmethylcarbinol (phenylethyl alcohol). The latter is then dehydrated in the vapor phase to styrene, using a TiO_2 catalyst at about 180 to 280°C. In a second version, isobutane is used instead of ethylbenzene, isobutylene being formed as the by-product. This can then be reacted with methanol to form MTBE, a gasoline additive (Sec. 7.9).

8.4   Methanol to Formaldehyde

The commercial production of formaldehyde started in Germany in about 1890, using the catalytic partial oxidation of methanol with air in a fuel-rich mixture. The catalyst was unsupported metallic copper, used at approximately atmospheric pressure, and the product was rapidly quenched by solution in water. After about 1910, copper was replaced by silver in processes used in Germany and the United States; this gave higher yields. A different process, apparently first put into use in the 1940s and 1950s, uses an iron molybdate catalyst under fuel-lean conditions (Reichhold-Skanska process). These two processes account for essentially all commercial manufacture of formaldehyde.

The possibility of direct conversion of methane to formaldehyde has been extensively studied, but it is not commercially practicable, probably because of the much greater reactivity of formaldehyde relative to methane. Methanol will decompose directly to formaldehyde and hydrogen, an endothermic reaction, but no catalyst appears to have been developed that does not also substantially decompose the formaldehyde further to carbon monoxide and hydrogen. The methanol-air explosive region is from about 6.7 to 36.5 vol % at atmospheric pressure and expands somewhat with increasing temperature. Operations must be outside these limits for safety. Some details concerning the two processes were published by Walker (1964) and Chauvel et al. (1973). A more recent brief description has been written by Davies et al. (1989).

8.4.1   Methanol-rich system (silver catalyst)

A methanol-air mixture (about 50:50 mol ratio) at marginally above atmospheric pressure, is passed through a fixed, thin catalyst bed consisting of silver wire gauze or silver crystals (0.5 to 3 mm in size). The exit temperature is about 600°C, and the contact time is about 0.01 s or less. The reaction is not equilibrium-limited but is highly mass-transfer-controlled, and operation is essentially adiabatic. The silver catalyst is more sensitive to iron-group impurities than the iron-molybdate catalyst described in the following. The reactor configuration is simple and much less costly than a multitube reactor with external cooling, as used with the iron molybdate catalyst, but the overall yield with the silver catalyst system, of the order of 90 percent, is less than with the iron-molybdate system. The operating temperature is well above the Tammann temperature, $T_m/2$ = 615 K (Sec. 4.5), and the silver undergoes major physical reconstruction during the reaction. Catalyst life can vary from several months to about two years, depending in part on the purity of the methanol.

The exit gases always contain considerable hydrogen, as well as water, so the reaction may be regarded as a mixture of partial oxidation and dehydrogenation.

$$CH_3OH + \tfrac{1}{2}O_2 \rightarrow HCHO + H_2O \qquad (8.14)$$

$$-\Delta H = 158 \text{ kJ/mol}$$

$$CH_3OH \rightarrow HCHO + H_2 \qquad (8.15)$$

$$-\Delta H = -84 \text{ kJ/mol}$$

Metallic silver as such has little catalytic activity for the decomposition of methanol, even at high temperatures. To be active, oxygen must be chemisorbed onto it. Methanol is not readily adsorbed on silver metal but is readily adsorbed onto the chemisorbed oxygen. The situation here is somewhat analogous to ethylene oxide formation, although at the much higher temperatures here, the chemisorbed oxygen is postulated to be monatomic. Since the feed ratio is oxygen-lean, the downstream portion of a packed bed may have little activity once the oxygen has been substantially consumed. Adsorptivity for oxygen decreases in this order: copper, silver, gold. The intermediate adsorptivity of silver makes this catalyst preferred over the other two.

From studies on metallic copper and silver, Wachs and Madix (1978) propose that the principal mechanism is:

$$CH_3OH(g) + O(ads) \rightarrow CH_3O(ads) + OH(ads) \qquad (8.16)$$

$$CH_3OH(g) + OH(ads) \rightarrow CH_3O + H_2O(g) \qquad (8.17)$$

$$2CH_3O(ads) \rightarrow 2CHOH(ads) + 2H(ads) \qquad (8.18)$$

$$2H(ads) \rightarrow H_2(g) \qquad (8.19)$$

This implies that the oxidation and dehydrogenation reactions do not occur as separate processes on different sites but are intimately related. They further suggest that at a high degree of oxygen coverage, formation of a formate becomes more important, which decreases selectivity. Therefore, a relatively low coverage of chemisorbed oxygen is optimum. The formate would rapidly decompose to form carbon dioxide and hydrogen or carbon monoxide and water.

A low concentration of steam is also frequently added to the feed to help eliminate carbon deposits on the catalyst, and this may allow a somewhat higher degree of conversion to be achieved before selectivity becomes unacceptably low. The product must be rapidly quenched to minimize decomposition of formaldehyde into carbon monoxide and hydrogen.

Considerable carbon dioxide is found in the by-products. This is probably not formed by oxidation of methanol directly and possibly is formed by catalytic oxidation of carbon monoxide.

If a single reactor is used, conversion is limited to about 70 percent of the methanol. The product is then distilled, and unconverted methanol is recycled. To achieve essentially complete reaction without recycling, it is necessary to use a second reactor with additional air introduced interstage, to avoid forming an explosive mixture initially.

This eliminates the cost of the distillation step, but the overall yield with respect to methanol is less.

8.4.2 Methanol-lean system (iron-molybdate catalyst)

The concentration of CH_3OH in air in this process is about 6 to 9 mol %. The reaction is more exothermic than that using a silver catalyst and requires cooling during reaction to keep the temperature down to an acceptable level. Thus a multitube reactor with tubes 15 to 25 mm in diameter is used, externally cooled with Dowtherm or a molten salt, with about 0.5-s superficial contact time at reactor conditions. The cooling medium is typically held at about 280°C and a hot spot along the tube develops with a temperature of about 340 to 380°C. The catalyst is unsupported $Fe_2(MoO_4)_3$, plus some excess MoO_3, in a typical weight ratio of about 80% MoO_3 and 20% Fe_2O_3. Excessive temperatures cause volatilization of MoO_3 and the formation of "molybdenum-deficient" iron molybdates. This reduces the selectivity and also causes loss of mechanical strength.

Excess MoO_3 added during preparation of the catalyst helps prevent formation of the molybdenum-deficient species. Nevertheless the molybdenum-iron ratio gradually drops during use, and typical lifetime is about 6 to 12 months. Small amounts of a chromium oxide or a cobalt oxide are also sometimes added, perhaps to help stabilize the iron-molybdate structure. Representative forms are 3.5 × 3.5 mm pellets or rings of OD × ID × h = 4 × 2 × 3.5 mm.

This catalyst becomes inert in the presence of excess methanol and requires a fairly high oxygen partial pressure to maintain its activity. Considerable excess air must thus be fed with the methanol. Nearly complete reaction is obtained in one pass, and reported yields are about 91 to 94 percent. Some carbon monoxide is formed by partial oxidation of the CH_2O product and some carbon dioxide and HCOOH are also formed. Air compression costs are substantial, so operation is with as high a methanol-air ratio as is compatible with safety and maintenance of an active catalyst. Figure 8.4 is a photograph of a plant having a capacity of 90,000 tons per year of formaldehyde, expressed in terms of the 37 wt % solution. On the right are the reactors, rather short and squat with tube lengths of about 3 ft, grouped around a large heat exchanger in the center. The (large) absorption tower for product recovery is on the left.

A redox-type mechanism presumably operates here, of the form

$$CH_3OH + Cat\text{-}O \rightarrow CH_2O(g) + H_2O(g) + Cat \qquad (8.20)$$

$$2Cat + O_2 \rightarrow 2Cat\text{-}O \qquad (8.21)$$

Figure 8.4   Formaldehyde plant in Castellanza (Varese), Italy. *(Courtesy of Montedison, S.p.A.)*

where Cat-O represents the catalyst in the oxidized form, and Cat, the reduced form. The active oxidizing agent is lattice oxygen, but the activity of molybdate-type catalysts for formation of formaldehyde appears also to be closely related to their acidity (Ai 1978). The acidity in turn may be affected by heat treatment and activation procedures.

Formaldehyde is usually transported as a 37-percent aqueous solution. Since shipping costs are significant, small-capacity plants located near the source of demand can be economic. The IFP process, which utilizes an iron-molybdate catalyst, is described in some detail by Le Page et al. (1987) together with information on catalyst preparation and use. A recent paper by Windes et al. (1989) on modeling a packed-bed reactor for this reaction contains a discussion of the reaction kinetics reported for this catalyst.

8.5 Butylenes to Butadiene

Normal butylenes may be converted to butadiene by oxidative dehydrogenation as an alternate to direct dehydrogenation (Sec. 9.17).

$$C_4H_8 + \tfrac{1}{2}O_2 \rightarrow C_4H_6 + H_2O \qquad (8.22)$$

$$-\Delta H = 121 \text{kJ/mol}$$

Unlike direct dehydrogenation, the reaction is not equilibrium-limited. Higher olefins, e.g., pentene, react similarly but give a variety of products. Isobutylene is converted mostly to combustion products; paraffins are relatively unreactive.

The major process used in the United States is based on technology developed by Petro-Tex. Their patent literature focuses on a variety of ferrites incorporating zinc, magnesium, or manganese. Chromium is also frequently added to help stabilize the catalyst against excessive reduction [Rennard & Kehl 1971; Massoth & Scarpiello 1971]. These structures may be written as $Zn(Cr_{2-x}Fe_x)O_4$ or $Mg(Cr_{2-x}Fe_x)O_4$. Maximum selectivity occurs with values of x of about 1. Sterrett and McIlvried (1974) report a kinetic study on an unsupported $ZnCrFeO_4$ spinel having approximately a 1:1:1 ratio of the three metals, and review earlier literature on oxidative dehydrogenation of butene. The surface area of this catalyst is in the range of 1 to 10 m^2/g, depending on the calcination temperature.

Studies of these and ferrite spinels containing various other metals such as copper and cobalt have also been reported in a series of papers by Hightower and coworkers (Gibson & Hightower 1976; Yin et al. 1988). There has been little patent activity since the late 1970s on ferrites for this reaction. The best ferrite catalysts appear to contain two phases, a pure spinel plus a small amount of α-Fe_2O_3. Bismuth-molybdate catalysts are also active and selective for this reaction (Batist et al. 1967, 1968), as is a phosphorous-tin oxide composition (Pitzer 1972). In a process described by British Petroleum Chemicals, reaction in the presence of steam and air is carried out at 400 to 450°C with a catalyst that may be a mixed oxide of antimony and tin. A detailed review focusing on kinetics and mechanism has been published by Kung and Kung (1985).

In the Petro-Tex process, a mixture of air and butenes in the presence of a high concentration of steam is reacted in a fixed-bed adiabatic reactor using a moderate stoichiometric excess of butenes at a pressure slightly above atmospheric. The ignition temperature is about 345 to

360°C, and the maximum allowable exit temperature is about 575 to 595°C to prevent catalyst deactivation. Essentially all the oxygen is consumed, and under representative operating conditions about 65 percent of the butylenes are converted to butadiene per pass, in about 93-percent selectivity, using a steam-butylenes feed mole ratio of about 12 (Welch et al. 1978). This ratio is set largely as the minimum needed to limit the adiabatic temperature rise to an acceptable level, which in turn is determined by the hydrocarbon-oxygen ratio and the extent of side reactions. The principal by-products are vinylacetylene, formaldehyde, acetaldehyde, and acrolein, plus carbon oxides. Some information about a similar process operated by Phillips was published by Hutson et al. (1974). Interest in these processes has decreased in recent years with the increasing production of butadiene as a coproduct in the thermal cracking of naphtha and gas oils (see also Sec. 9.17.).

The oxidative dehydrogenation of hydrocarbons in general was reviewed by Sharchenko (1969), who gives extensive references. The oxidative dehydrogenation of paraffins catalyzed by gaseous halogens such as bromine or iodine, either with or without a solid catalyst, has been studied extensively. No process based on this chemistry appears to have been commercialized, in part due to corrosion problems and the necessity for high halogen recovery.

8.6   Maleic Anhydride and Phthalic Anhydride

The reactions of commercial importance are: the oxidation of naphthalene or o-xylene to phthalic anhydride and the oxidation of benzene, n-butene, or n-butane to maleic anhydride.

$$\bigcirc + (7 + x)/2\,O_2 \longrightarrow \text{[maleic anhydride]} + 2\,H_2O + x\,CO_2 + (2 - x)\,CO \quad (8.23)$$

$$-\Delta H = 1870 \text{ kJ/mol for } x = 2$$

$$n\,C_4H_8 + 3\,O_2 \longrightarrow \text{[maleic anhydride]} + 3\,H_2O \quad (8.24)$$

$$-\Delta H = 1315 \text{ kJ/mol}$$

$$\text{[naphthalene]} + (7 + x)/2\,O_2 \longrightarrow \text{[phthalic anhydride]} + 2H_2O + xCO_2 + (2 - x)\,CO$$

$$-\Delta H = 1790 \text{ kJ/mol for } x = 2 \qquad (8.25)$$

$$\text{[o-xylene]} + 3O_2 \longrightarrow \text{[phthalic anhydride]} + 3H_2O \qquad (8.26)$$

$$-\Delta H = 1200 \text{ kJ/mol}$$

Some maleic anhydride may also be produced as a by-product in the oxidation of o-xylene, especially if it is carried out at relatively high temperatures. The main catalyst ingredient in each case is vanadia, but the support and other additives vary with the process and reactant. A very substantial literature exists in the form of patents and publications. The application of vanadium pentoxide for these types of reactions goes back to at least 1917, when Gibbs and Conover obtained a patent covering some of these uses.

8.6.1   Maleic anhydride

The catalytic partial oxidation of benzene in air to form maleic anhydride was described by Weiss and Downs in 1920, and first industrial production was in 1928. A representative catalyst comprises V_2O_4 and MoO_3 in a molar ratio of about 2, plus a small amount of Na_2O, on an alumina support. A multitube fixed-bed reactor is used with an air-benzene mole ratio of about 65 to 85. Pressure is slightly above atmospheric, and contact time is of the order of 0.5 to 1 s. (A typical reactor is diagrammed in Fig. 8.2.)

The reaction is highly exothermic, and considerable temperature gradients are typically encountered along a packed tube. The array of tubes is cooled with a molten inorganic salt mixture (e.g., 7% $NaNO_3$, 40% $NaNO_2$, and 53% KNO_3, which is a eutectic) held at about 375°C. The molten salt in turn is used to generate high-pressure steam. (In early processes mercury was used.) The benzene-air mixture is typically fed at about 200°C and is rapidly preheated in the first portion of the packed tubes (e.g., about the first 30 cm) to an ignition temperature of about 350°C. The reaction rate then becomes appreciable, and heat is transferred out rather than in.

Even with relatively small tubes, about 2 cm in inside diameter, the

rate of heat transfer is insufficient to hold the reacting gas nearly isothermal, and a hot zone develops part way down the tube that may
have a peak temperature as much as 100°C above that of the coolant.
The reacting gas then cools down near the end of the reactor tube as
the rate diminishes with depletion of reactant. In representative operation, 97- to 98-percent conversion is achieved with an initial selectivity of over 74 percent, which gradually drops with time. Under normal conditions catalyst life is of the order of 2 to 3 years.

Newer processes are based on catalytic oxidation of n-butylene (1-
butene and 2-butene) or n-butane. One advantage of the C_4 feedstocks
over benzene is that in the desired reaction no carbon is lost in forming
the desired product. For 100-percent conversion, the weight yield from
butane is about a third greater than that from benzene. Moreover,
benzene is a known carcinogen and in the United States the Environmental Protection Agency sets strict standards on benzene emissions.

Normal butylenes have become increasingly available as a
coproduct of thermal "steam" pyrolysis of naphthas, and processes to
oxidize the n-butylene in a C_4 fraction to maleic anhydride have been
developed by several companies, including Mitsubishi in Japan (fluid-
bed reactor) and Bayer and BASF in Germany (tubular fixed-bed reactor with molten salt cooling). The C_4 product from a steam cracker
will consist primarily of butenes and butadiene, plus smaller amounts
of butanes. Under optimum operating conditions, the butanes are
unreacted; isobutylene burns to carbon oxides and water; and the n-
butenes and butadiene are converted to maleic anhydride. Varma and
Saraf (1979), in a review with extensive references, summarize a large
number of patented catalyst compositions and discuss possible kinetics and reaction mechanism.

With current technology (1990) maleic anhydride yields from benzene are about 65 to 70 percent of theoretical versus about 45 to 55
percent of theoretical for butane or butene. Maleic anhydride is removed by scrubbing and some of the remaining gas is recycled and
mixed with fresh feed. The inflammability limit for C_4 hydrocarbons
in air is about 1.9 vol % versus about 1.4 percent for benzene, which is
an advantage. For maximum capacity, the feed composition is typically adjusted to be near the lower inflammability limit. For butene,
reaction temperatures of about 380 to 430°C are quoted; for n-butane,
about 400 to 480°C. Pressure is moderately above atmospheric, in the
neighborhood of 0.3 to 0.4 MPa, probably chosen to provide sufficient
pressure to force exit gases through downstream scrubbing and purification steps. For either n-butene or n-butane feedstocks, vanadium-
phosphate catalysts are used, but the required catalyst structure for
use with butane is considerably more complex than that for butene.

Maleic anhydride from n-butane. The first commercially viable maleic anhydride process starting with n-butane apparently was operated by Monsanto in 1974 in a plant converted from benzene feed. An extensive literature amounting to hundreds of papers and patents has appeared in the last 15 years, directed at determining the catalyst structure that provides maximum selectivity combined with acceptable durability when feeding butane. The optimum structures are quite complex, as is shown, and much remains to be learned about structure, methods of characterization, and suitable methods of manufacture. This may well be one of the most difficult industrial catalysts to prepare, to characterize, and to use reproducibly.

The preferred catalysts for fixed-bed reactors are unsupported vanadium phosphates containing small amounts of one or more promoters such as lithium, zinc, and molybdenum. The desired structure seems to be a crystalline material with considerable strains or defects (see below) and the role of promoters may well be that of introducing stable defects. A phosphorus-vanadium atomic ratio greater than unity is desired, and an optimum ratio appears to be about 1.2. The higher the ratio, the less active is the catalyst, but the longer the life. A slight excess of phosphate seems to inhibit the mobility of oxygen in the bulk catalyst, helping to stabilize the desired structure.

In a representative method of preparation, vanadium pentoxide is mixed with nearly anhydrous phosphoric acid and an organic solvent such as isobutyl alcohol. Anhydrous HCl is added to solubilize the V_2O_5. The mixture is heated and organic solvent removed by volatilization. The optimum structure appears to be very sensitive to small variations in water concentration and to water removal during preparation. The product is dried and calcined to yield the catalyst precursor, which is then pelletized or made into spheres. From Fourier-transform infrared (FT-IR) studies, a slight amount of alcohol or alcoholic residues appear to be retained in the precursor even after calcination. This produces disorders that carry over into the activated catalyst.

After loading the catalyst into the reactor, it is activated under carefully controlled conditions, which change the precursor into the actual active catalyst. This procedure seems to require net reducing conditions, but with the presence of some gaseous oxygen. Possibly a suitable butane-air mixture is utilized with a specified time-temperature ramp protocol. The presence of some oxygen may be needed to prevent loss of lattice oxygen as the remainder of organics are removed.

The use of an organic medium for catalyst preparation provides a catalyst considerably more selective than one made in an aqueous medium. The higher cost of catalyst manufacture in an organic medium here is readily justified economically; this is one of the few instances in which this is the case for an industrial catalyst. Another is the silver catalyst used for synthesis of ethylene oxide (see Sec. 8.3.).

Informative papers by Busca et al. (1986) and Horowitz et al. (1988) provide considerable insight into the structure of the optimum catalyst. Busca et al. prepared a number of vanadium-phosphate catalysts both in aqueous and organic media, characterized the catalyst precursor and activated catalyst by X-ray diffraction for each preparation, and determined the activity and selectivity of each activated catalyst. The precursor has the empirical formula written by different researchers as $(VO)_2 \cdot P_2O_7 \cdot 2\ H_2O$, $VO(HPO_4) \cdot 0.5\ H_2O$ or $(VO)_2H_4P_2O_9$, all of which are equivalent.

The activated catalyst has the formula $(VO)_2P_2O_7$. The transformation is "topotactic" in that the crystallites of the $(VO)_2P_2O_7$ look identical to the crystallites of the $VO(HPO_4) \cdot 0.5\ H_2O$ precursor, as observed by scanning electron microscopy, transmission electron microscopy, and electron diffraction. Of particular importance is the observation that the degree of disorder as revealed by X-ray diffraction peak heights and line widths is carried over from catalyst precursor to final catalyst; e.g., the most deformed precursor structure gives the most deformed active phase.

X-ray diffraction (XRD) studies have played an important role in characterizing the optimum catalyst, and they illustrate the power of XRD for obtaining useful insights in the preparation and use of an industrial catalyst. XRD patterns for both catalyst precursors and activated catalyst are reported in a variety of papers and are used in several patents to define the claimed composition.

XRD data, in general, may be given in one or more of three equivalent forms: (1) relative intensity at an angle, 2θ, at which significant reflection is observed, (2) the crystal face or plane from which the reflection occurs, and (3) the corresponding lattice spacing d, in Angstroms, between these planes. A possible source of confusion is that these planes in this case are indexed differently by different researchers. Considering the catalyst precursor, a significant reflection occurring at $2\theta = 30°$, with $d = 2.98$ Å is assigned the (202) designation by Bordes et al. (1984) and Busca et al. (1986). The same reflection is designated (220)(130) by Horowitz et al. (1988). The 220 and 130 reflections essentially overlap and therefore are added together by Horowitz and coworkers. Another significant reflection occurring at $2\theta = 15°$, with $d = 5.68$ Å is designated as the (010) reflection by Bordes and Busca and (001) by Horowitz.

The activated catalyst shows significant line intensities at $2\theta = 23°$, $d = 3.9$ Å, (020) reflection plane and at $2\theta = 28.5°$, $d = 3.1$ Å, (204) reflection plane. The (020) designation is used by Busca and Horowitz. It is termed the (200) reflection by Johnson et al. (1987). The active catalyst also exhibits some reflection at $2\theta = 30.0°$ ($d = 2.98$ Å), which might represent some residual (202) plane from the catalyst precursor.

These three lines, which dominate XRD patterns for the desired activated catalyst, as referred to in recent literature, were also the most intense reported in a catalyst patent by Schneider (1975). Schneider measured the XRD after activation in an air-butane mixture, and the desired species was termed the "B-Phase." An X-ray pattern for an "optimum precursor" is also reported in patents by Stefani and Fontana (1978).

One conclusion from the studies of both Busca and Horowitz is the importance of the 001 plane (010 in Busca nomenclature), which is the so-called cleavage plane or stacking plane ($d = 5.68$ Å in the precursor). For highest selectivity this plane must be strained or have stacking disorder. Such disorder is revealed by X-ray line broadening and diminished line intensity.

An aqueous preparation gives a high, sharp $d = 5.68$ Å line. In the various preparations with a mixture of isobutyl alcohol and benzyl alcohol, Busca et al. formed a series of precursors for which the line corresponding to $d = 5.68$ Å gradually became wider and its intensity dropped. This indicates increasing disorder in this plane. There seemed to be much less effect on the $d = 2.98$ Å spacing. Busca et al. also made an almost amorphous precursor with little or no reflection from the 010 plane. The most selective catalyst was one of an intermediate degree of disorder.

A patent by Edwards and Meyers (1988) bases their claims on a catalyst precursor having a characteristic powder X-ray diffraction pattern, which is contrasted to that for a less desirable catalyst precursor. The d spacings are essentially the same for the two, but in the desired precursor the lines are much broader and the relative intensities are very different, especially for the line spacings at 5.71 and 2.94 Å. In the desired precursor these are $d_{5.71}/d_{2.94} = 37/100$. In the less-desired precursor these are $d_{5.72}/d_{2.94} = 100/54$. Calcining the desired precursor in air at 371°C gave the same X-ray diffraction pattern as the uncalcined material.

The role of small amounts of promoters such as zinc, lithium, and molybdenum can be hypothesized as causing desirable defects in the 010 plane of the precursor (leading to the 020 plane of the active catalyst). Some studies show that X-ray line broadening of the 010 plane is anisotropic, indicating that one plane can be increased in area relative to another, i.e., that the aspect ratio of the crystallites might be altered so as to expose more of the 010 plane. Horowitz et al. added some *tetraethyl orthosilicate* (TEOS) in some of their preparations, introducing small amounts of silica into the final catalyst. This increased selectivity because of increased surface area, especially of the 010 plane.

They also reported that wet milling of the precursor in isopropanol led to a significant improvement in catalyst selectivity. This improvement was attributed to sliding of precursor platelets away from one another, exposing more (010) surface. Other factors, as yet only dimly perceived, may also be relevant. Some amorphous material, invisible to X-ray, may also be important, and little information is available on changes upon aging. In a recent study, Centi et al. (1989) characterized catalysts held for at least 700 hours in a reaction environment and present hypotheses on the nature of the active species.

The most plausible sequence of reactions involved in partial oxidation of either butane or butene is shown in Fig. 8.5. (Sampson & Shooter 1965). Each of the species shown has been detected in oxidation experiments and each by itself yields some maleic anhydride. With n-butane, the first step is rate-limiting, and only low levels of intermediates are found.

Hodnett (1985) provides an extensive and detailed review (including extensive references to the patent literature) of preparation and characterization methods for vanadium-phosphate catalysts for selective oxidation of C_4 hydrocarbons. Earlier extensive reviews were published by Varma and Saraf (1979), Voge and Adams (1967) and Sampson and Shooter (1965). The historical development of oxidation processes for maleic anhydride is described in a pithy review by Chinchen et al. (1987), which also details some of the economic con-

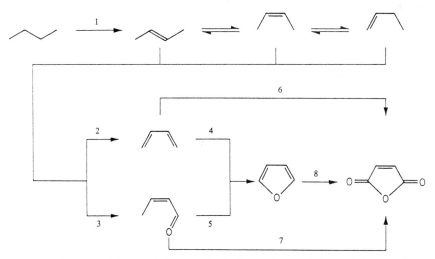

Figure 8.5 Possible molecular intermediates in the oxidation of linear C_4 hydrocarbons to maleic anhydride. *(Sampson and Shooter 1965)*

siderations that affect the use of competitive feedstocks. Commercial production in fixed-bed reactors is reviewed by Burnett et al. (1987).

As of 1990 about one-half the maleic anhydride capacity operating in the world used benzene as a feed (plants primarily in Europe and Japan), whereas the other half, mostly in the United States, used butane (a few used butene). However a major shift to butane feed appears to be underway. Current plants predominantly use a multitube fixed-bed reactor, but some new plants, utilizing butane as a feedstock, apply a new fluidized-bed technology (the Alma process from Alusuisse Italia and Lummus Crest or from BP Chemicals–Mitsui Toatsu Chemicals). The first of these to become commercial apparently was a Mitsui-BP plant started up in Japan in 1987. Several plants using the Alma process have been announced as being under design or construction as of 1990. With a fluidized bed, butane and air can be fed at separate locations in the reactor and therefore at a butane concentration on an overall basis that is above the inflammability limit.

As of 1990 du Pont was studying, on a pilot plant scale, a recirculating catalyst process (Contractor et al. 1988; see also Sec. 8.1). The catalyst in an oxidized state is contacted with butane in an entrained-bed reactor, in the absence of air. At the top of the reactor the catalyst, now in a reduced state, is separated from products, and it is reoxidized by contact with air in a second reactor. The oxidized catalyst is returned to the entrained-bed reactor. In effect, the redox mechanism described in Sec. 8.1 is carried out in two separate vessels rather than simultaneously.

With either a fluidized-bed or an entrained-bed reactor, a major problem is attrition resistance of the catalyst. Catalysts for these types of reactors are usually manufactured by a spray-drying process frequently incorporating colloidal silica. A novelty in this particular application is a method of catalyst preparation such that the colloidal silica, comprising about 10 percent of the whole, migrates to the outside of the spray droplets, forming an attrition-resistant porous eggshell around the catalyst particle (Bergna 1989). du Pont patents for the transport reactor process describe a vanadium-phosphate catalyst with silica and either indium, antimony, or tantalum as a promoter (Bergna 1988).

The principal use of maleic anhydride is for the manufacture of unsaturated polyester resins. It is also converted to fumaric acid and can be hydrogenated in steps to form a variety of products, notably 1,4-butanediol and tetrahydrofuran.

8.6.2 Phthalic anhydride

The first industrial process for making phthalic anhydride by catalytic air oxidation appeared in the 1920s, using refined naphthalene from coal tar in a fixed-bed reactor. In 1946 Chevron initiated production by the vapor-phase oxidation of o-xylene. The use of naphthalene received an impetus by the development of a fluidized-bed process (Sherwin-Williams and Badger), first commercialized in the early 1950s. This process gave good yields with high-purity naphthalene but uneconomic yields with o-xylene. Coupled with this was the development in the early 1960s of processes for production of naphthalene from petroleum by hydrodealkylation of alkyl naphthalenes present in certain refinery product streams (Sec. 9.18). Alkyl naphthalenes such as methylnaphthalene give considerably lower yields in the partial oxidation reaction than does naphthalene itself.

o-Xylene has become the preferred feed, and formation of phthalic anhydride from o-xylene in a multitube fixed-bed process has become the process of choice in most new installations. In the Von Heyden, *Badische Anilin und Soda Fabrik* (BASF) process, the reaction temperature is in the range of 400°C, pressure is slightly above atmospheric, contact time is of the order of 5 s, and few by-products other than carbon oxides are formed. In another version (e.g., Chevron), temperatures of about 400 to 475°C and a contact time of about 0.5 s are used, and an appreciable quantity of maleic anhydride and other by-products are formed. The higher-temperature process utilizes a smaller reactor and smaller catalyst load, but the yield is slightly lower.

Either process can also be used with naphthalene, either from petroleum or unrefined naphthalene from coal tar. In the Von Heyden process, the yield on a weight basis is about 82 percent with a naphthalene feed, and about 92 percent with o-xylene. (However, the stoichiometric yield is greater for naphthalene than for o-xylene.) The maximum concentration of aromatic in the feed is limited by the necessity to avoid an explosive mixture, and, in the case of o-xylene, this is about 1 vol %. The fluid-bed process (Sherwin-Williams and Badger) is now obsolescent.

Since feedstock and product are purchased and sold on the basis of weight, a considerable advantage of o-xylene over naphthalene as a feedstock is that no carbon is lost in forming the desired product. Hence, with 100-percent selectivity, a theoretical yield of 139.6 kg of product is possible per 100 kg of o-xylene fed. (Yields up to about 80 percent of theoretical have been reported.) The theoretical heat of reaction for naphthalene is substantially greater than for o-xylene, which exacerbates the heat-transfer problem in multitube fixed-bed reactors.

o-Xylene is also preferred because xylenes are readily available from catalytic reforming, and suitable processes have been developed for separation of o-xylene from its isomers. As a liquid, it is easier to transport and store than naphthalene. Commercially, material of about 95-percent purity is used as a feedstock. In Sec. 11.9, representative axial-temperature profiles are given for the partial oxidation of o-xylene to phthalic anhydride to show the effect of such variables as tube diameter and the wall temperature, based on a simplified kinetic model and data published by Froment (1967). Industrial reactors are generally operated so as to obtain essentially complete conversion of the reactant, as well as of phthalide and o-tolualdehyde formed as intermediates. This reduces purification costs.

A considerable variety of catalyst compositions, all based on vanadia, have been used. With naphthalene as a feedstock, a commercial catalyst composition consists of vanadium oxide and potassium sulfate on a silica support, similar to that used in sulfur dioxide oxidation. Optimum catalyst selectivity, activity, and stability is achieved when a considerable amount of pyrosulfate is present. This is obtained by adding a small amount of sulfur dioxide to a pure naphthalene feed or by pretreatment of coal-tar naphthalene to reduce its sulfur content to an optimum value.

The optimum sulfur level depends on the type of reactor. In a fluid-bed system this was a SO_3/K_2O ratio of about 2.0, achieved with a naphthalene feed containing about 0.1 wt % sulfur. The optimum in a tubular fixed-bed reactor is different, which may be ascribed to the existence of a hot spot in the fixed-bed case, so the composition of the catalyst at this elevated temperature would differ from that in contact with the same gas composition at a lower temperature. The effects of sulfur in naphthalene on the performance of fixed- and fluidized-bed reactors are also discussed by Saffer (1963).

With an o-xylene feed, the highest yields reported in the patent literature are for a vanadium oxide–titania catalyst. The catalytically active material, typically a powder of about 4% V_2O_5 and 96% TiO_2 (anatase) is applied as a thin layer (e.g., about 100 μm) on the outside of an inert core, presumably to minimize diffusion limitations. A support such as MgAl silicate is satisfactory. The principal reaction pathway is the partial oxidation of o-xylene to o-tolualdehyde, which in turn is converted to o-toluic acid, o-phthalide, and then phthalic anhydride in a series of reactions. With the use of titania the concentration of these intermediates in the final product is reduced. Some maleic anhydride is also formed. Bond (1989) proposes a "rake" mechanism based on the sequential reaction of the five surface intermediates.

Some core supports may contain small concentrations of potassium or sodium as an impurity, e.g., from a clay binder used in manufacture. This can slowly migrate to the catalytic layer, especially at high temperatures, and react with the vanadia, forming an alkali vanadyl vanadate that is less active and selective, e.g.,

$$Na_2O + 6V_2O_5 \rightarrow Na_2O \cdot V_2O_4 \cdot 5V_2O_5 + \tfrac{1}{2}O_2 \qquad (8.27)$$

In this event a small amount of SO_2 (e.g., ~100 ppm) may be added to the feed. Since V_2O_5 is weakly acidic, but SO_2 is strongly acidic, the SO_2 in effect pulls sodium (or potassium) out of the structure.

The relative rates of the different steps are affected by catalyst composition and by the particular mixtures of species present. Earlier kinetic schemes need to be modified for application to present-day catalysts supported on titania. A detailed review by Wainwright and Foster (1979) summarizes the older literature on reaction kinetics, mechanisms, and catalysts, covering oxidation of naphthalene as well as o-xylene.

Anatase is preferred to rutile as the titania support for reasons that are not completely clear. Bond et al. (1989) suggest as a possibility that anatase can be obtained as nonmicroporous particles of only a few nanometers in size, with corresponding surface area of about 10 m^2/g. (Supporting this as a coating on an inert core would minimize the possibility of diffusion limitations.) Gasior et al. (1987) report that, with time on stream, V_2O_5 spreads over the surface of anatase, but does not over rutile. Hausinger et al. (1988) show that the method of preparation and calcination of vanadia-titania catalysts can have a marked effect on catalyst structure. Vanadia supported on titania promotes the anatase-rutile transformation. A polyvanadate is formed on an anatase surface, but calcination at 500°C converts the anatase to rutile with a marked decrease in surface area and incorporation of V^{+4} into the rutile lattice.

Evidence is accumulating that the site of catalytic activity is a full VO_x monolayer (Bond 1989; Bond et al. 1989). Any uncovered portions of the TiO_2 surface may cause nonselective oxidation. Industrial catalysts on low-area anatase contain several times a monolayer equivalent (Bond et al. 1989), which is postulated to be only a source of VO_x to maintain as complete a monolayer as possible. From a study by Cristiani et al. (1989) utilizing infrared and laser-Raman techniques, it was concluded that the monolayer comprised monooxovanadyl species, accompanied by V_xO_y "clusters."

Dicarboxylic acids such as terephthalic acid (1,4-benzene dicarboxylic acid) are too unstable to be manufactured by vapor-phase catalytic oxidation. Instead, the process of choice is liquid-phase oxidation by air of o-xylene dissolved in acetic acid, using a homogeneous catalyst system (Mid-Century, Amoco process).

8.7 Vinyl Acetate

A mixture of ethylene, oxygen, and acetic acid in the vapor phase, with ethylene in considerable excess, is mixed with a recycle stream and is passed over a fixed-bed catalyst at about 150 to 175°C and about 0.5- to 1.0-MPa pressure to form vinyl acetate. The oxygen concentration is about 10 percent, chosen to stay out of the inflammability region. The reaction is

$$C_2H_4 + CH_3COOH + \tfrac{1}{2}O_2 \rightarrow CH_2\!\!=\!\!CH\!-\!\!O\!-\!\!C(O)CH_3 + H_2O$$

$$-\Delta H = 176 \text{ kJ/mol} \qquad (8.28)$$

The catalyst contains palladium on an acid-resistant support such as silica, in the form of 4- to 5-mm spheres. α-Al_2O_3 is also satisfactory. Several percent of potassium acetate is added to the catalyst to increase catalyst activity and to reduce oxidation to carbon dioxide. The potassium acetate slowly migrates from the carrier and must be replaced by injection into the feed stream.

The reaction is highly exothermic, and a multitube reactor with, e.g., 2.5-cm-ID tubes is used, the heat being removed by boiling water in the shell. About 10- to 20-percent conversion of ethylene is obtained per pass, with 60- to 70-percent consumption of oxygen. The overall selectivity is 91 to 94 percent, based on ethylene reacted. About 1 percent of the ethylene forms acetaldehyde, and carbon dioxide is the primary additional by-product.

Reaction of acetic acid with the oxygen is apparently negligible; it is converted only to vinyl acetate, in amounts corresponding to 15 to 30 percent of the acetic acid fed. The product is rapidly cooled, vinyl acetate is removed by scrubbing with an organic solvent such as propylene glycol, and carbon dioxide is removed by scrubbing with a base such as aqueous, hot alkali carbonate. The remaining stream is mixed with fresh feed and recycled. Allowing the concentration of carbon dioxide and other inert gases, such as nitrogen and argon brought in with the oxygen, to build up to a certain extent is desirable to help keep the oxygen concentration below the explosive limit.

The process, first put into commercial operation in about 1968, was developed almost simultaneously by Bayer and Hoechst in Germany and National Distillers (U.S. Industrial Chemicals) in the United States, and is the process of choice for new plants. It replaces an earlier liquid-phase process utilizing a homogeneous palladium and copper chloride redox catalyst with ethylene, similar to that in the Wacker process for manufacture of acetaldehyde from ethylene. Corrosion problems in the liquid-phase ethylene process were especially severe, largely because of HCl, which is formed as an intermediate, and the process is no longer operated. An earlier process based on acetylene was the process of choice in the 1960s but is probably now obsolete. Acetylene and acetic acid were reacted at about 180 to 230°C over zinc acetate deposited on carbon, in a multitube reactor. Further details on this and competitive processes are given by Stobaugh et al. (1972) and by Krekeler and Kronig (1967).

A mechanistic study by Nakamura and Yasui (1970) of this reaction on a palladium catalyst revealed that no vinyl acetate is formed from ethylene and acetic acid in the absence of oxygen. They concluded that acetic acid is activated by abstraction of hydrogen by palladium in the presence of oxygen. Ethylene is adsorbed with abstraction of hydrogen by palladium even in the absence of oxygen. They thus hypothesized that vinyl acetate is formed from combination of dissociatively adsorbed acetic acid and dissociatively adsorbed ethylene, the surface reaction being rate-determining under industrial reaction conditions.

In their work at 120°C, the addition of potassium acetate increased the rate of reaction on a 1 wt % Pd/Al$_2$O$_3$ catalyst as much as tenfold. The maximum activity was achieved with about 2 to 3 wt % potassium acetate, after which it decreased. Since the compound is slowly lost by volatilization, maintenance of the proper level of potassium acetate under industrial reaction conditions is important.

Of other alkali metal acetates, those of cesium and rubidium are comparable to potassium in activity; sodium and lithium are less active; and alkaline earth acetates are generally even less. Of other potassium salts, those in which the anion can be readily replaced by an acetate ion are about as active as potassium acetate. A compound such as potassium chloride showed no activity, presumably because the chloride ion is not easily replaced by an acetate ion. In addition to promoting hydrogen abstraction from adsorbed acetic acid, the potassium is postulated to weaken Pd-O bonds in a palladium-acetate surface compound.

Nakamura and Yasui developed a rate expression from their data that is a starting point for modeling this reaction. However, the kinetics are probably very complicated. Judging from the reaction conditions, a liquid phase is probably present in at least some of the pores of the catalyst under at least some portion of the reaction conditions. (The boiling point of acetic acid at atmospheric pressure is 119°C.)

A commercial catalyst contains about 2 wt % Pd and also gold, in a weight ratio of palladium to gold of about 3:1 (Bartsch 1978, 1979). Gold is inert but it apparently helps inactivate the support (Nakamura et al. 1978) and improves catalyst life, activity, and selectivity. The reaction is highly diffusion-limited, which tends to accelerate side reactions; the heavy metals are therefore deposited in a thin band near the outside surface. However, during commercial operation some of the palladium migrates towards the pellet center and the palladium crystallites grow. The mechanism may be similar to a solution/deposition process observed with palladium in the presence of other oxygenated species (Sec. 6.4.3). The gold remains stationary.

From propylene, acetic acid, and oxygen, allyl acetate is formed, in much higher selectivity than in the equivalent liquid-phase reaction using a palladium salt and cocatalysts.

Most vinyl acetate is converted to polyvinyl acetate as an emulsion polymer used in paints, adhesives, coatings, etc., or it is processed into polyvinyl alcohol (used in adhesives, sizings, etc.) or polyvinyl butyral. The latter is used as a laminate in safety glass. Some vinyl acetate is copolymerized with vinyl chloride or other monomers to form an emulsion copolymer, also used in paints and coatings. Vinyl alcohol is unstable and therefore cannot be polymerized directly.

8.8   Oxychlorination

A wide variety of chlorinated compounds are manufactured by the chlorination of a hydrocarbon, hydrogen chloride being produced as a by-product. Hydrogen chloride is difficult to transport and overall is produced in quantities greater than those needed in industry. Consequently, there has long been interest in processes to convert hydrogen chloride directly back to chlorine, either in a separate process or simultaneously during the chlorination process. In an old procedure, the *Deacon process*, the direct reaction

$$4HCl + O_2 \rightarrow 2Cl_2 + 2H_2O \qquad (8.29)$$

was catalyzed by a copper chloride catalyst at about 600°C. Particular difficulties are volatilization of the metal chloride at this reaction temperature and corrosion, which is especially severe for a mixture of water and hydrogen chloride at an elevated temperature. The conversion for this exothermic reaction may also be limited by equilibrium.

After World War II a commercial fluidized-bed process (Shell) was developed using a catalyst containing potassium chloride and a rare earth chloride, e.g., lanthanum chloride, in addition to copper chlorides. This exhibited suitable activity at about 420°C. The potassium salt appears to reduce volatility and the lanthanum salt markedly increases activity. A competitive process (Kel-chlor) for reaction (8.29) uses nitrogen oxide compounds in the presence of about 70 to 80% sulfuric acid as reaction intermediates rather than a heterogeneous catalyst. The process may operate at 0.1 to 1.5 MPa and temperatures of about 130 to 180°C.

Chlorination and oxidation of the hydrogen chloride product can also be caused to occur simultaneously, termed *oxychlorination*. The most important process is the conversion of ethylene to 1,2-dichloroethane (ethylene dichloride), which in turn is converted to vinyl chloride by pyrolysis:

$$CH_2{=}CH_2 + 2HCl + \tfrac{1}{2}O_2 \rightarrow CH_2ClCH_2Cl + H_2O \qquad (8.30)$$

$$- \Delta H \,'= 119 \text{ kJ/mol}$$

$$CH_2ClCH_2Cl \rightarrow CH_2{=}CHCl + HCl \qquad (8.31)$$

Because of the overall stoichiometry of the process, some ethylene is also reacted directly with chlorine to form ethylene dichloride.

$$CH_2{=}CH_2 + Cl_2 \rightarrow CH_2ClCH_2Cl \qquad (8.32)$$

Reaction (8.32) may be carried out with a catalyst such as ferric chloride, at 50 to 60°C, using liquid dichloroethane as a reaction medium. Homogeneous reaction in the vapor phase may be carried out at 370 to 500°C. In the latter case some vinyl chloride and hydrogen chloride may also be formed. More than 90 percent of U.S. production capacity for vinyl chloride utilizes this so-called *balanced technology*, which came into practice in the 1960s. In earlier technology, acetylene was reacted with hydrogen chloride to form vinyl chloride using a mercury(II) chloride/carbon catalyst, in a multitube reactor cooled by boiling water. This process is still practiced to a lesser extent.

For the oxychlorination reaction, the catalyst is typically cupric chloride on alumina, modified with potassium chloride to reduce the volatility of the copper chloride. The latter may be held onto the catalyst by bonding with OH groups on alumina to form a structure such as —Al—O—CuCl. The reaction temperature is 250 to 315°C, and the pressure is atmospheric or slightly higher. The conversion of hydrogen chloride decreases at higher temperatures, possibly because of decreased adsorption of hydrogen chloride onto the catalyst. There are some indications that the dichloroethane product is more strongly adsorbed than the reactants and thereby inhibits the rate. Carrubba and Spencer (1970) report a kinetic study of the reaction using a copper chloride/alumina catalyst at 180°C.

The feed stream typically contains an excess of ethylene and oxygen to obtain essentially complete conversion of hydrogen chloride. Steam may be added to bring the composition below the explosive limit. The reaction is highly exothermic, and either a multitube fixed-bed or a fluid-bed reactor may be used, with air or oxygen. In a process utilized by Pechiney-St. Gobain, ethylene, hydrogen chloride, and air are reacted at 280 to 480°C and 0.2- to 0.8-MPa pressure in a fluidized-bed reactor using a copper salt/oxide as the catalyst.

Combining reactions (8.30) and (8.31) is clearly desirable, and a number of catalyst compositions have been patented. However, no commercial process to do so has apparently been put in operation. Typical process flow sheets and further details are given by Wimer and Feathers (1976) and Reich (1976). The catalyst in the Shell version of the Deacon process is a molten salt under reaction conditions held in the pores of a support; in oxychlorination the catalyst may also be molten under some conditions. Catalyst composition and reaction mechanisms are reviewed by Kenney (1975) and Villadsen and Livbjerg (1978) in conjunction with molten salt systems in general.

Oxychlorination of ethylene is reviewed by Naworski and Velez (1983).

A process to oxychlorinate methane (Transcat, C-E Lummus) (*Chem. Eng.* 1974) has been described that would use a molten salt mixture of cupric chloride, cuprous chloride, and potassium chloride (which depresses the melting point). Pressure is below 0.7 MPa and temperatures are about 370 to 450°C. The molten salt is circulated by gas lifts between two reactors, an oxidizing reactor and a chlorination/oxychlorination reactor. In the first reactor the molten salt flows downward in a packed bed against a stream of air. Waste chlorocarbons are pyrolyzed elsewhere, and their products are also fed to this reactor. Copper chloride is oxidized to $CuO \cdot Cl_2$, some CuCl reacts with Cl_2 to form $CuCl_2$ and some reacts with HCl and O_2 in air to form $CuCl_2$ and H_2O. In the second reactor methane is converted to various chloromethanes by chlorination, and some of the HCl formed is converted to water and Cl_2 in situ by oxygen released from the molten salt. This process has apparently not been commercialized.

Although 90 percent of more of the HCl consumed in the United States is produced as a by-product, it is shipped primarily as an aqueous solution, and transportation costs can be significant. Hence, a small amount of HCl is produced by direct reaction of Cl_2 and H_2, "chlorine burning," where regional economics supports this method.

8.9   Sulfuric Acid

Sulfuric acid accounts for the greatest consumption of any inorganic chemical, most of it being used for manufacture of phosphate fertilizers and processing of nonferrous metal ores. In the nineteenth century it was manufactured by the lead chamber process in which dilute sulfur dioxide, usually produced by burning iron pyrites or elemental sulfur in air, was contacted with nitrogen oxides and passed slowly through a series of chambers (usually lined with lead inside for inertness). This provided time for a complex series of reactions to take place in both the gas and the liquid phases, leading to the formation of dilute sulfuric acid. The nitrogen oxides and an intermediate unstable compound $HNOSO_4$, nitrosylsulfuric acid, acted as a homogeneous catalyst and were recovered for reuse. An advantage of the process was that relatively impure gases, as from smelters, could be reacted without extensive prepurification; but concentrated acid could not be produced directly, the equipment required was huge and cumbersome, and the process has long been obsolete.

The use of a heterogeneous catalyst for the reaction

$$SO_2 + \tfrac{1}{2}O_2 \rightleftharpoons SO_3 \qquad\qquad (8.33)$$

$$-\Delta H^{0}{}_{900K} = 95.8 \text{ kJ/mol}$$

became commercial in Europe toward the end of the nineteenth century, spurred by the fact that this process permitted the direct production of fuming sulfuric acid, "oleums," consisting of SO_3 dissolved in H_2SO_4. These products were particularly desirable for sulfonation reactions in the growing dye industry. The SO_3 formed is dissolved in 98% H_2SO_4 since, if it is attempted to dissolve the SO_3 in water directly or into a weaker acid, the water vapor pressure causes the formation of an acid mist that is difficult to remove. The fortified H_2SO_4 formed may then be diluted to the desired strength.

In the early plants the catalyst was platinum-supported on an acid-resistant material, usually asbestos, magnesium sulfate, or silica gel. These materials gradually were replaced between 1920 and 1940 by a catalyst comprising vanadium oxide and potassium sulfate on a silica support that, although slightly less active, is cheaper and less susceptible to poisoning. All plants constructed since World War II presumably use a vanadium-type catalyst.

The equilibrium for reaction (8.33) as a function of temperature is shown in Fig. 8.6 for an initial composition of 8.0 mol % SO_2, 13% O_2, and 79% N_2 at atmospheric pressure. Since the reaction reverses at higher temperatures, the reactor usually consists of four trays in series, which operate adiabatically at slightly above atmospheric pres-

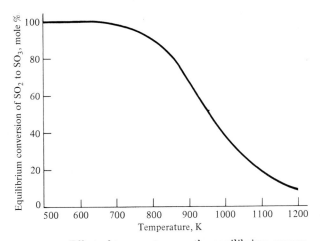

Figure 8.6   Effect of temperature on the equilibrium conversion of sulfur dioxide to sulfur trioxide (initial sulfur dioxide concentration of 8.0 percent by volume in air).

sure. The reacting gas is cooled between the trays. The inlet SO_2 concentration is typically about 7 percent (from a metallurgical smelter operation) to 10.5 percent (from elemental sulfur combustion).

With an inlet gas containing about 9% SO_2 the temperature entering the first tray is adjusted to about 420°C. It leaves at about 600°C, and the heat in this stream is usually recovered in a waste-heat steam boiler. The temperature drop across subsequent trays is typically 50 to 60°C, 10 to 15°C, and 5°C, respectively, and the gas is cooled by heat exchangers between trays. Typically, about 75 percent of the total conversion occurs on the first tray, and only 2 percent or so on the last. The inlet temperature to each succeeding tray is adjusted to an optimum value that varies with circumstances. An important consideration is that the rate of reaction drops rather dramatically in the region below about 440°C because of the peculiar nature of the catalyst (see later). In a sulfur-burning plant additional air may be supplied after the second and third passes to provide additional oxygen for the reaction. This results in a somewhat lower required catalyst loading but slightly higher SO_2 emissions from the final absorption tower.

The catalyst layers are from about 45 to 75 cm deep, and the cost of the catalyst is a large portion of the cost of the loaded reactor. A plant that produces 1000 tons of acid per day will contain 150,000 to 200,000 liters of catalyst. The catalyst is extremely long-lived, 10 or more years not being unusual, and a common procedure is to occasionally screen or replace the catalyst on the first tray on which dust, scale, and poisons slowly accumulate.

The overall conversion is typically 99.7 percent or more and is determined primarily by air pollution control rather than by internal economics. To meet air pollution requirements limiting SO_2 concentrations to about 300 to 1000 ppm in the discharge to the atmosphere, SO_3 is substantially removed by absorption from product gases after the third tray, and the remaining SO_2 is reacted further on the fourth tray.

Figure 8.7 is a schematic diagram of a representative converter design. Only a portion of the gas from the second tray is removed for cooling, conditions being adjusted so that the mixture of the cooled gas and the uncooled gas is at the desired temperature for entering the third tray. The gas leaving the third tray is cooled against gas returning to the fourth tray by a heat exchanger, passes to an absorber, and returns through the heat exchanger to the fourth tray. Heat is then recovered, and the gas passes to a second absorber. The use of two absorbers increases the overall conversion and minimizes SO_2 discharge to the atmosphere. Figure 8.8 is a photograph of a sulfuric acid plant having a capacity of 850 tons of acid per day. The converter is on the left, and one of the heat exchangers is in the right foreground.

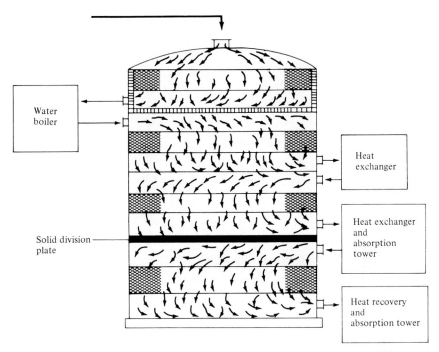

Figure 8.7 Representative sulfur dioxide converter design. *(Courtesy of Monsanto Enviro Chem Systems, Inc.)*

The usual catalyst comprises a mixture of vanadia and potassium sulfate on a silica support, the vanadium-potassium atomic ratio being in the range of 2 to 3.5, and the vanadium content in the range of 5 to 9 wt % V_2O_5. A representative commercial catalyst in its activated state has the composition 13 wt % K_2O, 6.9 wt % V_2O_5, 0.5 Na_2O, 19.9% SO_3, with the remainder silica gel or kieselguhr (diatomaceous earth). In a typical manufacturing process, kieselguhr that has been acid-washed (to remove iron and other impurities) and calcined is mixed with ammonium vanadate and potassium hydroxide, plus some potassium silicate that acts as a bonding agent. The thick dough is extruded, air-dried, and calcined in contact with SO_2 or an SO_2-SO_3 mixture to convert it to the final chemical form. The reaction of SO_2 with alkali and its oxidation is relatively exothermic, and, desirably, it is carried out before the catalyst is placed into service in the reactor.

These catalysts are unusual in that the potassium and vanadium compounds react with one another and with SO_2 and SO_3 to form a mixture of complex potassium vanadia pyrosulfates, which is partly or completely liquid under reaction conditions (Tandy 1956). The

Figure 8.8   Sulfuric acid plant at Scarlino/Follonica (Grosseto), Italy. *(Courtesy of Montedison S.p.A.)*

pyrosulfates have lower melting points than the corresponding sulfates. This melt forms a film on the surface of the pores in the inert silica support, which can migrate under operating conditions.

The composition of the melt changes with temperature and gas composition and with a change in operating conditions. This influences its activity. If the temperature is changed, many hours may be required before a new steady-state rate is reached, especially at lower temperatures. Various models have been proposed for ways in which the liquid may be distributed on the support, and optimal liquid loadings have been suggested; but these depend on the model assumed. These theoretical aspects have been reviewed in detail by Livbjerg et al. (1974) and Villadsen and Livbjerg (1978).

Commercial catalysts are typically extrudates about 5.5 mm in diameter by about 8 mm in length. A larger size, for example, 8 × 11 mm, may be placed on the first tray, in order to lower pressure drop, especially since dirt, scale, etc. build up in this location. In some cases a vanadium oxide catalyst of slightly different composition is placed on the final tray of the converter, the catalyst having higher activity for the partially converted gases. The average pore size of these catalysts is in the micrometer range, and the surface area is about 1 m^2/g, a value that does not seem to change much with the melt conditions.

If one considers the various alkalis as promoters, according to Tandy (1956), maintenance of the V^{5+} state is enhanced in the order Cs > Rb > K > Na. That the +4 form is less active for this reaction than the +5 form is reasonably clear. The ratio of the +4 to the +5 form is enhanced at lower temperatures and at lower values of the ratio P_{SO_2}/P_{SO_3}. All commercially used catalysts contain potassium, and many of them some sodium as well.

Studies on commercial catalysts agree in concluding that the rate of reaction drops markedly at temperatures below about 420 to 460°C (Villadsen and Livbjerg 1978). The apparent activation energy is much higher in the lower temperature region. The deactivation at lower temperatures is caused by the increased presence of the V(IV) form and the precipitation of active vanadium species. In a detailed study Boghosian et al. (1989) isolated and determined the structure of the various V(IV) and V(III) crystalline compounds precipitated under various SO_2 reaction conditions. They also observed that the drop in catalytic activity occurred simultaneously with the formation of vanadium compounds of low solubility. Heat treatment at a temperature above about 470°C causes the low-valence vanadium compounds to decompose, reoxidize, and redissolve. The position of the break in the Arrhenius plots depends on the nature and quantity of the alkali promoter, the alkali-vanadium ratio and the SO_3/SO_2 ratio.

Sulfur dioxide in air can be oxidized to sulfur trioxide by bubbling it through a potassium sulfate-vanadia melt (Haldor-Topsøe & Nielsen 1947). Such a melt also catalyzes other oxidation reactions for which solid vanadium oxide is a catalyst, e.g., the partial oxidation of o-xylene to phthalic anhydride (Satterfield & Loftus 1965). However, in the latter case the rate on a volume basis is low compared with that observed with a solid catalyst.

A large number of kinetic expressions to represent the rate over the whole range of industrial conditions have been reported. Livbjerg and Villadsen (1972) list 12 and Urbanek and Trela (1980) list 29. In part they represent studies under different experimental conditions, but they also conflict with one another in some degree, which is not surprising in view of the unusual behavior of the catalyst. The rate of reaction is moderately limited by diffusion. On 6 × 6 mm pellets, effectiveness factors in the range of 0.3 to 0.8 for representative industrial conditions have been estimated (Livbjerg & Villadsen 1972), although it is difficult to do so quantitatively because of the complex kinetics.

Details on the older catalyst compositions and processes are given in the book by Duecker and West (1959). Donovan et al. (1983) review catalyst formulations, testing, and deactivation, giving extensive references. The reaction was intensively studied by Boreskov and his coworkers for many years, and a report on a kinetic study (Boreskov et al. 1967) reviews earlier work. Herce et al. (1977) report kinetic data at 0.1, 0.5, and 1.0 MPa for a vanadia catalyst containing barium oxide instead of a potassium compound, although commercially there seems to be little economic incentive to operate a catalytic reactor at much above atmospheric pressure. In a review of the use of molten salts as catalysts, Kenney (1975) discusses the kinetics of the reaction. Villadsen and Livbjerg (1978) cover the same area in great detail in a later review, with particular attention to composition of these melts as a function of the reaction conditions. Urbanek and Trela (1980) consider reactor design in some detail. See also the review by Kenney (1980). The historical development of catalytic SO_2 oxidation is covered briefly by Davies (1987) and Davies et al. (1989). The latter also provides a pithy summary of the subject.

8.10   Ammonia Oxidation

The basis for present-day nitric acid manufacture stems from work by Kuhlmann, who filed a patent in 1838 for oxidation of ammonia in air over platinum sponge to form nitric oxide. Ostwald and coworkers studied this reaction on a pilot scale during 1901 to 1904, leading to the first commercial plant in Germany in 1906. This had a capacity of 300 kg of nitric acid per day. Use of platinum in the form of a gauze, the present-day configuration, was patented by Kaiser in 1909. Early industrial ammonia was primarily a by-product of coking of coal and was relatively impure, but this was soon replaced by relatively pure and cheap ammonia from the Haber process (Sec. 10.5). This process stimulated the advent of large-scale nitric acid production from ammonia oxidation in the 1920s. Worldwide, some 75 to 80 percent of the nitric acid produced today is used for manufacture of fertilizer. Other uses are for explosives and oxidation of chemical intermediates.

In present-day practice a mixture of ammonia and air is passed downward through a pad of fine platinum-alloy gauzes at a pressure

Figure 8.9   Ammonia oxidation reactors. *(Courtesy of Johnson Matthey & Co., Ltd. and ICI Agricultural Division.)*

ranging from slightly above atmospheric to about 0.9 MPa (Fig. 8.9). The desired reaction is:

$$4NH_3 + 5O_2 \rightarrow 4NO + 6H_2O \qquad (8.34)$$

$$-\Delta H_{298} = 227 \text{ kJ/molNH}_3$$

The stoichiometric ratio for the reaction corresponds to 14.2 mol % NH_3, but the explosive limit of NH_3 in air is 12.4 percent at 0.8 MPa and slightly more at 0.1 MPa. Hence the NH_3 concentration used does not exceed about 11 percent in a high-pressure plant and about 13.5 percent at atmospheric pressure. The highly exothermic reaction is extremely rapid, being complete in about 1 ms or less, and is highly mass-transfer-controlled. Therefore, the gas composition at the catalyst surface is different from that in the bulk. Intermediates such as NH, HNO, and NH_2OH have been postulated, but little is actually known about the reaction mechanism.

To initiate the reaction, the catalyst must be preheated, as by use of a flame, to a temperature at which the reaction becomes self-starting. After this the reactor heats itself up to a steady-state reaction temperature. Conditions for starting an exothermic reaction such as this and for maintaining the reactor stable have been extensively treated in the chemical engineering and other literature for many years. An analysis of the factors determining the starting and stability phenomena in ammonia oxidation was published in 1918 by Liljenroth and further developed by Wagner in 1945.

The exit gases are rapidly cooled by placing the gauze pad on a ceramic support that, in turn, is positioned on top of a heat exchanger. NO in the cooled gases is allowed to oxidize to NO_2 homogeneously, and the NO_2 is then absorbed into water, accompanied by further oxidation, to form HNO_3. The oxidation and absorption are always carried out at elevated pressure, from about 0.5 MPa to 0.8 or 0.9 MPa. The catalytic oxidation of NH_3 may be carried out at approximately atmospheric pressure, followed by compression of product gas, or it may be carried out at a pressure dictated by the downstream operations without intermediate compression. The latter is the more common practice.

Increased pressure increases the rate of mass transfer of NH_3 and O_2 to the catalyst surface, and hence increases the rate of reaction. Thus, the catalyst inventory can be less, and a smaller reactor can be used. However, at the optimum reaction conditions the selectivity is slightly less and platinum losses are greater than with atmospheric-pressure operation. At atmospheric pressure, the optimum gauze temperature is about 810 to 850°C; at 0.8 MPa, about 920 to 940°C. The yield is about 97 to 98 percent for atmospheric-pressure processes and about 95 percent for operation at 0.7 to 0.9 MPa, the remainder of the NH_3 appearing as N_2. Platinum is lost from the gauze by volatilization of platinum oxide [Eq. (8.38)] and, to a lesser extent, by mechanical losses.

NH_3 also reacts homogeneously with NO to form N_2 by the reaction

$$4NH_3 + 6NO \rightarrow 5N_2 + 6H_2O \qquad (8.35)$$

$$-\Delta H = 1810 \text{ kJ/mol}$$

Figure 8.10   Installation of new catalyst gauzes in an ammonia oxidation plant. *(Courtesy of Johnson Matthey & Co., Ltd. and Thames Nitrogen Co., Ltd.)*

This undesirable reaction may occur if the flow through the gauze pad is uneven, allowing some NH_3 to escape downstream. For this reason the pad is built up of individual flat gauzes laid very carefully on one another to ensure that no free spaces exist between them (Fig. 8.10). At excessively low flow rates some NO may also be lost by the catalytic decomposition of NO

$$2NO \rightarrow N_2 + O_2 \qquad (8.36)$$

The oxidation of NH_3 to elemental nitrogen may also be significant:

$$4NH_3 + 3O_2 \rightarrow 2N_2 + 6H_2O \qquad (8.37)$$

$$-\Delta H = 1265 \text{ kJ/mol}$$

A representative pad is about 5 mm thick, and may be as much as 4 m or more in diameter. Since the pressure drop is so low, careful engineering is required to obtain even distribution of gas flow. A long cone-type entrance section is usually placed above the pad for this purpose (Fig. 8.9). The pad may contain as many as 40 gauzes, but reaction is essentially complete on the first two or three, when using 80-mesh gauze at atmospheric pressure. The additional gauzes may increase the overall efficiency by increasing the pressure drop and thereby causing more uniform gas distribution and temperature. Some of the gauzes are also needed to take over the reaction as the first gauzes disintegrate or become inactivated (see the following). However, the overall rate of precious-metal loss increases with the number of gauzes in the pad. In some designs the lower portion of the catalyst pack is replaced with a porous pad made of a nickel-chrome alloy, which reduces the platinum inventory required while providing the minimum pressure drop needed.

Fresh gauze is not very active, but, during the first few days of reaction, reconstruction of the metal occurs with complex outgrowths and deep fissuring. The gauzes become rough, as shown in Fig. 8.11, and the activity is greatly enhanced. The restructuring occurs primarily on those gauzes on which the major portion of the reaction is occurring, so major differences are seen between the first, the second, and the third gauzes, and between the top and bottom surfaces of the active gauzes. Electron microscope studies indicate that reconstruction of active catalyst surfaces probably occurs constantly throughout the working life of the catalyst. This reconstruction is associated with the reaction itself, since it does not occur at reaction temperature in the presence of either ammonia alone or oxygen alone.

During operation, platinum is lost at a fairly steady rate, caused primarily by the reaction

$$Pt(s) + O_2 \rightleftharpoons PtO_2(g) \tag{8.38}$$

The vapor pressure of platinum metal itself (e.g., 8.9×10^{-7} Pa or 6.76×10^{-9} torr at 1570°C) is too low for platinum volatilization to be a significant mechanism. The equilibrium of reaction (8.38) is shifted to the right at higher temperatures. The rate of loss is governed by the mass transport of slightly volatile PtO_2 from the surface of the catalyst (Nowak 1969), so it increases at higher temperatures and higher flow rates. The PtO_2 is reconverted to the metallic form downstream from the reactor by the reverse of reaction (8.38). Some platinum may be recovered by filters, some may be deposited on downstream heat-exchange surfaces, and some may also settle out in a variety of other locations.

For pressure operation (e.g., about 0.8 MPa), flow rates, "loadings" vary from about 40 to 100 short tons N_2 per (day) (meter)^2. (This use of mixed units is conventional. A short ton equals 2000 pounds.) Corresponding platinum losses are about 1.2 to 1.8 g Pt per short ton N_2 converted. A "getter" system (Holzmann 1968) is used in some plants

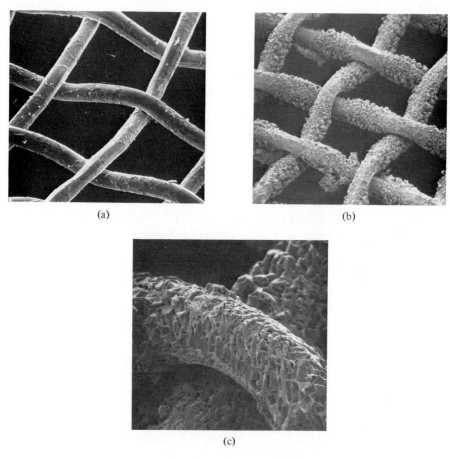

(a)   (b)

(c)

Figure 8.11   Scanning electron micrographs of 10% Rh-90% Pt gauze wire 0.075 mm (0.003 in) in diameter. (a) Original gauze, as drawn, showing uniform grain structure and absence of nodules on the wires. (b) The gauze in part (a) after one-half the normal gauze life installed in a nitric acid plant, showing the nodular pattern typical of an active gauze. (c) An enlarged view of the crossover point of two gauze wires in part (b) showing the characteristic octagonal crystal structure and the nodules, which are concentrated on the wire surfaces between crossover points. [Courtesy of Platinum Metals Review, vol. 15, p. 52 (1971)]

in which gauzes of pure palladium or a 20% gold–80% palladium alloy are placed directly below the platinum-alloy catalyst pad. The palladium immediately alloys with volatilized platinum oxide to form a solid solution.

The platinum recovery is also mass-transfer-controlled until the gauze has increased in weight about 80 percent, at which time its efficiency drops rather sharply. The recovery gauze pack therefore can be designed so its effective life approximately matches that of the platinum gauze pad above it, whereupon the entire unit can be removed for precious-metal recovery and replaced with a new unit. Palladium is the effective agent in the getter pad. Gold, if used, is present only to enhance mechanical properties. Some palladium is also lost from the getter gauze pad by volatilization.

The platinum loss occurs predominantly from the top gauzes. If a getter system is not used, from time to time the gauze pack may be removed and new platinum gauzes be placed directly above the support while the older gauzes are replaced on the top. This eliminates the activation period.

The addition of a few percent of rhodium to the platinum increases conversion efficiency and reduces catalyst loss (Handforth & Tilley 1934). Hence, the platinum alloy in the gauzes usually consists of 95% platinum-5% rhodium or 90% platinum-10% rhodium, the latter generally being preferred for high-pressure, high-temperature catalytic reaction. Rhodium in small amounts contributes mechanical strength to the alloy, but concentrations higher than above 10 percent result in a more brittle material that is more difficult to fabricate. Rhodium is also more expensive than platinum. A combination of 90% platinum, 5% palladium, 5% rhodium may also be used, in which half the rhodium is replaced by much less expensive palladium, apparently without loss of yield. The standard gauze is 80 mesh per inch (31.5 wires per centimeter) woven from wire 0.003 in (0.075 mm) in diameter. This represents a reasonable optimum between the desire for fine wire and high area on the one hand and mechanical requirements on the other. Sometimes a coarser gauze is interspersed occasionally among the finer gauzes, for mechanical reasons.

At atmospheric pressure platinum is preferentially lost by volatilization, and the surface of the alloy becomes enriched with rhodium, which is nearly as active as platinum. However, operating conditions are near the boundary separating rhodium and a rhodium oxide as the stable phase. Rhodium oxides are favored by lower temperatures, high oxygen partial pressures, and higher rhodium content of the alloy. Some rhodium may be lost by formation of RhO_2, which is less volatile than PtO_2. Solid Rh_2O_3, which is relatively unreactive, may also be formed and may blanket some of the platinum, thereby inactivating it (Harbord 1974). Since formation of Rh_2O_3 is favored by lower temperatures, a drop of the order of 50°C below normal operating temperatures could cause a platinum-rhodium gauze to become inactive (Sperner & Hohmann 1976). Segregation of rhodium at the surface is readily shown by electron microprobe studies (Sec. 5.5.4 and Fig. 8.12).

A loss in yield can also be produced by iron contamination of the gauzes from adventitious impurities in the plant (iron is a good ammonia-decomposition catalyst) or from iron acquired during fabri-

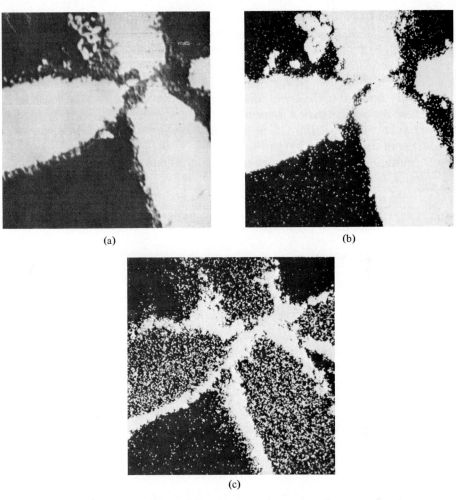

(a)

(b)

(c)

Figure 8.12   Electron microprobe and X-ray images of spent inactive gauze showing segregation of rhodium at the surface. (*a*) Electron image of cross section of gauze. (*b*) Platinum X-ray image. (*c*) Rhodium X-ray image. *[Courtesy of Platinum Metals Review, vol. 15, p. 52 (1971).]*

cation. Catalyst activity can be markedly affected by small variations in surface-iron concentration; see, e.g., Stacey (1980).

Various base metal catalysts have long been studied as possible replacements for platinum-alloy catalysts, and a composition of 90% Fe_2O_3, 5% Mn_2O_3, and 5% Bi_2O_3 was used during World War I as a substitute. Cobalt oxide alone and combinations of cobalt oxide with other oxides such as iron oxide and chromium oxide, supported or unsupported, in fixed or fluidized beds, have also been studied. However, the base metal catalysts are not economically competitive with the platinum-alloy system. The active species seems to be a Co(II, III) oxide which is reduced to an inactive Co(II) form with ammonia concentrations in air above about 7 percent. The 7-percent limitation on NH_3 concentration may also be in part to avoid overheating the catalyst. The cobalt catalyst is very susceptible to sulfur poisoning. Temkin (1979) states that Co_3O_4 is the best of the nonplatinum catalysts and that a selectivity near 95 percent can be achieved at a reaction temperature of 700 to 750°C. He also discusses reaction mechanisms on this and platinum catalysts.

Ammonia oxidation on conventional catalysts is briefly reviewed by Davies et al. (1989).

8.11   Synthesis of Hydrogen Cyanide

The principal present-day process for manufacture of hydrogen cyanide was developed by Andrussow from studies in the early 1930s. A mixture of methane, ammonia, and air is passed through a platinum-alloy gauze pad in a manner closely analogous to that used in ammonia oxidation. The desired reaction may be written as

$$CH_4 + NH_3 + \tfrac{3}{2}O_2 \rightarrow HCN + 3H_2O \qquad (8.39)$$

$$-\Delta H = 482 \text{ kJ/mol}$$

The product gas also contains appreciable amounts of H_2 and CO as well as unreacted NH_3 and a small amount of CH_4 in addition to N_2 from the air. Natural gas and NH_3 are each usually fed in slight stoichiometric excess to air as expressed by reaction (8.39), and some degree of preheat may or may not be used.

The catalyst is a pad of 90% Pt-10% Rh woven screens like that used for NH_3 oxidation and is supported on a ceramic structure. This structure in turn is placed directly atop a heat exchanger for rapid quenching of reaction products, since HCN reacts homogeneously and rapidly with the water formed in the initial reaction:

$$HCN + H_2O \rightarrow NH_3 + CO \qquad (8.40)$$

Under equilibrium conditions the HCN concentration in reaction (8.40) is negligible.

The reaction pressure is about 0.2 MPa, the temperature is about 1100 to 1150°C, and contact time is of the order of a millisecond. Lower temperatures may lead to carbon formation, which reduces reactivity and can cause mechanical breakup of the gauze. The yield based on NH_3 fed is typically about 70 percent, and NH_3 is recovered from the product gas for reuse. As with NH_3 oxidation, traces of iron contamination on the platinum catalyst reduce yield and hence promote coke deposition.

Platinum losses in this reaction are small, presumably because formation of volatile platinum oxides is less likely in the overall reducing environment. A new gauze pack does not reach full activity and selectivity until after a period of 2 to 3 days, during which the gauze undergoes a major rearrangement with a large increase in roughness and surface area (Fig. 8.13). The activity and selectivity then slowly decline with time over a period of months. The addition of a trace of sulfur-containing compounds during initial operation reportedly de-

(a)   (b)

(c)

Figure 8.13 Appearance of leading gauze in the pack after prolonged exposure in the Andrussow process: 0.076 mm (0.003 in.) wire diameter and 1024 mesh/cm^2 (80 mesh/ in.). (a) Magnification about X40. Note the matte appearance and considerable reduction in apertures of the gauze. (b) Scanning electron micrograph of part (a). Note transformation of formerly solid wire into a mass of crystallites, many with well-developed pyramidal faces. (c) Same as part (b), further enlargement. [Courtesy of Platinum Metals Review, vol. 22, p. 131 (1978)]

creases the activation period. The reason for the effect is unknown, although electron photomicrographs show that it causes the catalyst structure to rearrange more rapidly.

Schmidt and Luss (1971) report on the detailed examination by various instruments of platinum-rhodium gauze catalysts after being used for NH_3 oxidation or the HCN reaction, the latter with and without sulfur treatment. Pan (1971) reports on morphological changes of a platinum-rhodium gauze catalyst after use in a 10-cm-ID pilot plant reactor. Flytzani-Stephanopoulos et al. (1977) describe surface morphologies of platinum catalysts as observed by SEM, after being used in various oxidation reactions.

Earlier studies of the reaction have been published by Andrussow (1951) and Pfeil and Hoffmann (1963). Pan and Roth (1968) report information on conversion and selectivity of NH_3 to HCN as a function of CH_4/NH_3 molar ratio and the ratio of air to reactants (CH_4 and NH_3), obtained in a 10-cm-ID reactor. The NH_3 may react to form HCN, it may pass through unreacted, or it may decompose to the elements. At air-reactant mole ratios lower than about 2.8, the HCN yield dropped off substantially. Also, the catalyst can become inactivated by carbon deposits if insufficient air is provided. Above an air-reactant ratio of about 3.25 the mixture becomes explosive.

Representative values for the maximum yield of HCN based on NH_3 were about 85 percent at a CH_4/NH_3 molar ratio of about 1.0 and an air/($CH_4 + NH_3$) ratio of 2.8, or about 88 percent at a CH_4/NH_3 mol ratio of about 1.6 and air/($CH_4 + NH_3$) ratio of 3.25. An increasing fraction of the NH_3 was found to pass through the gauze pad unreacted as the CH_4/NH_3 ratio was increased (e.g., above 0.8), termed *leakage*. The fraction of NH_3 decomposed and therefore unrecoverable increases as the CH_4/NH_3 ratio is decreased below about 1.2.

The ratio of NH_3/CH_4 chosen varies somewhat depending on whether emphasis is on yield or on production. For a fixed feed-gas temperature to the reactor, the reaction temperature changes with reactant ratios and mass flow rate, and this may also affect yield and conversion. In an industrial reactor it may not be easy to obtain as high yields as those reported by Pan and Roth, because of the difficulty of achieving uniform flow over a large-diameter, thin pad of gauze and the possible occurrence of downstream reactions.

Waletzko and Schmidt (1988) modeled the HCN synthesis by combining 13 simultaneous surface reactions among NH_3, CH_4, O_2, NO, H_2, and CO. Individual rates for each of the reactions had been previously measured on polycrystalline platinum, in many cases by Schmidt and coworkers, so there were no adjustable parameters except for the possibility of concentration gradients between bulk and catalyst surface. Predicted HCN selectivities and an optimum with feed composition agreed closely with that observed experimentally, giving credence to the validity of the model.

The fact that their model gave reasonably good agreement between predicted thickness of a gauze pack and that used industrially helps support their assumption of no mass-transfer limitations between gauze surface and flowing gas stream. Ammonia oxidation alone on a gauze pack of similar thickness is mass-transfer-limited, but there reaction is substantially complete on about 3 gauzes whereas the entire pack participates in the Andrussow synthesis. Further, the metal reconstruction in the latter case seems to develop a very extensive increase in surface area.

The meticulous work of Schmidt and coworkers is an impressive tour-de-force of simulating a complex heterogeneous catalytic reaction from first principles. The model predicts that the reactor should operate at the highest temperature possible and that higher pressures would increase production. It also predicts behavior under reaction conditions inaccessible industrially.

In an alternative process (Degussa), which is not widely used, a mixture of methane and NH_3 is passed through an array of ceramic tubes about 2 m in length and 2 cm in diameter, coated internally with a platinum-containing catalyst layer and heated externally. Reaction occurs at 1200 to 1300°C, and H_2 is formed as a by-product. The reaction is highly endothermic.

$$CH_4 + NH_3 \rightarrow HCN + 3H_2 \qquad (8.41)$$

$$-\Delta H = -250 \text{ kJ/mol}$$

Studies of this reaction are reported by Koberstein (1973), who used a reactor tube nearly identical to those used industrially. No consecutive reactions reportedly occur, and, with this particular catalyst, ammonia decomposition reportedly is negligible. Most of the reaction occurs in a short portion of the tube and largely under mass-transfer-controlling conditions; the first portion of the tube is required for heat-up and the last for cooling. Because of the large difference in molecular weight between H_2 and the other species present and the large temperature gradient between wall and gas at the exit, Koberstein calculates that considerable separation of the products occurs by thermal diffusion.

A higher concentration of HCN is produced in this process than in the Andrussow process, which lowers subsequent costs of purification; but the process is sensitive to operate and seems to be economic only in a small installation and where natural gas is expensive.

Some HCN is also produced as a by-product of manufacture of

acrylonitrile. HCN is used primarily to make adiponitrile by reaction with butadiene (for nylon 66) and methyl methylacrylate via reaction with acetone and esterification with methanol. Methyl methylacrylate is polymerized to form transparent plastics such as Lucite and Plexiglas and protective coatings. Some HCN is also used to make chelating agents.

8.12   Control of Vehicle Engine Emissions

The exhaust from the spark-ignition internal combustion engine of an automobile or light truck contains small concentrations of hydrocarbons and CO from incomplete combustion of fuel, and of nitric oxide (NO) from nitrogen fixation at the high temperature of combustion. These contaminants are a major contributor to air pollution and one of particular concern in urban areas. (At lower temperatures NO may be further oxidized to NO_2. The two species are frequently lumped together and designated as NO_x.)

Federal legislation in the United States, which went into effect for 1975-model cars, established maximum permissible emission levels for automobiles in terms of the emissions of three pollutants, expressed as grams of hydrocarbons, CO, and NO per mile traveled. The concentrations are averaged in a detailed test procedure that simulates representative modes of operation of an automobile during warm-up and driving after the engine reaches normal operating temperature.

Permissible levels for individual pollutants have been gradually lowered, and those for California have generally been more stringent than for the remainder of the United States. For the 1977 model year, the U.S. standards, in grams per mile* were hydrocarbons, 1.5; CO, 15; and NO_x, 2.0. To meet these standards combined with desired engine performance, so-called driveability, required the almost universal use of a catalyst to oxidize CO and hydrocarbons in the exhaust to CO_2 and H_2O. The NO_x standard was generally met by exhaust-gas recirculation to lower the combustion temperature and, hence, NO formation. For the model year 1981, the NO_x standard was lowered to 1.0 g/mile, which required a major change in catalyst design and formulation (Sec. 8.12.1). An interesting feature of the standards is that, since they are expressed as grams per mile, it is easier for a smaller car to meet the standards than a larger vehicle. New legislation will require a further reduction in emissions in the early 1990s. By the

---

*Somewhat surprisingly, this use of mixed metric and English units seems to have elicited no comment from either scientists, technologists, or the lay public. Standards in Europe are expressed in terms of grams per kilometer.

original legislation, the catalyst system in the new vehicle must generally meet specified standards for 50,000 mi or 5 years, whichever comes first, but the required life will likely be extended in the near future.

The catalyst application to automobiles is unique. It was the first large-scale use of a catalyst in a consumer product, supposed to perform for at least 5 years without attention by technically trained people, or indeed by anyone at all. Nearly complete oxidation of CO and hydrocarbons and control of NO_x is required of an intermittent gaseous stream whose temperature, composition, and flow rate vary in an erratic pattern and which may contain traces of any of a wide variety of catalyst poisons from possible fuel additives, lubricating oil, and corrosion.* Further, the unit must be compact because of stringent volume limitations, and the thermal mass must be as low as possible so the catalyst can reach ignition temperature rapidly, whereupon the emission control starts. The catalyst bed must operate at an extremely low pressure drop in order to minimize power loss from the engine. The sums of money expended for research and development of this single product stretch into the hundreds of millions of dollars and probably exceed that for any other single catalyst application.

In spite of intensive study, no catalyst composition has yet been developed that exhibits the requisite activity and durability when the fuel contains lead alkyls, commonly added in the past to raise the octane number of gasoline (Sec. 9.3), or phosphorus compounds. Hence, nonleaded gasoline must be used. Various base metal oxides exhibit good catalytic activity for oxidation, one of the most active being copper chromite. However, they may be insufficiently resistant to sintering at high temperatures to meet durability standards, and they are less active than noble catalysts at the low temperatures of the engine warm-up period. They also may be more susceptible to poisoning from NO_x and SO_2 in the exhaust gases. Some base oxide compositions may also deteriorate when subjected alternately to a net oxidizing and a net reducing environment.

---

*The potential cumulative effect of even traces of poisons in the reacting gases in contact with a catalyst can be vividly seen in this application. On average, an automobile burns its weight in fuel every year. With a 1000-kg car, over a 5-year period about 5000 kg of fuel would be consumed at an air-fuel weight ratio of about 14.5:1. About 72,500 kg of air with the products of combustion contact the catalyst. If the usual leaded gasoline containing 3 g of lead per gallon were to be used, 5000 g of lead would pass through a catalyst on which about 1 to 2 g of noble metal is supported. Even with "lead-free" gasoline, which is specified as containing no more than 0.05 g of lead per gallon, over a 5-year period this amounts to about 80 g. (Typical lead levels in "nonleaded" gasoline are actually a small fraction of this value.) With a sulfur content of about 300 ppm in gasoline, which is the U.S. average, about 2 kg of sulfur dioxide will contact the catalyst.

The catalysts developed for oxidation of CO and hydrocarbons in the 1975–1980 period were in all cases supported platinum or platinum plus palladium. Either of two catalyst configurations has been used. In one, the noble metal is supported on alumina beads held in a thin layer in a rather flat pancake-like alloy-steel container. The gases flow down through the layer. In the second, a honeycomb monolith is used consisting of a block of parallel, nonintersecting channels. (See Figs. 4.15, 4.16, and 4.17.) This is usually composed of cordierite, a magnesium-aluminum silicate, $Mg_2Al_3(AlSi_5O_{18})$, which has a low coefficient of thermal expansion and is mechanically strong. The monolith surfaces are covered with a very thin "washcoat" layer of alumina, and the noble metal is impregnated onto this.

The open cross-sectional area of the monolith is typically 70 percent or so of the total, and the number of cells per square inch range from 200 to 400 (31 to 62 cells per square centimeter), the corresponding wall thicknesses being, for example, 10 or 6 mils (0.25 or 0.15 mm), respectively. The material of higher cell count is somewhat more expensive to fabricate but allows a smaller catalyst unit to be utilized. The less the mass, the more rapidly it becomes heated up to the ignition temperature. For the same reason, specially fabricated alumina pellets of low mass are used in the packed-bed configuration. The ignition temperature with present noble-metal catalysts is about 250 to 300°C. Emissions during the warm-up period produce a substantial fraction of the total allowed by the test procedure, so rapid warm-up of the catalyst assumes considerable importance.

Platinum is more active for oxidation of paraffin hydrocarbons; palladium, for oxidation of CO and possibly unsaturated hydrocarbons. Platinum and palladium are found together in ores located predominantly in the U.S.S.R. and South Africa. Their individual price in the marketplace is dictated by the relative demand for the two metals compared with the ratio in which they occur in nature. The net demand for platinum in the Western world has increased more or less steadily from about 2,500,000 oz t per year in 1978 to about 3,500,000 oz t per year in 1989. Net use (gross minus recovery) in automobile catalysts accounts for about one-half of the platinum demand. About one-third of the demand was for jewelry, mostly in Japan. The net amount purchased for investment has been an increasing fraction of the total but fluctuates greatly from year to year. This investment demand has been stimulated in recent years by the appearance of several legal tender coins and medallions struck in platinum. Recovery of platinum from auto catalysts is only recently becoming appreciable and amounted to about 175,000 oz t in 1989.

Over the past several years about 80 percent of the net platinum supply has come from South Africa, about 5 percent as a by-product of nickel refining from the Inco operations at Sudbury, Canada, and almost all of the remainder from the U.S.S.R. The platinum from the U.S.S.R. is probably a by-product of nickel operations, and the ratio of palladium to platinum appears to be much higher than that in South African ores. The amount from the Inco operations depends on the primary demand for nickel, whereas the South African ores are mined for primary production of platinum and palladium; there other precious metals and nickel are produced as by-products. The only platinum production in the United States is from the Stillwater operations in Montana, but this is small relative to other sources.

Palladium demand in 1989 in the Western world amounted to 3,300,000 oz t. About one-half of this was in the electronics industry for use largely in conductive inks and protective coatings. About 30 percent was for dental alloys. Palladium can be interchanged for gold in many uses, so market prices for the two metals tend to move in tandem.

In South Africa, ores are mined primarily from an ore body termed the Merensky Reef. In recent years there has been gradual development of another ore body known as the UG2 reef. In the Merensky ore the platinum-group metals (pgm) content is about 0.2 oz t per ton of ore. The relative weight proportions of the pgm are about as follows: platinum, 1; palladium, 0.6 to 0.4; ruthenium, 0.15 to 0.07; rhodium, 0.06 to 0.04; iridium, 0.02 to 0.01; osmium ~ 0.002. Some osmium and iridium are also recovered as by-products of refining gold from certain South African ores. This concentrate is termed *osmiridium* and typically is about one-third osmium, one-third iridium, and about one-sixth platinum. Of the four minor platinum-group metals, the demand for rhodium (about 330,000 oz t in 1989) is high for use in three-way auto catalysts (see the following), and this use accounts for three-fourths of all rhodium available in the Western world. About two-thirds of the rhodium comes from South Africa and about one-third from the U.S.S.R. The comparatively small demand for ruthenium and iridium is well within mine capacities. There is little interest in osmium.

In the United States little platinum is used in jewelry. About two-thirds of the total net platinum demand is for motor vehicle catalysts. The production of the other pgm is as a by-product, so changes in demand can markedly affect price. Market prices for platinum in the past decade have varied in the range of about $300 to $600 per troy ounce. That for palladium has varied from $80 to $160 per troy ounce. The high demand for rhodium has caused its price in recent years to rise to the neighborhood of $1000 to $1500 per troy oz. Ruthenium prices have long hovered at about $60 to $70 per troy ounce. Iridium prices have been at the level of about $250 to $300 per troy ounce for many years. (Prices and market demands given in the foregoing have been taken largely from the annual reports *Platinum* prepared by the Johnson Matthey Co.) In comparison, in recent years market prices for such base metals as nickel, chromium, molybdenum, and cobalt, which are used as catalysts, have been in the range of $2 to $20 per pound of metal.

Since platinum-group metals are expensive, the loading used in auto catalysts is the minimum necessary to meet standards. This works out to an amount of noble metal in the range typically of about 1 to 2 g per catalyst unit.

The catalyst temperature is in the range of 400 to 600°C during normal operation, but may rise several hundred degrees above this under extreme driving conditions or with engine malfunction. The reaction is highly mass-transfer-limited after the engine reaches operating temperature, and the most effective use of the noble metal catalyst is to deposit it in a relatively thin layer near the outside catalyst surface. Poisons generally accumulate on the outermost surface of the porous support; so optimally the noble-metal layer should probably be displaced slightly into the interior to prolong catalyst life. This is sometimes termed an *eggshell*-type deposit.

8.12.1 Simultaneous removal of CO, hydrocarbons and NO_x

The more stringent limitations set in the United States for NO_x emissions from automobiles for model years 1981 and later required a major change in catalyst design. No catalysts of sufficient activity for decomposition of NO_x are known, and NO_x must therefore be removed by reduction to N_2 while still achieving control of CO and hydrocarbons. More than one type of catalyst configuration may be utilized, depending on engine characteristics and other design factors.

The solution that has been generally applied emerged from the finding that the concentrations of hydrocarbons, CO, and NO_x can all be reduced to the desired level simultaneously in a single catalyst unit if it is operated in a narrow range of air-fuel ratio that is approximately stoichiometric. This procedure requires precise control of the fuel-air mixture fed to the automobile engine at all operating conditions, to achieve this narrow, so-called "window" of composition. Generally, an oxygen sensor in the engine exhaust stream with a feedback control system is required. This type of unit is termed a *three-way catalyst* (TWC) because all three pollutants are removed simultaneously.

The most active catalyst is platinum, but some of the NO_x is reduced to NH_3 instead of N_2, which is not desired. The most effective catalyst for conversion of NO_x to N_2 is one in which appreciable rhodium is added to the platinum. However there is no primary production of rhodium anywhere in the world; it is produced as a by-product of production of platinum and palladium. The ratio of rhodium to platinum in South African ores, e.g., is about 0.06 to 0.04, but a higher ratio is desired in the catalyst, causing a rapid escalation in rhodium market prices in recent years.

In some cases a manufacturer employs a dual catalyst unit, the first unit being a three-way catalyst followed by an oxidation catalyst with additional air being added to the exhaust ahead of the oxidation catalyst. The two units may be housed in the same container or may be separated. Where space is at a premium, the first unit may be placed as close to the engine as possible, for rapid light-off. However, the trend seems to be toward closed-loop control with a single TWC in which rhodium is an essential ingredient. Some base-metal catalysts such as nickel or molybdenum oxide may also be added. Lesser amounts of palladium may also be added, but it may be less useful in this application than in a strictly oxidation-type catalyst. All automobile catalysts contain some quantity of platinum or palladium or both.

The control signal oscillations produce oscillations in the air-fuel ratio in the exhaust, with a frequency of about one per second (1 Hz). The consequent operation of the catalyst in a nonsteady-state manner is of considerable importance in designing an optimum catalyst. The alumina contains a stabilizer such as barium or lanthanum to minimize high-temperature sintering. Almost all catalysts also contain ceria, which seems to have several effects. In addition to helping stabilize alumina, it may act in an oxygen storage capacity, adsorbing oxygen during the oxygen-rich portion of an oscillation and utilizing this oxygen to oxidize CO and hydrocarbons during the fuel-rich portion, although evidence for this mechanism is murky. Base metals may contribute to this effect. The ceria and other species may also enhance CO conversion to CO_2 by the water-gas shift reaction with water vapor, if oxygen is not present. Similarly, hydrocarbon conversion may be enhanced by the steam-reforming reaction.

Other subtle interactions among the many variables, which are too complex to summarize here, may be encountered. One of these is that segregation of the noble metals may be desirable, e.g., by preparing separate layers within the outermost portions of an alumina support or by supporting each noble metal on an optimum support for that element. Alloy formation can cause less desirable reactions and the nature of the support can affect dispersion and chemical structure of the noble metals in different ways.

Monolith supports are used in 90 percent or more of all catalysts, largely because of durability problems with pellets. The use of low-density pellets to improve light-off characteristics seems to have caused problems with pellet attrition and mechanical breakup. The monolith walls are coated with a thin layer of alumina which, after firing, has a surface area of 80 to 100 m^2/g. The alumina is 20 to 30 wt % of the total, so for the final catalyst the surface area is about 20 m^2/g. There has been considerable interest in metallic monoliths that could be very compact and light off rapidly, but they require special alloys and methods of treatment and may be too costly at present for widespread use.

Exhaust emission standards and emission test procedures for other countries besides the United States are summarized by Taylor (1987). As of 1990, catalytic converters were needed for cars in the United States, Canada, Australia, and Japan. Regulations and economic incentives in Western Europe as of 1990 varied considerably in different countries, but the new European Economic Community legislation is causing a rapid increase in the fraction of new cars equipped with catalytic converters. The Western European situation as of 1987 was discussed by Groenendaal (1987) in some detail. The net annual demand for noble metals for catalyst units there will evidently increase rapidly in the next several years, whereas that in the United States may decrease as recycling from junked cars becomes a major source, offset possibly by increased metal loadings required to meet new, more stringent legislation.

An extensive literature is available on automobile catalysts. Among recent publications the proceedings of a symposium are noteworthy (Crucq & Frennet 1987). Useful reviews by Taylor (1984, 1987) treat the entire subject. An earlier review by Kummer (1980) summarizes the extensive study of base-metal catalysts for oxidation catalysts and the ways in which noble metal catalysts are superior. A later review (Kummer 1986) with many references focuses on the use of noble metals and the three-way catalyst system. Gandhi and Shelef (1987) discuss some of the possible mechanisms involved. Cooper et al. (1987) discuss aspects of preparation, performance, and durability. Howitt (1987) gives considerable information on catalyst supports, particularly the ceramic monoliths, and the variety of requirements that these must meet. Harrison et al. (1982) review the catalysis of reactions involving reduction or decomposition of nitrogen oxides, giving extensive references and treating both base and noble metal catalysts. Emphasis is on mechanisms. In older literature, Shelef (1975) reviews the reactions of NO and its removal from auto exhaust and Shelef et al. (1978) review poisoning of auto catalysts.

8.12.2 Diesel particulate emissions

Diesel engines, because they operate at higher compression ratios, are considerably more fuel-efficient than gasoline-fueled engines. Diesel engines have long been used for heavy truck and bus propulsion. Diesel engines for automobiles, which are manufactured mostly in Europe, account for only a few percent of the total for autos worldwide. Concern with diesel engine exhaust centers on particulate emissions. These particles are very small, in the range of 0.1 μm and can remain suspended in the air for long periods of time. The particles are carbonaceous and can readily adsorb sulfates and other species. Being so small, the particles may be deposited deep in the lungs and they are implicated as aggravating a variety of diseases.

Early U.S. emission control requirements were based on opacity standards for the smoke in diesel exhaust from heavy duty trucks and buses. These were succeeded in the 1980s by particulate standards in terms of grams per mile set for cars, trucks, and buses. These standards could be met in part by engine modifications. To meet the most severe standards, however, a trapping system is also required, in which the trap is occasionally regenerated by burning the deposit. As of 1990, the trap-oxidizers are just beginning to be introduced commercially. A variety of trap designs have been tested; one of the most promising is a wall-flow monolith filter on which an oxidizing catalyst is deposited. A variety of both base and noble metal catalysts have been studied, and many of the considerations applicable to oxidizing catalyst units for gasoline-powered cars apply here.

A large variety of uses of catalytic combustion beyond that in automobiles have been applied for many years. In some cases a gaseous stream may contain CO and hydrocarbons in sufficiently high concentration to represent energy that is recoverable, but the fuel is of insufficient concentration to support normal combustion. Catalytic combustion for primary energy production, as in stationary gas turbines, shows promise of producing significantly lower emissions, especially of NO_x, than do conventional combustors. The reactions taking place are probably partly catalytic and partly thermal, and in some cases the catalyst may primarily play the role of a flame holder. In all cases the catalyst is a supported noble metal. For some applications a principal limitation is to develop a rugged support that is stable at temperatures that may be as high as 1500°C.

8.13   Reduction of NO_x from Stationary Sources

Before emission controls of any sort were established, the burning of fossil fuels for generation of steam heat, electricity, and for general industrial activity contributed about as much NO_x to the atmosphere as that from traffic. NO_x from large furnaces is dissipated into the atmosphere by chimneys, but it is a source of photochemical smog, and contributes to acid rain. Starting in the early 1970s a policy has gradually evolved in various countries, notably Japan, the United States and Germany, to establish a program of reducing emission levels of NO_x in flue gases from fossil-fuel-fired power stations. This reduction can be done by various methods of combustion control or by a variety of flue gas treatments.

A proven method that has been rapidly brought into practice, notably in Japan, is *selective catalytic reduction* (SCR) with NH_3. As of the late 1980s, more than 100 utility boilers in Japan had been equipped with SCR units, mostly on coal- or oil-fired boilers, although a few were fired with gas. These SCR units are usually combined with other control techniques. A variety of situations may be encountered, but of particular importance is the presence of SO_x and dust and fly ash when coal or oil is burned. Catalyst performance is also affected by the substantial concentration of steam and O_2 invariably present.

One of the most effective catalysts is about 7 wt % vanadia on titania. To avoid plugging, this catalyst in turn is used on a rather open support that permits parallel flue gas flow such as honeycombs or parallel plates. Alternately, catalyst particles may be confined in wire mesh with flue gas and dust flowing through parallel channels. A representative honeycomb (monolith) has square holes of 5- to 10-mm size and walls about 1 mm thick, dimensions much larger than those used in automobile converters. These larger holes also allow low pressure drop, which is vitally important where the goal of the operation is power production. There is less necessity here for the very compact catalyst unit required in vehicles.

Typically, about 0.6 to 0.9 mol of NH_3 are introduced per mol of NO_x present, which removes 60 to 85 percent of the NO_x, leaving 1 to 5 ppm of NH_3 unreacted. A higher ratio of NH_3/NO_x increases NO_x removal, but then NH_3 bypassing "slip" increases. The optimum temperature is in the region of 300 to 400°C. NO can be completely reduced at lower temperatures, but SO_2 is oxidized to SO_3 by the vanadia. Compounds, such as NH_4HSO_4 and $(NH_4)_2S_2O_7$, that will deposit on the catalyst below 250 to 300°C are also formed. The oxidation of NH_3 to NO begins to become appreciable at 400°C.

The most active catalyst is formed when the vanadia is supported on anatase rather than rutile. The nature of the vanadia-titania surface compounds may be somewhat different with the two forms of titania, but the effect here may be largely caused by the fact that anatase usually has a higher surface area than rutile. When a residual oil is used as fuel, the flue gas will contain vanadium, which deposits on the catalyst and may increase the catalyst activity. Other supports such as silica and carbon are less effective, but a vanadia on titania may in turn be supported on silica or other material. A detailed and lengthy review by Bosch and Janssen (1988) covers fundamentals and technology with comprehensive references.

A homogeneous gas-phase reduction process in which NO_x is selectively reduced to N_2 and H_2O by NH_3 was developed by Exxon. The temperature required is within a fairly narrow range of about 900 to 1000°C, so the NH_3 is introduced into the upper portion of the boiler. However, it is difficult to operate within this temperature range in a larger plant. Capital investment is lower than with SCR units, but NO_x reduction is only about 50 percent, and higher NH_3/NO_x ratios are required. NH_3 bypassing is greater and some of it may be oxidized to NO_x.

For many years NO_x emissions from nitric acid plants or chemical operations emitting NO_x fumes have been controlled by a nonselective catalytic reduction using hydrogen, carbon monoxide, or hydrocarbons as reducing agents on a supported palladium catalyst. A representative composition of the tail gas from a nitric acid plant (dry basis) is 2 to 3% O_2, 0.3 to 0.4% NO_x, and the remainder N_2. The oxygen present must first be consumed and the gas stream must be preheated to an initial (ignition) temperature in the range of 200 to 400°C, depending on the reducing agent. The reactor operates adiabatically and the temperature increase through the reactor is about 150°C for each percent of oxygen present.

The above types of units have been generally replaced with selective catalytic reduction units using NH_3 as the reducing agent. Sulfur compounds and dust are not present, so optimum catalyst units and operation may be slightly different than those for utility flue gas. Catalysts are generally supported vanadia, operated at temperatures of about 200 to 350°C. Here operation must be controlled to prevent the formation of ammonium nitrate and nitrides.

SCR systems utilizing NH_3 have been gradually coming into use for a variety of exhaust or flue gases from other operations. These include gas-turbine- and diesel-engine-powered plants, fluidized-bed boilers, and fluidized catalytic cracking plants.

8.14   Literature

Most recent overall treatments of partial oxidation catalysis have focused on possible catalyst structures and reaction mechanisms. Haber (1981) gives an extensive review of the crystallography of various types of catalysts, most of which involve metal-oxide bonding. Dadyburjor et al. (1979) review selective oxidation of hydrocarbons on composite oxides, with emphasis on possible mechanisms. A briefer review on the same subject is that of Cullis and Hucknall (1982). Closely related is a review by Bielan'ski and Haber (1979) on oxygen in catalysis on transition metal oxides and a book by Kiselev and Krylov (1989) on adsorption and catalysis on transition metals and their oxides. Clayton and Norval (1980) review briefly oxidation over copper, silver, and gold catalysts, again with emphasis on mechanism. Boreskov (1982) gives a detailed review of theory and mechanisms for the catalytic activation of dioxygen (O_2). Chinchen et al. (1987) cover the historical development of processes for oxidation of SO_2, of NH_3 and for the production of maleic anhydride.

In the earlier literature, the book by Hucknall (1974) discusses the selective oxidation of olefins and alkanes, but it does not cover aromatic or heterocyclic compounds. The review by Sampson and Shooter (1965) treats ethylene, propylene, butane, butylene, benzene, naphthalene, and o-xylene. Voge and Adams (1967) cover the catalytic oxidation of olefins, from ethylene to pentenes. The book by Germain (1969) treats hydrocarbon reactions in general, with particular emphasis on mechanism, and includes well over 1000 references. Sharchenko (1969) reviews oxidative dehydrogenation of hydrocarbons with extensive references, many on work in the U.S.S.R. Carrá and Forzatti (1977) summarize mechanisms and kinetic expressions for a variety of reactions, and some of the factors involved in reactor design.

References

Ai, M.: *J. Catal.*, **54**, 426 (1978).

Andrussow, L.: *Angew. Chemie*, **63**, 21 (1951).

Bartsch, R. C., U.S. Patents 4,119,567 (October 10, 1978) and 4,158,737 (January 19, 1979).

Batist, Ph.A., A. H. W. M. Der Kinderen, Y. Leeuwenburgh, F. A. M. G. Metz, and G. C. A. Schuit: *J. Catal.*, **12**, 45 (1968).

Batist, Ph.A., C. J. Kapteijns, B. C. Lippens, and G. C. A. Schuit: *J. Catal.*, **7**, 33 (1967).

Bergna, H. E.: U.S. Patents 4,677,084 and 4,769,477 (1988) to du Pont.

Bergna, H. E., in S. A. Bradley, M. J. Gattuso and R. J. Bertolacini (eds.): *Characterization and Catalyst Development: An Interactive Approach*, ACS Symposium Series No. 411, 1989.

Berty, J. M., in B. E. Leach (ed.): *Applied Industrial Catalysis*, vol. 1, Academic, New York, 1983, p. 207.

Bielan'ski, A. and J. Haber, *Catal. Rev.—Sci. Eng.*, **19**, 1 (1979).

Boghosian, S., R. Fehrmann, N. J. Bjerrum, and G. N. Papatheodorou: *J. Catal.*, **119**, 121 (1989).

Bond, G. C.: *J. Catal.*, **116**, 531 (1989).

Bond, G. C., S. Flamerz, and R. Shukri: *Faraday Discuss. Chem. Soc.*, **89**, 65 (1989).

Bordes, E., P. Courtine, and J. W. Johnson: *J. Solid State Chem.*, **55**, 270 (1984).

Boreskov, G. K., in J. R. Anderson and M. Boudart (eds.): *Catalysis: Science and Technology*, Vol. 3, Springer Verlag, New York, 1982, p. 39.

Boreskov, G. K., R. A. Buyanov, and A. A. Ivanov: *Kinet. Catal.*, **8**, 126 (1967).

Bosch, H. and F. Janssen: *Catalysis Today*, **2**, 369 (1988).

Burnett, J. C., R. A. Keppel, and W. D. Robinson: *Catalysis Today*, **1**, 537 (1987).

Busca, G., F. Cavani, G. Centi, and F. Trifiro: *J. Catal.*, **99**, 400 (1986).

Calderbank, P. H., and A. D. Caldwell: *Adv. Chem. Ser. No. 109*, 1972, p. 38.

Carrá, S., and P. Forzatti: *Catal. Rev.—Sci. Eng.*, **15**, 1, (1977).

Carrubba, R. V., and J. L. Spencer: *Ind. Eng. Chem., Process Des. Dev.*, **9**, 414 (1970).

Centi, G., F. Trifiro, G. Busca, J. Ebner, and J. Gleaves: *Faraday Discuss. Chem. Soc.*, **87**, 215 (1989).

Chauvel, A. R., P. R. Courty, R. Maux, and C. Petitpas: *Hydrocarbon Process.*, September 1973, p. 179.

Chem. Eng., June 24, 1974, p. 114.

Chinchen, G., P. Davies, and R. J. Sampson, in J. R. Anderson and M. Boudart, (eds.): *Catalysis: Science and Technology*, vol. 8, Springer Verlag, New York, 1987, p. 1.

Clayton, R. W., and S. V. Norval, in: *Catalysis*, vol. 3, The Chemical Society, London, 1980, p. 70.

Contractor, R. M., H. E. Bergna, H. S. Horowitz, C. M. Blackstone, U. Chowdhry and A. W. Sleight in J. W. Ward (ed.): *Catalysis 1987*, Elsevier, Amsterdam, 1988.

Cooper, B. J., W. D. J. Evans, and B. Harrison, in A. Crucq and A. Frennet (eds.): *Catalysis and Automotive Pollution Control*, Elsevier, Amsterdam, 1987, p. 117.

Cristiani, C., P. Forzatti, and G. Busca: *J. Catal.*, **116**, 586 (1989).

Crucq, A., and A. Frennet (eds.): *Catalysis and Automotive Pollution Control*, Elsevier, Amsterdam, 1987.

Cullis, C. F., and D. J. Hucknall: *Catalysis*, vol. 5, The Royal Society of Chemistry, London, 1982, p. 273.

Dadyburjor, D. B., S. S. Jewur, and E. Ruckenstein: *Catal. Rev.—Sci. Eng.*, **19**, 293 (1979).

Dalin, M. A., I. K. Kolchin, and B. R. Serebryakov: *Acrylonitrile*, Technomic Pub. Co., Westport, Conn., 1971.

Davies, P., in J. R. Anderson and M. Boudart (eds.): *Catalysis: Science and Technology*, vol. 8, Springer Verlag, New York, 1987, p. 8.

Davies, P., R. T. Donald, and N. H. Harbord, in M. V. Twigg (ed.): *Catalyst Handbook*, 2nd ed., Wolfe, London, 1989, p. 469.

Donovan, J. R., R. D. Stolk, and M. L. Unland, in B. E. Leach (ed.): *Applied Industrial Catalysis*, vol. 2, Academic, New York, 1983, p. 245.

Driscoll, D. J., K. D. Campbell, and J. H. Lunsford: *Adv. Catal.*, **35**, 139 (1987).

Duecker, W. W., and J. R. West: *The Manufacture of Sulfuric Acid*, Reinhold, New York, 1959.

Edwards, R. C., and B. L. Meyers: U.S. Patent 4,732,885 (1988) to Amoco Corp.

Faraday Discussions of the Chemical Society, No. 87, *Catalysis by Well Characterized Materials*, Royal Society of Chemistry, London, 1989.

Flytzani-Stephanopoulos, M., S. Wong, and L. D. Schmidt: *J. Catal.*, **49**, 51 (1977).

Froment, G. F.: *Ind. Eng. Chem.*, **59**(2), 23 (1967).

Gans, M., and B. J. Ozero: *Hydrocarbon Process.*, March 1976, p. 73.

Gasior, M., J. Haber, and T. Machej: *Appl. Catal.*, **33**, 1 (1987).

Gates, B. C., J. R. Katzer, and G. C. A. Schuit: *Chemistry of Catalytic Processes*, McGraw-Hill, New York, 1979.

Germain, J. E.: *Catalytic Conversion of Hydrocarbons*, Academic, New York, 1969.

Germain, J. E.: *Intra-Sci. Chem. Rep.*, **6**, 101 (1972).

Gandhi, H. S., and M. Shelef, in A. Crucq and A. Frennet (eds.): *Catalysis and Automotive Pollution Control*, Elsevier, Amsterdam, 1987, p. 199.

Gibson, M. A., and J. W. Hightower: *J. Catal.*, **41**, 420, 431 (1976) (and earlier studies).

Grasselli, R. K., and J. D. Burrington: *Adv. Catal.*, **30**, 133 (1981).

Grasselli, R. K., G. Centi, and F. Trifuro: *Appl. Catal.*, **57**, 149 (1990).

Groenendaal, W., in A. Crucq, and A. Frennet (eds.): *Catalysis and Automotive Pollution Control*, Elsevier, Amsterdam, 1987, p. 81.

Haber, J.: *Int. Chem. Eng.*, **15**, 21 (1975). [See also *Z. für Chem.*, **13**(7), 241 (1973).]

Haber, J., in J. R. Anderson and M. Boudart (eds.): *Catalysis: Science and Technology*, vol. 2, Springer Verlag, New York, 1981, p. 14.

Hahn, A. V. G.: *The Petrochemical Industry: Market and Economics*, McGraw-Hill, New York, 1970.

Haldor-Topsøe, F. A. and A. Nielsen: *Trans. Dan. Acad. Sci.*, **1**, 18 (1947).

Hancock, E. G. (ed.): *Propylene and its Industrial Derivatives*, Benn, London, 1973.

Handforth, S. L., and J. N. Tilley: *Ind. Eng. Chem.*, **26**, 1288 (1934).

Harbord, N. H.: *Platinum Met. Rev.*, **18**, 97 (1974).

Harrison, B., M. Wyatt, and K. G. Gough: *Catalysis*, vol. 5, The Royal Society of Chemistry, London, 1982, p. 127.

Hausinger, G., H. Schmelz, and H. Knözinger: *Appl. Catal.*, **39**, 267 (1988).

Herce, J. L., J. B. Gros, and R. Bugarel: *Chem. Eng. Sci.*, **32**, 729 (1977).

Higgins, R., and P. Hayden: *Catalysis*, vol. 1, The Chemical Society, London, 1977, Chap. 5, p. 168.

Hodnett, B. K.: *Catal. Rev.—Sci. Eng.*, **27**, 373 (1985).
Holzmann, H.: *Chem.—Ing.—Tech.*, **40**, 1229 (1968).
Horowitz, H. S., C. M. Blackstone, A. W. Sleight, and G. Teufer: *Appl. Catal.*, **38**, 193 (1988).
Howitt, J. S., in A. Crucq, and A. Frennet (eds.): *Catalysis and Automotive Pollution Control*, Elsevier, Amsterdam, 1987, p. 301.
Hucknall, D. J.: *Selective Oxidation of Hydrocarbons*, Academic, New York, 1974.
Hutson, T., R. D. Skinner, and R. S. Logan: *Hydrocarbon Process.*, June 1974, p. 133.
Johnson, J. W., D. C. Johnston, and A. J. Jacobson, in B. Delmon, P. Grange, P. A. Jacobs, and G. Poncelet (eds.): *Preparation of Catalysts, IV*, Elsevier, Amsterdam, 1987, p. 181.
Kenney, C. N.: *Catal. Rev.—Sci. Eng.*, **11**, 197 (1975).
Kenney, C. N.: *Catalysis*, vol. 3, The Chemical Society, London, 1980, p. 123.
Kiguchi, L., T. Kumazawa, and T. Nakai: *Hydrocarbon Process.*, March 1976, p. 69.
Kilty, P. A., and W. M. H. Sachtler: *Catal. Rev.—Sci. Eng.*, **10**, 1 (1974).
Kiselev, V. F., and O. V. Krylov: *Adsorption and Catalysis on Transition Metals and their Oxides*, Springer Verlag, New York, 1989.
Klink, A., E. Paul, J. Gillin, and W. Sklarz: *Proceedings of the Fourth International/Sixth European Symposium on Chemical Reaction Engineering*, DECHEMA, 1976, p. 327.
Koberstein, E.: *Ind. Eng. Chem., Process Des. Dev.*, **12**, 444 (1973).
Kolchin, I. K.: *Khim. Prom.*, **49**(11), 815 (1973).
Krekeler, H., and W. Kronig: *Seventh World Petroleum Congress*, vol. 5, Elsevier, Amsterdam, 1967, p. 41.
Kummer, J. T.: *J. Phys. Chem.*, **90**, 4747 (1986).
Kummer, J. T., in *Progress in Energy and Combustion Science*, vol. 6, Pergamon, Elmsford, N.Y., 1980, p. 177.
Kung, H. H., and M. C. Kung: *Adv. Catal.*, **33**, 159 (1985).
Law, G. H., and H. C. Chitwood: U.S. Patent 2,279,469 (1942).
Le Page, J. F., et al.: *Applied Heterogeneous Catalysis*, Technip, Paris, 1987.
Liljenroth, F. G.: *Chem. Metall. Eng.*, **19**(6), 287 (1918).
Livbjerg, H. B. and J. Villadsen: *Chem. Eng. Sci.*, **27**, 21 (1972).
Livbjerg, H. B., B. Sorenson, and J. Villadsen: *Adv. Chem. Ser.*, **133**, 1974, p. 242.
Mars, P., and D. W. van Krevelen: *Chem. Eng. Sci.*, **3** (special supplement), 41 (1954).
Massoth, F. E., and D. A. Scarpiello: *J. Catal.*, **21**, 294 (1971).
Nakamura, M., Y. Fujiwara, and T. Yasui: U.S. Patent 4,087,622 (1978) to Bayer.
Nakamura, S., and T. Yasui: *J. Catal.*, **17**, 366 (1970).
Naworski, J. S., and E. S. Velez, in B. E. Leach (ed.): *Applied Industrial Catalysis*, vol. 1, Academic, New York, 1983, p. 239.
Nielsen, R. P., and J. H. La Rochelle: U.S. Patents 3,962,136 (1976) and 4,012,425 (1977).
Nowak, E. J.: *Chem. Eng. Sci.*, **21**, 19 (1966); **24**, 421 (1969).
Pan, B. Y. K.: *J. Catal.*, **21**, 27 (1971).
Pan, B. Y. K. and R. G. Roth: *Ind. Eng. Chem., Process Des. Dev.*, **7**, 53 (1968). [See also B. Y. K. Pan, *Ind. Eng. Chem., Process Des. Dev.*, **8**, 262 (1969).]
Pfeil, E., and P. Hoffmann: *Ber. Bunsenges. physik. Chem.*, **67**, 229 (1963).
Pitzer, E. W.: *Ind. Eng. Chem., Prod. Res. Dev.*, **11**, 299 (1972).
Reich, P.: *Hydrocarbon Process.*, March 1976, p. 85.
Rennard, R. J., and W. L. Kehl: *J. Catal.*, **21**, 282 (1971).
Sachtler, W. M. H., G. J. Dargelo, J. Fahrenfort, and R. J. H. Voorhoeve: *Rec. Tran. Chem.*, **89**, 460 (1970).
Sachtler, W. M. H., and N. H. deBoer: *Third Congress on Catalysis*, North-Holland, Amsterdam, 1965, p. 252.
Saffer, A.: in *Catalysis in Practice, Symposium*, Institution of Chemical Engineers, London, 1963, p. 54.
Sajkowski, D. J., and M. Boudart: *Catal. Rev.—Sci. Eng.*, **29**, 325 (1987).
Sampson, R. J., and D. Shooter: *Oxid. Combust. Rev.*, **1**, 223 (1965).
Satterfield, C. N., and J. Loftus: *AIChE J.*, **11**, 1103 (1965).

Schmidt, L. D., and D. Luss: *J. Catal.*, **22**, 269 (1971).
Schneider, R. A.: U.S. Patent 3,864,280 (1975) (to Chevron Research Co.).
Sharchenko, V. K.: *Int. Chem. Eng.*, **9**, 1 (1969).
Shelef, M.: *Catal. Rev.—Sci. Eng.*, **11**, 1 (1975).
Shelef, M., K. Otto, and N. C. Otto: *Adv. Catal.*, **27**, 311 (1978).
Sleight, A. W., and W. J. Linn: *Ann. N.Y. Acad. Sci.*, **272**, 22 (1976).
Snyder, T. P., and C. G. Hill, Jr.: *Catal. Rev.—Sci. Eng.*, **31**, 43 (1989).
Sperner, F., and W. Hohmann: *Platinum Met. Rev.*, **20**, 12 (1976).
Stacey, M. H.: *Catalysis*, vol. 3, The Chemical Society, London, 1980, p. 98.
Stefani, G., and P. Fontana: U.S. Patents 4,085,122 and 4,100,106 (1978).
Sterrett, J. S., and H. G. McIlvried: *Ind. Eng. Chem., Process Des. Dev.*, **13**, 54 (1974).
Stobaugh, R. B., W. C. Allen, Jr., and Van R. H. Sternberg: *Hydrocarbon Process.*, May 1972, p. 153.
Tandy, G. H.: *J. Appl. Chem.*, **6**, 68 (1956).
Taylor, K. C., in J. R. Anderson and M. Boudart (eds.): *Catalysis: Science and Technology*, vol. 5, Springer Verlag, New York, 1984, p. 119.
Taylor, K. C., in A. Crucq and A. Frennet (eds.): *Catalysis and Automotive Pollution Control*, Elsevier, 1987, p. 97.
Temkin: *Adv. Catal.*, **28**, 173, 1979.
Urbanek, A. and M. Trela: *Catal. Rev.*, **21**, 73 (1980).
van Santen, R. A. and H. P. C. E. Kuipers: *Adv. Catal.*, **35**, 265 (1987).
van Santen, R. A., in M. J. Phillips and M. Ternan (eds.): *Proceedings, 9th International Congress on Catalysis*, The Chemical Institute of Canada, Ottawa, 1988, p. 1152.
Varma, R. L., and D. N. Saraf: *Ind. Eng. Chem., Prod. Res. Dev.*, **18**, 7 (1979).
Villadsen, J., and H. Livbjerg: *Catal. Rev.—Sci. Eng.*, **17**, 203 (1978).
Voge, H. H., and C. R. Adams: *Adv. Catal.*, **17**, 151 (1967).
Wachs, I. E., and R. J. Madix: *J. Catal.*, **53**, 208 (1978).
Wagner, C.: *Chem. Tech. (Chem. Fabr., Neue Folge)*, **18**, 1, 28 (1945).
Wainwright, M. S., and N. R. Foster: *Catal. Rev.—Sci. Eng.*, **19**, 211 (1979).
Waletzko, N., and L. D. Schmidt: *AIChE J.*, **34**, 1146 (1988).
Walker, J. F.: *Formaldehyde*, 3rd ed., Reinhold, New York, 1964.
Welch, L. M., L. J. Croce, and H. F. Christmann: *Hydrocarbon Process.*, November 1978, p. 131.
Wimer, W. E., and R. E. Feathers: *Hydrocarbon Process.*, March 1976, p. 81.
Windes, L. C., M. J. Schwedock, and W. H. Ray: *Chem. Eng. Comm.*, **78**, 1 (1989).
Yin, C-R. J., T-J. Park, and J. W. Hightower, in M. J. Phillips and M. Ternan (eds.): *Proceedings, 9th International Congress on Catalysis*, The Chemical Institute of Canada, Ottawa, 1988, p. 1570, and vol. 5, p. 508.
Zomerdijk, J. C., and M. W. Hall: *Catal. Rev.—Sci. Eng.*, **23**, 163 (1981).

Chapter

9

Processing of Petroleum and Hydrocarbons

The largest-volume catalytic processes are found in the refining of petroleum. Catalytic reforming, catalytic cracking, hydrocracking, and hydrodesulfurization are carried out on a very large scale, and catalytic hydrotreating is used to improve the quality of various products and intermediate feedstocks. The primary products are a range of fuels, but a small yet growing fraction of the crude oil processed, in the range of 5 to 10 percent, is converted to chemicals. The most important, in terms of quantity produced, are ethylene, propylene, butylenes, 1,3-butadiene, and benzene, toluene, and xylene (BTX). The BTX aromatic compounds are produced primarily by catalytic reforming. Toluene and xylene in particular are in demand as high-octane components in gasoline. Benzene and xylene are required for chemical manufacture, and toluene to a lesser extent.

Some low-molecular-weight olefins* are produced as a by-product of refinery operations such as catalytic cracking. A mixture of olefins and a wide variety of other compounds is also produced by thermal cracking of various hydrocarbon feedstocks in the presence of steam, so-called *steam cracking*. The composition of the product varies substantially, depending on the feedstock (e.g., ethane in contrast to various distillate fractions) and the severity of the cracking reaction. Steam cracking is operated primarily to produce ethylene, but is also

---

*The commonly used nomenclature in the petroleum and petrochemical industries for several classes of compounds differs from the IUPAC nomenclature. The industry nomenclature is generally used here since that is the form usually found in the relevant literature. Some synonyms are as follows: paraffins (acyclic alkanes), olefins (alkenes), cycloalkanes (naphthenes), propylene (propene), butylene (various butenes).

a major source of propylene, butadiene (1,3-butadiene), and *pyrolysis gasoline*, which contains substantial benzene.

Acetylene has also been an important chemical, produced by subjecting natural gas or other hydrocarbons to very high temperatures. For ethane cracking to produce ethylene, typical temperatures are 750 to 900°C, and for formation of acetylene, about 1200°C. These are set by equilibrium considerations. The use of acetylene as the starting point for chemical manufacture has been superseded by several processes based on lower-cost olefins. The use of acetylene for production of vinyl chloride has been replaced by ethylene, and use of acetylene for the manufacture of acrylonitrile has been replaced by propylene. However, steam cracking of heavier feedstocks produces significant quantities of acetylene, which then becomes available priced as a by-product.

For treatments of petroleum processing in general, see, e.g., the books by Hobson and Pohl (1973), Speight (1980) and Gary and Handwerk (1975). The petrochemicals industry is treated in a book by Spitz (1988).

9.1 Composition of Petroleum

Petroleum consists predominantly of various hydrocarbons but also contains lesser amounts of sulfur, nitrogen, and oxygen in the form of a variety of organic compounds. Small amounts of vanadium and nickel are also present, mostly in the form of porphyrins and related structures. Elemental sulfur is also found in small amounts in some crude oils. The distribution of type of compound and of molecular weights varies greatly with location and the particular formation (depth) from which the crude oil was obtained. In primary recovery methods, the crude oil is forced to the surface by the natural energy of the reservoir. This energy may be from natural gas under pressure, either dissolved in the oil or present in a cap over the oil, or from the surrounding water.

Some portion of the petroleum always remains in the formation after primary recovery, and a variety of "secondary" and "tertiary" methods are being increasingly applied to recover additional petroleum from depleted fields or to increase the recovery rate from partially exhausted fields. These include injection of energy from the surface, as by pressurization with carbon dioxide or water, injection of steam to lower viscosity, or use of surface-active agents or low-viscosity solvents to assist the flow of oil.

Petroleum recovered in primary production is accompanied by natural gas, which typically contains 80 to 90 percent methane. The remaining hydrocarbons are primarily ethane, propane, and butane, in quantities decreasing in this order. Gas containing appreciable amounts of these higher hydrocarbons is termed *wet gas*. Natural gas recovered in the absence of petroleum, as in Western Europe, frequently contains no more than 3 or 4 percent of hydrocarbons other than methane and is termed *dry gas*. Most of the natural gas in the United States is wet gas. In either case considerable quantities of hydrogen sulfide, carbon dioxide, and/or nitrogen may also be present. In some U.S. production areas, the gas contains helium in concentrations that can be economically recovered. C_2 to C_4 hydrocarbons are removed from wet gas by absorption in an oil or, in some newer plants, by a cryogenic process. Ethane is an important feedstock for manufacture of ethylene by thermal (steam) cracking. The C_3 and C_4 gases may be sold as *liquefied petroleum gas* or used as a feedstock for thermal cracking. In the United States the amount of butanes separated from natural gas is considerably more than the amount separated from refinery streams.

The hydrocarbons in petroleum are primarily paraffins, aromatic ring compounds, and *naphthenes* (these are saturated rings with five or six C atoms in the ring, not to be confused with *naphthalenes*). No olefins or acetylenes are present. Petroleum may be classified by composition loosely into *paraffinic-base* and *asphaltic-base* crudes, some being intermediate in character. Paraffinic-base crudes contain considerable quantities of paraffins (alkanes), which may be linear or branched. They are more highly concentrated in the lower-boiling fractions. The major portion of the crude, however, consists of ring compounds, either aromatic or naphthenic or both. The asphaltic-base crudes are so named because they contain a larger quantity of asphaltenes (ill-defined high-molecular-weight material—see Sec. 9.15). The intermediate-boiling fractions of asphaltic crudes are usually more aromatic than naphthenic in character.

The concentration of paraffins decreases in the higher-boiling fractions of all crude oils. They are mostly branched. The single-ring compounds (both aromatic and naphthenic) in light fractions of many crudes usually have one, two, or three short alkyl chains. Molecular complexity increases with molecular weight, and multiple-ring structures occur in the higher-boiling fractions. These rings may be linked by alkyl groups, be conjugated (as in bicyclohexyl), or fused [as in decahydronaphthalene (Decalin) or naphthalene]. In a multiple-ring structure some rings may be aromatic and others saturated.

Sulfur and nitrogen compounds are the most important impurities in petroleum from the point of view of catalytic processing of distillate fractions. Organic sulfur compounds occur in all crude oils, in amounts varying from as little as 0.05 wt % sulfur to as high as 5 wt %. Hydrogen sulfide is also often present, and sometimes there are traces of elemental sulfur. The sulfur content (expressed as a weight fraction) increases with overall molecular weight, so a residual fraction will have a considerably higher sulfur content than the crude from which it is derived. In the low-boiling fractions, the principal sulfur compounds are organic sulfides or disulfides, mercaptans (thiols; R-S-H, in which R is an aliphatic group or a saturated cyclic ring), and thiophenes. In higher-boiling fractions sulfur is present largely in the form of thiophene derivatives such as benzo- and dibenzothiophenes. The nonheterocyclic sulfur compounds are the less stable thermally, and they may react or be substantially decomposed during distillation.

Most crude oils contain 0.1 wt % nitrogen or less, but some heavy asphaltic-base crudes may contain up to about 0.9 wt %. Shale oil derived from retorting U.S. western shales contains up to 2 wt % nitrogen, and so-called synthetic crudes derived from coal or tar sands may contain up to about 1 wt % nitrogen. As with sulfur compounds, the nitrogen content increases with molecular weight of the crude-oil fraction. The structures of the various nitrogen compounds have not been as well characterized as those of the sulfur compounds. Those identified and of most importance in hydroprocessing are mostly heterocyclic, and they are typically grouped into basic compounds (e.g., pyridines and quinolines, which may have alkyl substituents) and nonbasic compounds (derivatives of indole, pyrrole, and carbazole).

Oxygen is present in low- and medium-boiling-range fractions of petroleum, primarily as aliphatic and cyclic carboxylic acids and, sometimes, in small amounts, as phenols. Vanadium and nickel are found in crude oil in concentrations from as low as 3 ppm to 500 to 600 ppm, the weight ratio of vanadium to nickel typically being 5:1 to 10:1. These are found mostly in the asphaltenes, which are in the residual fraction. Hence, high metal content is typically associated with asphaltic-base crudes of high asphaltene content.

9.2 Fractionation

The first step in processing is to separate the crude oil by fractional distillation into cuts characterized by their boiling point range. These cuts may vary considerably from one refiner to another, depending on the subsequent use to which they are put; they may be "wide" or "narrow," and they may overlap one another somewhat. Table 9.1 lists those typically obtained, in order of decreasing volatility. For the more volatile fractions, a range limit may be described by a carbon number instead of a boiling point. The last column describes typical uses for the fraction. The boiling point range is typically presented in terms of fraction volatilized versus temperature as determined by a

TABLE 9.1   Representative Fractions from Distillation of Petroleum

Fraction	Component range and/or boiling point range, °C (°F)	Typical use
1. Gas	Up to C_4	Burned as fuel. Ethane may be thermally cracked to produce ethylene. Propane or a mixture of propane and butane may be sold as liquified petroleum gas (LPG).
2. Straight-run gasoline	$C_4 - C_5$	Blended into gasoline, isomerized or used as a chemical feedstock.
3. Virgin naphtha (light distillate)	$C_5 - 150$ (300)	Used as a feed to catalytic reformer or blended into gasoline.
4. Heavy naphtha (kerosene)	120—200 (250–400) (Up to ~C_{15})	Jet fuel, kerosene.
5. Light gas oil	200–310 (400–600) (Up to ~C_{20})	Used as No. 2 distillate fuel oil, or blending stock for jet fuel and/or diesel fuel.
6. Gas oil (heavy distillate)	Up to ~ 350 (650) (~C_{25})	Used as a feed to catalytic cracker or sold as heavy fuel oil.
7. Atmospheric residual	~350+(650+)	Various uses. May be distilled under vacuum to produce vacuum-gas oil, coked, or burned as fuel.
8. Vacuum residual	~560+(1050+) equivalent boiling point	Various. Some is hydrotreated catalytically.

standardized method. The test is tedious and it is usually simulated by a gas-chromatographic procedure (ASTM D 2887).

Different crude oils vary greatly in the boiling-point distribution of their components. A light crude from Algeria, Libya, or Nigeria may contain as much as 30 percent in the boiling point range up to about 200°C, whereas a heavy crude, as found in Venezuela, may have hardly any material boiling below 200°C but may contain 35 to 50 percent with an equivalent boiling point above 560°C (1050°F).

The highest temperature to which crude is usually subjected in distillation at atmospheric pressure is about 350°C (650°F). This is primarily to avoid appreciable decomposition but also to avoid excessive viscosity of the nondistilled product (residue) at ambient temperatures (high *pour point*), which would make it difficult to store and pump. The atmospheric residue can be further separated by vacuum distillation into one or more *heavy gas oils*. A final "nondistillable" fraction is left, so-called *vacuum residual*. This is sometimes described as having an equivalent boiling point at one atmosphere of, say 1000°F+ or 1050°F+ (560°C+). In fact it frequently contains a considerable quantity of material, e.g., 40 percent or so, having an atmospheric boiling point below this temperature. The heavy gas oils may be sent to a catalytic cracker or hydrocracker, or, if they are of appropriate composition, they may be further processed into lubricating oils or waxes.

The relative demand for various petroleum products varies considerably in different parts of the world. Historically, in the United States the refining of petroleum has centered on the manufacture of gasoline for motor cars. Gasoline has accounted for 40 to 50 percent of the total demand for petroleum products in the United States for the last several decades. This is in part because of the emphasis on private car transportation and the abundant supply of natural gas that provided a considerable portion of the overall fuel demands. In contrast, in Western Europe and Japan, emphasis has historically been more on production of fuel oils, and gasoline accounts for a much smaller percent of the crude oil demand. Large U.S. refineries have tended to include a substantial variety of chemical processes that are integrated with one another and directed at production of gasoline. In some of the world refineries may do little more than distill crude oil into fractions.

9.3   Motor Fuels

The traditional fuel for spark-ignition in internal combustion engines (Otto cycle) has been gasoline, blended from hydrocarbons produced from various refinery processes. Because of increasing concern for control of air pollution, the formulation of gasoline and other motor fuels is becoming more precise and more specifically tailored to local atmospheric conditions and variations in climate. In many cases it is necessary or expedient to add one or more of a variety of oxygenated species. Nevertheless, the two principal requirements for a motor fuel are:

1. The fuel must have a suitable volatility range. Some portion must vaporize readily in the manifold of the engine when cold so that it may be started, yet the mixture must not be so volatile that it causes vapor lock when the engine is hot. *Vapor lock* is the formation of bubbles of gasoline vapor in critical locations in the fuel system, such as the fuel pump or carburetor, which interferes with engine performance. The heaviest components must be vaporizable, and the fuel as a whole must be sufficiently nonviscous that it flows freely in cold weather. The composition to provide this is modified somewhat in different climates and from summer to winter to provide approximately the same volatility under these different conditions. The suitable hydrocarbons are primarily those in the C_5 to C_8 range, to which some C_4 may be added to achieve necessary volatility.

2. The fuel must have an octane number equal to or exceeding some minimum value. The higher the compression ratio, the higher is the

octane number required of the fuel, but the more efficiently the engine can be operated.

The octane number in essence is a quantitative but imprecise measure of the maximum compression ratio at which a particular fuel can be utilized in an internal combustion engine without some of the fuel-air mixture undergoing premature self-ignition. The fuel-air mixture in the cylinder is ignited by a spark, but the advancing flame front compresses the remaining mixture until it may reach the point of self-ignition before being ignited by the flame. This causes an excessive rate of pressure increase, termed *knocking*, which reduces the engine power. Under severe conditions it can cause engine damage. The octane number of a fuel is obtained by comparing its knocking characteristics with various blends of isooctane (2,2,4-trimethylpentane), arbitrarily assigned a value of 100, and *n*-heptane, assigned a value of 0. The blends of those two compounds are termed the *primary reference fuels*. A fuel that matches the knocking characteristics of a mixture of 90 parts isooctane and 10 parts *n*-heptane by volume is assigned an octane number of 90.

The octane number is measured in a standardized, single-cylinder variable-compression-ratio engine in which conditions of incipient knock can be determined. The engine can be operated in either of two ways. One simulates mild operating conditions and is termed the *research method* or *F-1 method*; the other simulates severe operating conditions such as high-speed, high-load conditions and is termed the *motor method* or *F-2 method*. The *research octane number* (RON) is always higher than the *motor octane number* (MON) (for octane numbers of 100 and below), the difference between the two being termed the *sensitivity*. The research octane number is that most frequently cited in the literature.

Operation of the actual engine on the road is, of course, the ultimate test, and this is also affected by variables such as engine design, spark timing, age, and carbon deposits in the cylinders. *Road octane numbers* (RdON) may be obtained by operation of a car on the road or on a chassis dynanometer, although these data are more expensive to obtain. Empirical relationships may thus be developed between RdON on the one hand and RON and MON on the other for each significant variety of vehicle, and these formulas are used by the refiner as a guide in the blending of gasoline.

Mixtures of hydrocarbons do not behave by the additive rule defined by isooctane and *n*-heptane mixtures. Some compounds such as toluene and xylene contribute very significantly to the antiknock characteristics of a paraffinic-base or other base stock and are therefore assigned a high *blending octane number*, whereas a compound such as benzene is less effective and is assigned a much lower blending number. Table 9.2 gives the research octane numbers of some representative pure hydrocarbons and, for comparison, a representative blending octane number. The blending number depends on the other components in the final mixture and the concentration of a specified compound in the final mixture.

The use of octane numbers in practice is a complex but highly developed procedure, but some general trends are clearly shown by Table 9.2. For a given molecular weight, branched paraffins have much higher octane numbers than linear (normal) paraffins, and the highest octane numbers are obtained when the side groups are bunched together in the center of the chain (2, 2, 3-trimethylpentane has the highest octane number of the octanes). The octane number of paraffins increases markedly with decreasing carbon number. An olefin generally has a higher octane number than the corresponding paraffin, and the octane number is greater if the double bond is in the center portion of the molecule. Diolefins tend to form gums on storage and are undesirable.

Aromatic compounds have among the highest octane numbers, but they are also much in demand as feedstocks for chemical manufacture. They are produced primarily by catalytic reforming (Sec. 9.5) in which a major reaction is dehydrogenation of naphthenes. The product from a reformer varies with the nature of the feedstock and with *severity* of operation (essentially reaction temperature). An operation to form a product with a research octane number of 95 typically yields about 60 percent aromatics in the product fraction consisting of C_5 and higher hydrocarbons. A typical aromatic composition is: benzene, 10%; toluene, 47%; xylenes, 32%; remainder (e.g., ethylbenzene), 11%. However, benzene is a known carcinogen and the concentration of benzene in gasoline in the near future will probably be restricted to a value not greater than about 1 to 2 percent. Its concentration in reformate can be reduced to some extent by increasing the boiling point range of the feedstock to the reformer.

Toluene is useful for its combination of high octane number and suitable volatility. Its floor price is set by its value as a blending stock in gasoline; its ceiling price, by its feedstock value to produce benzene in hydrodealkylation units, for use as a chemical feedstock. In effect benzene by itself does not knock, but it does not blend nearly as effectively with other gasoline components as do most other compounds.

Xylenes and ethylbenzene have considerably higher boiling points than C_8 paraffins and olefins. Although their octane numbers are high, they are not sufficiently volatile to be allowed to make up a large fraction of the total. The total aromatic content of gasoline is determined in part by an economic balance among various sources of oc-

TABLE 9.2   Octane Numbers of Selected Compounds (Research Method)

Compound	Octane number		Boiling point, °C
	Actual	Blending*	
Paraffins			
Methane	>120		−161
Ethane	118		−88
n-Propane	112		−42
n-Butane	93	113	0
n-Pentane	62	62	36
n-Hexane	25	19	69
n-Heptane	0	0	98
2,2,4-isooctane	100	100	
Other trimethyl pentanes			
(2,2,3-; 2,3,3-; 2,3,4-)	103–106		⎫
Dimethyl hexanes	55–75		⎬ 99–119
Methyl heptanes	22–33		⎭
Naphthenes			
Cyclopentane	101	141	49
Methylcyclopentane	91	107	72
Cyclohexane	83	110	81
Higher alkyl cyclopentanes	80–70		88–132 and up
and alkyl cyclohexanes	and less		
Olefins compared to paraffins			
2-Methyl-1-hexene	91		91
2-Methylhexane	42		90
3-Methyl-2-pentene	97		68
3-Methylpentane	74		63
Aromatics			
Benzene	>100	99	80
Toluene	120	124	111
m-Xylene	117	145	139
Alcohols			
Methanol	106 (92)[†]	134–138[§]	65
Ethanol	99	128–135[§]	78.5
2-Propanol	90		82
Methyl tert-butyl ether (MTBE)	117 (101)[†]	118[‡]	55
Tert-amyl methyl ether (TAME)		112[‡]	

*Based on 20 vol % of the compound in 80 vol % of a 60:40 mixture of isooctane and n-heptane, using a linear scale.
†Motor octane number.
‡Based on 5 to 20 vol % of the compound blended with unleaded regular gasoline of a base RON of 89.
§Based on 10 vol % of the compound blended with an unleaded gasoline of a base RON of 90 to 93.

tane number blending stocks, but high concentrations may lead to smoke in the exhaust and carbon buildup in the engine. Most of the fuel mixture must also be more volatile than toluene, and a distribution of high-octane compounds throughout the volatility range is desirable. The maximum aromatic content of gasoline is typically about 30 percent to avoid carbon buildup in engines and exhaust smoke.

Some compounds and mixtures have octane numbers greater than 100, as calculated by an extrapolation procedure, and in these cases the F-2 number may exceed F-1. Various alcohols and ethers also have high octane numbers or high blending octane numbers. Methanol and ethanol are good blending components, but trace amounts of water in blends with gasoline can cause phase separation. Ethanol is of interest in that it can be readily produced from biomass, and it has been added to gasoline at various times during the past half-century or more in various countries, in concentrations of up to about 10 percent. Ethers of suitable boiling point can be manufactured from olefins and methanol. With ethers, phase separation with traces of water is less of a problem, and they are effective additives for increasing octane number.

Methyl *tert*-butyl ether (MTBE) has become a favored source of high-octane components, in part because it has similar blending characteristics to the hydrocarbons in gasoline. MTBE is manufactured from isobutylene and methanol utilizing an ion-exchange-resin catalyst (Sec. 7.9). Isobutylene is formed in catalytic cracking, steam cracking, and catalytic reforming. It can also be produced by isomerization of n-butenes or n-butanes or dehydrogenation of isobutane, but this substantially increases the cost of the MTBE. A Houdry-type dehydrogenation process applied to a C_4 paraffin stream produces butadiene, n-butylenes and isobutylene (Sec. 9.17.1). Isobutylene is also in demand for manufacture of butyl rubber and viscosity improvers in lube oils.

In the United States, present government regulations limit the amount of oxygenates allowed in gasolines to typically about 2.0 percent oxygen by weight, although waivers have been issued. Some concerns still remain about the effect of various oxygenates in gasolines on engine durability, compatibility with fuel system components, etc., especially with methanol.

With mounting concern about air-pollution control, the formulation of gasolines is becoming increasingly affected by the atmospheric reactivity and volatility of various gasoline components that contribute excessively to ground-level smog formation. This is of particular importance in areas of high air pollution such as Los Angeles. The overall problem is complex but it affects various catalytic processes. For example, isopentenes are much more atmospherically reactive than paraffins and the various oxygenate additives. However, these isopentenes can be converted to *tert*-amyl methyl ether (TAME) by reaction with methanol in a process similar to that used to synthesize MTBE. TAME is a useful gasoline additive, and plants to manufacture TAME are in operation in Europe. The more volatile fraction ("light end") of the gasoline fraction from a fluid catalytic cracker is the feed stream, and the critical C_5 olefins are converted to ether.

Increased attention is also being directed to motor fuels alternate to gasoline. Natural gas and propane have high octane numbers but require high-pressure vessels for storage. Methanol can be made readily by present technology from coal, natural gas, or petroleum fractions, but it is poisonous, corrosive, and has about 40 percent less energy than gasoline. Ethanol can be made by fermentation from corn or various plant material, but it is expensive unless subsidized. It has been used extensively in Brazil, partly "neat" (100 percent) and partly blended into gasoline. In all cases considerable modification of engine and fuel system may be required. Alternative fuels are reviewed by Ecklund and Mills (1989).

Previously, the octane number of gasoline has been increased by addition of alkyl lead compounds. A chemical or physical blend of tetraethyl lead and tetramethyl lead is usually used to achieve a range of volatility. Addition of ethylene dichloride and ethylene dibromide is also necessary to avoid the undesired buildup of nonvolatile lead deposits in the engine cylinders and cylinder head. With these compounds, volatile lead oxyhalides are formed and are emitted in the exhaust.

Until about 1970 almost all gasoline in the United States contained up to about 3 g of lead per gallon (0.8 g per liter). Beginning with the 1975-model automobile manufacture in the United States, most cars have been equipped with catalyst units to reduce automobile pollution by oxidizing most of the CO and hydrocarbons in the exhaust gas to CO_2 and H_2O and reduce NO_x formed in the combustion process (Sec. 8.12.1). In spite of extensive study, no catalyst system has yet been developed having acceptable activity and durability with gasoline containing the lead alkyls and accompanying organohalogen compounds. Catalysts are gradually inactivated by lead compounds, and alumina, the usual catalyst support, is gradually attacked by halogen acids formed from the ethylene dichloride and ethylene dibromide.

Cars equipped with catalysts of present design must use motor fuel in which the requisite octane number is obtained without the addition of lead compounds. Concern with the health hazards of emitting lead compounds into the environment led to a program in the United

States of gradually reducing the maximum allowable concentration of lead in gasoline in general so that the use of lead is now being completely phased out. A similar scenario is at an earlier stage in Europe.

Gasoline is blended from several sources in the refinery to form the so-called gasoline pool. The principal sources are the portion of the product of suitable volatility from:

1. Catalytic cracking

2. Catalytic reforming

3. Hydrocracking

4. Alkylation

5. Straight-run gasoline

Some n-butane may also be added. *Alkylation* in the fuels industry refers to the reaction, catalyzed by sulfuric acid or nearly anhydrous hydrogen fluoride, of C_3 to C_5 olefins with isobutane to form C_7 to C_9 isoparaffins. A large excess of isobutane is used to minimize polymerization of the olefins with themselves. Two liquid phases are present. The reaction can also be catalyzed by acidic zeolites, but no commercial process based on zeolites or other solid acids appears to have been put into practice.

Very few refineries operate all four of the aforementioned catalytic processes, so the extent to which an individual refiner draws on various sources for gasoline components varies substantially from case to case and depends on such factors as the fraction of the crude oil processed to be converted to gasoline, the scale of operations, the demand for aromatics for sale as chemicals, and the outside supply of high-octane components.

The gradual phase-out of lead additives in gasoline has required a variety of changes in petroleum processing to produce high-octane components. These include switching from monometallic to bimetallic catalysts in reformers and operation at higher severity (Sec. 9.5), use of modified "octane catalysts" in fluid catalytic cracking (Sec. 9.4), use of C_5-C_6 isomerization, and use of oxygenated components, especially MTBE. As of 1990, ethanol was being blended into U.S. gasoline, downstream of the refinery, to the extent of about 60,000 barrels per day, comprising 0.8 vol % of U.S. gasoline. MTBE was being blended at the refinery at the rate of about 100,000 barrels per day to comprise about 1.4 vol % of the overall U.S. pool. The efforts to increase high-octane components are accompanied by reducing or eliminating the lowest-octane blending stocks, such as straight-run gasoline, raffinate (paraffins remaining from extraction of aromatics from reformate), and naphthas from thermal cracking. Environmental concerns to reduce hydrocarbon evaporative emissions by lowering volatility also result in less use of butanes, which are otherwise a cheap source of "front-end" octane components.

Hoffman (1980) gives an extensive table of octane ratings (RON and MON) of various typical refinery streams, both unleaded and leaded, as well as a table of RON and MON values of oxygenated hydrocarbons as used neat or in blends. Pierce and Logwinuk (1985) compare a variety of ways in which refinery operations may be modified to obtain "octane enhancement" and give the octane ratings of the different refinery streams that may be blended into gasoline.

Diesel fuel. Diesel engines are the primary power units on heavy-duty trucks, buses, and ships and are used in a small fraction of automobiles. Fuel efficiency is greater than in spark-ignition engines since compression ratios are substantially higher. Ignition is by adiabatic compression, thus the reaction properties of diesel fuel are in essence the opposite of those required for gasoline; normal paraffins are desired and aromatics must be minimized. The quality of diesel fuel is characterized by the *cetane number*, analogous to the octane number used for gasoline. The standard is a mixture of n-hexadecane ($C_{16}H_{34}$—"cetane") assigned a number of 100 and α-methyl naphthalene, assigned a number of 0. (n-Hexadecane is the highest-molecular-weight n-paraffin that is liquid at room temperature.)

As marketed, diesel fuel typically has a cetane number of about 50. With lower cetane numbers, fuel ignites later in the cycle and combustion is less efficient. Additionally, a low pour point* is required, so a completely n-paraffin ("waxy") fuel would be unsatisfactory, and a slight degree of branching is desired. Diesel fuel typically is about C_{10} to C_{20} in composition.

The standard method of determining the cetane number is by the ASTM D613 engine test. The time interval between start of fuel injection and ignition is measured as the compression ratio is varied. This is then compared to that for reference fuels, usually secondary references. Usually an engine test is unnecessary and a cetane index, satisfactory for most purposes, is calculated by the ASTM method D-976-80. This utilizes two physical properties of the fuel, the mid-point of the boiling-point curve (determined by ASTM D-86) and the API gravity (ASTM D-287). (The higher the API gravity, the less dense is the

---

*The pour point is the highest temperature at which a hydrocarbon product will flow, as determined by a prescribed test.

fuel.) Fuel composition would be a more fundamental basis for development of an improved cetane index and Pande and Hardy (1989) discuss a trial index based on a study of 53 fuels from a variety of sources.

9.4 Catalytic Cracking

The demand for gasoline relative to other liquid fuels in the United States has exceeded the fraction of crude petroleum having a suitable range of volatility ever since the advent of the mass-produced automobile. That large molecules could be thermally (noncatalytically) decomposed to form smaller ones has long been known. With the growth in demand for gasoline just prior to World War I, commercial processes appeared utilizing thermal cracking to increase the fraction of petroleum that could be utilized for gasoline.

Clays, especially after various treatments, were also long known to be active for hydrocarbon reactions. Eugene Houdry recognized the improved gasoline quality obtainable from decomposition reactions utilizing clay catalysts and developed a commercial process, first put in operation in 1936. This process utilized an acid-treated montmorillonite in a fixed-bed reactor operated cyclically. Cracking, which is endothermic, was carried out for about 10 minutes. The bed was then purged with steam and carbonaceous deposits were burned off with air, thus restoring the catalyst activity and reheating the catalyst bed. Two or more reactors were operated in parallel, each at a different stage of the overall cycle. Shortly before World War II, the commercialization of catalytic cracking was further spurred by the fact that the product had an octane number greater than that from thermal cracking, and a large demand developed for high-octane gasoline for propeller-driven aircraft.

Acid-treated montmorillonite catalysts are sensitive to high-temperature regeneration. Iron, present in the crystal lattice, becomes active in the presence of sulfur compounds. It is then oxidized during regeneration and catalyzes the undesired formation of coke and hydrogen. Other acid-treated clays were also used, but these were superseded by synthetic silica-alumina, a homogeneous xerogel containing 10 to 20 percent Al_2O_3 and free of iron. Various semisynthetic materials have also been used. In the 1960s these catalysts in turn were generally replaced by compositions containing several percent of zeolite H-Y (Sec. 7.7) dispersed in an amorphous silica-alumina matrix. These newer catalysts further increased the yield of gasoline from a specified amount of crude oil. Later, modified forms of zeolite Y, so-called ultrastable Y, gradually replaced H-Y. Other acidic compositions such as silica-magnesia also cause cracking, but none has been used commercially to a significant extent. The early development of cracking catalysts, their properties and characterization, are described by Ries (1952), by Ryland et al. (1960), and by Oblad et al. (1951).

The activity of virgin cracking catalysts drops rapidly during the first few seconds of contact time and then more slowly thereafter. For industrial purposes, reaction measurements are generally made on *equilibrium catalyst*, which is material that has been subjected to a sufficient number of cycles of reaction and regeneration so that essentially steady-state properties have been achieved.

Carbonaceous deposits (coke) are rapidly formed on the catalyst, and the reactor configuration must provide a means whereby a catalyst can be regenerated by burning off the coke with air after a short contact time. The original fixed-bed cyclic process was soon superseded by a moving-bed process in which reaction and regeneration occurred in different portions of the vessel. A fluidized-bed process was developed in the United States just prior to World War II and became the dominant process worldwide in the 1950s and 1960s. Finely divided catalyst is rapidly recirculated back and forth between the reactor and a regenerator in which deposited coke is removed by combustion with air. The heat required for the endothermic cracking reactions is supplied by the sensible heat of the catalyst from the regenerator, the catalyst being mixed with fresh feedstock. Close coupling between the two units of the process is required. The two units are separated by steam purges, and among the many requirements for a commercial catalyst are resistance to deactivation by steam at the high temperatures in the reactor, and resistance to attrition.

With the advent of zeolite fluid cracking catalysts, reactor configurations were modified to exploit most effectively the properties of these newer materials. Optimum operation corresponds to higher temperatures and shorter contact times, so the fluid-bed reactor has been generally replaced by a *riser cracker*. A representative design is shown in Fig. 9.1. The feed is mixed with and vaporized by contact with hot, regenerated catalyst and passes upwards concurrently with the catalyst in a vertical pipe. Essentially, plug flow occurs at velocities of about 20 ft/s, an order of magnitude greater than that in conventional dense fluidized beds. Contact times of the order of 2 to 4 s are achieved.

With typical zeolite catalysts the reaction temperature is in the neighborhood of 520 to 540°C, decreasing moderately from bottom to top since the reaction is endothermic. The weight ratio of catalyst to oil typically has values of about 4.5 to 5.5 and the cracking tempera-

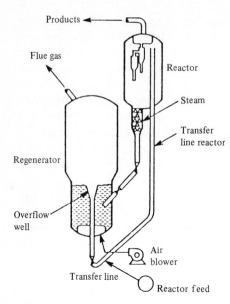

Products ←

Flue gas

Reactor

Steam

Transfer
line reactor

Regenerator

Overflow
well

Air
blower

Transfer line

Reactor feed

Figure 9.1 Fluid catalytic cracker and regenerator. Diagram from Davison Catalagram #65. (*Maselli and Peters 1985*)

ture is controlled by the preheat temperature of the oil feed and the rate of catalyst recirculation. Pressure is about 0.2 to 0.3 MPa. Regeneration continues to be carried out in a separate fluid-bed reactor, at a temperature of about 700°C.

In some installations, the gas leaving the regenerator contains a fairly high CO content and this is burned in a "CO boiler" in which steam is generated. However, particularly in more recent installations, obtaining as high a ratio of CO_2 to CO as possible in the gases leaving the regenerator is desirable, partly in order to maximize heat utilization in the form of hot catalyst (the heat of combustion of carbon at 800 K to form CO_2 is 395 kJ/mol but is only 123 kJ/mol to form CO). It is also desired to minimize afterburning of CO in the dilute phase above the regenerator fluid bed, which may damage the catalyst, and CO discharged to the atmosphere must also be limited to meet air-pollution-control standards.

Many years ago small amounts of chromia were sometimes added to a silica-alumina catalyst to promote CO oxidation in the regenerator, but this lowered catalyst selectivity in the cracking reactor. A more recent development, put into substantial commercial practice, has been to incorporate minute amounts of platinum (of the order of 1 to 10 ppm) into conventional cracking catalyst (Schwartz 1978; Hemler & Stine 1979). This concentration is sufficiently small that the reactions in the cracking reactor are not noticeably altered, but sufficiently great to increase significantly the combustion of CO in the regenerator.

The platinum may also be furnished in the form of a separate solid additive, which allows the platinum level in the circulating system to be increased rapidly when desired, so as to adjust to variations in feed composition to the cracking reactor. By designing the solid to have an attrition rate greater than that of the cracking catalyst, it can be preferentially removed from the system, so the platinum level could also be rapidly decreased if desired. Although platinum is expensive and is lost with the catalyst fines, the amounts here are so small that this application is economical.

Thermal cracking for the production of gasoline is no longer practiced, but thermal cracking of a variety of feedstocks in the presence of steam (steam cracking) is utilized to produce ethylene, propylene, etc., for chemical manufacture. The viscosity of the residue from distillation may be decreased by a mild thermal cracking termed *visbreaking*, or the residue may be converted to petroleum coke and lighter products by a severe thermal cracking operation.

Classically, the feed to the catalytic cracking reactor has been any distilled fraction, atmospheric- or vacuum-distilled, that is to be reduced in molecular weight. Usually it is a fraction with an initial boiling point above about 200°C since more volatile material can be processed into gasoline. However, the range of feedstocks used has been steadily expanding and now includes topped whole crudes and various residual fractions, if they are low in metals and asphaltene content. They may also include vacuum gas oils from visbreaking or coking units, solvent deasphalted oils, and hydrodemetallized residues. The feed thus may contain a wide range of types of hydrocarbons and molecular weights. If considerable organosulfur is present, this may be lowered by catalytic desulfurization before being fed to the catalytic cracker.

The reactions that occur in the catalytic cracker are complex, and the products formed are considerably different from those from thermal cracking. All cracking catalysts are highly acidic, and the mechanisms of these various reactions involve the formation of carbocation intermediates, discussed in Sec. 7.5.

Almost all cracking catalysts now in commercial use incorporate 10 to 20 percent zeolite H-Y in one form or another. For manufacture, the zeolite is mixed with an amorphous silica-alumina hydrogel and/ or clays pretreated in various ways. This is then washed, base-exchanged to remove contaminant ions such as Na^+ and SO_4^{2-}, spray dried, and calcined. The resulting microspheroidal fluid catalyst particles average about 50 μm in diameter and comprise a matrix surrounding the zeolite particles, which are typically about 1 μm or less in diameter. The properties of the matrix can be varied so as to contribute either little or considerable activity to the entire catalyst particle. Small amounts of other zeolites may also be added, as well as additives for sulfur transfer (see the following) and for inactivation of heavy metals if they are in the feed.

With the gradual phase-out of lead alkyl additives to gasoline, there has been increased attention on obtaining high-octane components by a variety of modifications and new processing schemes in petroleum refining. In catalytic cracking, emphasis has shifted toward making gasoline-range product of higher octane number, even at the expense of some loss in yield. This has been achieved by use of aluminum-deficient forms of zeolite H-Y, "ultrastable Y" (Sec. 7.7) in the catalyst. Total worldwide consumption of cracking catalysts as of 1990 was about 1000 tons per day, and about one-third of this contained this type of zeolite. These are sometimes termed *octane cracking catalysts*.

Most of the sulfur compounds in the feed, typically 80 to 95 percent, are converted to H_2S during catalytic cracking and are subsequently removed by selective absorption from the gas fraction of the product. However, sulfur in the coke deposits on the catalyst is converted to SO_x (SO_2 and SO_3) in the regenerator. Discharge to the atmosphere must be minimized to protect air quality. Feedstock hydrodesulfurization and flue-gas desulfurization are costly, but an effective procedure is to incorporate into the catalyst a material that transfers SO_x in the regenerator back to the catalytic reactor where it is reduced to H_2S.

The transfer agent may be an alumina, which operates primarily by adsorption/desorption or a heavy metal oxide that is converted to a sulfide/sulfate in the regenerator. By a combination of hydrolysis in the steam purge and reduction in the catalytic reactor, this is converted back to the metal oxide. The patent literature describes rare-earth oxides or platinum on alumina as possibilities. The platinum increases oxidation of CO to CO_2 and SO_2 to SO_3, which increases SO_x adsorption. These transfer agents may be incorporated into the cracking catalyst or, more frequently, added separately to form a mechanical mixture. [See Hirschberg and Bertolacini (1988) and Rheaume and Ritter (1988).]

A large number of selective variations in commercial cracking catalyst formulations are available in order to provide an economical optimum for each refiner's own particular set of circumstances. Wear and Mott (1988) discuss the many interactions between catalyst composition and desired process objectives. According to their survey in 1988, over 100 different fluid catalytic cracking (FCC) catalysts were being used in 153 operating units in North America.

A nondistilled feedstock typically contains various amounts of nickel and vanadium compounds present in the original crude and iron present from contamination. These compounds deposit on the catalyst. Nickel and iron cause primarily nonselective cracking and coke formation; vanadium oxides, formed in the regenerator, may attack the structure of the zeolite, as well as accelerate undesired side reactions. Compounds of antimony added to the circulating catalyst passivate nickel; methods for control of vanadia are less satisfactory, but a variety of other passivators may be used, including compounds of bismuth, tin, and $CaTiO_3$. In practice, only feedstocks having metal contents below 20 to 30 ppm are usually acceptable.

About one-half the product from catalytic cracking is of the volatility range suitable for gasoline, and this comprises some 30 to 50 percent of the total gasoline pool, some of which must first be upgraded, e.g., by hydrogen treatment. The balance between gasoline and heavier fractions can be altered to a considerable degree by catalyst composition and operating conditions. The hydrocarbon composition is, of course, quite different from that of uncracked material (straight run) of the same boiling point range. The sulfur and nitrogen content is usually higher than in the straight-run fraction since the concentration of these impurities increases with molecular weight of the crude fraction. The product from the catalytic cracker is typically separated by distillation into streams that may be further processed as follows:

1. C_4 *and lighter fraction.* The C_4 fraction, which may include some C_5, may be fed to an alkylation unit in which the isoparaffins react with C_4 olefins. n-Butane may be added to gasoline. Isobutylene is a feedstock for MTBE. C_2-C_3 is sold as liquefied petroleum gas (LPG). C_2-C_4 may be a feedstock to a thermal cracker.

2. *Light catalytic naphtha,* bp 18 to 93°C (65 to 200°F). This cut goes to the gasoline pool, or a C_5-C_6 fraction may be isomerized first to increase its octane number.

3. *Intermediate catalytic naphtha,* bp 93 to 165°C (200 to 330°F). A light hydrogen treatment may be necessary for this fraction to lower the diolefin content. (Diolefins tend to form gums on storage.) Hydrogenation of the monoolefins should be avoided to prevent lowering the octane number, and excessive consumption of hydrogen, which is expensive. This fraction has a lower octane number than that of the light catalytic naphtha, and it may be fed to a catalytic reformer to improve the octane rating. (The light and intermediate naphtha may also be treated as a single stream.)

4. *Heavy catalytic naphtha,* bp 150 to 235°C (300 to 450°F). The aro-

matics may be extracted from this fraction; the paraffins may then be used for jet fuel or diesel fuel. Otherwise, this fraction may be fed to a hydrocracker, or it may be blended into heating oil.

5. *Fraction above 235°C (450°F)*. This fraction is highly aromatic. It may be hydrodesulfurized and used as fuel, or recycled to the catalytic cracker (sometimes it is termed *cycle oil*, even if it is not recycled). Aromatic rings do not crack appreciably and must be presaturated (hydrogenated) to cause significant ring breakage.

Literature.   An extensive literature exists on catalysts and reactions. Early reviews are available by Haensel (1951), Voge (1958), and Ryland et al. (1960). In later literature, Venuto and Habib (1978) review the interactions between reactor equipment, nature of feedstocks and of catalysts, while Gates et al. (1979) discuss mechanisms and commercial performance characteristics. Wojciechowski and Corma (1986) review catalytic cracking with emphasis on kinetics and mechanisms. The proceedings of a symposium (Occelli 1988) contain papers providing a wealth of detail on fluid catalytic cracking, centering on commercial applications. Scherzer (1989), in an extensive and detailed review, discusses a variety of scientific and technical aspects of cracking catalysts containing zeolites. These include preparation, manufacturing processes, the various catalyst and matrix components, physical characterization, reaction mechanisms, and correlations between catalyst composition and catalytic properties. A historical review has been published by Avidan et al. (1990).

9.5   Catalytic Reforming

The principal objective of catalytic reforming is to process a hydrocarbon fraction, having a volatility range suitable for use in gasoline, so as to increase its octane number, but without significantly changing the molecular weight. Catalytic reforming is also the principal source of the chemicals benzene, toluene, and xylenes. Catalytic reforming is utilized on a major scale in petroleum refining; the quantity of feedstock so processed in the United States is nearly one-quarter of the total crude oil processed.

   The first commercial catalytic reforming process in the United States was introduced in 1939, stimulated by the wartime demand for high-octane gasoline for propeller-driven aircraft, and for aromatic chemicals such as toluene for use in making trinitrotoluene (TNT). A molybdena/alumina catalyst was utilized in a fixed-bed reactor operated under a high pressure of hydrogen. It was soon followed by processes utilizing a similar catalyst in a moving-bed or fluidized-bed reactor. The catalyst became coked rapidly, thus requiring frequent regeneration, and these processes gradually became uneconomic during the 1950s upon the development of a catalyst consisting of platinum on an acidic alumina.

The platinum catalyst was utilized in a fixed-bed reactor and was introduced in 1949 by the Universal Oil Products Co. based on work by Haensel and his coworkers. Hydrogen, formed in the process, was recycled through the reactor to maintain a sufficiently high hydrogen partial pressure so that coke-forming reactions could be minimized. Thus, the reactor could be operated for periods of many months before regeneration was needed. This was the first use of a precious metal catalyst in the petroleum industry, and it was followed rapidly by a number of related processes utilizing platinum that differed primarily in the nature of the support.

That the support needed to be acidic was recognized, but there are a number of subtleties about the optimum acidity that were gradually revealed through intensive research. In the first UOP catalyst, the alumina contained combined halogen, as fluoride or chloride. This had poor tolerance to low concentrations of water vapor as formed in regeneration, which removed halogen from the support. The halogen could be replaced and its effectiveness substantially restored by adding to the feed a small amount of an organohalogen compound that decomposed in the reactor. Better tolerance to water was achieved by using a silica-alumina base that contained no halogen. The silica-alumina had to be treated to achieve a controlled degree of acidity, but silica-alumina is not now used since it causes excessive hydrocracking. The next development was the use of η-alumina as a base, which has an inherently stronger acidity than the more common γ form (see Sec. 4.5.1 and Fig. 7.4), but η-alumina is not now widely used since acidity can be more effectively controlled with chloride addition.

A wide variety of reactions are involved in catalytic reforming, consisting primarily of dehydrogenation and isomerization reactions, plus some hydrocracking. The rates of reaction decrease in the approximate order shown in Table 9.3, which lists for each type of reaction a specific example for a C_6 hydrocarbon. The equilibrium constant K (partial pressures in atmospheres) and heat of reaction ΔH are for 500°C (Edmonds 1975). The hydrogen produced by reforming is an important by-product since it can be used for hydrodesulfurization and hydrotreating in other portions of a refinery. The catalyst consists of platinum or, more commonly, platinum plus rhenium, iridium, or tin, supported on acidified alumina.

The first three reactions listed in Table 9.3 occur very rapidly, essentially to equilibrium. The olefins concentration in the final product

TABLE 9.3   Representative Catalytic Reforming Reactions

Reaction	K	ΔH, kJ/mol
1. Dehydrogenation of naphthenes to aromatics	6×10^5	+221
(cyclohexane $\longrightarrow$ benzene $+ 3H_2$)		
2. Dehydrogenation of paraffins to olefins	$\sim 4 \times 10^{-2}$	$\sim +130$
$C_6H_{14} \longrightarrow C_6H_{12} + H_2$		
3. Isomerization of alkyl cyclopentanes	8.6×10^{-2}	-15.9
(methylcyclopentane $\longrightarrow$ cyclohexane)		
4. Isomerization of n-paraffins to isoparaffins	~ 1	~ 5
$n\text{-}C_6H_{14} \longrightarrow \text{iso-}C_6H_{14}$		
5. Dehydrocyclization of paraffins to aromatics		
$n\text{-}C_6H_{14} \longrightarrow C_6H_6 + 4H_2$		
6. Hydrocracking of paraffins		
$C_6H_{14} + H_2 \longrightarrow \text{olefins and paraffins}$		

SOURCE: Edmonds (1975).

is low since they are thermodynamically unfavored, but olefin formation is an intermediate step in paraffin isomerization (see the following). The equilibrium of reaction 3 is likewise unfavorable, but the reaction is driven to the right by the rapid dehydrogenation of the cycloparaffin formed by isomerization. The combined reaction is termed *dehydroisomerization*. The dehydroisomerization of alkyl cyclopentanes is an important reaction since the ratio of their concentration to that of alkyl cyclohexanes varies between about 0.5 to 1.5 in representative straight-run naphthas.

The isomerization of n-C_6H_{14} to the isoparaffins does not normally proceed to the equilibrium distribution of dimethyl butanes. The *dehydrocyclization* of an n-paraffin may also occur, but the rate is relatively low, increasing with molecular weight of the paraffin. The mechanism from n-hexane is believed to involve the intermediate formation of methylcyclopentane and methylcyclopentene.

9.5.1   Catalyst dual functionality

The catalyst is the classic example of *dual functionality* in that, in order for isomerization, dehydrocyclization, or hydrocracking to occur, both metallic sites (e.g., platinum) and acidic sites must be present on the catalyst surface. The isomerization of, e.g., an n-paraffin to an isoparaffin does not proceed directly, but via dehydrogenation to an n-olefin. This in turn is isomerized to an isoolefin, which is then hydrogenated to the corresponding isoparaffin. The hydrogenation-dehydrogenation steps proceed on the platinum sites; the isomerization, on acidic sites.

The concept of a dual-function catalyst with two distinctly different kinds of sites was introduced by Mills et al. (1953) through work with catalysts containing only an acidic function, only a dehydrogenation function, or both. Later Weisz (1962) showed by studies with mechanical mixtures that the intermediates are true gas-phase species that are transported by gaseous diffusion between the different sites. For example, under comparable conditions, little isomerization of hexane occurs on either a platinum/silica catalyst alone or silica-alumina catalyst (acidic) alone, but a mechanical mixture is quite active (Table 9.4). These data were obtained at 373°C with a 5:1 molar ratio of hydrogen to n-hexane. Studies with n-heptane isomerization show that with platinum/silica or platinum/carbon little reaction occurred (Fig. 9.2), but a mechanical mixture of either of these with silica-alumina gave much more reaction. The three upper curves show that the smaller the component particle sizes used, the more the isomerization rate increased. The finest particle mixture gave results comparable to platinum impregnated on silica-alumina.

Weisz and others [see, e.g., Thomas and Thomas (1967, p. 338)] have calculated so-called intimacy requirements concerning the maximum distance between sites that can be allowed without diffusion becoming a significant rate-limiting step. This requirement is a function of other variables such as rate of individual reactions and thermodynamic equilibria. For some of the other reactions occurring in reforming, such as dehydrocyclization of an n-paraffin such as n-hexane, mechanical mixtures are not very effective (Sinfelt 1964). Presumably some key intermediate, perhaps a diolefin, is formed that is not easily desorbed. In that event the intermediate would have to migrate by surface diffusion to a nearby acid site or interact with a nearby acidic site.

TABLE 9.4 Hexane Isomerization on Mechanical Catalyst Mixtures

Catalyst charge to reactor	Wt % conversion to isohexanes
10 cm^3 of platinum/silica	0.9
10 cm^3 of silica-alumina	0.3
Mixture of 10 cm^3 of each of above	6.8

SOURCE: Weisz (1962).

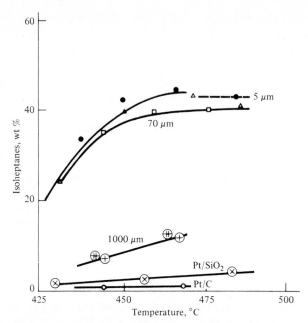

Figure 9.2   Isomerization of *n*-heptane, conversion versus temperature. Pt/C, 1000 μm (○); Pt/SiO₂, 1000 μm (⊗); Pt/SiO₂ + SiO₂·Al₂O₃, 1000 μm (⊕); Pt/C +SiO₂·Al₂O₃, 1000 μm (⊕); supported Pt + SiO₂·Al₂O₃, 70 μm (□); supported Pt + SiO₂·Al₂O₃, 5 μm (△); Pt impregnated on SiO₂·Al₂O₃, (●). (*Weisz 1962. Reprinted with permission from Advances in Catalysis. Copyright by Academic Press.*)

Comparisons of a mechanical mixture of different monofunctional catalysts with a single multifunctional catalyst must be made carefully to ensure that the results are truly significant, especially if the kinetics are complicated. Even if the same total loadings of active components are used, differences in contact time and concentration profiles between the two sets of experiments may contribute their own subtle effects. Figure 9.3 generalizes the concept of dual functionality to a larger variety of reactions of importance in catalytic reforming (Mills et al. 1953), taking the C_6 hydrocarbons as an example. A number of the reactions observed involve several steps in sequence.

In view of the distribution of products obtained in reforming reactions over a molybdena catalyst, this may also be termed bifunctional, in which both functions are shown by a single compound. This finding can be rationalized by attributing the acidic property to the metal oxide and the hydrogenation-dehydrogenation function to the metal ions. Multifunctional catalysts were reviewed by Weisz (1962) and by Sinfelt (1964).

In addition to its role in providing sites for hydrogenation-dehydro-

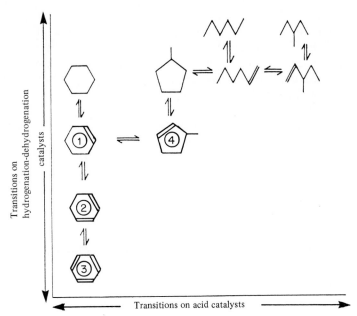

Figure 9.3 Sequence of reactions on a dual-function catalyst. C_6 hydrocarbons used as an example. (*Mills et al. 1953. Reprinted with permission from Industrial and Engineering Chemistry. Copyright by the American Chemical Society.*)

genation reactions to occur, platinum also acts to minimize the rate of formation of carbonaceous deposits. Hydrogen chemisorbs onto the platinum with dissociation and appears to diffuse along the surface of the catalyst, perhaps along carbonaceous deposits. (This phenomenon of adsorption followed by surface diffusion is sometimes termed *spillover.*) (Sec. 6.4.2) Coke precursors are hydrogenated, which improves their desorption from the catalyst. The rate of coke formation is a function of hydrogen pressure. The minimum concentration of platinum that can be practicably used on the catalyst is set more by that needed to keep the catalyst "clean" rather than the amount needed to provide an adequate number of metallic sites. This minimum amount in turn is determined in part by the nature of the feedstock and operating conditions.

For straight-run naphtha from distillation, a practicable minimum platinum content is in the neighborhood of 0.2 to 0.3 wt %, depending in part on the frequency of regeneration. Cracked stocks (e.g., naphtha from a catalytic cracker or from steam cracking) can also be fed to a reformer, but the presence of olefins, and especially diolefins, causes a much more rapid increase in the rate of coking. This effect can be overcome to some extent by use of a higher platinum content. Under industrial operating conditions and with industrial catalysts, the hydrogenation-dehydrogenation reactions appear to be essentially in equilibrium, and the sites are so close to one another that diffusion is not rate-limiting. The rate-limiting processes are the isomerization reactions on the acid sites. Some isomerization occurs on metallic sites, but this is not a major contribution under industrial reaction conditions.

Optimum operating conditions are determined by an economic balance among several factors. The equilibrium for dehydrogenation reactions is favored by high temperatures and low hydrogen partial pressure, but this increases the rate at which the catalyst becomes inactivated by coke deposits. Higher platinum loadings decrease the rate of inactivation, but the catalyst is then more costly.

Beginning in about 1968, an improved catalyst consisting of a mixture of platinum and rhenium, a *bimetallic catalyst*, supported on an acidic alumina (Kluksdahl 1968) came to replace much of the commercial use of the earlier platinum/alumina catalyst. A mixture of platinum and iridium, or platinum and tin has also come to be used. These bimetallic catalysts may initially be slightly less active than the all-platinum catalysts, but they maintain their activity over longer periods of time because of a slower rate of formation of coke deposits on the metal function (coke on the alumina support is of lesser importance). They may generally be used at lower hydrogen pressure, which allows an increased degree of dehydrocyclization of paraffins to aromatics to occur and reduces hydrocracking. The octane number of the reformate (the product from the reformer) is then increased and, generally, a higher yield of C_5+ product and of hydrogen is obtained.

9.5.2 Reactor configurations

At least three reactor configurations have been used. In each case, in effect, multiple adiabatic reactors are operated in series, the product being reheated between reactors. The early conventional reforming process using a Pt/Al_2O_3 catalyst consisted of three (occasionally four) fixed-bed reactors with furnace reheaters between the units. In a representative four-reactor system, the temperature drop along each reactor would be about 55, 40, 20, and 5°C, respectively. In this configuration the catalyst is distributed nonuniformly, the first reactor containing the least amount, and the last reactor, the most. Approximately every 6 months or so the entire group of units is shut down, carbonaceous and sulfur compounds accumulated on the catalyst are burned off, and then the entire unit is put back on stream. These reformers are termed *semiregenerative*. They have the advantage that the catalyst composition can be varied from beginning to end of the beds for optimum performance. For example, a predominantly dehydrogenation catalyst could be used upstream.

Later the trend was to *cyclic* reactors in which four to six fixed-bed units are operated in series, one being shut down for regeneration at all times. In this case a temperature drop of about 25 to 30°C is taken through each reactor, and the catalyst is distributed uniformly among all reactors. One or two reactors may be regenerated each day, and since carbonaceous deposits are removed quite frequently, a higher rate of formation is allowable. These reactors can be operated satisfactorily at lower pressures and lower recycle-gas ratios than the semiregenerative units, allowing an increased yield to form gasoline. The cyclic units also provide a higher degree of flexibility to accommodate varying feedstocks, changing octane number requirements, etc.

Since the mid-seventies the preferred design for new installations, developed by UOP, consists of a continuous moving bed comprising three radial-gas-flow reactors stacked on top of one another, with external interheaters. Addition and withdrawal of catalyst is continuous, and the average residence time of the catalyst can be varied from a few days to a month or more. This reactor design minimizes pressure drop and facilitates catalyst circulation. The withdrawn catalyst is regenerated and reactivated in a separate vessel and returned to the reactor. The design is sometimes termed *continuous catalytic reforming* (CCR).

Representative operating conditions in semiregenerative or cyclic reactors are about 480°C and 2 MPa with an all-platinum catalyst, about 1 MPa with a platinum-rhenium catalyst. In the semiregenerative reformers, the temperature is gradually raised as the catalyst deactivates so as to keep the octane number of the product nearly constant. An upper limit of about 520 to 550°C is set by materials of construction or furnace capacity. When this temperature is reached, the reactor is shut down and the catalyst is regenerated. Instead, the run may be terminated by excessive pressure drop, caused by coke buildup, or by decline in yield.

Operating conditions in the various reactors are also determined by the nature of the feedstock and the uses to which the product is to be put. With *low-severity* operation (essentially lower temperatures), only dehydrogenation reactions and dehydroisomerization of alkyl cyclopentanes occur. A high yield (volume basis) of material in the suitable boiling range for gasoline, but of lower octane number, is obtained. *High-severity* operation, achieved primarily by higher temperatures, increases the aromatics content (via, in part, dehydrocyclization reactions), but hydrocracking also increases. The yield of C_5+ products drops, but its aromatics content and octane number increases.

If aromatic chemicals are to be produced, a reformer is usually run at high severity to produce a more concentrated aromatics product and thereby reduce the cost of subsequent processing (extraction, fractionation). However, an increased portion of the feed becomes hydrocracked material that is too volatile to use in gasoline. Beyond operating conditions, the percentage of the feedstock converted to aromatics depends largely on the naphthenic content of the feed. Much Middle East crude is high in paraffins and produces lower yields of aromatics than can be obtained with most U.S. or South American crudes.

9.5.3 Catalyst compositions

Hundreds of patents have been issued on catalyst compositions. All commercially used reforming catalysts contain platinum, either alone or in a combination with another metal. In the monometallic forms the platinum content is typically 0.35 to 0.6 wt %. The bimetallic catalysts with rhenium are typically about 0.3 wt % platinum and 0.3 wt % rhenium, termed a *balanced composition*, but in some formulations the rhenium-platinum ratio is considerably greater than unity. Platinum-tin catalysts typically contain about 0.3 wt % tin, and the platinum content is in the range of 0.5 to 0.3 wt %.

The minimum platinum content is set by an otherwise excessive rate of coking and is also affected by the nature of the feedstock. (Diolefins, for example, cause more rapid coking, which can be counteracted by a higher platinum content.) For maximum utilization of a very expensive material, the platinum is spread out in as finely divided form as possible. A large fraction of the total platinum atoms present are on the surface in a commercial catalyst. The support is almost always an alumina, acidified by the incorporation into the structure of about 1% chloride. The use of chloroplatinic acid for impregnation leads to the natural incorporation of chloride into the alumina during preparation. Unless suitable measures are taken, acidity is gradually lost during reaction, but this is restored by adding small amounts of an organic chloride to the feedstock. Presumably this decomposes to release HCl, which is adsorbed by the alumina.

The bimetallic catalysts are sometimes referred to as *alloy catalysts*, but the actual form under reaction conditions is unknown. The structure may also gradually change upon repeated regenerations.

All these catalysts are gradually poisoned by sulfur compounds in the feed that, being predominantly in the divalent state, adsorb on and coordinate with metal sites, but a small amount of sulfur may be beneficial. The platinum monometallic catalysts may be operated satisfactorily with sulfur levels in the feedstock up to the range of 10 to 50 ppm, depending partly on the platinum loading on the catalyst and the frequency of regeneration that is practicable. The Re-Pt/Al$_2$O$_3$ catalysts are more sensitive to sulfur poisoning, but a small amount of sulfur is needed for optimum performance. This is typically 1 to 3 ppm in the feed for a platinum-rhenium ratio of unity, but perhaps as low as 0.1 ppm of sulfur for a high-rhenium–low-platinum catalyst. The platinum-tin catalysts are less sensitive to sulfur level than the platinum-rhenium catalysts. These low sulfur levels usually necessitate prior hydrodesulfurization of the feed. Consequently, a refinery not possessing such equipment may be able to use only the all-platinum catalyst.

A new platinum or platinum-bimetallic catalyst may cause an excessive degree of hydrocracking, which, being exothermic, may result in an excessive temperature rise. Hence, a low concentration of a sulfur compound may be introduced into the feed initially to avoid this behavior. This treatment method is sometimes referred to as *tempering* or "taking the edge off" a catalyst. When the sulfur compound in the feed is removed, the adsorbed sulfur material is slowly hydrogenated to H$_2$S and desorbed. Avoiding excessive initial activity also reduces the subsequent rate of buildup of coke deposits and prolongs catalyst life. Apparently, some very active sites that cause hydrocracking, polymerization, and condensation reactions are poisoned by this procedure.

In any event too high a sulfur concentration leads to excessive coking and rapid deactivation. Basic nitrogen compounds adsorb on acid sites and reduce isomerization and cracking activity, but they have little effect on dehydrogenation activity. Tiny amounts of arsenic (which is found in shale oil) or of other heavy metals can produce irreversible poisoning.

With the platinum-rhenium catalyst an unacceptably high rate of hydrogenolysis is observed unless a small amount of sulfur is always present. Coke formation is then reduced and selectivity for dehydrogenation of paraffins to the corresponding olefins is enhanced. These effects appear to be caused by some form of a surface structure that may be written as ReS$_{ads}$, which acts to divide the platinum surface into very small clusters of the order of 1 to 3 platinum atoms (Biloen et al. 1980). Under industrial conditions most of the rhenium is visualized to be in the sulfided state. The platinum is partly in the zero-valent form and partly as PtS$_x$, and is adjacent to the rhenium.

These generalizations appear to apply to platinum-tin also, although tin may modify acid sites as well. Tin presumably divides platinum into small clusters in the same fashion as ReS_{ads}, but the presence of sulfur is not required. Tin is an inactive component, whereas rhenium by itself is active for hydrocarbon transformations and must therefore be in the sulfur-modified form.

The interpretation of these observations thus is essentially that the surface geometry is modified to reduce structure-sensitive reactions. Basically, sulfurization or the presence of tin suppresses reactions occurring in metallic cluster sites, so selectivity to isomerization is increased. In the same way, small deposits of coke can also cause similar effects. Excessive sulfur leads to more rapid coke formation and higher rate of deactivation.

Various other subtle effects are of importance in practice. Rhenium oxide has high cracking functionality and is more difficult to reduce unless it is adjacent to platinum. The optimum presulfiding procedure for platinum-rhenium is sensitive to temperature, vapor composition, and other variables.

The preferred catalyst also depends on the equipment available. The best performance for platinum-tin catalysts occurs with frequent regeneration so Pt-Sn is the catalyst of choice for the CCR units. They may also be used in cyclic units but not semiregenerative units. Platinum-tin catalysts can withstand more coke than Pt-Re and if operated at relatively low pressure (e.g., 0.7 MPa) they give more C_5+ product and less $C_1 + C_2$. The H_2 produced is consequently of higher purity. Although the platinum-tin is shorter lived than platinum-rhenium, this is not important if they are used in the CCR moving-bed unit or in cyclic units with frequent regeneration.

With platinum-iridium catalysts, metal agglomeration can occur readily upon regeneration, so careful control during oxidation is needed to obtain the desired degree of redispersion (Garten and Sinfelt 1980). Therefore they are not usually used in cyclic reactors where regeneration has to be done fairly rapidly. Their primary use is in semiregenerative reactors where more time is available to control burnoff and re-activation. With platinum-iridium, sulfur is adsorbed and desorbed more readily than with platinum-rhenium, so in the event of an upset in which a higher sulfur content in the feed is contacted with the catalyst, the reformer changes in performance more slowly with the platinum-rhenium catalyst, allowing operators more time to adjust reactor conditions. The platinum-iridium catalysts are more active than platinum-rhenium catalysts under comparable conditions. The strictly limited availability of iridium is also a possible limiting factor on its industrial use.

Many other multimetallic catalysts containing platinum have been patented. Platinum-germanium and platinum-lead appear to have been used in a few industrial installations worldwide, but there is little substantial or sustained interest in these compositions.

All of these reforming catalysts have lifetimes measured in years. In reprocessing, typically the entire catalyst is dissolved. Platinum recovery from the catalyst is in the neighborhood of 99 percent, that of iridium or rhenium about 93 to 95 percent.

Regeneration is accomplished by carefully burning coke off the catalyst, avoiding overheating that might cause damage. In a representative procedure, an inert gas, usually N_2, is circulated through the catalyst bed and then air is introduced to provide an initial oxygen content of about 1 percent. After the more reactive portion of the deposits has been removed, the oxygen content may be raised, for example, to 2 percent and the inlet temperature raised to 480 to 500°C, or a substantially higher oxygen content may be used. These conditions are held until all carbon is removed.

The catalyst is then typically contacted with a low concentration of HCl or a chloro compound and steam, in the presence of 5 to 10% O_2, to reacidify the alumina and disperse the metal. This seems to involve the intermediate formation of oxides and oxychlorides of platinum that have appreciable volatility or surface mobility. The final stage in regeneration is usually an *oxygen soak* in which catalyst is contacted with air alone. The catalyst is then reduced with H_2 before being put back on stream. The entire process is centered on achieving maximum metal redispersion (Sec. 6.4).

9.5.4 Literature

The early development of catalytic reforming processes and understanding of the chemical reactions involved was reviewed by Ciapetta et al. (1958). Reactions on chromia, which is effective for dehydrocyclization of paraffins to aromatics, and molybdena are described in considerable detail. A later review by Ciapetta and Wallace (1971) discussed Pt/Al_2O_3 and $Pt\text{-}Re/Al_2O_3$ catalysts and the reforming reactions they catalyze. Gates et al. (1979) review mechanisms and industrial performance. A detailed review by Biswas et al. (1988) discusses poisoning, coking, and the role of sulfur on activity and selectivity of reforming catalysts. Edgar (1983) gives a brief overall summary of catalytic reforming as it is carried out in refineries. The IFP (Institut Français du Petrole) reforming process is described by Le Page et al. (1987).

A detailed treatment of bimetallic catalysts (Sinfelt 1983) summarizes an extensive series of fundamental and applied studies carried out over more than two decades by one of the premier researchers in this area and his colleagues. Sinfelt (1981) also reviews catalytic reforming in general. An engaging personal account of the early development of the platinum reforming catalyst and the process based on it was published by Sterba and Haensel (1976). The great industrial importance of this process has led to much fundamental research on methods of obtaining a high degree of dispersion of platinum and other metals on alumina, and on characterization of such dispersions. It has also stimulated many studies of the effect of particle size on reactivity and structure sensitivity (Chap. 6).

9.6   Cyclization

9.6.1   From C_6-C_7 paraffins

In a detailed and key paper, Bernard (1980) reported studies that led to the development of an unusual monofunctional, nonacidic catalyst for cyclization of n-hexane on zeolite L in the K-form, containing platinum. On classical metal-acidic bifunctional catalysts, n-hexane aromatization is relatively slow because the main pathway involves a carbenium ion producing methyl cyclopentane, which is then isomerized into cyclohexane and in turn dehydrogenated to benzene. In competition are hydrocracking and other isomerization reactions that increase with acidity.

More recent studies by Tamm et al. (1987) elaborate on the mechanism on zeolite L. The key step is the ring closure on a metal site of n-hexane to cyclohexane, which then rapidly dehydrogenates to benzene. Methyl pentanes and methyl cyclopentane must be converted first to n-hexane as an intermediate. Zeolite L's superior performance to zeolite X or Y may be associated with a tight confinement in the zeolite channel that forces the n-hexane to bend around. (L zeolite is one-dimensional with pores of about 0.74-nm aperture leading to cavities of about $0.48 \times 1.24 \times 1.07$ nm. See Table 7.3.) Derouane and Vanderveken (1988) have reviewed the literature and proposed a more specific confinement mechanism to interpret data on effects of the nature of paraffin carbon number and isomer structure on selectivity and activity.

An industrial catalyst is partly barium-exchanged and has the approximate formula (0.6 to 0.8 wt %) $Pt/Ba_2K_5Al_9Si_{27}O_{72}$. The platinum is nearly 100 percent dispersed in the form of particles of 0.8 to 1.0 nm or less, located within the zeolite channels. A key feature is a low rate of coke fouling, attributed to the particular zeolite support.

This catalyst is the basis of the Chevron Aromax process (Tamm et al. 1987; Hughes et al. 1986, 1987). Representative reaction conditions are 500°C, a (H_2/HC) mole ratio of 6 and total pressure of 0.4 to 1.0

MPa. This process is an alternative to isomerization and reforming as a method of increasing the octane number of light straight-run naphthas. However, benzene is carcinogenic, and its concentration in gasoline must be limited; the process may be directed more to chemical production than to fuels. Isomerization on a dual-function catalyst is suitable for C_5-C_6 fractions that do not contain too much C_6, but C_7 compounds crack readily.

9.6.2   From C_3-C_4 paraffins

The Cyclar process for conversion of *liquefied petroleum gas* (LPG) to aromatics was announced jointly by UOP and British Petroleum (BP) in 1984, termed by them *dehydrocyclodimerization*. It converts a relatively inexpensive feedstock to aromatics (benzene, toluene, and xylene), which are in strong demand. The catalyst is a high-silica zeolite, possibly ZSM-5, containing gallium. The preferred catalyst appears to have gallium impregnated into the zeolite rather than substituted into the framework. The overall reaction forms a product with substantially lower hydrogen-carbon ratio than the feed, and the excess hydrogen is rejected largely as H_2 rather than lower-molecular-weight hydrocarbons—a useful feature.

The major reaction steps are paraffin dehydrogenation to olefins that crack, oligomerize, and cyclize to aromatics. The intermediate olefins react rapidly; so their concentration at any time is very low if there are no olefins in the feed. The overall reaction is endothermic, and the UOP continuous reactor with continuous catalyst regeneration (CCR), as developed for catalytic reforming, is utilized (Sec. 9.5.2). Here it consists of four beds with interheaters. The overall wt % yield of aromatics from fresh feed is about 65 percent, of which about 92 wt % is BTX, together with about 2000 *standard cubic feet* (SCF) of hydrogen per barrel processed. This is recovered and used elsewhere. The remainder is fuel gas, methane and ethane. More details are given by Doolan and Pujado (1989).

As of 1989, a commercial Cyclar unit of about 1000-barrels-per-day capacity was under construction at the BP Grangemouth refinery in the U.K.

9.7   Isomerization

9.7.1   Paraffin isomerization

Paraffins in the C_5 and C_6 range may be isomerized in order to increase the octane number of a light blending stock for gasoline. (*n*-Pentane has a research octane number of 62 compared with a value of 92 for isopentane.) Similar octane numbers are desirable for the various volatility fractions in gasoline, so paraffin isomerization is a method of achieving so-called front end high octane. The process is closely related to catalytic reforming, but aims at achieving a closer approach to equilibrium with respect to paraffin isomerization reactions. Paraffin isomerization has become of more importance as the use of lead additives is gradually phased out, but paraffin isomerization is used to a much lesser extent than reforming.

Under equilibrium conditions the highest concentrations of the highly branched paraffins, which have the highest octane numbers, occur at the lowest temperature (Fig. 9.4). Hence, a highly active catalyst is needed. Such a catalyst is similar to that used in reforming but usually has somewhat stronger acidity. The catalysts most extensively studied and patented are dual-function, consisting of platinum or palladium on a zeolite. The catalyst of choice appears to consist of H-mordenite and platinum in an alumina matrix. The sodium content must be very low, but feed sulfur levels up to 35 ppm on a continuous basis can be tolerated. The process is not used on C_7 or higher paraffins, because excessive cracking (undesired) occurs on these highly acidic catalysts.

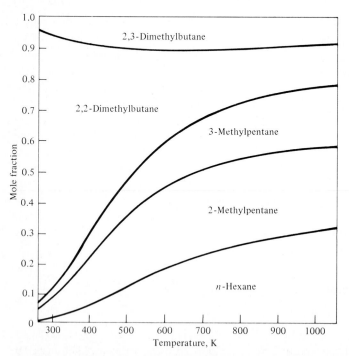

Figure 9.4 Equilibrium concentrations of five hexanes in the gaseous phase (width of band measures mole fraction of indicated isomer at equilibrium). (*Rossini et al. 1941*)

Representative reaction conditions are about 260°C and about 2.6 MPa, using a H_2-hydrocarbon mole ratio with values of about 1 to 4. This is a considerably lower temperature and higher pressure than that in reforming. The high hydrogen pressure is to minimize coke formation. The reaction appears to be about zero order with respect to both hydrogen and hydrocarbon partial pressure.

This process, as applied to C_5-C_8 hydrocarbons, first became commercial in about 1966 but apparently has had few new developments since the mid-1970s. A variety of high-paraffinic fractions of suitable volatility may be processed, such as light straight-run naphtha, product from hydrocrackers, raffinate from extraction of aromatics from reformate, etc. The Shell Hysomer process, introduced in 1970, is representative (Minachev & Isakov 1976; Bolton 1976). It is described in further detail by Kouwenhoven and van Zijil Langhout (1971). In this process unconverted n-paraffins in the product are removed by adsorption in a shape-selective molecular sieve, desorbed by stripping with hydrogen, and recycled to the isomerization reactor. This allows total conversion of the original feed. Asselin et al. (1972) review catalysts, mechanisms, and processes and refer to earlier reviews for more details.

During and after World War II the isomerization of n-butane to isobutane was carried out in a large number of plants to supply isobutane for alkylation with C_4 olefins to synthesize high-octane components for gasoline. This process originally used Friedel-Crafts-type catalysts, such as $AlCl_3$ or chlorided alumina, but these were superseded in the 1960s by the use of platinum on acidic supports very similar to those used in reforming and C_5-C_6 paraffin isomerization.

A widely used process for C_4 isomerization was developed by UOP and termed by them *Butamer*, and a similar process was developed by BP. Typical operating conditions are 150 to 200°C and 1.5 to 3.0 MPa, and product composition was near equilibrium. With the increasing availability of isobutane from catalytic cracking, the C_4 isomerization processes gradually became uneconomic and by the 1980s were no longer being operated. However, by 1990 growing concerns about emissions of hydrocarbons to the atmosphere was leading to requirements for decreased volatility of gasolines and hence decreased use of n-butane. Simultaneously, the increased demand for isobutane for synthesis of MTBE will probably lead to a return in the near future to some commercial use of C_4 catalytic isomerization.

9.7.2 Xylene isomerization

A mixture of the xylene isomers and ethylbenzene is readily available as the C_8 aromatic fraction from catalytic reforming. An essentially equilibrium mixture of xylene isomers and benzene may also be made by disproportionation of toluene using, e.g., a ZSM-5 catalyst, but this process is of lesser importance commercially. p-Xylene is in high demand for conversion to terephthalic acid or methyl terephthalate, one of the two monomers combined in polyester polymers, used to make fiber, films, packaging materials, and containers. o-Xylene, used to make phthalic anhydride (Sec. 8.6.2) is of moderate but lesser interest. There is little demand for m-xylene. p-Xylene may be separated from the mixture of the three xylenes and ethylbenzene by a zeolite adsorption process (UOP Parex process) or by low-temperature fractional crystallization. The remaining stream can then be reacted catalytically to cause conversion to the equilibrium composition of the three xylenes.

Unlike paraffin isomerization, equilibrium here is not appreciably affected by temperature. An essentially equilibrium composition can be readily achieved at about 400°C using platinum/silica-alumina in the presence of hydrogen to minimize coke formation (Bolton 1976). A commercial process, used in the 1960s and 1970s based on this type of catalyst is Octafining (Uhlig and Pfefferle 1970), developed by Engelhard. Representative reaction conditions are about 430 to 480°C and 1 to 2 MPa.

Separating ethylbenzene from the mixture of xylenes by distillation is expensive, and the usefulness of xylene-isomerization catalysts has, to a considerable degree, rested on their ability to convert ethylbenzene in the mixture with xylenes to xylenes or other useful products. In the Octafining process, ethylbenzene was converted to xylenes by a reaction that seems to involve the formation of ethylcyclohexane as an intermediate. Silica-alumina alone will cause isomerization of the xylenes to occur, but not conversion of ethylbenzene. In the absence of platinum and hydrogen, carbonaceous deposits build up rapidly.

In the mid 1970s this catalyst gradually was replaced by catalysts based on the medium-pore zeolite ZSM-5 [Mobil, see Chen and Garwood (1986)], or borosilicate molecular sieves [Amoco, see Kutz (1988)] that appear to provide a higher yield and more valuable by-products. The borosilicate catalysts are somewhat less active than those based on ZSM-5 and are optimally used at somewhat different temperatures and hydrogen partial pressures.

A product molecular-sieving effect does not seem to be very significant with respect to xylene isomerization with either catalyst since the xylene isomer distribution in the product is essentially that for equilibrium. However, the zeolite pore size does affect the distribution of by-products, as shown by comparison with zeolites of substantially different pore sizes. The by-product distribution is somewhat different for the two catalysts, and this is also affected by the degree of purity of the feedstock and the nature of impurities. For some applications the hydrogen functionality is increased by incorporating a small amount of a nonnoble metal into the catalyst.

All the foregoing processes operate in the vapor phase. A liquid-phase process using a zeolite ZSM-5 catalyst has been described but does not appear to have been commercialized, perhaps because of insufficient activity for conversion of ethylbenzene.

9.8 Molybdenum Sulfide Catalysts

Molybdenum sulfide catalysts first became of technical interest in the 1920s in conjunction with high-pressure hydrogenation processes for liquefaction of coals. Immediately preceding and during World War II, sulfide catalysts began to be applied to petroleum processing, initially in catalytic hydrodesulfurization for sulfur removal. Subsequent applications include removal of nitrogen by *hydrodenitrogenation* (HDN), *hydrodemetallization* (HDM), to remove vanadium and nickel, *hydrodeoxygenation* (HDO), and hydrogenation.

Each of these groups of reactions will be discussed separately. Because of the complex mixture of compounds present in most fuels processing, more than one of these categories of reactions usually occurs simultaneously. Hydrodesulfurization has been the most intensively studied, and the HDS of thiophene and thiophene derivatives has been frequently used as model compound reactions. Molybdenum sulfide is usually promoted with cobalt or nickel and almost always supported on γ-Al_2O_3. In industrial catalysts the weight ratio, usually expressed in terms of MoO_3 to CoO, is usually about 3 to 4. Tungsten sulfides, promoted with cobalt or nickel have also been used industrially for decades, but to a lesser extent, possibly in part because of the greater cost of tungsten compared with molybdenum. Tungsten acts in an analogous fashion to molybdenum. Cobalt-molybdenum catalysts have undergone intensive scrutiny, but many aspects of their structure and mechanism of action are still uncertain.

$CoMo/Al_2O_3$ and $NiMo/Al_2O_3$ catalysts are usually made by impregnation of γ-Al_2O_3 with an aqueous solution of ammonium molybdate and cobalt (or nickel) nitrate. This precursor is dried and calcined, which converts the molybdenum to MoO_3. Before use the MoO_3 is transformed into MoS_2 by treatment with a mixture of H_2S and H_2 or a feed containing sulfur compounds and H_2. The resulting molybdenum catalyst is almost completely sulfided. If the precursor is first reduced (to MoO_2), it is much more difficult to sulfide, and considerable oxygen may remain in the catalyst. Such a catalyst may be considerably less active than a properly sulfided catalyst and may show different reaction selectivity. This precaution should be taken into account when evaluating the literature. The oxide precursor is usually sulfided in situ, but catalyst may also be supplied by the manufacturer presulfided, which reduces downtime and simplifies startup. The cobalt-molybdenum catalysts are largely used when emphasis is on hydrodesulfurization.

MoS_2 has a layered structure with weak interactions between the sulfur atoms in adjacent layers. (MoS_2 is an excellent lubricant.) Most of the cobalt is adsorbed onto the edges of the MoS_2 crystallites or is present as Co_9S_8 crystallites on the support. The former structure is usually referred to as the Co-Mo-S phase, and this is believed to be the principal active site. Some cobalt can also occupy tetrahedral sites in the γ-Al_2O_3 lattice, but this is presumably inactive. A high cobalt-molybdenum ratio and high sulfidation temperature favor formation of Co_9S_8.

Cobalt in the Co-Mo-S structure acts as a chemical promoter, possibly by improving hydrogen adsorption. However, the situation is somewhat confused since cobalt sulfide and nickel sulfide are comparable in activity for HDS to that of MoS_2. (Nickel sulfide is used commercially as a hydrogenation catalyst). A principal barrier to a better understanding of these catalysts is the lack of a suitable method for determining their active surface area.

A review by Prins et al. (1989) discusses the evidence for structure and promoter function in cobalt-molybdenum HDS catalysts. Chianelli (1985) has made detailed studies of the trends of activity of the various transition metal sulfides for the HDS of dibenzothiophene (DBT). He presents correlations of activity with respect to position in the periodic table, heat of formation of the sulfide, number of d electrons, etc. H. Topsøe and coworkers have been responsible for much of the evidence for the importance of the Co-Mo-S-type structure in HDS. Their work and related work are discussed in a review by Topsøe and Clausen (1985). See also a review by Topsøe et al. (1984) and a symposium edited by Occelli and Anthony (1989).

Although there appear to be strong interactions between the cobalt-molybdenum sulfides and an Al_2O_3 support, the promoting effect of cobalt (or nickel) on MoS_2 does not require the presence of γ-Al_2O_3. Cobalt-molybdenum has a much weaker interaction with a silica support than an alumina support, which suggests that three-dimensional MoS_2 crystallites would then be favored. A cobalt-molybdenum catalyst supported on silica is used in a Shell residue hydroconversion process (Sec. 9.15). Use of carbon as a catalyst support has received considerable attention, as reviewed by Abotsi and Scaroni (1989). Such catalysts may have high HDS activity and have been of some industrial interest as possibly allowing an inexpensive method of recovering heavy metals from spent catalyst by a simple combustion process. However, no commercial use of such a catalyst seems to have been reported.

Keely et al. (1985) compare several variations on effect of CoMo/ Al_2O_3 catalyst preparation methods on HDS activity for a light cycle oil. They found that a cobalt-ammonia carbonate is preferred to cobalt nitrate (the latter however is cheaper). There was no appreciable difference between use of ammonium molybdate (2.5 NH_3/MoO_3) and ammonium heptamolybdate.

Industrially, a solution containing both cobalt and molybdenum, or nickel and molybdenum is usually used for simultaneous impregnation. Frequently some phosphoric acid is also added, which can have several desirable effects, especially with nickel-molybdenum. Phosphate stabilizes the impregnating solution and, upon impregnation, converts the Al_2O_3 surface to a (basic) aluminum phosphate. Coke formation tends to be suppressed, which may be caused by a decrease in acidity. The phosphate apparently does not alter the Co-Mo-S (or Ni-Mo-S) structure but it makes the Al_2O_3 harder and may decrease sintering. Sequential impregnation of cobalt and molybdenum has sometimes been reported to yield an improved catalyst, but it is doubtful that the higher manufacturing cost can be justified in commercial operations.

The choice between a CoMo/Al_2O_3 catalyst versus a NiMo/Al_2O_3 catalyst involves several considerations. Cobalt-molybdenum is generally preferred for HDS activity; nickel-molybdenum for HDN and hydrogen uptake in processing unsaturated fuels. Examples of the latter are saturation of aromatics to improve cetane number, or hydrotreating a gas oil to make a feed to a fluid catalytic cracker or to improve thermal stability and color. However, nickel-molybdenum catalysts have substantial HDS activity and may be preferred for HDS when the feedstock contains substantial products from catalytic cracking. In some cases the decision between the two catalysts is based largely on a relative cost basis. A cobalt-nickel-molybdenum catalyst has also been used.

Literature. Earlier reviews on catalyst structure, reaction mechanisms, and kinetic models were published by Furimsky (1980), Ratnasamy and Sivasanker (1980), Mitchell (1981), by Schuit and Gates (1973), in a book by Gates et al. (1979), by Schuman and Shalit (1970), and by McKinley (1957). The book by Weisser and Landa (1973) gives a detailed treatment of sulfide catalysts and reactions catalyzed by them, with copious references. The nature of sulfur compounds in petroleum is summarized by Drushel (1970) and work over many years on characterization of sulfur in petroleum at the U.S. Bureau of Mines is summarized by Coleman et al. (1970). Moyes (1988) reviews theories of sulfide activity and hydrogen sorption by sulfide catalysts, but notes in conclusion that there is no simple relationship between hydrogen sorption and HDS activity. (See also the literature references at the end of Sec. 9.9, and 9.15)

9.9 Hydrodesulfurization (HDS)

The sulfur content of a crude oil varies greatly with its origin. The highly paraffinic crudes from North Africa (Libya, Algeria) and from Nigeria and Indonesia may contain as little as 0.2 wt % sulfur and a very low metal content (e.g. ~3 ppm). In the Near East a light Arabian crude may contain typically 1.5 wt % sulfur; and a Kuwait crude, 2.5 to 4 wt % sulfur. The metal contents are of the order of 10 to 30 ppm. Midcontinent U.S. crudes may vary from 0.2 to 2.5 wt % sulfur. Heavy crudes, having a large nonvolatile fraction, are usually high in sulfur content and may also have a relatively high metal content. Thus, Venezuelan crude oils typically contain 2 to 4 wt % sulfur, and as much as 400 to 500 ppm of metals.

The sulfur content increases progressively with the boiling point of the fraction, as illustrated in Table 9.5 for Kuwait crude. The metals are found almost entirely in the residuum and greatly complicate HDS processes applied to a residuum. Deposits are formed inside catalyst pores or on the outside surfaces of catalyst pellets, which ultimately cause plugging and catalyst deactivation.

The sulfur content of petroleum fractions must be reduced for a variety of reasons:

1. The maximum acceptable sulfur content in the feed to a catalytic reformer is determined by the nature of the catalyst. Bimetallic reforming catalysts are especially sensitive, and the sulfur content must be limited to the vicinity of 1 ppm or less.

TABLE 9.5 Variation of Sulfur Content of a Kuwait Crude Oil With Boiling Point

Fraction; boiling point range, °C (°F)	Sulfur content, wt %
Naphtha; C_4-150 (300)	0.02
Kerosene; 150–230 (300–450)	0.175
Furnace oil; 230–345 (450–650)	1.23
Heavy furnace oil; 345–370 (650–700)	2.37
Heavy gas oil; 350–550 (660–1020)	2.91
Residue; >370 (700)	4.22
Residue; >550 (1020)	5.12

SOURCE: F. W. B. Porter el al., British Patent 710,342, in Schuman and Shalit (1970), p. 293.

2. Air-pollution-control standards require removal of, in some cases, 80 percent or more of the sulfur otherwise present in various fuel oils.

3. Much of the sulfur in a gas oil fed to a catalytic cracker may be deposited in the form of coke, the sulfur content of which is converted to sulfur dioxide in the regenerator and emitted to the atmosphere in the combustion gases. To limit air pollution from this source, the sulfur content of the gas oil may be reduced before being fed to the catalytic cracking unit.

4. The organosulfur content of the feed to a hydrocracker must be reduced to avoid poisoning of the hydrocracking catalyst.

5. Reduction of sulfur content reduces corrosion during refining and handling and improves the odor of the product.

The process used for this purpose is catalytic treatment with hydrogen to convert the various sulfur compounds present to hydrogen sulfide.* The hydrogen sulfide is readily separated and converted to elemental sulfur, a convenient form for handling, by the Claus process. Here some of the hydrogen sulfide is oxidized to sulfur dioxide by air, and sulfur is formed by the overall reaction:

$$2H_2S + SO_2 \rightarrow 3S \downarrow + 2H_2O \tag{9.1}$$

The usual catalyst is a form of alumina. Grancher (1978) discussed reaction kinetics and the process.

Interest in hydrodesulfurization was initially stimulated by the availability of hydrogen from catalytic reformers. However, the demand for hydrogen for hydrodesulfurization and hydrotreating now often outstrips that available in a given refinery, and it must then be generated specifically for these purposes. Under a suitable set of circumstances, sufficient hydrogen may be formed from dehydrogenation side reactions in the hydrodesulfurization reactor, and this can be continuously recycled back to the inlet. An example occurs with a charge stock that is high in naphthenes, low in olefins, and operated under conditions such that considerable dehydrogenation of naphthenes to aromatics also occurs (e.g., Autofining, a British Petroleum process).

During hydrodesulfurization a number of other hydrogenation reac-

---

*Sulfur compounds may also be removed by adsorption on a bed of zinc oxide, which is thereby converted to zinc sulfide. The maximum reaction temperature is about 400°C, limited by side reactions of the feedstock being treated. Only those sulfur compounds that are readily decomposed thermally to H_2S can be removed. This includes mercaptans and disulfides, but most sulfides and all thiophenes are relatively stable at the maximum temperature of operation. The spent zinc oxide is not regenerated, and the process is only practicable for removal of traces of sulfur.

tions occur—some desired and some not desired. Diolefins are readily hydrogenated, which improves the stability of the product and reduces gum formation. The nitrogen content may also be somewhat reduced by hydrodenitrogenation, which occurs simultaneously with HDS (see Sec. 9.10). Basic nitrogen compounds inhibit the catalytic cracking reaction by adsorption on acid sites, and they accelerate the formation of coke. This is an additional reason for hydrogen pretreatment of the gas oil feed to a catalytic cracker. Multiring aromatic compounds will not crack significantly, so hydrogenation of one or more of these rings is also desirable before the feedstock goes to a catalytic cracker. The single-ring aromatics that are particularly desirable for gasoline are thus obtained in the product. For such a product, minimizing the hydrogenation of monoolefins and of aromatics in the feed is desirable in order not to reduce octane number. This goal can usually be accomplished by careful control of temperature and pressure.

Hydrogen is expensive to manufacture, so all hydrodesulfurization and hydrotreating processes are operated to optimize the desired reactions yet minimize hydrogen consumption. Operating conditions may vary substantially with the particular distillate fraction to be treated. A *straight-run* or *virgin fraction* (that separated from crude oil by distillation only) may have a substantially different chemical composition than a fraction of the same boiling-point range that has been subjected previously to chemical reaction, such as catalytic cracking.

For low-boiling-point and middle-boiling-point distillates (up to about 350°C), representative HDS reaction conditions are about 300 to 400°C, and 0.7 to 5 MPa hydrogen pressure. The higher the boiling point of the feedstock, the higher is the sulfur content (Table 9.5) and the less reactive are the sulfur compounds present. More severe conditions (higher temperature and pressure and longer contact time) are then needed. Combinations of high pressure (for example, 7 MPa) and low temperature (for example, 300°C) are generally avoided, if possible, to minimize excessive consumption of hydrogen. Usually a considerable excess of hydrogen over that needed stoichiometrically is fed to the reactor inlet, and the hydrogen remaining in the exit gases is recycled to the inlet (with some purge to remove product gases and impurities in the hydrogen).

Hydrodesulfurization and hydrogenation reactions are exothermic. Most reactors are adiabatic fixed beds and may be multistage. Cooling is usually provided by injecting additional hydrogen between the stages, termed *cold-shot cooling*. The feed at reaction conditions may be all vapor, mixed vapor and liquid, or essentially all liquid. In the latter two cases the liquid is usually caused to flow concurrently downward with the gas through a fixed catalyst bed, termed a *trickle-bed reactor*.

Alternately, for reaction of a heavy or residual oil, the "H-oil" or "L-C fining" process has been used in a few installations. Liquid and hydrogen gas are passed upwards through an ebullating bed of small catalyst particles. This process minimizes accumulation of solid deposits on the outside surface of catalyst particles, e.g., vanadium and nickel compounds from residual oils; provides good temperature control; and provides a convenient method of removing working catalyst and continuously adding new catalyst.

The sulfur is present largely in the form of thiols (mercaptans), sulfides, disulfides, and various thiophenes and thiophene derivatives. Mercaptans and sulfides react to form hydrogen sulfide and hydrocarbons.

$$RSSR' + H_2 \rightarrow RH + R'H + H_2S \qquad (9.2)$$

$$RSH + H_2 \rightarrow RH + H_2S \qquad (9.3)$$

$$RSR' + 2H_2 \rightarrow RH + R'H + H_2S \qquad (9.4)$$

where R and R' are various hydrocarbon groups.

The order of reactivity is about RSH > R—S—S—R' > R—S—R' > thiophenes. Reactivity decreases with increased molecular size and varies depending on whether R is an aliphatic or aromatic group. Among thiophene derivatives, reactivity under industrial conditions decreases in about the following order: thiophene > benzothiophene ≃ dibenzothiophene > alkyl-substituted benzothiophenes. The alkyl thiophenes are in general less reactive than thiophene, but there is considerable variation with location of the alkyl group. Methyl groups in the 2 and 5 position cause the greatest inhibition, presumably by steric effects.

The main reaction pathway for thiophene is:

$$\text{(thiophene ring)} + 3H_2 \longrightarrow H_2S + C_4H_8 \quad \text{(mixed isomers)} \qquad (9.5)$$

Small amounts of butadiene are formed, possibly as an intermediate, but this is rapidly hydrogenated to a butene. The butenes in turn are more slowly hydrogenated to butane. The thiophene ring is not hydrogenated before sulfur is removed, although the first step may involve an essentially simultaneous removal of a sulfur atom and donation of two hydrogen atoms to the structure. Thiophane (the completely hydrogenated analogue of thiophene) is found in small amounts in the absence of basic nitrogen compounds. In their presence, little or no thiophane is observed (Satterfield et al. 1980). Thiophane may be formed by a side reaction, but, in any event, it is much more reactive than thiophene.

A kinetic study of thiophene hydrodesulfurization at atmospheric pressure and 235 to 265°C on a commercial $CoMo/Al_2O_3$ catalyst in a differential reactor (Satterfield & Roberts 1968) showed that the reaction is inhibited by hydrogen sulfide. The rate could be expressed by a Langmuir-Hinshelwood-type expression as follows:

$$-r = \frac{kP_TP_H}{(1 + K_TP_T + K_SP_S)^2} \tag{9.6}$$

The subscript T refers to thiophene, S to hydrogen sulfide, and H to hydrogen.) This and other studies indicate that the hydrodesulfurization and subsequent hydrogenation reactions occur on separate sites. In a power-law expression, the HDS reaction appears to be between half and first order with respect to hydrogen at pressures above atmospheric. It is severely inhibited by basic nitrogen compounds.

In the case of benzothiophene, substituted or unsubstituted, the thiophene ring is hydrogenated to the thiophane derivative before the sulfur atom is removed, in contrast to the behavior of thiophene.

$$\tag{9.7}$$

Other steps may also be involved in the reaction network. As with thiophene, methyl substitution reduces reactivity.

Dibenzothiophene reacts primarily to form biphenyl, plus smaller amounts of phenylcyclohexane.

$$\tag{9.8}$$

The aforementioned products are typical of those found in industrial processing. Biphenyl may be hydrogenated further to phenylcyclohexane, but there is good evidence that some phenylcyclohexane is formed as an initial reaction product. Again, other steps of lesser importance or involving transitory intermediates should be considered in a detailed reaction network (Broderick et al. 1980).

Thiophene and dibenzothiophene have been used extensively as model compounds for characterization of HDS reactions. Vrinat (1983) lists the various kinetic expressions that have been published for these two reactions, as well as the lesser amount of information on benzothiophene.

All the hydrodesulfurization reactions are essentially irreversible under most industrial conditions, although if extremely low sulfur content (e.g., less than 1 ppm) is desired, this may be limited by thermodynamic considerations. Thus, a minimum sulfur content may be set by a reaction of the type:

$$RCH{=}R'CH + H_2S \rightleftharpoons \text{mercaptans} + H_2 \tag{9.9}$$

Such a reaction is exothermic and is shifted to the right by lower temperatures.

The HDS catalyst is almost always $CoMo/Al_2O_3$, sometimes $NiMo/Al_2O_3$ (see Sec. 9.8), which is sulfided before use. The ratio of molybdenum to cobalt is always considerably greater than 1, a representative composition being 3 wt % CoO and 12 wt % MoO_3.

Catalytic hydrodesulfurization is reviewed by Gates et al. (1979) and Grange (1980). Desulfurization of heavy oils and residua is the subject of a book by Speight (1981). Kinetics and chemistry are reviewed by Zdražil (1982) and Vrinat (1983). See also the references at the end of Sec. 9.8.

The term *sweetening process* is applied to any of a variety of methods for removing objectionable odors from various petroleum products. The odors are caused primarily by mercaptans. These may be removed by extractive or adsorptive processes or by catalytic air oxidation in the liquid phase to form disulfides, which are innocuous. The patent literature indicates that supported metal phthalocyanines are effective, such as cobalt phthalocyanine on a carbon support. Other methods of sulfur removal are discussed in Sec. 10.1.4.

9.10   Hydrodenitrogenation (HDN)

Organonitrogen compounds are present in smaller concentrations in crude oil than are sulfur compounds. The weight ratio of nitrogen to sulfur varies from about 1:2 in some high-nitrogen crudes to between 1:5 and 1:10 in other crudes. A high-nitrogen California crude may contain about 0.9 wt % nitrogen and a Caribbean crude about 0.4 wt % nitrogen (together with 2.5 to 4.0 wt % sulfur), but in many crude oils the nitrogen content is in the vicinity of 0.1 wt %. Some of the organonitrogen compounds are converted to ammonia during hydrodesulfurization, but the nitrogen compounds are in general less reactive. Thus, desulfurization of a Caribbean heavy fraction to reduce the sulfur content from 4 to 1 wt % might typically lower the nitrogen content from 0.4 wt % to about 0.25 wt %. As with sulfur compounds, the nitrogen content of distillate fractions increases with boiling point.

Nitrogen reduction is required mostly to minimize catalyst poisoning in subsequent processing. Nitrogen compounds, especially those that are basic, can be a major source of coke formation in catalytic cracking, and they are strong poisons for acid functionality in this and other types of catalysts as well. Nitrogen reduction may also be needed to meet product specifications such as stability. With heavier fuels such as burner oils it may be necessary to meet NO_x emission standards upon combustion. Also some multiring N-heterocyclics may have carcinogenic activity.

The nature of nitrogen and oxygen compounds in petroleum is summarized by Snyder (1970). In crude oils, nitrogen is present largely in the form of heterocyclic compounds having five-membered pyrollic rings or six-membered pyridinic rings. The nonheterocyclic compounds include anilines, nitriles, and aliphatic amines. The last type undergo HDN readily and therefore are of little concern in industrial HDN.

Crude shale oil is produced from oil shale by thermal retorting, which decomposes the less stable nitrogen compounds and yields a product typically containing about 1 wt % nitrogen in the naphtha fraction and about 2 wt % nitrogen total. More than two-thirds of these are N-heterocyclics. Oxygen compounds are present in amounts of 1 wt % oxygen or more, and sulfur compounds are about 1 wt %. Both are distributed more or less uniformly through the boiling-point range, in contrast to the distribution found in natural crude oils. The pyridinic compounds (quinolines, pyridines, acridines) are strong bases, whereas pyrollic compounds (indoles, pyrroles, carbazoles) are weak bases or nonbasic. (See Table 9.6)

Less is known about the hydrodenitrogenation of heterocyclic nitrogen compounds than of the analogous reactions with heterocyclic sulfur compounds. In general, the heterocyclic ring must first be saturated before ring fracture at a C—N bond can occur. Nitrogen is removed from the resulting amine or aniline as ammonia. Aliphatic amines react readily, but aromatic amines are less reactive. With pyridine, the ring is first hydrogenated to piperidine, which forms, in turn, pentylamine and pentane plus ammonia (McIlvried 1971).

$$\text{(pyridine)} \xrightarrow{+3H_2} \text{(piperidine)} \xrightarrow{+H_2} C_5H_{11}NH_2 \xrightarrow{+H_2} C_5H_{12} + NH_3 \quad (9.10)$$

TABLE 9.6   Representative Heterocyclic Nitrogen Compounds

Name	Formula	Structure
Pyrrole	C_4H_5N	
Indole	C_8H_7N	
Carbazole	$C_{12}H_9N$	
Pyridine	C_5H_5N	
Quinoline	C_9H_7N	
Acridine	$C_{13}H_9N$	

On a nickel-molybdenum catalyst, which accelerates hydrogenation reactions, the first step can proceed to a nearly equilibrium concentration of piperidine (Satterfield & Cocchetto 1975; Satterfield et al. 1980). Hence, with increased temperature, the overall HDN rate can go through a maximum, as has been observed at 1.1 MPa. At the higher hydrogen pressures of usual industrial interest, however, this may not be observed.

Most model compound HDN studies have been restricted to the six-membered heterocyclic compounds, particularly pyridine, alkyl pyridines, and quinoline. Quinoline HDN has been studied in some detail at pressures and temperatures of industrial relevance on a sulfided $NiMo/Al_2O_3$ industrial catalyst. Its reaction network, shown in Fig. 9.5, illustrates the complexity of this representative reaction (Satterfield & Cocchetto 1981). Several features bear comment:

1. Hydrogenation of the heterocyclic ring is required before nitrogen removal can occur. (This has been shown for all heterocyclic com-

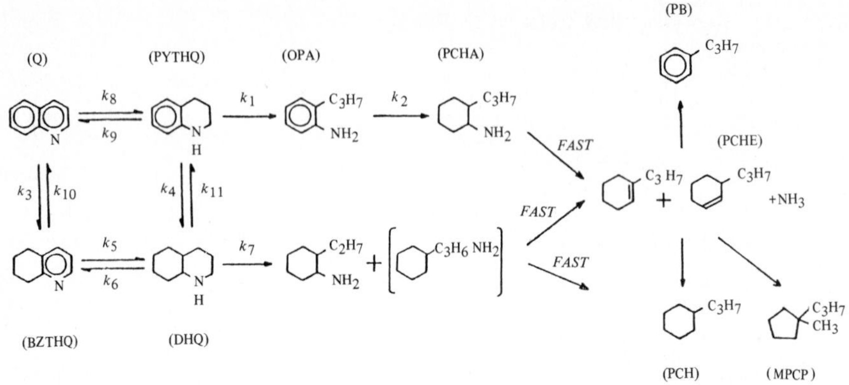

(PB)

(Q)   (PYTHQ)   (OPA)   (PCHA)

k_8, k_9 ... k_1 ... C$_3$H$_7$, NH$_2$ ... k_2 ... C$_3$H$_7$, NH$_2$ ... FAST ... C$_3$H$_7$ (PCHE)

k_3 | k_{10} ... k_4 | k_{11} ... FAST ... C$_3$H$_7$ + C$_3$H$_7$ +NH$_3$

k_5, k_6 ... k_7 ... C$_2$H$_7$, NH$_2$ + [C$_3$H$_6$ NH$_2$] ... FAST ... C$_3$H$_7$ ... C$_3$H$_7$, CH$_3$

(BZTHQ)   (DHQ)   (PCH)   (MPCP)

Q	Quinoline
PyTHQ	Py (or 1,2,3,4)-tetrahydroquinoline
BzTHQ	Bz (or 5,6,7,8)-tetrahydroquinoline
DHQ	Decahydroquinoline (cis and trans isomers)
OPA	o-propylaniline
PCHA	propylcyclohexylamine
PB	propylbenzene
PCHE	propylcyclohexene (1,1 or 1,2)
PCH	propylcyclohexane
MPCP	1,1-methylopropylcyclopentane

Figure 9.5 Reaction network for the hydrodenitrogenation of quinoline. (*Satterfield and Cocchetto 1981. Reprinted with permission from the American Chemical Society.*)

pounds studied.) Hydrogenation of quinoline, Q, to PyTHQ occurs so rapidly that the two compounds are in essential equilibrium. The rate of hydrogenation of quinoline, Q, to BzTHQ is much slower, even though there are some indications that BzTHQ may be thermodynamically more stable than PyTHQ.

2. All the reactions among the two-ring compounds are potentially reversible, as has been shown by studies with the individual compounds.

3. The main reaction path is from quinoline to PyTHQ to DHQ under typical reaction conditions, but the route through OPA may become more important at lower hydrogen pressures.

4. OPA by itself is more reactive than the other heterocyclic nitrogen compounds present, but in a mixture with them it becomes relatively unreactive. OPA is relatively nonbasic and is not readily adsorbed onto the catalyst in the presence of the heterocyclics, which are strongly basic.

5. An important intermediate in the downstream reaction is propylcyclohexene (PCHE), which may be either dehydrogenated to propylbenzene or hydrogenated to propylcyclohexane (PCH). The dominant product is PCH, and this is favored under equilibrium conditions.

A detailed study of the kinetics of this reaction showed that some of the reaction intermediates are more strongly adsorbed than either quinoline or final products, and it is necessary to take this into account in formulating a suitable rate expression. (See Sec. 9.14.)

The overall reaction network is seen to be a complex of hydrogenation and hydrogenolysis reactions. With quinoline, the hydrogenation reactions at representative conditions seem to proceed more rapidly than the hydrogenolysis reactions, but the latter generally have higher activation energies and therefore become less rate-limiting at higher temperatures. The fact that the nitrogen ring must be saturated before nitrogen removal can occur can lead to some confusion in interpreting model compound studies because considerable hydrogen may be taken up before any actual HDN occurs. Also, one must distinguish between degree of disappearance of a starting compound and complete conversion of all nitrogen compounds.

In industrial hydroprocessing, H_2S is almost invariably present. It has been shown to increase the HDN of pyridine (Satterfield et al. 1975), presumably by increasing catalyst acidity. Likewise H_2S produces a significant increase in the HDN of quinoline, caused by an increase in the rate of the acid-catalyzed (hydrogenolysis) reactions in the network and decrease in their activation energy. H_2S has little effect on the hydrogenation-dehydrogenation reactions (Satterfield & Gültekin 1981; Yang & Satterfield 1983, 1984). Water vapor also increases the HDN rate of quinoline, but its effect is much less than that of H_2S and is scarcely noticeable in the presence of H_2S (Satterfield & Smith 1986).

Fewer studies have been reported on five-membered nitrogen heterocyclic compounds, largely because of experimental difficulties. These compounds are less stable thermally and have very low solubilities in liquids that can be used to carry them into the reactor. Indole has been studied the most. The sequence of reactions involves saturation of the heterocyclic ring to form indoline, followed by C—N bond hydrogenolysis to form o-ethyl aniline.

Several precautions should be noted in evaluating model compound studies of HDN. Use of nonsulfided catalysts gives unrepresentative results; indeed, a minimum partial pressure of H_2S is required even with sulfided catalysts to obtain maximum catalyst activity and reaction behavior representative of industrial conditions. In practice, sufficient sulfur is usually present to maintain the catalyst in the fully sulfided condition. Behavior of mixtures can be far different from that of single compounds, because of competitive adsorption effects. Pulse-type reactors here as elsewhere can give misleading results. Reaction characteristics at atmospheric pressure are far different from those under industrial conditions.

More details on HDN may be found in the recent reviews by Ho (1988) and Ledoux (1988) and an earlier review by Katzer and

Sivasubramian (1979). Hydrodenitrogenation is seldom carried out as a separate process, but is one in the overall set of complex reactions that can occur in catalytic hydrotreating.

9.11   Hydrodeoxygenation (HDO)

Oxygenated compounds are present in only small concentrations in petroleum, but increase in concentration with boiling point. Little is known about the structure of these higher-molecular-weight substances. The lower-molecular-weight molecules are mostly carboxylic acids and phenols which are readily removed in any hydrogenation treatment. Some of them tend to cause foaming, but except for this phenomenon, oxygen content here is of little concern.

In liquid fuels derived from coal, shale, tar sands, or biomass, however, substantial quantities of oxygenated organic compounds may be present. Some of these compounds can cause corrosion and fuel instability, but it is not clear that oxygen content as such needs to be reduced for other reasons. A detailed analysis of a representative liquid fuel from coal is given in a series of papers by Gates and coworkers (1983–1986). Oxygen is present largely as phenolic and furan derivatives, but some of the heterocyclics present contain both oxygen and nitrogen in the same molecule, such as in hydroxypyridines and hydroxyanilines.

Less information is available on model oxygenated compound reactives than for sulfur and nitrogen compounds. Those studies available are mostly on phenol and its derivatives, benzofuran and dibenzofuran. Some of these were performed at atmospheric pressure, under which conditions the reaction network is considerably different from that at industrial pressures. The subject is reviewed by Furimsky (1983).

The HDO reactions of an alkyl phenol or benzofuran are quite similar to the reactions of analogous compounds containing nitrogen, namely an alkyl aniline and indole. C—O bonds and C—N bonds are of similar strength, and resonance energies of R—Ar—OH and R—Ar—NH$_2$ are about the same. The principal reaction networks for benzofuran and for o-ethyl phenol are shown in Fig. 9.6 (Lee & Ollis 1984). With o-ethyl phenol, the benzene ring is first saturated. It then undergoes hydrogenolysis to form H$_2$O and ethyl cyclohexenes, which then react as in the HDN reaction. Benzofuran forms 2,3-dihydrobenzofuran, which is converted to o-ethyl phenol, which in turn reacts as in the foregoing.

The HDO network of dibenzofuran (DBF) is shown in Fig. 9.7 (LaVopa & Satterfield 1987). This is based on studies on a sulfided

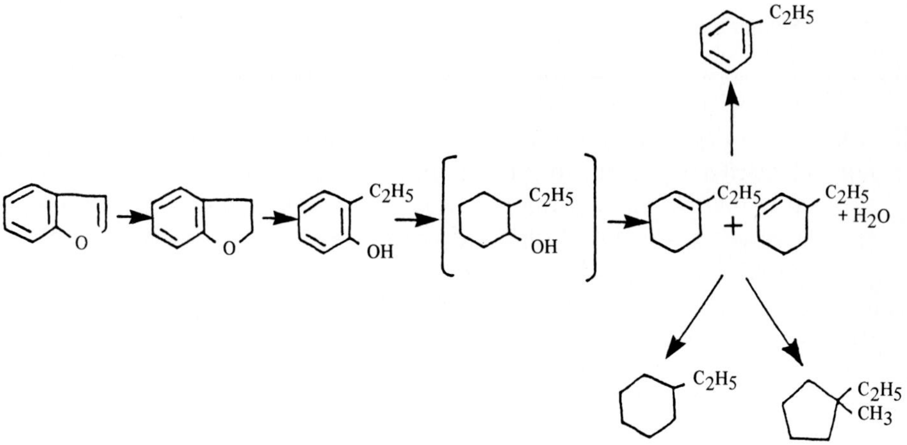

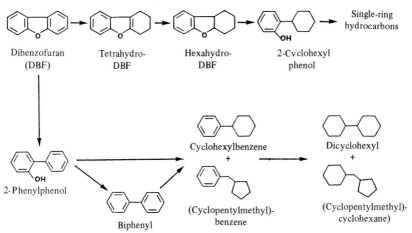

Figure 9.6 Reaction network for the hydrodeoxygenation of benzofuran. (*Adapted from Lee and Ollis 1984*)

Dibenzofuran (DBF)	Tetrahydro-DBF	Hexahydro-DBF	2-Cyclohexyl phenol	Single-ring hydrocarbons

2-Phenylphenol

Cyclohexylbenzene +

Biphenyl

(Cyclopentylmethyl)-benzene

Dicyclohexyl +

(Cyclopentylmethyl)-cyclohexane

Figure 9.7 Reaction network for the hydrodeoxygenation of dibenzofuran. (*La Vopa and Satterfield 1987. Reprinted with permission from* Energy and Fuels. *Copyright 1987 by American Chemical Society.*)

NiMo/Al$_2$O$_3$ catalyst at 350 to 390°C and 7.0 MPa. Two parallel reactions occur initially; the first is hydrogenation of a benzene ring in DBF that then proceeds through a series of intermediates to form single-ring hydrocarbons. The second is hydrogenolysis of DBF to form 2-phenyl phenol, which then reacts rapidly to form biphenyl and various double-ring compounds. The first reaction pathway was predominant under the conditions studied. All the oxygen-containing intermediates are more reactive than DBF.

9.12   Hydrodemetallation (HDM)

Crude oil contains small quantities of nickel and vanadium in the form of high-molecular-weight organometallic compounds. During distillation they become concentrated in the residual fraction. Practically none of them are present in the fraction of < 500°C and only a little in the 500 to 600°C fraction. Representative concentrations in the atmospheric residua are, e.g., 6 ppm Ni and 33 ppm V in that from light Arabian crude, 28 ppm Ni and 78 ppm V in heavy Arabian crude, to 114 ppm Ni and 387 ppm V in a representative Venezuelan crude (Quann et al. 1988).

A portion of the metals are present in the form of porphyrins, in which the metal atom is surrounded by four pyrrole-type rings. The nonporphyrinic structures comprise a wide variety of organometallic complexes. To a large extent these organometallic compounds are associated with asphaltenes in the residua, and HDM as practiced commercially is not a separate reaction but rather one of a group that includes HDS, HDN, and hydrogenation. Unlike the others, in HDM metals are deposited on the catalyst, in the form of sulfides, causing irreversible fouling so that catalyst replacement costs can be a major source of expense. High catalyst pore volume and an optimum pore size distribution assume considerable importance to obtain high metals loading before the catalyst becomes too inactive.

The catalyst usually is a supported molybdenum, but a number of reactor configurations provide for two-stage processing in which the first stage utilizes a cheap, sacrificial catalyst to provide high metals removal followed by a second stage utilizing a fairly conventional CoMo/Al$_2$O$_3$ or NiMo/Al$_2$O$_3$ catalyst for HDS and HDN. The deposited metals may themselves contribute considerable catalytic activity. This can be either desirable or undesirable, depending on circumstances.

Only a small number of model compound HDM studies of metal porphyrins have been reported, notably by Wei and coworkers. The first step is a reversible hydrogenation followed by a series of hydrogenation-hydrogenolysis reactions culminating in metal deposition. Further details on reaction kinetics and approaches to catalyst design are given in an extensive detailed review by Quann et al. (1988) and in a briefer review by Wei (1987) and Pereira et al. (1987). See also Sec. 9.15 on residua conversion.

9.13   Hydrocracking

Hydrocracking is a combination of catalytic cracking and hydrogenation and is carried out under substantial pressure. The hydrogen hydrogenates coke precursors on the catalyst and thereby minimizes the rate of coke formation such that a catalyst life of the order of a year or more can be achieved before regeneration is required. Hydrocracking processes were developed in Germany and in England in the 1930s to supply aviation gasoline for military purposes. The catalyst consisted of various metal sulfides such as tungsten sulfide, unsupported or supported. High pressures were required, over 20 MPa.

The continuing development of catalysts, including two-stage processes with two different types of catalysts, led to the appearance in the 1960s of dual-function catalysts. The balance between metallic function and acid function in these catalysts may be substantially varied, such that a variety of feedstocks can be processed, to produce a considerable variety of products. In the early 1960s the focus of attention was particularly on conversion of distillates in the 200 to 350°C range to gasoline. Later, emphasis was placed on the versatility of a particular process to be operated so as to maximize gasoline production in the summer and fuel oils in the winter.

Modern hydrocracking processes were developed primarily to process feeds having a high content of polycyclic aromatic compounds, which are relatively unreactive in catalytic cracking. These feeds include heavy vacuum-gas oils, deasphalted vacuum residuum, heavy gas oil from petroleum coking, and catalytic cycle oil. However, a great variety of situations may be encountered and the desired products can include lubricating oils, diesel fuel, and various chemicals, in addition to distillates of various boiling points and properties.

The reaction temperature is lower than that in catalytic cracking, in the range of 200 to 400°C, and the hydrogen pressure may vary from 1 to 10 MPa, depending on the feedstock and type of reactions desired. The minimum hydrogen pressure is usually set by that required to minimize the rate of coke formation, but too high a hydrogen pressure causes excessive hydrogen consumption. The excess reaction of hydrogen may also lower product quality, e.g., by converting aromatics to naphthenes, thereby lowering the octane number of a gasoline fraction.

A highly aromatic feed is generally needed to make a high-octane gasoline fraction directly from the hydrocracker. With feeds of lower aromaticity, the naphtha fraction of the product must generally be fed to a reformer to increase the octane number. In the usual hydrocracker operation, recycling is used to extinction; i.e., all the feed is eventually converted to a product boiling below a specified maximum temperature.

A variety of catalysts and processing designs may be used commercially depending on the feedstock and desired product. These are all dual-function catalysts, but in many cases a mechanical mixture of two monofunctional catalysts performs similarly.* The basic principle in catalyst design is to obtain a balance between hydrogen-transfer functionality and cracking functionality to achieve the desired slate of products without coke deposition. Excessive acidity tends to cause coking, but this can be overcome with higher hydrogenation functionality. Higher hydrogen pressure is, of course, also effective but has other disadvantages. Either a noble metal (usually palladium) or nonnoble metals may be used in a variety of combinations with various supports.

Representative are NiMo or NiW on silica-alumina of various Si/Al ratios, on a halogenated Al_2O_3 or on a zeolite. NiMo or NiW are more tolerant to sulfur compounds than is palladium, but are less active. Used on an amorphous support, they are representative compositions for mild hydrocracking and production of heavier distillates and lubricating-oil base stocks. NiMo on a zeolite can be more active and crack mainly to gasoline and jet fuel. Palladium on ultrastable zeolitic Y is used for manufacture of middle distillate fuel. By varying the palladium concentration the balance between, e.g., naphtha and turbine fuel can be controlled.

The noble-metal catalysts are poisoned by low concentrations of organosulfur and organonitrogen compounds, so the feedstocks are usually first fed to a hydrodesulfurizer (HDS) reactor in which these substances are converted to H_2S and NH_3, respectively. The zeolite catalysts can tolerate greater concentrations of H_2S and NH_3 than can silica-alumina, hence with their use, separating the NH_3 and H_2S formed in the desulfurizer from the remainder of the product before it is passed to the hydrocracker is usually unnecessary. This results in considerable cost savings. The non-noble metal catalysts must be kept in a sulfided state, so a minimum concentration of H_2S, e.g., of the order of 30 ppm, must be maintained in the reacting gases.

The degree of hydrocracking can be caused to vary over a wide range. Typically, 50 percent or more of the products are of a boiling-point range below that of the feed. At the other extreme, a mild hydrocracking may be caused to occur in what is otherwise essentially a hydrotreating process.

An unusual feature of hydrocracking is that there is essentially no limitation on the degree of reaction. Larger molecules continue to crack into smaller molecules. The overall reaction is exothermic, so reactor design must provide methods of monitoring temperature excur-

---

*Selective hydrocracking, in which the molecule fissions in the center, requires an acidic site. Hydrocracking at the end C—C bond to form CH_4 proceeds on platinum by itself (see Chap. 6), but the rate of this reaction is generally negligible under industrial conditions.

sions that might be preliminary to a runaway reaction, sometimes termed demethylation.

Vacuum gas oils from residuum upgrading processes are of increasing importance as hydrocracker feedstocks. They are more difficult to hydrocrack than the same fraction derived directly from crude, because of their higher content of polycyclic aromatic hydrocarbons (PAH), which are alkylated. Mono- and diaromatic structures predominate, but compounds containing up to five or six aromatic rings have been identified. In commercial operation, the product from the hydrocracker is usually distilled and the heavy fraction recycled.

Small amounts of higher-molecular-weight cyclic compounds containing up to 10 or more rings, of varying degrees of saturation, may be formed, and this can be of concern industrially. Depending on the catalyst, these compounds may be formed faster than they are hydrocracked, and thus they build up in the recycled stream. They may cause catalyst deactivation, but a more important problem may be their limited solubility. Thus they can deposit downstream on valves, heat exchangers, etc. A paper by Sullivan et al. (1989) gives detailed information on these various molecular transformations upon hydrocracking and hydrotreating.

The first hydrocracking process utilizing zeolites was commercialized by Union Oil and Exxon in 1964. Operating characteristics of a number of installations of this process are detailed by Bolton (1976). The chemical reactions occurring in hydrocracking are discussed in more detail by Langlois and Sullivan (1969). Reactions and processes are treated in a symposium chaired by Watkins and Hutchings (1972) and in a symposium organized by Ward and Qader (1975). Vlugter and Van'T Spijker (1971) review catalyst compositions for the hydrocracking of residua and distillates to produce a variety of products.

9.14 Interaction Effects

With mixtures of compounds, a variety of interactions can occur between starting substances; intermediates of appreciable stability, and H_2S, NH_3, and H_2O formed. H_2S keeps $CoMo/Al_2O_3$ or $NiMo/Al_2O_3$ in its fully sulfided form. High concentrations of H_2S above the minimum needed for this purpose also moderately increase the rate of acid-catalyzed reactions such as hydrogenolysis and isomerization. Water in the concentrations formed by HDO reactions has only slight effects, and these are overshadowed by that of H_2S. NH_3 as a base poisons acid sites, but other nitrogen compounds are usually much more strongly adsorbed. There are also many subtleties in these interactions too complex to be considered here.

The most marked effects are caused by the nitrogen compounds, which can inhibit HDS and HDO reactions as well as hydrogenation and hydrocracking. Inhibition by nitrogen compounds that are not sterically hindered can be correlated to their basicity as measured by proton affinity. In a recent study (La Vopa & Satterfield 1988), this correlation was shown for thiophene HDS in which the poisoning effect was expressed as an inhibition adsorption constant derived from Langmuir-Hinshelwood kinetics. These inhibitor adsorption constants correlated well with measures of inhibition of the HDO of dibenzofuran, even when the nitrogen compound underwent considerable reaction and when allowing for the inhibiting effects of reaction intermediates was necessary.

The correlation for thiophene inhibition versus proton affinity is shown in Fig. 9.8. The two nitrogen compounds below the correlating line are both sterically hindered. There is no correlation with volatility, which is plausible since boiling point is largely determined by rel-

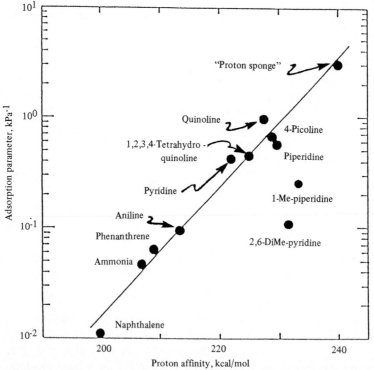

Figure 9.8 Adsorption parameters from thiophene rate measurements correlate with basicity of nitrogen compounds present, as measured by proton affinity. (*La Vopa and Satterfield 1988. Copyright J. Catalysis. Reprinted with permission from Academic Press.*)

atively weak van der Waals forces that are not involved in chemisorption. The order of adsorption strength for various nitrogen compounds derived here for thiophene HDS agrees generally with that reported for nitrogen poisoning of hydroprocessing catalysts and of acidic cracking catalysts.

The foregoing discussion shows that attempts to list various compounds in order of decreasing reactivity under hydrotreating conditions must be hedged with many qualifications. However, certain broad generalizations may be helpful. In real coal liquids, HDS > HDN > HDO is usually observed. In comparing analogous molecular structures, dibenzothiophene (DBT) > dibenzofuran (DBF) > (probably) acridine and carbazole. Compounds with analogous chemical structures have considerably different boiling points, e.g., that for DBT is 332°C; for DBF, 287°C; and for acridine and carbazole, 345 and 355°C. Since feedstocks are separated by volatility, within a particular distilled fraction oxygenated compounds tend to have a higher average molecular weight than sulfur compounds, and these in turn will be higher than that of nitrogen compounds. Thus, from a technical point of view, one may wish to compare the reactivity of quinoline more closely with that of dibenzofuran than with benzofuran.

Bearing in mind these various limitations, a list of relative reactivities in a model compound mixture published by Rollman (1977) is helpful (Table 9.7.). These were obtained by starting with a standard feed comprising nine components in nearly molar ratios. Heterocyclics were represented by dibenzothiophene, quinoline, and dibenzofuran. The others were mostly various aromatic hydrocarbons. Systematically, each of the heterocyclic compounds was replaced, one at a time, with another heterocyclic compound containing the same characteristic element, e.g., quinoline by indole or o-ethylaniline. The change in reactivity was calculated assuming first-order kinetics and expressed in an arbitrary scale relative to the rate of hydrogenation of naphthalene to tetralin.

9.15   Conversion of Residua and Heavy Oils

Residua, and especially vacuum residua, in the past have usually been fed to a thermal coking unit or blended with lighter oils to produce fuel oil. More recently, processing low-quality heavy crude oils and various residual fractions into transportation fuels—motor gasoline, diesel and jet fuels—has been increasingly economical. These feedstocks have a much lower hydrogen-carbon ratio than the desired products, so overall carbon rejection or hydrogen addition is necessary. A variety of processes are commercial or nearly so. Carbon may

TABLE 9.7   Relative Reactivities of Selected
Heterocyclic Compounds

Compound	Structure	Reactivity
Dibenzofuran		0.4
Indole		0.9
2, 3 Benzofuran		1.0
o-Ethylaniline		1.1
o-Ethylphenol		1.2
Quinoline		1.3
2-Phenylphenol		1.4
Benzothiophene		3.4
Dibenzothiophene		3.6
p-Cresol		5.2

be concentrated into a residual by-product by thermal reactions, such as visbreaking or delayed coking, that produce lower-molecular-weight liquids, or the crude may be deasphalted. Alternately, by catalytic hydrotreating, much of the feedstock is converted directly into oil products. Various combinations of thermal, catalytic, and gasification processes may also be used. If the residuum has a low metal content (e.g., < ~30 ppm), low nitrogen content (e.g., < ~2000 ppm), and Ramsbottom carbon (see the following) of about 5 wt % or less, subjection to a catalytic cracker may be practical. (The asphalt fraction can be coked or blended into a high-sulfur fuel oil.)

The definition of a heavy oil is somewhat arbitrary, but typically 20 to 70 percent of the contents remain in the nonvolatile residue after atmospheric distillation. Sulfur content typically ranges from 3 to 6 wt %, and nitrogen up to 1 wt %. Metals (nickel and vanadium) content can range up to several hundred parts per million. Asphaltenes can comprise up to 30 percent of the residua. Heavy oils, bitumens, and residua are also frequently characterized by a carbon residue content. This content is measured by an empirical test in which a sample is heated in a loosely closed container at a controlled high temperature. The sample both evaporates and cracks, leaving behind a carbonaceous residue. Either of two similar types of apparatus is used, and the amount of residue is accordingly termed Ramsbottom carbon residue or Conradson carbon residue, according to the test (see ASTM D-189 and D-524). This essentially provides a measure of the coke-forming tendency of the heavy oil or residuum during catalytic hydrotreatment. Coking is much greater than that observed with distillates.

Processing characteristics are also substantially affected by the fraction of the oil or residua termed asphaltenes. This is defined as the fraction that precipitates when the sample is treated with 40 volumes of n-pentane per volume of sample. The solubilized fraction (termed *maltenes*) is further divided into two groups, *resins* and *oils* by solution in liquid propane and an adsorption-and-elution procedure. The degree of separation into the two groups may vary somewhat with details of the procedure. (See ASTM D2007.)

Asphaltenes are a complex mixture of high-boiling, polynuclear aromatic, polar compounds and they contain a large fraction of sulfur, nitrogen, and metal impurities. Some metal impurities may also be found in the resin fraction. Little is known about the asphaltene structures, although they appear to form loosely associated aromatic sheets. The reported molecular weights vary substantially with the measurement method, and the higher-molecular-weight material appears to be colloidal. During catalytic reaction the asphaltenes presumably dissociate and break up in poorly understood ways. The carbon residue, as measured in the foregoing, increases in an irregular fashion with asphaltene content.

A variety of residua hydrotreatment processes are commercial. In general, the goal is to reduce the content of sulfur, metals, and asphaltenes and produce lighter products by hydrocracking. In some cases the goal is a broad improvement in quality of the crude to make it suitable for a conventional refining process, e.g., catalytic cracking. Alternately, the focus may be on producing a heavy fuel oil with a much lower sulfur content, or it may be on achieving maximum conversion to lighter products. The relative emphasis on the various reactions varies greatly with the type of feedstock, type of process, catalyst, and reaction conditions. The process chosen may also center about providing flexibility to vary from predominantly desulfurization to hydrocracking, depending on market conditions and available feedstock.

In some cases two or three stages are used in which the first stage contains an inexpensive sacrificial catalyst to remove most of the metals, even though little HDS occurs. This may, e.g., be a low-molybdenum catalyst that initiates deposits of nickel, which in turn cause much of the subsequent HDM. The second stage contains a more or less conventional $NiMo/Al_2O_3$ or $CoMo/Al_2O_3$ catalyst. An acidic support, e.g. silica-alumina, may be used for high hydrocracking activity or a low-acidity or nonacidic support if coking is to be minimized. The reactors may be fixed-bed, moving-bed or ebullating reactors.

The selection of the optimum catalyst or sets of catalysts varies from case to case. The catalysts are usually extrudates, 1/16-in (1.5 mm) diameter being representative for fixed beds, 1/32-in (0.8 mm) for ebullating beds. A diagram of an ebullating-bed reactor is shown in Fig. 9.9. The vessel is nearly filled with liquid in which catalyst is suspended by the upward flow of liquid and hydrogen is introduced at the bottom. Liquid is recirculated from top to bottom and product as vapor is removed from the top. The moving-bed or ebullating-bed reactors allow more or less continuous addition and withdrawal of catalyst without interruption and therefore are of particular advantage for processing feedstocks of very poor quality, e.g., those of high residue and metal content.

The reactions can be substantially diffusion-limited, and deposition of metals and carbonaceous deposits cause changes in the diffusion characteristics with time. In fixed-bed reactors the maximum metal deposit typically occurs near the outside of the catalyst pellets, especially initially and near the reactor inlet. The deposit profile varies with distance down the reactor and with time. Vanadium removal rates are generally faster than those of nickel. The desired reaction characteristics vary with circumstances, but typically include degree of sulfur removal, degree of conversion of "nondistillable" material to more volatile products, and achievement of high metals pickup before the catalyst becomes unacceptably inactive.

Optimum catalysts typically have a rather broad range of pore sizes,

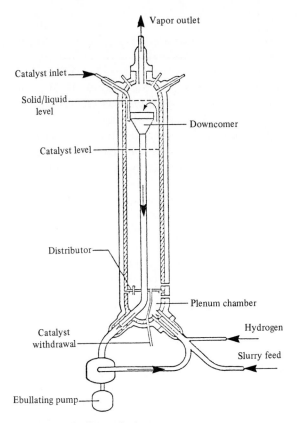

Figure 9.9   Ebullating bed reactor.

e.g., micropores and mesopores (up to about 10-nm diameter) to provide sufficient surface area and macropores (~0.1 to 1.0 μm) to allow
easy movement of large molecules. The primary mechanisms for catalyst deactivation are pore-mouth plugging, metals poisoning, and
coke deposition. Catalyst composition, particle size, shape, and pore
structure are manipulated to achieve an optimum. Some portion of the
reactions is probably thermal rather than catalytic.

Some of the processes for coal liquefaction involve suspending finely
divided coal in a liquid in the presence of a catalyst such as CoMo/
Al_2O_3 and treating it with hydrogen at elevated pressure and temperature in an ebullating-bed reactor. The process is similar to residue
hydrotreatment. The reactions occurring are complicated, and diffusion effects and clogging of catalyst pores by finely divided solids in
the coal play an important role.

Further details are available in the review by Quann et al. (1988)
and in a book by Speight (1981). These give considerable detail about

commercial reactor technologies, as does a review by Dautzenberg and De Deken (1984). An earlier comprehensive review of the general reaction-engineering aspects of hydroprocessing was published by Weekman (1976). Trickle-bed reactors as used for hydrodesulfurization and other processes were reviewed by Satterfield (1975), and mass transfer in heterogeneous catalysis in general is treated in the book by Satterfield (1970). Recent books on multiphase reactors include those by Shah (1979), Ramachandran and Chaudhari (1983), Gianetto and Silveston (1986), and Fan (1989). The last, on gas-liquid-solid fluidization engineering, includes a substantial chapter on hydrotreating and conversion of residua.

A review by Oelderik et al. (1989) discusses upgrading of residua with particular attention to Shell hydroconversion technology, which has reached commercialization in a plant near Rotterdam. This process uses a novel, moving-bed "bunker reactor" in the first stage, primarily aimed at metals removal. This reactor is followed by fixed-bed reactors that perform desulfurization. Hydrocracking occurs in both reactors. The catalyst in the bunker reactor is a NiMo or CoMo on a spherical silica support that allows metal sulfides to be extracted from spent catalyst and coke to be burned, after which the catalyst can be reused.

9.16 Hydrotreating

This term, synonymous with *hydroprocessing* or *hydrofining*, is used in a general way to include a variety of catalytic hydrogenation processes used in fuels refining or for purification of products such as industrial solvents. These may be grouped into processes for improving the quality of a final product or processes in which the hydrotreated stream becomes the feedstock for a subsequent process that benefits from the pretreatment. The term may include processes in which emphasis is on hydrodesulfurization, as well as those in which emphasis is on saturation of some or all of various unsaturated species present in a feedstock. Hydrotreatment implies little change in volatility in contrast to hydrocracking.

As examples of the first group of processes, hydrotreating may be used as a finishing process in the manufacture of lubricants and various special oils, to improve their color and stability. The catalyst is typically $CoMo/Al_2O_3$ or $NiMo/Al_2O_3$, which is sulfided before use. A minimum concentration of hydrogen sulfide must be present in the reactor environment to maintain the catalyst in the fully sulfided form. Sufficient hydrogen sulfide is usually formed from the sulfur compounds present. In its absence, the catalyst ages faster, perhaps because nickel sulfide becomes reduced to the metal, which then sinters and loses area. If necessary, a small amount of hydrogen sulfide or decomposable organic sulfide may be deliberately added to prevent this effect. Le Page et al. (1987) give an overview of catalysts, kinetics, and processes for hydrorefining in general and hydrotreating to refine lube-oil blending stocks. Galiasso et al. (1984) review the hydrotreatment of cracked light gas oil.

Another application as a finishing process is the partial hydrogenation of *pyrolysis gasoline*, the product fraction of the volatility range of gasoline produced from any one of a number of pyrolysis processes, such as steam cracking, coking, or visbreaking. The product is too unstable to be incorporated directly into gasoline, and mild hydrogenation of diolefins and other gum-formers stabilizes it. Typical catalysts are palladium, nickel, or nickel-tungsten, each supported on alumina. The choice depends on various factors including composition of the pyrolysis gasoline, and nature and amounts of poisons present, such as sulfur compounds. Le Page et al. (1987) describe the IFP (Institut Français du Pétrole) process in detail including information on kinetics and effects of poisons.

As another example, jet fuel specifications often include a *luminometer number*. This number is a measure of the carbon-forming propensity of the fuel and hence of smoke emissions and of radiation heat-transfer characteristics in the aircraft engine combustion chamber. These factors are related essentially to the aromatics content of the fuel. A portion of the feed to the jet fuel "pool" may be hydrogenated to limit the aromatics content to an acceptable level. Likewise, for diesel fuel, paraffins are needed rather than aromatics to achieve the desired self-ignition properties; these are characterized by a *cetane number*.

As an intermediate processing step, hydrotreating is used to improve the quality of a feedstock. Thus, hydrodesulfurization is often necessary before a feedstock can be catalytically reformed. Before being fed to a catalytic cracker, a gas-oil fraction may be hydrotreated to accomplish several objectives simultaneously.

1. Prior hydrodesulfurization provides a means for control of air pollution because some of the sulfur present in a feedstock will be deposited in the form of coke on the cracking catalyst. This may be emitted to the air in the cracking catalyst regenerator.

2. HDN removes nitrogen compounds that otherwise deactivate acidic sites on cracking catalysts and also contribute to coke formation.

3. Saturation of an aromatic ring is required to cause it to crack. Without such prior saturation, multiring aromatic compounds pass through a catalytic cracking reactor and undergo little or no reaction.

9.17   Dehydrogenation

9.17.1   Dehydrogenation of butane and butene

Processes to dehydrogenate n-butane or n-butene to butadiene were hastily developed and put into commercial application in the United States at the beginning of World War II for synthetic rubber production when sources of natural rubber were suddenly cut off. The reactions are endothermic and thermodynamically limited.

$$C_4H_{10} \rightarrow C_4H_8 + H_2 \qquad (9.11)$$

$$C_4H_8 \rightarrow C_4H_6 + H_2 \qquad (9.12)$$

The ΔH for each reaction is about 134 kJ/mol. Since the number of moles increases on reaction, improved conversion at equilibrium is obtained by operation at as low a partial pressure of hydrocarbon as feasible. For favorable equilibrium, a temperature of 500 to 600°C is needed for reaction (9.11) and 600 to 700°C for reaction (9.12). The Houdry dehydrogenation processes, of long standing, can be modified to dehydrogenate n-butane to n-butene, n-butene to butadiene, or a mixture of butane and butene to butadiene.

For a process oriented toward butadiene, n-butane or n-butenes are preheated to about 620°C and passed through a bed of 18 to 20 wt % chromia on alumina in the form of 3- to 4-mm pellets, to which considerable inert material is added to provide additional heat capacity. The beds are wide, horizontal, and only about 1 m thick, to minimize pressure drop. The total pressure is about 10 to 20 kPa (vacuum operation), and the contact time is about 0.2 s.

Several reactors are used in parallel. Each reactor operates essentially adiabatically, and after about 5 to 10 min the feed is switched to another reactor. The first reactor is purged by evacuation, and carbon deposits are then burned off by blowing with air, which reheats the bed. The bed is then again evacuated, and the cycle is repeated. The reaction temperature is about 625 to 675°C. Above about 700°C, excessive polymerization and coking occur and the undesirable formation of acetylenes is increased. Below about 600°C the rate becomes uneconomically low. The total cycle time is about 15 to 30 min, so a minimum of three reactors is needed to achieve continuous operation. Commercially, as many as eight have been used.

A mixture of butadiene and butenes is produced, from which butadiene is separated and butenes and unreacted butane are recycled. The overall yield of butadiene from butane is about 60 percent. Information on kinetics, catalyst coking, and reactor design and a guide to the earlier literature is provided by Dumez and Froment (1976). The process has also been described by Craig and Dufallo (1979).

In another process, butane is converted to butenes at about 1 atm over a chromia-alumina catalyst at about 600°C. Operation is cyclic. About once an hour the feed is stopped and coke deposits are removed by passing flue gas containing 2 to 3 percent O_2 over the catalyst.

n-Butenes may also be converted to butadiene by mixing with steam in a mole ratio of steam to butenes of about 10:1 at 600 to 700°C and passing it over an unsupported iron oxide-chromia promoted with a potassium compound. The steam supplies the heat required for the endothermic reaction. The usual composition, known as Shell 105 catalyst, is about 90% Fe_2O_3-4% Cr_2O_3-6% K_2CO_3. The stable form of iron under reaction conditions is probably Fe_3O_4, which is stabilized by the chromia. The catalyst is calcined at high temperatures for strength, and this results in a low area, of the order of 2 m^2/g. The potassium compound helps promote the reaction of carbon with steam and hence helps keep coke deposits from forming. At the reaction temperature, K_2CO_3 is appreciably volatile and is slowly lost. Hence, it must be replenished by addition to the feed. A chromia-alumina catalyst, as used, e.g., in the Houdry process, is not stable in the presence of steam.

Butadiene is also produced as one of the products from thermal (steam) cracking of naphtha and gas oil. Historically, most of the butadiene consumed in Europe and Japan has come from steam cracking. In the United States about 30 percent of the supply was produced by catalytic dehydrogenation in 1980, but as of 1990 about 95 percent of U.S. consumption was from steam cracking or imports. Interest in processes for olefin manufacture has, however, been growing. In particular, dehydrogenation of isobutane is required to supply the rapidly increasing demands for isobutylene to produce MTBE as a gasoline additive, and high-purity propylene is needed for fiber manufacture.

The historical development of dehydrogenation catalysts and processes is reviewed by Kearby (1955) and Hornaday et al. (1961). Chromia-alumina has a complex structure that may be markedly affected by the method of preparation and has received much study. If prepared by impregnation of alumina, the chromia is present as clusters of tiny crystallites that only partially cover the alumina. Chromia-alumina can be regarded as a dual-function catalyst that has both acidic and dehydrogenation functions. Its physical and chemical properties are reviewed by Poole and MacIver (1967). Carrà and Forni (1972) discuss kinetics and possible reaction mechanisms.

9.17.2 Styrene from ethylbenzene

Traditionally, ethylbenzene was made by alkylation of benzene with ethylene using an aluminum chloride catalyst, but in more modern processes developed by Mobil and UOP and used in several commercial plants, a ZSM-5 catalyst is used instead. Its pore structure apparently inhibits the formation of polyalkylated aromatics usually formed to some degree on non-shape-selective catalysts. A high mole ratio of benzene to ethylene in the feed values (in the range of 5 to 20) is used to achieve high selectivity. Reaction conditions are 1.4 to 2.7 MPa and temperatures above 370°C. A more recent development by Unocal is a zeolite catalyst, probably an H-Y type, that allows the reaction to take place at milder temperatures in the liquid phase and requires regeneration only once a year. It reportedly is to be used in a plant under construction in Japan in 1988 by Nippon Steel/Shin-Daikyowa.

Ethylbenzene may be dehydrogenated to styrene using catalysts similar to those used for dehydrogenating butene to butadiene, although dehydrogenation here is easier to carry out.

$$
\underset{\text{CH}_2\text{CH}_3}{\bigcirc} \longrightarrow \underset{\text{CH}=\text{CH}_2}{\bigcirc} + \text{H}_2 \qquad (9.13)
$$

$$-\Delta H = -121 \text{ kJ/mol}$$

Chromia is poisoned in the presence of steam, and one catalyst used commercially is an unsupported iron oxide promoted with a potassium compound such as Shell 105 (see the foregoing). Other promoters may also be present. Even though this is a low-area catalyst with large pores, the reaction is substantially diffusion-limited on 6-mm particles. Selectivity is improved with smaller sizes, but these cause an increased pressure drop, which is not desired. Commercially 4- to 6-mm-diameter extrudates are used.

The process is operated typically with a mole ratio of steam-ethylbenzene having values of 10 to 15, at about atmospheric pressure. The steam provides the heat for this highly endothermic reaction. The temperature is about 600 to 650°C, and contact time is of the order of 1 s. Two adiabatic fixed-bed reactors with reheat in between are used. Styrene yields of about 90 percent are achieved at conversions of 40 to 60 percent. Some toluene is produced as a by-product.

For maximum conversion and yield, such reactors and ancillary equipment are especially designed to provide a minimum pressure drop, so a radial fixed-bed reactor may be utilized. Catalyst life is of the order of 1 to 2 years. Kearby (1955) gives equilibrium data and describes early catalyst compositions, and Lee (1974) describes detailed studies with iron oxide catalysts and with commercial Shell 105 catalyst.

The potassium promoter migrates with time toward the center of the pellets (Lee 1974) because the center is slightly cooler than the outside, caused by the endothermic reaction. Potassium also migrates downstream. Maximum activity occurs at a level of a few percent potassium; hence, the potassium migration causes the outside of the catalyst pellet to deactivate, from loss of potassium, and causes the center also to deactivate, from accumulation of excess potassium. Potassium is present largely as the hydroxide at the reactor inlet, caused by the high steam pressure, but substantially in the form of carbonate toward the exit because of CO_2 formed as a by-product. The carbonate is much less volatile than the hydroxide, and this also affects the migration pattern of the potassium. Muhler et al. (1988) present evidence for a model of the iron oxide structure based on a variety of instrumental techniques.

9.18 Hydrodealkylation

Hydrodealkylation is the hydrocracking of an alkyl aromatic to form a paraffin and an unsubstituted aromatic ring. Commercially, toluene and other alkyl benzenes are converted to benzene, or alkyl naphthalenes are converted to naphthalene.

$$C_6H_5CH_3 + H_2 \rightarrow C_6H_6 + CH_4 \qquad (9.14)$$

$$\text{Methylnaphthalene} + H_2 \rightarrow \text{naphthalene} + CH_4$$

$$-\Delta H \sim 50 \text{ kJ/mol } CH_4 \qquad (9.15)$$

Typical operating conditions are 500 to 600°C, 3 to 7 MPa, and a H_2-feed mole ratio having values in the range of 5 to 15, utilizing an adiabatic reactor. Operating conditions are nearly the same for the two reactions and are chosen so as to achieve good yields and reaction rates without ring hydrogenation. The feedstock may be toluene (Houdry "Detol" process) or a highly aromatic stream such as a reformate or "cycle oil" from catalytic gas-oil cracking or a light oil from coking of coal.

The Houdry "Litol" process has been used commercially since 1964 and is described by Dufallo et al. (1981). It was originally developed to produce benzene from the C_6–C_8 fraction of coal tar liquids from coking of coal. Typically these liquids contain 70 to 75% benzene, 18 to 20% toluene, 6 to 8% C_8 aromatics, plus small amounts of naphthenes, paraffins, olefins, diolefins, and sulfur compounds. In the Litol process this is first partly hydrogenated to remove compounds that readily polymerize, and then the stream is contacted with a chromia-alumina catalyst at about 600°C, which causes dehydrogenation of naphthenes, hydrocracking and dealkylation of other hydrocarbons, and additional desulfurization. This treatment converts the C_6–C_7 fraction of the product into essentially benzene and toluene. The exothermic nature of the reaction means that it can potentially run away. This requires careful attention to the design and operation of the reactor.

Under reaction conditions equilibrium amounts of saturated ring compounds, e.g., cyclohexane, are very small. The dealkylation reactions are essentially irreversible, and mole yields in the range of 95 to 97 percent are achieved for, e.g., conversion of toluene to benzene. The large excess of hydrogen minimizes side reactions and coke formation on the catalyst. One or two adiabatic reactors are used in series.

The reactions may also be carried out thermally at slightly higher temperature and pressure, and both catalytic and noncatalytic processes have been practiced commercially. The thermal processes are more flexible with respect to feedstock, but the catalytic processes permit higher yields and conversion per pass and lower hydrogen consumption. The catalyst is a low-sodium chromia-alumina. Hydrodealkylation in general is reviewed by Asselin (1964), and naphthalene from petroleum by Ballard (1965).

Most naphthalene is used as a charge stock for manufacture of phthalic anhydride (Sec. 8.6.2). Alkyl naphthalenes, if used as the feedstock for this partial oxidation reaction, provide an unsatisfactory yield. The economic incentive to operate hydrodealkylation to form naphthalene is therefore closely related to the price and availability of o-xylene, the alternate feedstock for phthalic anhydride manufacture.

Benzene is a widely used starting material for chemical synthesis, but there are few uses for toluene. The economic incentive for dealkylation of toluene to benzene varies greatly with time and location and is influenced by many factors. Most benzene and toluene is produced by catalytic reforming in which the quantities of toluene produced are generally greater than those of benzene. However, toluene is a better high-octane blending component for gasoline than is benzene, and the benzene content of gasoline must be strictly limited because it is carcinogenic. Some benzene is also produced as a by-product of thermal steam cracking and by specific processes (Sec. 9.6).

9.19   Regeneration of Coked Catalysts by Combustion

In many hydrocarbon and related reactions, such as catalytic cracking, reforming, hydrodesulfurization, and various dehydrogenations, carbonaceous deposits (so-called coke) are gradually formed on the surface of the catalyst. The continuing accumulation of these deposits reduces the activity of the catalyst to the point that it must be regenerated. This buildup of coke may become significant in a few seconds, as in catalytic cracking, or only over a period of many months, as in some catalytic reforming processes.

The deposit of coke causes a reduction in catalytic activity by blocking active sites. The distribution of the deposit can vary greatly with the situation, and mathematical analyses of the simpler cases are similar to those used to describe catalyst poisoning. At one extreme, a strongly adsorbed poison deposits initially at the pore mouths (near the external surface of catalyst pellets) and on the topmost layers of a fixed bed of catalyst. The outer zone of the catalyst thus becomes an effectively inert annulus through which reactants must diffuse to reach active surface. The thickness of this inert annulus in a pellet grows with time, and the thickness of the top layers of catalyst-containing deposits likewise increases.

Simultaneously, pores may become choked if deposits significantly reduce pore size, leading to various diffusion-limiting effects. The resulting effects on activity and selectivity of a fixed bed of catalyst can evidently be highly complex, and their consideration is outside the scope of the present treatment. The subject was analyzed in considerable detail in an early analysis by Wheeler (1951, 1955) and is covered in extensive reviews by Butt (1972, 1984).

The character of these coke deposits is complex and varies substantially with the conditions under which they were formed, and with subsequent treatments. In some cases, especially when formed at relatively low temperatures, they are essentially an ill-defined, high-molecular-weight polymer, much of which can be removed by washing with a solvent. Appleby et al. (1962) made a detailed characterization of the coke formed in catalytic cracking and showed that it consisted of large aggregates of polynuclear aromatic molecules comprising essentially condensed systems of fused aromatic rings, plus strongly adsorbed portions of products of the reaction. X-ray diffraction studies likewise show that, when deposited at a high temperature (e.g., 400 to 500°C), a substantial portion of the coke is in a pseudographite form.

Even so, the coke may contain considerable hydrogen, a representative empirical formula being between CH_1 and $CH_{0.5}$, provided that heavy metals are not present on the catalyst in a metallic form. In the latter case, the deposits usually contain little hydrogen (see also Sec. 9.19.2). Bell (1987) describes structure and composition of carbonaceous deposits on catalysts as revealed by modern spectroscopic methods.

The usual technique of regenerating a coked catalyst is by combustion with diluted oxygen, although steam or steam plus air is sometimes used. The following discussion focuses first on oxidative combustion in a single pellet or in a differential reactor. Representative methods used in practice are then treated.

If the effectiveness factor for the primary catalytic reaction is essentially unity (Chap. 11) and the catalyst is uniform in intrinsic activity, the coke usually is distributed uniformly through the catalyst. If the effectiveness factor for the regeneration reaction likewise approaches unity, the oxygen gradient through the pellet is negligible, and the coke concentration decreases uniformly throughout the pellet during the combustion reaction.

At a sufficiently high temperature, the regeneration reaction may become diffusion-limited, and oxygen reacts as fast as it is transported to the carbon. In a sphere, reaction then occurs solely at a spherical interface that moves progressively to the center, and the rate is limited by the rate of diffusion of oxygen through a shell of carbon-free porous solid. These facts may be visually demonstrated by cutting a pellet in half after partial removal of coke. With some catalysts, the effect may be demonstrated by submerging a pellet in a liquid of the same refractive index, e.g., silica-alumina beads in benzene or other suitable hydrocarbon. Under highly diffusion-controlled regeneration conditions, one sees a black sphere, surrounded concentrically by a white or light-gray spherical shell from which all the coke has been removed. Under intermediate conditions, a progressive darkening toward the center is visible.

9.19.1 Intrinsic kinetics: Nature of coke deposits

A substantial number of reports are available on the rate of combustion in air of carbonaceous deposits in porous catalysts, both on the intrinsic kinetics and under diffusion-controlled conditions. In many of the studies, particularly earlier ones, operating conditions were poorly controlled, the reactor was not truly differential, or measurements were made in the transition zone between intrinsic and diffusion control. All these factors make interpretation difficult.

An atom of carbon in graphite occupies about 0.04 nm^2 of cross-sectional area; if each atom of carbon in coke occupies the same area, a monoatomic layer of carbon on an oxide-type catalyst or support would comprise about 5 wt % carbon for each 100 m^2/g of surface area. Studies by Weisz and Goodwin (1966) on silica-alumina catalysts of about 250 m^2/g surface area indicated that, up to about 6 wt % carbon, the rate of combustion was proportional to the amount of carbon present; i.e., all atoms of the coke were presumably equally accessible to oxygen. At higher coke contents (e.g., 7 to 20 wt % carbon on silica-alumina) the rate for the first 50 percent or so of reaction was less than proportional to the amount of carbon present, indicating that some of the carbon atoms were initially inaccessible, but in the latter part of the reaction the rate again became first order with respect to total carbon present. The same type of behavior at high coke contents has been reported by others.

Considerable hydrogen may be present in the coke, and, if so, it is removed preferentially in the early stages of the regeneration. If some of the deposit is essentially a hydrocarbon polymer, this may be decomposed and volatilized in the pores, and the products then burn homogeneously outside the catalyst pores. In the best controlled laboratory studies, investigators of the regeneration reactions have pretreated their coked catalyst before combustion at elevated temperatures in an inert atmosphere in order to eliminate most of the volatile matter present or to further decompose the coke and thereby obtain more reproducible results. In most laboratory studies, the coke has been deposited from a hydrocarbon vapor under non-diffusion-limiting conditions, which at moderate carbon loadings seem to provide a true monolayer.

Coke formation on zeolites can be markedly affected by the zeolite pore structure, as discussed in Sec. 7.7.8.

9.19.2 Carbon gasification kinetics

Close agreement has been reported of first-order reaction rate constants for combustion of monolayer coke deposits when they are formed on inert supports or acidic cracking catalysts not containing transition metals. Data were reported by Weisz and Goodwin (1966) for coke burnoff from silica-alumina, silica-alumina Durabead, silica-magnesia, fuller's earth (an adsorbent clay), or Filtrol 110 (a cracking catalyst derived from natural clay). There was no effect of support on the rate, and the same results were obtained on silica-alumina with deposits from laboratory cracking of gas oil, naphtha, cumene, or propylene. Johnson and Mayland (1955) also reported in an earlier study that the specific burning rates of carbon on silica-alumina, silica-magnesia, clay, silica gel, and cracking catalysts were approximately the same, although detailed information about the kinetics on the various supports was not developed.

The equation for the first-order rate constant is shown in Fig. 9.10 and is given by Weisz and Goodwin (1966).

$$k = 1.9 \times 10^8 \, e^{-157/RT} \; \text{sec}^{-1} \cdot \text{atm}^{-1} \tag{9.16}$$

where the expression for the rate of reaction per unit volume of pellet is

$$-r = k P_{O_2} c_C \tag{9.17}$$

and c_C is the moles of carbon present per cubic centimeter of pellet.

Several earlier investigators show results that agree closely with

Eq. (9.16), so it may be taken as representative of the intrinsic combustion rate of monolayer carbon on a noncatalytic surface. There is some controversy concerning the order of the reaction with respect to oxygen under various conditions. Most investigators indicate that it is nearly proportional to the first power in the range from about 10 to 100 kPa partial pressure of oxygen and at the temperatures of interest in catalyst regeneration. These rates are quite close to those reported for oxidation of graphite.

The presence in the porous structure of transition metals or other catalysts can greatly accelerate the rate of carbon oxidation. For example, Weisz and Goodwin reported that a chromia-alumina catalyst showed rates two to three orders of magnitude greater than that observed on silica-alumina, although the activation energy remains the same (Fig. 9.10). Bowman (1956) showed intermediate catalytic activity for carbon oxidation on a molybdena-alumina catalyst, and a similar activation energy. Platinum/alumina reforming catalysts also are catalytic for carbon oxidation and can be rapidly regenerated at relatively lower temperatures and lower oxygen concentration.

The initially rapid rates reported by some investigators may represent desorption of volatile hydrocarbons or further cracking combined with desorption, with much of the combustion of the products occurring homogeneously in either case. The rapid reaction of hydrogen present in the coke, which would occur initially, may also be erroneously interpreted as combustion of carbon if reaction is measured by disappearance of oxygen. Steam formed in the catalyst pores by the reaction of hydrogen in the coke may also accelerate the gasification of the carbon. In some commercial operations, all catalyst particles are probably not completely regenerated at each cycle, and there is an opportunity for multilayered carbon deposits to build up, even at low overall coke levels.

The regeneration reaction may become limited by the diffusion of oxygen into the pores at a temperature in the range of 450°C or higher, depending on catalyst size, pore structure, and other variables (Satterfield 1970, Chap. 5). Regeneration of coked zeolite catalysts can be complex and can be affected by the uneven distribution of coke within various portions of the zeolite pore structure (Sec. 7.7.8).

9.19.3 Regeneration of coked catalysts in practice

A considerable variety of regeneration procedures may be used depending on circumstances and, in particular, on catalyst composition. If regeneration is required often, a continuous process must provide a facility for continuous burnoff separate from the reactor, as in the

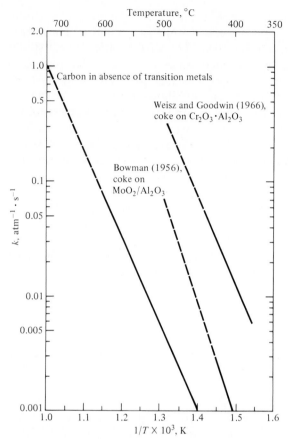

Figure 9.10   First-order reaction rate constants for oxidation of coke deposits. Dashed lines indicate extrapolated data.

fluidized-bed regenerators used in conjunction with fluid catalytic cracking processes. Alternately, a cyclic fixed-bed process may be designed in which reaction and coke-burnoff steps follow in sequence, separated by purge steps to avoid the formation of explosive gas mixtures. An example is the Houdry process for converting butane to butadiene.

If regeneration is required only at intervals of several months or longer, a fixed-bed unit can be shut down for the period of time required for regeneration and then put back on stream. If this interruption is too lengthy, (it may require two to three days), or if regeneration is difficult to achieve in the reactor vessel, the coked catalyst may be quickly replaced with fresh catalyst and the regeneration carried out elsewhere.

The regeneration procedures used for a fixed bed of catalyst usually involve several common characteristic steps in sequence. The bed is first purged of hydrogen and hydrocarbons with an inert gas, usually at an elevated temperature that may exceed that used for regeneration as such. For regeneration, temperatures throughout the bed are held within a fairly moderate range, sufficiently high to secure an adequate rate of coke removal but not so high as to damage the catalyst.

In a representative procedure, the initial bed temperature is about 350°C. With hot nitrogen recirculating through the system and means for removing CO_2 and H_2O from the exit gas, air is added to the inlet to comprise typically 0.2 to 0.5 % O_2 in the gas. The oxygen reacts rapidly on contact with the carbonaceous deposit, so the burning takes place within a fairly narrow zone that moves slowly through the reactor. Its location can be monitored by thermocouples that show the movement of the accompanying hot spot. The maximum inlet O_2 concentration is limited to that needed to keep the temperature hot spot below an acceptable level. After breakthrough of oxygen from the exit, the inlet oxygen level is increased in increments until the entire bed is subjected to an oxygen level typically in the range of 5 to 10 % O_2. Simultaneously, the inlet gas temperature may be raised.

The details of a regeneration procedure are highly specific to circumstances. Not only may they vary substantially from the foregoing generic description, but even with one particular reactor the procedure may vary considerably with each regeneration and it may be altered *ad hoc* as the burning proceeds. Frequently, much of the carbonaceous deposits are found in the interstices between catalyst particles, or deposited on inert material in a guard bed, or on the top of the catalyst bed. Such deposits are formed primarily by a thermal reaction, and the extent of laydown is then more or less independent of the nature of the catalyst.

These deposits increase the pressure drop through a reactor and may also cause uneven distribution of reactants through the bed. In contrast, "catalytic coke" is deposited on the surface of the catalyst and possibly at pore mouths and affects reaction selectivity and activity, but not pressure drop. This coke distribution may vary considerably throughout pellets and throughout the bed, thus affecting the appropriate burnoff procedure. Whether the burnoff occurs in a zone-like manner or more broadly through the bed can be controlled to some extent by the inlet temperature and oxygen concentration. The higher the temperature and oxygen concentration, the more zone-like will be the regeneration.

Bed regeneration may be required to restore pressure drop to an acceptably low level or to restore reactor performance. If the catalyst contains a noble metal such as platinum, the regeneration procedure may be followed by an "oxygen soak" to redistribute the metal (See Sec. 6.4).

The foregoing discussion considers deposits containing only carbon and hydrogen. If sulfur compounds are present, the sulfur is oxidized to SO_2 and SO_3 and, with an alumina-based catalyst, much may be adsorbed onto the catalyst. Under subsequent reducing conditions the adsorbed SO_x is reduced to H_2S and leaves with reaction products.

The burnoff of catalytic coke is treated in considerable detail by Hughes (1984), who presents quantitative analyses showing such effects as bed temperature profiles versus time for several cases of interest. See also Byrne et al. (1986). Butt (1984) gives a broad review of catalyst deactivation and regeneration, in effect bringing up to date an earlier review (Butt 1972). Hatcher and Burton (1984) present the results of an experimental study of regeneration of a molybdenum catalyst and a fixed-bed simulation. Ellingham and Garrett (1984) give a brief account of the practicalities of off-site oxidative regeneration of catalysts and their reclamation, focusing on sulfided CoMo and NiMo catalysts. HDS catalysts are usually regenerated off-site where air-pollution-control facilities are available.

References

Abotsi, G. M. K., and A. W. Scaroni: *Fuel Proc. Tech.*, **22**, 107 (1989).

Appleby, W. G., J. W. Gibson, and G. M. Good: *Ind. Eng. Chem., Process Des. Dev.*, **1**, 102 (1962).

Asselin, G. F., in J. J. McKetta, Jr. (ed.): *Advances in Petroleum Chemistry and Refining*, vol. 9, Wiley, New York, 1964, p. 284.

Asselin, G. F., H. S. Bloch, G. R. Donaldson, V. Haensel, and E. L. Pollitzer: *Am. Chem. Soc., Div. Pet. Chem., Prepr.*, **17**(3), B4 (1972).

Avidan, A. A., M. Edwards, and H. Owen: *Rev. Chem. Eng.*, **6**, 1 (1990).

Ballard, H. D., Jr., in J. J. McKetta, Jr. (ed.): *Advances in Petroleum Chemistry and Refining*, vol. 10, Wiley, New York, 1965, p. 219.

Bell, A. T., in E. E. Petersen and A. T. Bell (eds.): *Catalyst Deactivation*, Dekker, New York, 1987, p. 235.

Bernard, J. R., in L. V. C. Rees (ed.): *Proceedings of the Fifth International Conference on Zeolites*, Heyden, London, 1980.

Biloen, P., J. N. Helle, H. Verbeek, F. M. Dautzenberg, and W. M. H. Sachtler: *J. Catal.*, **63**, 112 (1980).

Biswas, J., G. M. Bickle, P. G. Gray, D. D. Do, and J. Barbier: *Catal. Rev.—Sci. Eng.*, **30**, 161 (1988).

Bolton, A. P., in J. A. Rabo (ed.): *Zeolite Chemistry and Catalysis, ACS Monogr. No. 171*, 1976, p. 714.

Bowman, W. H.: Sc. D. thesis, M.I.T., Cambridge, Mass., 1956.

Broderick, A. V., A. V. Sapre, N. K. Nag, V. H. J. de Beer, B. C. Gates, and H. Kwart: *J. Catal.*, **61**, 523 (1980).

Butt, J. B.: *Adv. Chem. Ser., No. 109*, 1972, p. 259.

Butt, J. B., in J. R. Anderson and M. Boudart (eds.): *Catalysis: Science and Technology*, vol. 6, Springer, 1984, p. 1.

Byrne, A., R. Hughes, and J. Santamaria-Ramiro: *Chem. Eng. Sci.*, **41**, 773 (1986).

Carrà, S., and L. Forni: *Catal. Rev.*, **5**, 159 (1972).

Chen, N. Y., and W. E. Garwood: *Catal. Rev.—Sci. Eng.*, **28**, 185 (1986).

Chianelli, R. R., in H. Heinemann, and G. A. Somorjai (eds.): *Catalysis and Surface Science*, Dekker, New York, 1985, p. 61; also published in *Catal. Rev.—Sci. Eng.*, **26**(3, 4) (1985).

Ciapetta, F. G., R. M. Dobres, and R. W. Baker in P. H. Emmett (ed.): *Catalysis*, vol. 6, Reinhold, New York, 1958, p. 495.

Ciapetta, F. G., and D. N. Wallace: *Catal. Rev.*, **5**, 67 (1971).

Coleman, H. J., R. L. Hopkins, and C. J. Thompson: *Am. Chem. Soc., Div. Pet. Chem., Prepr.*, **15**(3), A17 (1970).

Craig, R. G. and J. M. Dufallo: *Chem. Eng. Progress*, February 1979, p. 62.

Dautzenberg, F. M., and J. C. De Deken: *Catal. Rev.—Sci. Eng.*, **26**, 421 (1984).

Derouane, E. G., and D. J. Vanderveken: *Appl. Catal.*, **45**, L15 (1988).

Doolan, P. C., and P. R. Pujado: *Hydrocarbon Process.*, September 1989, p. 72.

Drushel, H. V.: *Am. Chem. Soc., Div. Pet. Chem., Prepr.*, **15**(2), C13 (1970).

Dufallo, J. M., D. C. Spence, and W. A. Schwartz: *Chem. Eng. Progress*, Jan. 1981, p. 56.

Dumez, F. J., and G. F. Froment: *Ind. Eng. Chem., Process Des. Dev.*, **15**, 291 (1976).

Ecklund, E. E., and G. A. Mills: *Chemtech*, **19**, 549, 626 (1989).

Edgar, M. D., in B. E. Leach (ed.): *Applied Industrial Catalysis*, vol. 1, Academic, New York, 1983, p. 123.

Edmonds, T., in J. M. Tedder, A. Nechvatal, and A. H. Jubb: *Basic Organic Chemistry, Part 5: Industrial Products*, Wiley, New York, 1975, p. 58.

Ellingham, R. E. and J. Garrett, in B. E. Leach (ed.): *Applied Industrial Catalysis*, Vol. 3, Academic, New York, 1984, p. 25.

Fan, L-S.: *Gas-Liquid-Solid Fluidization Engineering*, Butterworths, 1989.

Furimsky, E.: *Catal. Rev.—Sci. Eng.*, **22**, 371 (1980).

Furimsky, E.: *Catal. Rev.—Sci. Eng.*, **25**, 421 (1983).

Galiasso, R., W. Garcia, M. M. Ramirez de Agudelo, and P. Andreu: *Catal. Rev.—Sci. Eng.*, **26**, 445 (1984).

Garten, R. L., and J. H. Sinfelt: *J. Catal.*, **62**, 127 (1980).

Gary, J. H. and G. E. Handwerk: *Petroleum Refining: Technology and Economics*, Dekker, New York, 1975.

Gates, B. C., J. R. Katzer, and G. C. A. Schuit: *Chemistry of Catalytic Processes*, McGraw-Hill, New York, 1979.

Gates, B. C., and coauthors: *Ind. Eng. Chem., Process Des. Dev.*, **22**, 292, 298 (1983); **23**, 773 (1984); **24**, 92 (1985); **25**, 40, 618 (1986).

Gianetto, A. and P. L. Silveston: *Multiphase Chemical Reactors: Theory, Design, Scale-Up*, 1986, Hemisphere.

Grancher, P.: *Hydrocarbon Process.*, July 1978, p. 155; September 1978, p. 257.

Grange, P.: *Catal. Rev.—Sci. Eng.*, **21**, 135 (1980).

Haensel, V.: *Adv. Catal.*, **3**, 179 (1951).

Hatcher, W. J., and T. H. Burton: *I. Chem. E. Symposium Series No. 87* (Eighth International Symposium on Chemical Reaction Engineering), Institute of Chemical Engineers, 1984.

Hemler, C. L., Jr., and L. O. Stine: U.S. Patent 4,148,751 (April 10, 1979) to UOP, Inc.

Hirschberg, E. H., and R. J. Bertolacini, in M. L. Occelli (ed.): *Fluid Catalytic Cracking, ACS Symposium Series No. 375*, 1988, p. 114.

Ho, T. C.: *Catal. Rev.—Sci. Eng.*, **30**, 117 (1988).

Hobson, G. D., and W. Pohl (eds.): *Modern Petroleum Technology*, 4th ed., Wiley, New York, 1973.

Hoffman, H. L.: *Hydrocarbon Process.*, February 1980, p. 57.

Hornaday, G. F., F. M. Ferrell, and G. A. Mills, in J. J. McKetta (ed.): *Advances in Petroleum Chemistry and Refining*, vol. 4, Wiley, New York, 1961, p. 451.

Hughes, R.: *Deactivation of Catalysts*, Academic, New York, 1984, p. 242.

Hughes, T. R., W. C. Buss, P. W. Tamm, and R. L. Jacobson, in Y. Murakami, A. Iijima, and J. W. Ward (eds.): *New Developments in Zeolite Science and Technology*, Elsevier, Amsterdam, 1986, p. 725.

Hughes, T. R., R. L. Jacobsen, and P. W. Tamm, in J. W. Ward (ed.): *Catalysis 1987*, Elsevier, Amsterdam, 1987, p. 317.

Johnson, M. F. L., and H. C. Mayland: *Ind. Eng. Chem.*, **47**, 127 (1955).

Katzer, J. R., and R. Sivasubramian: *Catal. Rev.—Sci. Eng.*, **20**, 155 (1979).

Kearby, K., in B. T. Brooks et al. (eds.): *The Chemistry of Petroleum Hydrocarbons*, vol. 2, Reinhold, New York, 1955, p. 221. See also P. H. Emmett (ed.): *Catalysis*, vol. 3, Reinhold, New York, 1955, p. 453.

Keely, W. M., P. Jerus, E. K. Dienes, and A. L. Hausberger, in H. Heinemann, and G. A. Somorjai (eds.): *Catalysis and Surface Science*, Dekker, New York, 1985, p. 183; also published in *Catal. Rev.—Sci. Eng.*, **26**(3, 4) (1985).

Kluksdahl, H. E.: U.S. Patent 3,415,737 (1968).

Kouwenhoven, H. W. and W. C. van Zijil Langhout: *Chem. Eng. Progress*, **67**(4), 65 (1971).

Kutz, N., in W. H. Flank and T. E. Whyte, Jr. (eds.): *Perspectives in Molecular Sieve Science*, ACS Symposium Series No. 368, 1988.

Langlois, G. E., and R. F. Sullivan: *Am. Chem. Soc., Div. Pet. Chem., Prepr.*, **14**(4), D18 (1969).

La Vopa, V., and C. N. Satterfield: *Energy & Fuels*, **1**, 323 (1987).

La Vopa, V., and C. N. Satterfield: *J. Catal.*, **110**, 375 (1988).

Ledoux, M. J.: in *Catalysis*, vol. 7, The Chemical Society, London, 1988, p. 125.

Lee, C-L., and D. F. Ollis: *J. Catal.*, **87**, 325 (1984).

Lee, E. H.: *Catal. Rev.*, **8**, 285 (1974).

Le Page, J. F., et al.: *Applied Heterogeneous Catalysis*, Technip, Paris, 1987.

Maselli, J. M., and A. W. Peters: *Catal. Rev.—Sci. Eng.*, **26**, 223 (1985).

McIlvried, H. G.: *Ind. Eng. Chem., Process Des. Dev.*, **10**, 125 (1971).

McKinley, J. B., in P. H. Emmett (ed.): *Catalysis*, vol. 5, Reinhold, New York, 1957, p. 405.

Mills, G. A., H. Heinemann, T. H. Milliken, and A. G. Oblad: *Ind. Eng. Chem.*, **45**, 134 (1953).

Minachev, Kh. M., and Ya. I. Isakov, in J. A. Rabo (ed.): *Zeolite Chemistry and Catalysis*, ACS Monogr. No. 171, 1976, p. 552.

Mitchell, P. C. H.: *Catalysis*, Vol. 4, 1981, Royal Society of Chemistry, London.

Moyes, R. B., in Z. Paál and P. G. Menon (eds.): *Hydrogen Effects in Catalysis*, Dekker, New York, 1988, p. 583.

Muhler, M., R. Schlögl, and G. Ertl, in M. J. Phillips and M. Ternan (eds.): *Proceedings of the Ninth International Congress on Catalysis*, The Chemical Institute of Canada, Ottawa, 1988, p. 1758.

Oblad, A. G., T. H. Milliken, Jr., and G. A. Mills: *Adv. Catal.*, **3**, 199 (1951).

Occelli, M. L. (ed.): *Fluid Catalytic Cracking*, ACS Symposium Series No. 375, 1988.

Occelli, M. L., and R. G. Anthony (eds.): *Hydrotreating Catalysts: Preparation, Characterization, and Performance*, Elsevier, Amsterdam, 1989.

Oelderik, J. M., S. T. Sie, and D. Bode: *Appl. Catal.*, **47**, 1 (1989).

Pande, S. G. and D. R. Hardy: *Energy & Fuels*, **3**, 308 (1989). *Fuel*, **69**, 437 (1990).

Pereira, C. J., R. G. Donnelly, and L. L. Hegedus, in E. E. Petersen and A. T. Bell (eds.): *Catalyst Deactivation*, Dekker, New York, 1987, p. 315.

Pierce, V. E., and A. K. Logwinuk: *Hydrocarbon Process.*, September 1985, p. 75.

Poole, C. P., Jr., and D. S. MacIver: *Adv. Catal.*, **17**, 223 (1967).

Prins, R., V. H. J. De Beer, G. A. Somorjai: *Catal. Rev.—Sci. Eng.*, **31**, 1 (1989).

Quann, R. J., R. A. Ware, C-W. Hung, and J. Wei: *Adv. Chem. Eng.*, **14**, 95 (1988).

Ramachandran, P. A. and R. V. Chaudhari: *Three-Phase Catalytic Reactors*, Gordon & Breach, London, 1983.

Ratnasamy, P., and S. Sivasanker: *Catal. Rev.—Sci. Eng.*, **22**, 401 (1980).

Rheaume, L., and R. E. Ritter, in M. L. Occelli (ed.): *Fluid Catalytic Cracking*, ACS Symposium Series No. 375, 1988, p. 146.

Ries, H. E.: *Adv. Catal.*, **4**, 88 (1952).

Rollmann, L. D.: *J. Catal.*, **46**, 243 (1977).

Rossini, F. D., E. J. Prosen, and K. S. Pitzer: *J. Res. Nat. Bur. Stand.*, **27**, 529 (1941).

Ryland, L. B., M. W. Tamele, and J. N. Wilson, in P. H. Emmett (ed.): *Catalysis*, vol. 7, Reinhold, New York, 1960, p. 1.

Satterfield, C. N.: *AIChE J.*, **21**, 209 (1975).

Satterfield, C. N.: *Mass Transfer in Heterogeneous Catalysis*, M.I.T. Press, Cambridge, Mass., 1970. Reprint edition, Krieger, Melbourne, Florida, 1981.

Satterfield, C. N. and J. F. Cocchetto: *AIChE J.*, **21**, 1107 (1975).

Satterfield, C. N., and J. F. Cocchetto: *Ind. Eng. Chem., Proc. Des. Dev.*, **20**, 53 (1981).
Satterfield, C. N., and S. Gültekin: *Ind. Eng. Chem., Proc. Des. Dev.*, **20**, 62 (1981).
Satterfield, C. N., M. Modell, and J. F. Mayer: *AIChE J.*, **21**, 1100 (1975).
Satterfield, C. N., M. Modell, and J. A. Wilkens: *Ind. Eng. Chem., Proc. Des. Dev.*, **19**, 154 (1980).
Satterfield, C. N., and G. W. Roberts: *AIChE J.*, **14**, 159 (1968).
Satterfield, C. N., and C. M. Smith: *Ind. Eng. Chem., Proc. Des. Dev.*, **25**, 942 (1986).
Scherzer, J.: *Catal. Rev.—Sci. Eng.*, **31**, 215 (1989).
Schuit, G. C. A., and B. C. Gates: *AIChE J.*, **19**, 417 (1973).
Schuman, S. C., and H. Shalit: *Catal. Rev.*, **4**, 245 (1970).
Schwartz, A. B.: U.S. Patent 4,072,600 (February 7, 1978) to Mobil.
Shah, Y. T.: *Gas-Liquid-Solid Reactor Design*, McGraw-Hill, New York, 1979.
Sinfelt, J. H.: *Adv. Chem. Eng.*, **5**, 37 (1964).
Sinfelt, J. H., in J. R. Anderson and M. Boudart (eds.): *Catalysis: Science and Technology*, Springer, 1981, vol. 1, p. 257.
Sinfelt, J. H.: *Bimetallic Catalysts: Discoveries, Concepts and Applications*, Wiley, New York, 1983.
Snyder, L. R.: *Am. Chem. Soc., Div. Pet. Chem., Prepr.*, **15**(2), C44 (1970).
Speight, J. G.: *The Chemistry and Technology of Petroleum*, Dekker, 1980.
Speight, J. G.: *The Desulfurization of Heavy Oils and Residua*, Dekker, New York, 1981.
Spitz, P. H.: *Petrochemicals: The Rise of an Industry*, Wiley, New York, 1988.
Sterba, M. J., and V. Haensel: *Ind. Eng. Chem., Prod. Res. Dev.*, **15**, 2 (1976).
Sullivan, R. F., M. M. Boduszynski, and J. C. Fetzer: *Energy & Fuels*, **3**, 603 (1989).
Tamm, P. W., D. H. Mohr, and C. R. Wilson, in J. W. Ward (ed.): *Catalysis 1987*, Elsevier, Amsterdam, 1987, p. 335.
Thomas, J. M., and W. J. Thomas: *Introduction to the Principles of Heterogeneous Catalysis*, Academic, New York, 1967.
Topsøe, H., R. Candia, N-Y. Topsøe, and B. S. Clausen: *Bull. Soc. Chim. Belg.*, **93**, 783 (1984).
Topsøe, H., and B. S. Clausen, in H. Heinemann and G. A. Somorjai (eds.): *Catalysis and Surface Science*, Dekker, New York, 1985, p. 95; also published in *Catal. Rev.—Sci. Eng.*, **26**(3, 4) (1985).
Uhlig, H. F., and W. C. Pfefferle: *Adv. Chem. Ser., No. 97*, 1970, p. 204.
Venuto, P. B., and E. T. Habib: *Catal. Rev.—Sci. Eng.*, **18**, 1 (1978). Also published as *Fluid Catalytic Cracking with Zeolite Catalysts*, Dekker, New York, 1979.
Vlugter, J. C., and P. Van'T Spijker: *Eighth World Petroleum Congress*, vol. 4, Applied Science Publishers, London, 1971, p. 159.
Voge, H. H., in P. H. Emmett (ed.): *Catalysis*, vol. 6, Reinhold, New York, 1958, p. 407.
Vrinat, M. L.: *Appl. Catal.*, **6**, 137 (1983).
Ward, J. W. (ed.): *Catalysis 1987*, Elsevier, Amsterdam, 1987.
Ward, J. W. and S. A. Qader: "Hydrocracking and Hydrotreating," *ACS Symp. Ser. No. 20*, 1975.
Watkins, C. H., and L. E. Hutchings (chairpersons): *Symposium on Advances in Distillate and Residual Oil Technology*, Am. Chem. Soc., Div. Pet. Chem., Prepr., **17**(4), G3 (1972).
Wear, C. C., and R. W. Mott: *Oil Gas J.*, July 25, 1988 (30), p. 71.
Weekman, V. W.: *Fourth International/Sixth European Chemical Reaction Engineering Symposium*, DECHEMA, Frankfurt am Main, 1976, p. 615.
Wei, J., in L. L. Hegedus (ed.): *Catalyst Design: Progress and Perspectives*, Wiley, New York, 1987, p. 245.
Weisser, O., and S. Landa: *Sulphide Catalysts, Their Properties and Applications*, English translation, Pergamon, Elmsford, N.Y., 1973.
Weisz, P.: *Adv. Catal.*, **13**, 137 (1962).
Weisz, P., and R. D. Goodwin: *J. Catal.*, **6**, 227 (1966).
Wheeler, A.: *Adv. Catal.*, **3**, 249 (1951).
Wheeler, A., in P. H. Emmett (ed.): *Catalysis*, Vol. 2, Reinhold, New York, 1955.

Wojciechowski, B. W., and A. Corma: *Catalytic Cracking: Catalysts, Chemistry and Kinetics*, Dekker, New York, 1986.
Yang, S. H., and C. N. Satterfield: *J. Catal.*, **81**, 168 (1983).
Yang, S. H., and C. N. Satterfield: *Ind. Eng. Chem., Proc. Des. Dev.*, **23**, 20 (1984).
Zdražil, M.: *Appl. Catal.*, **4**, 107 (1982).

Synthesis Gas and Associated Processes

This chapter is devoted to a closely related group of industrial catalytic processes, many of which are carried out on a large scale and have been of industrial significance for many decades. These processes center around synthesis gas, a mixture of carbon monoxide and hydrogen, which may be made by a variety of methods, either catalytic or noncatalytic, by reacting natural gas, petroleum residua, or coal with steam, air, and/or oxygen. Various quantities of CO_2 and N_2 may also be present. The catalytic processes are steam reforming of a variety of hydrocarbon feedstocks ranging from natural gas to naphtha or a light gas oil. The synthesis gas may then be reacted over a heterogeneous catalyst to form methanol, paraffins (Fischer-Tropsch synthesis), or methane. With a homogeneous catalyst containing cobalt or rhodium, synthesis gas may be reacted with an olefin to form an aldehyde (oxosynthesis). Extensive current research and development work also suggests the future possibility of economic conversion of synthesis gas into chemical feedstocks such as olefins and aromatics and other chemical products.

For the manufacture of hydrogen for hydrogenation reactions or for ammonia synthesis, all the carbon monoxide must be substantially removed. This is accomplished primarily by the water-gas shift reaction, which converts carbon monoxide by reaction with added steam into carbon dioxide and additional hydrogen. The carbon dioxide is then removed by absorption. The catalytic synthesis of methane has been used as a method of purification of the traces of carbon oxides then remaining. It has also been of interest as a method of converting petroleum fractions or coal to *synthetic natural gas* (SNG) via the formation of synthesis gas. Certain selected hydrogenation processes are discussed in Sec. 6.7.

TABLE 10.1   Free Energy Change ($\Delta G°$) of Selected Reactions of Synthesis Gas, kJ/mol

Reaction	Temperature, °C				
	27	127	227	327	427
$CO + 2H_2 \rightarrow CH_3OH$	−26.4	−3.35	+20.9	+45.2	+69.9
$2CO + 4H_2 \rightarrow C_2H_5OH + H_2O$	−	−74.6	−27.1	+21.2	−
$4CO + 8H_2 \rightarrow C_4H_9OH + 3H_2O$	−	−199.3	−102.5	−3.95	−
$2CO \rightarrow CO_2 + C$	−119.6	−101.8	−83.8	−65.9	−47.9
$CO + 3H_2 \rightarrow CH_4 + H_2O$	−141.8	−119.6	−96.3	−72.4	−47.9
$2CO + 2H_2 \rightarrow CH_4 + CO_2$	−170.3	−143.9	−116.7	−88.9	−60.0
$nCO + 2nH_2 \rightarrow C_nH_{2n} + nH_2O$ ($n = 2$)	−114.0	−81.0	−46.5	−11.18	+24.7
$nCO + (2n + 1)H_2 \rightarrow C_nH_{2n+2} + nH_2O$ ($n = 2$)	−214.9	−169.4	−122.2	−73.8	−24.6

Table 10.1 lists the standard free-energy change as a function of temperature for a number of synthesis reactions of interest. All these reactions, being exothermic, have the most favorable product equilibrium at the lowest temperature. Some reactions, such as synthesis of paraffins, are favorable over the whole temperature range of interest. In each case there is a volume contraction upon reaction; so increased pressure is helpful. The formation of methanol is the most unfavorable reaction and requires high pressure, a relatively low temperature, and an active catalyst to cause it to proceed even to a modest degree. Considerably lower pressures suffice for methanation and Fischer-Tropsch synthesis. With the monohydric alcohols, the equilibrium becomes progressively more favorable with increase in molecular weight (Storch et al. 1951), but their relative distribution in the product from catalytic synthesis is just the opposite (Sec. 10.4.4), being governed by kinetics rather than thermodynamics.

10.1   Steam Reforming

Steam is reacted catalytically with natural gas (primarily methane) or with hydrocarbon feedstocks such as naphthas to form a mixture of H_2, CO, CO_2, and CH_4. The term *steam reforming* should not be confused with *catalytic reforming* or with *steam cracking*, the latter being a noncatalyzed process. The commercial catalyst is in all cases a supported nickel, but there are considerable variations in the nature of the support and in the promoters present. Cobalt and iron are less effective than nickel. The platinum-group metals are highly active but are too expensive.

Starting with hydrocarbons higher than methane, the main course of the reaction appears to be the conversion of the hydrocarbons to carbon monoxide and hydrogen, followed by their reaction to form methane. The water-gas shift reaction [Eq. (10.3)] accompanies these reactions.

$$C_nH_m + nH_2O \rightarrow nCO + (n + [m/2])H_2 \tag{10.1}$$

$$-\Delta H_{298} < 0$$

$$CO + 3H_2 \rightleftharpoons CH_4 + H_2O \tag{10.2}$$

$$-\Delta H_{298} = 206 \text{ kJ/mol}$$

$$CO + H_2O \rightleftharpoons CO_2 + H_2 \tag{10.3}$$

$$-\Delta H_{298} = 41.2 \text{ kJ/mol}$$

Under reaction conditions of industrial interest, the amounts of hydrocarbons other than methane present at equilibrium are vanishingly small and reactions (10.2) and (10.3) nearly approach equilibrium.

10.1.1   Formation and reactions of carbon

Avoiding conditions leading to carbon deposition is particularly important since this can cause blockage of catalyst pores and catalyst deterioration, leading to premature reactor shutdown. A necessary, but not sufficient, requirement is that operating conditions lie outside those in which solid carbon can be formed under equilibrium, as from carbon monoxide or methane:

$$2 CO \rightleftharpoons C + CO_2 \tag{10.4}$$

$$-\Delta H_{298} = 172.5 \text{ kJ/mol}$$

$$CH_4 \rightleftharpoons C + 2H_2 \tag{10.5}$$

$$-\Delta H_{298} = -75 \text{ kJ/mol}$$

Carbon can be present in a form thermodynamically more active than graphite, so that, e.g., the equilibrium ratio CO/CO_2 or CH_4/H_2 can be higher than that calculated for β-graphite. This form of carbon is sometimes termed *Dent carbon* in the earlier literature, from the early work of Dent and Cobb (1929), and Dent et al. (1945). The free energy of this carbon may exceed that of β-graphite by as much as 21 kJ/mol when formed at about 350°C, and up to 15 kJ/mol at 500°C. The properties of the carbon also may be influenced by the nature of the support. Rostrup-Nielsen (1975) has reported that the limiting conditions at which coke formation occurred on nickel by reactions (10.4) and (10.5) seemed to be a function of the nickel crystallite size.

The coke formed on the smallest crystallites showed the greatest deviation from graphite. (See also Sec. 6.5.)

Solid carbon can be formed and can accumulate under conditions in which it would not be present under equilibrium conditions, when reactions leading to its formation are intrinsically faster than those leading to its disappearance. These kinetic matters can be greatly influenced by catalyst composition and by the nature of the hydrocarbons present.

Carbon formation can be eliminated in practice by use of a sufficiently high ratio of steam to hydrocarbon, but that required may be considerably above that called for by thermodynamic equilibrium. For economical operation, reduction of this ratio to the minimum consistent with adequate catalyst life is desirable. Homogeneous thermal cracking of paraffins can occur simultaneously with the catalytic reaction of the paraffin with steam, and this reaction may also form carbon. The homogeneous reaction has a higher activation energy than the catalytic steam reaction and becomes significant above about 650 to 700°C (Bridger and Chinchen 1970). To minimize carbon deposits formed by homogeneous processes, a hydrocarbon-steam mixture should not be subjected to excessively high temperatures before the hydrocarbon has been substantially reacted catalytically.

The relative rates of carbon formation on nickel catalysts, from various hydrocarbons (Bridger and Chinchen 1970, p. 74; Rostrup-Nielsen 1977; Rostrup-Nielsen 1984) are about as follows:

Ethylene > > benzene,toluene > n-heptane > n-hexane

> cyclohexane > trimethylbutane ~

n-butane ~ carbon monoxide > methane

Carbon formation from natural gas is generally not a significant problem, but it can be much more serious with other hydrocarbons. Aromatics such as benzene and toluene are more conducive to coke formation than paraffins and are reformed more slowly. They typically may be present in the order of several percent in a light naphtha, and a sensitive method of monitoring the slow loss of catalyst activity with a naphtha feedstock is by following the gradual increase in aromatics concentration in the product.

The nature of the carbon deposit varies considerably with operating conditions and causes catalyst deactivation in different ways. Rostrup-Nielsen and Tøttrup (1979) and Rostrup-Nielsen (1984) distinguish three forms. Under steam reforming conditions, the carbon deposit dominating at temperatures below about 500°C is the result of slow polymerization of CH_x structures to form an *encapsulating film*. That dominating above about 450°C is *carbon-filament* growth (Sec. 6.5).

Above 600°C, thermal cracking of hydrocarbons causes deposition of carbon precursors on the catalyst, which forms *pyrolytic carbon*. Rostrup-Nielsen and Nielsen (1985) further discuss criteria for carbon-free operation.

The rate of the carbon-steam reaction is about 2 to 3 times faster than the rate of the carbon-carbon dioxide reaction, but the reaction rate of carbon with hydrogen is insignificant. One of the objectives of catalyst formulation is to catalyze the carbon-steam reaction. This is achieved by addition of an alkaline substance, which may act, in part, by neutralizing acid sites that catalyze cracking reactions. The alkali may also adsorb and dissociate water, providing a mechanism for reacting deposited carbon with an oxygen-containing species.

10.1.2 Applications of steam reforming

Steam reforming may be aimed at any one of several applications with, consequently, substantially different operating conditions.

The most important ones are:

1. Conversion of a naphtha to *substitute natural gas*, a gas with a high CH_4 content.

2. Conversion of a naphtha to a mixture of CH_4, CO, and H_2, so-called *town gas*, which has a heating value of about 500 Btu/ft^3 (1 Btu/ft^3 = 27,680 J/m^3). This is sometimes termed *medium Btu gas*. The product can also be converted to gas of a higher heating value by subsequent methanation.

3. Conversion of a naphtha or natural gas in a several-step process to a 3:1 mole ratio of H_2-N_2 for synthesis of ammonia.

4. Formation of a CO-H_2 mixture for synthesis of methanol, use in oxosynthesis, or Fischer-Tropsch synthesis.

5. Manufacture of H_2.

The first two processes were of considerable interest in the period of the 1940s to the 1960s in locations around the world where natural gas was not readily available. With the subsequent increased and widespread availability of natural gas, interest in these processes dropped. (See also Sec. 10.6.)

Figure 10.1 shows the calculated equilibrium composition of the product gas from n-heptane under representative reaction conditions. Figure 10.2 shows typical reforming conditions for the various aforementioned applications (Rostrup-Nielsen 1975, pp. 23 and 25). The formation of methane is favored at lower temperatures, so in applications where high conversion of methane is desired, high reactor exit

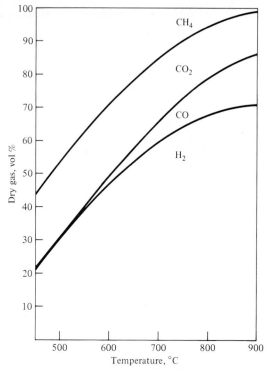

Figure 10.1 Equilibrium composition (dry basis) from steam reforming of n-heptane. Pressure: 3 MPa. H_2O/C = 4.0 mol/atom. Width of band indicates percentage of specified component present. (*Rostrup-Nielsen 1975, p. 23*)

temperatures are required. Other figures showing gas composition as a function of temperature, pressure, and steam ratio for methane and naphtha feedstocks are given by Ridler and Twigg (1989). Slack and James (1974, part I) give tables relating the percentage of methane converted at equilibrium as a function of pressure and steam-methane ratio.

For conversion of naphtha to a high-methane product using a low H_2O-C ratio in the feed-gas mixture, the overall heat of reaction may be slightly exothermic. For all other cases the reaction is endothermic, and highly so when the hydrocarbon is converted essentially completely to carbon oxides and hydrogen. For conversion of natural gas to synthesis gas, the natural gas is mixed with steam, in a mole ratio of about 1:3 to 1:4, and passed over the catalyst. The catalyst is typically held in one or two banks of vertical high-alloy steel (e.g., 20% nickel and 25% chromium) tubes, 9 to 16 cm in internal diameter and 6 to 12 m long, heated in a box-type furnace. Feed enters the reactors

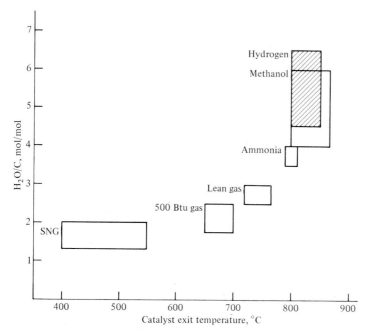

Figure 10.2 Typical reforming conditions for various applications. (*Rostrup-Nielsen 1975, p. 25*)

at about 500°C and products leave at a temperature of about 800 to 850°C, the external wall temperature being about 900°C (Rostrup-Nielsen 1975, p. 31). Pressure is in the range of about 1.5 to 3 MPa or possibly higher, in part because often the product gas is to be used at elevated pressure.

The maximum exit temperature allowable at the desired pressure is set largely by metallurgical limitations on the reactor tubes. Operating conditions may vary somewhat with the properties of the feedstock such as the nature and amounts of higher hydrocarbons present and impurities such as sulfur compounds. The methane content in the exit gas should be as low as practicable. This condition is favored by high temperature, but the exit temperature is determined by an economic balance on the entire process. Methane is generally inert in ammonia synthesis or in hydrogenation reactions. It is detrimental only because it reduces the partial pressure of the reacting gases and because, in its purge from the overall system, some valuable synthesis gas or hydrogen is also lost.

In the generation of hydrogen for use in hydrogenation reactors or hydroprocessing in refineries, the methane content in the exit gas is typically in the range of 1 to 3 percent (dry basis). The CH_4 present typically equals the equilibrium content as calculated for a temperature within about 25°C of the exit temperature. For technical purposes the approach to equilibrium is sometimes expressed by a phrase such as "the exit temperature is within x°C of the equilibrium temperature." For generation of gas for ammonia synthesis, CH_4 content is typically in the range of 10 percent (dry basis) (Sec. 10.5). Reactor temperatures are some 100 to 200°C lower for naphtha conversion than for methane conversion. Even when the product will be utilized at essentially atmospheric pressure, operation at elevated reactor pressure is usually economically advantageous. High pressure reduces the reactor volume necessary, and pressure drop through the bed is less for a specified mass flow rate, thus reducing compression costs. Natural gas and refinery gases are also generally available under pressure.

For ammonia synthesis, reduction of the methane content in the product gases from the primary reformer to a very low level is desirable in order to minimize the purge of methane in the subsequent ammonia synthesis step. To do this and to introduce nitrogen, the exit gas from the primary reformer, which contains up to about 10% methane (dry basis) is mixed with air and fed to a secondary, adiabatic reformer. Here the exothermic reaction of methane and air supplies heat to raise the temperature another 150 to 200°C, i.e., to the neighborhood of 1000°C or higher. Such temperatures would be difficult to achieve with externally fired metal-alloy tubes. The amount of air introduced is adjusted to form the ultimate 1:3 N_2-H_2 ratio required for ammonia-synthesis gas. The primary and secondary reformer operations clearly must be closely coupled to provide the necessary overall mass and thermal balance. Typically, the secondary reactor is refractory-lined, and the catalyst is nickel supported on a form of alumina that is thermally and mechanically resistant at these very high temperatures. Sometimes a nickel supported on chromia-alumina, which has high thermal resistance, is placed in the top portion of the bed in the secondary reformer.

Product gas is then cooled, additional steam is added, and additional H_2 is produced by passing the mixture through a water-gas shift reactor (Sec. 10.3). CO_2 is then removed by absorption, as by use of an amine-promoted aqueous K_2CO_3 solution. Remaining traces of CO and CO_2 are removed by applying the methanation reaction (Sec. 10.6). For making feed gas for synthesis of CH_3OH or for the Oxo process (CO-H_2 ratios of 1:2 or 1, respectively), the shift reaction is not used. CO_2 is added or H_2 removed for the overall mass balance.

Figure 10.3 is a photograph of the reforming operations of a large ammonia-synthesis plant. The primary reformer is in the center and consists of two furnace chambers with eight rows of burners on the side walls. Gases enter through inlet hairpins apparent at the top. The

Figure 10.3 Reforming operations of a 1250 metric ton/day ammonia plant. Anic, Manfredonia. (*Courtesy of J. R. Rostrup-Nielsen*)

vertical cylindrical vessel to the immediate left is the waste-heat boiler to which the exit gases from the secondary reformer are passed (the secondary reformer is hidden behind the waste-heat boiler). The high- and low-temperature shift reactors are contained together in the large vertical vessel to the far left. To the immediate right of the primary reformer is the stack for reformer flue gas and to its right is the compressor house.

10.1.3 Reforming catalysts

The high temperature of the steam-reforming reaction and the presence of steam set stringent requirements on the formulation of the supported nickel catalyst. Silica, unless suitably combined, may be slowly volatilized by steam at these temperatures, leading to catalyst degradation and deposition of silica downstream, an effect which is accelerated at higher pressures. Transition aluminas such as γ and η are not stable. The support is therefore a low-area, refractory-type material. In early processes operating at pressures up to about 0.3 MPa, the most common support was a calcium aluminate silicate, which was inexpensive and gradually became stronger with use. This catalyst support was unsatisfactory at higher pressures (up to about 3 MPa) because of migration of silica at the higher steam partial pressures.

In the early 1960s this support was replaced with a low-silica calcium aluminate; it, however, had a lower crush strength, gradually lost strength on use, and lost activity by gradual formation of nickel aluminate. This support, in turn, was replaced with a low-area α-alumina that, although more expensive, was mechanically stronger and longer lasting. Potassium compounds or other alkaline substances are frequently added to accelerate carbon-removal reactions. However, they may be slowly lost from the catalyst by volatilization and be deposited downstream on heat-exchange surfaces or on other catalyst beds. Minimizing the sintering of nickel is also important, and this is related to support composition and method of catalyst preparation.

The catalyst formulation may vary somewhat depending on whether the feedstock is to be methane, light hydrocarbons, or a naphtha, since the propensity to coke formation varies with feedstock composition. Table 10.2 lists the composition of several industrial reforming catalysts. The presence of alkali accelerates carbon-removal reactions but reduces catalyst activity, and alkali may cause corrosion and/or fouling problems downstream. For a natural-gas feed the use of alkali is usually unnecessary, and a higher-activity catalyst may be used instead. With a naphtha, control of carbon-forming reactions is more important, and alkali or alkaline earth substances are often added for this purpose.

The most effective alkali is K_2O, which is mobile on the catalyst surfaces but may be slowly lost by volatilization. In ICI catalyst 46-1 (Table 10.2), potassium is in the form of kalsilite $K_2O \cdot Al_2O_3 \cdot SiO_2$. This reacts slowly with CO_2 to form K_2CO_3, which is then rapidly hydrolyzed to KOH. This formulation avoids an excessive rate of loss of volatile potassium compound. Either alkaline or alkaline earth substances enhance steam adsorption. With naphtha reforming, the higher hydrocarbons are converted in the top of the bed, so that only CH_4 reforming occurs thereafter. Consequently, one catalyst formulation may be used in the first half of the reactor and a second in the lower half. Some catalyst compositions may contain sulfate, which, during the initial reduction and first hours of operation, is converted to H_2S and passes downstream. Unless this gas is vented or the H_2S otherwise controlled, it may poison downstream catalysts, such as those in the water-gas shift reactors.

The total surface of these catalysts is about 2 to 3 m^2/g, and that of the nickel metal, after being subjected to operating conditions, is about 0.5 m^2/g. The corresponding crystallite size is about 1 μm. Catalyst life is typically one to three years. As catalyst activity gradually drops, the furnace temperature is gradually raised to maintain the reaction rate constant. After a period, one or more "hot bands" may appear on the outside of the tubes, caused by a local drop in the rate of the endothermal reaction that keeps the tube walls below the firing temperature. These bands can be brought about by carbon deposition within the pores of the catalyst, which can ultimately lead to disinte-

TABLE 10.2 Composition of Typical Industrial Steam Reforming Catalysts

Producer*	Catalyst	Feedstock	Components, wt %						
			NiO	Al_2O_3	MgO	$MgAl_2O_4$	CaO	SiO_2	K_2O
BGC	CRG B	Naphtha	79	20–21	—	—	—	—	0.75–3.3
ICI	46-1	Naphtha	22	26	11	—	13	16	7
ICI	57-3	Natural gas	12	78	—	—	10	(0.1)	
Topsøe	RKS-1	Natural gas	15	—	—	85	—	(0.1)	
Topsøe	R67	Natural gas/LPG	15	—	—	85	—	(0.1)	
Topsøe	RKNR	Naphtha	34	12	54				
UCI	C-11-9	Natural gas	11–20†						
UCI	G-56	Light hydrocarbons	15–25†						
UCI	G-90	Light hydrocarbons	7–15†						

*BGC = British Gas Corp.; ICI = Imperial Chemical Industries Ltd.; UCI = United Catalysts Inc.
†Balance consists of unspecified refractory.
SOURCE: Rostrup-Nielsen (1984, p. 31).

gration of the pellet to powder. The process can be self-accelerating since the increased internal reactor temperature accelerates carbon deposition by reactions such as $CH_4 \to C + 2H_2$. The tube wall temperature may thus be increased to a level at which a metallurgical limitation necessitates shutdown of that tube. The hot spots typically occur at some position intermediate between inlet and exit, where the combination of hydrocarbon concentration and temperature maximizes the rate of carbon deposition.

Shutdown may also be indicated when the pressure drop reaches an uneconomic level, caused by accumulation of fines. Fines generation in turn may be caused by carbon formation and enhanced by plant upsets. Carbon can sometimes be removed satisfactorily by steaming, after which the catalyst is rereduced and the reactor put back on stream. Even when the catalyst is operating satisfactorily, it may be replaced during a scheduled general plant shutdown, as a precaution against a forced shutdown that might be required if it were to be extended to its full life. Shutdown and startup procedures are rather specific since at elevated temperatures too high a hydrocarbon concentration can cause coke deposits and too high a steam concentration can lead to overoxidation.

Nickel catalysts are very sensitive to poisoning by sulfur compounds, and the sulfur content of the feed gas must be reduced to a value below about 0.2 to 0.5 ppm in commercial operations. The coverage of adsorbed sulfur is determined by the ratio P_{H_2S}-P_{H_2}. The nickel becomes saturated at a value of this ratio of the order of 10^{-3} of that at which bulk Ni_3S_2 is formed at equilibrium. This illustrates the fact that surface chemisorbed species can exist under equilibrium conditions where the equivalent bulk solid does not exist. The poisoning is reversible; if sulfur is completely eliminated from the feed gas, the surface nickel sulfide is reduced back to elemental nickel. However, sulfur inhibits the rate of carbon formation so partial poisoning of an active nickel catalyst may be desirable in some cases, e.g., to produce a low-H_2/CO synthesis gas (Dibbern et al. 1986; Rostrup-Nielsen & Alstrup, 1988). This is an application of structure sensitivity as discussed in Sec. 6.1.1.

For industrial reactors there has been a trend toward use of sturdy rings, pellets pierced with multiple holes, "wagon wheels," and other unusual shapes. This is to achieve high void fraction, for minimum pressure drop, increased catalyst effectiveness factor, and possibly greater bed thermal conductivity. (See Fig. 4.2 and 4.3.) There are large gradients of temperature and composition between the bulk gas and the outside of catalyst pellets, as well as both axially and radially in an industrial packed tube. Thus, obtaining intrinsic kinetic information for practicable catalysts under industrial operating conditions is difficult. The rate of reforming appears to be approximately first order in methane, possibly inhibited to some extent by carbon monoxide and/or hydrogen. Kinetic studies are reviewed by Temkin (1979) and Van Hook (1980). Ridler and Twigg (1989) give an extensive tabulation of published rate equations for methane and other paraffins plus toluene, together with useful remarks on each study. Rostrup-Nielsen (1984) also discusses kinetics and catalysis in detail. Catalysts are also reviewed by Ross (1983). Bridger (1980) reviews the literature with emphasis on the period after 1974.

10.1.4 Reforming processes

The first steam reformers were started up in Germany by BASF about 1926 to 1928 and in the United States by the Standard Oil Co. of New Jersey (now Exxon) in 1930. For the production of hydrogen, these were usually designed for operation at slightly above atmospheric pressure; beginning in the 1950s, pressures were increased in new designs up to levels in the range of 0.4 to 1 MPa. In the 1960s pressures in the range of 3 MPa came into use, particularly for integrated steam-reforming and ammonia-synthesis plants. Increased pressure is unfavorable for conversion of methane to carbon monoxide and hydrogen, but this is compensated for by the high temperatures obtained in secondary reforming. Other industrial developments and many further details on catalysts and processes are provided by Ridler and Twigg (1989), in the book by Rostrup-Nielsen (1975), and a later detailed treatise (Rostrup-Nielsen, 1984). Much of the foregoing discussion has been drawn from these sources.

For the production of hydrogen for refinery use, typically feed gas or naphtha is desulfurized, mixed with steam, and reformed, and the product gas will be passed through high- and low-temperature water-gas shift converters. Carbon dioxide is removed by absorption, and the remaining low concentration of carbon oxides removed by conversion to methane.

With a natural gas or refinery gas consisting of light hydrocarbons, the sulfur compounds and other acid gases present may be reduced to a level below 60 to 80 vol ppm by scrubbing with a solution of an organic base such as monoethanolamine. The sulfur level may then be reduced to less than 1 ppm by adsorption at 20 to 50°C on activated carbon impregnated with a metal. This adsorbent is regenerated by steaming at about 160°C or higher. The effectiveness of scrubbing for removal of sulfur compounds varies greatly with their nature. Carbon adsorption is less effective with sulfur compounds of low boiling points, such as H_2S and COS; it is also less effective in the presence of higher-boiling-point hydrocarbons.

A variety of other processes may be used for removing mercaptans and other sulfur compounds from a feed stream. Mercaptans may be oxidized with air to disulfides, which are then removed by caustic scrubbing, or sulfur compounds may be removed by adsorption on zeolites. Catalytic hydrodesulfurization is usually used with feed streams consisting of naphthas and higher hydrocarbons in which the sulfur compounds present are not removable by scrubbing. Various sulfur compounds may also be removed by adsorption on hot ZnO, which is then discarded (Sec. 9.9). ZnO is effective with a much wider range of substances than is activated carbon, but the fact that it is nonregenerable makes its use costly except with low sulfur concentrations. Other possible poisons such as chloride and arsenic must also be controlled. Carnell (1989) gives a detailed treatment of feedstock purification and discusses the use of ZnO in some detail.

Synthesis gas may be prepared by a variety of noncatalytic methods. The first large-scale industrial uses were for the synthesis of ammonia and methanol, the synthesis gas being made by reacting coke with steam and air in a cyclic process. Steam was injected into a bed of hot coke to form carbon monoxide and hydrogen, thus termed *water gas*. The temperature dropped because of the endothermic reaction; after a period the bed was reheated by injection of air, and the cycle was repeated. Coke was used instead of coal to avoid problems from the formation of tar and other volatiles and impurities.

From the period of about 1910 to 1940, processes based on coke were predominant. After World War II they were gradually replaced by catalytic processes utilizing natural gas (especially in the United States, where supplies were plentiful and inexpensive) and naphtha (in Europe, where petroleum became a low-cost source of fuel, replacing coal). Today partial oxidation (noncatalytic) processes are of practical interest for conversion to synthesis gas of carbonaceous substances not readily reacted catalytically, such as heavy hydrocarbon feedstocks, coal, and other solids. Typically, oxygen, steam, and the feedstock are passed through an unpacked reactor at substantial pressure and 1400 to 1600°C, or a fluidized-bed reactor may be used. The synthesis gas is then purified.

10.2 Fischer-Tropsch Synthesis

The Fischer-Tropsch synthesis is broadly defined as the reductive polymerization (oligomerization) of CO by H_2 to form organic products containing primarily carbon and hydrogen. Lesser amounts of oxygenated products such as alcohols may also be formed. Beginning in the early 1920s Fischer and his coworkers studied a variety of catalyst compositions for the conversion of synthesis gas to fuels. In 1923 Fischer and Tropsch, working at the Kaiser Wilhelm Institute, reported that a liquid product was obtained at 10 to 15 MPa and 400 to 450°C using alkalized iron turnings as the catalyst. This was termed the "Synthol process," and the same term has been applied to an entrained-bed synthesis process developed later and currently used in South Africa.

Iron catalysts performed poorly at atmospheric pressure, and after study of many catalysts, they developed a cobalt catalyst promoted with ThO_2 and MgO, supported on kieselguhr, that operated satisfactorily at "normal pressure." This led to the construction in about 1936 by Ruhrchemie of the first commercial plant. By 1941 fifteen plants were in operation. Nine of these were in Germany, with a total rated output of about 16,000 barrels per day (for petroleum, 1 bbl = 42 gal = 0.519 m^3). These plants all used a cobalt catalyst in fixed-bed reactors, the plants being designed to run at essentially atmospheric pressure. The product consisted of a broad slate of gasoline, diesel oil, waxes, and detergents. However, the catalyst became coated with waxy products and required frequent regeneration by treatment with hydrogen or solvent extraction. The rise and fall of this process was highly related to demands for liquid fuels in World War II since Germany has no significant indigenous petroleum but considerable bituminous coal.

In the United States, concern about depletion of petroleum resources led to increased interest in processes for synthesizing liquid fuels. The U.S. Synthetic Fuels Acts of 1944, which expired in 1953, authorized an extensive research and development program at the U.S. Bureau of Mines. In 1938 Hydrocarbon Research in the United States had acquired the rights from Ruhrchemie to Fischer-Tropsch synthesis outside Germany. In the early 1950s Carthage Hydrocol, Inc., formed by a consortium of petroleum companies, built a plant at Brownsville, Texas, based on a process developed by Hydrocarbon Research. Natural gas was reformed to synthesis gas and converted to liquids utilizing an alkalized iron catalyst in a fluidized-bed reactor. Reaction conditions were about 315°C and 1.8 MPa. This plant was designed to produce 360,000 tons per year of liquid fuels and 40,000 tons per year of chemical products, but it never operated satisfactorily and was closed in 1957. One factor was that natural gas, originally available for a few cents per million Btu because it could only be used locally, began to increase in value with the construction of a vast pipeline network for its distribution throughout the United States. Moreover, plentiful supplies of petroleum became available from new discoveries, notably in the Middle East.

In 1955 an installation in Coalbrook (Sasolburg), South Africa began operation using an iron catalyst in fixed-bed and entrained-bed reactors with a combined capacity of about 5000 barrels per day, producing a broad spectrum of chemicals as well as fuels. This and subsequent plants are state-owned and are known as SASOL (South African Synthetic Oil Limited). A much larger scale plant, known as SASOL-II, was constructed at Secunda and came into operation about 1980, with a capacity of about 50,000 barrels per day. A third plant, also at Secunda, of similar capacity and design came into operation about 1984. Both of these later plants use an entrained-bed process* which, together with ancillary operations, is aimed primarily at producing gasoline.

These plants utilize synthesis gas derived from coal. South Africa has large coal reserves but essentially no petroleum, and these plants supply more than half of South Africa's consumption needs of liquid fuels. A fourth plant, utilizing an iron catalyst and synthesis gas derived from natural gas, was under design as of 1990. In 1989 it was announced that a Fischer-Tropsch synthesis plant with a capacity of about 500,000 metric tons per year was to be constructed in Sarawak, Malaysia by a consortium headed by Shell and including Mitsubishi and others. Synthesis gas derived from natural gas was to be converted utilizing a cobalt catalyst in a multitube fixed-bed reactor. Completion was scheduled for late 1992.

The fixed-bed reactors at SASOL operate at about 220°C and 2.7 MPa, using a precipitated iron catalyst heavily promoted with potassium with the objective of making primarily high-molecular-weight waxy products. The entrained-bed reactors operate at about 320°C and 2.2 MPa with a reduced fused-magnetite catalyst of considerably lower potassium content, with the objective of producing primarily products with a boiling-point range suitable for gasoline. The entrained-bed process accounts for most of the capacity.

With the advent of the commercial MTG process for conversion of methanol directly to high-octane gasoline, (Sec. 7.7.9), the fact that Fischer-Tropsch synthesis produces primarily straight-chain hydrocarbons makes it of particular interest for manufacture of diesel fuel (about C_{10}-C_{20}) and jet fuel. By optimizing catalyst composition and operating conditions to maximize high-molecular-weight products, separation of the C_{10}-C_{20} fraction and hydrocracking of the C_{20} + in a second step allows a high fraction of the synthesized product to be con-

---

*Finely divided catalyst and synthesis gas flow upward cocurrently in a pipe-like reactor at a high velocity (perhaps about 20 ft/s.). This is somewhat similar to the entrained-bed process used in fluid catalytic cracking, an endothermic reaction, except that heat exchangers are placed in the SASOL entrained-bed reactors to remove heat from the highly exothermic Fischer-Tropsch reaction.

verted into the C_{10}-C_{20} range. (In the SASOL operation the wax fraction is purified and sold as a chemical product.)

10.2.1 Mechanism

Iron has been studied much more than cobalt, and the discussion here focuses on what is known about iron. The weight of the evidence is that the key step is the dissociation of adsorbed CO to form surface carbon C_s as the required intermediate, termed the *carbide theory*. The C_s may be, or develop into, more than one form of carbon; it may undergo Fischer-Tropsch synthesis reactions as outlined below, it may aggregate into relatively unreactive graphitic-like carbon, or it may diffuse into the iron to form iron carbides. The main synthesis steps are probably as follows.

CO can dissociate from an adsorbed form via

$$CO_g \rightarrow CO_s \rightarrow C_s + O_s \tag{10.6}$$

or by Boudouard disproportionation of CO,

$$2\,CO \rightarrow C_s + CO_2 \tag{10.7}$$

The adsorbed oxygen atoms, O_s, in Eq. (10.6) can be removed by reaction with adsorbed hydrogen to form water. If H_2 pressure is low, the O_s can react with CO to form CO_2, but these conditions are unlikely under usual synthesis conditions. The C_s reacts with adsorbed dissociated hydrogen either to form methane (via Eq. 10.8) or hydrocarbons (via Eqs. 10.9 to 10.12).

$$C_s + H_s \rightarrow CH_s \xrightarrow{H_s} CH_{2,s} \xrightarrow{H_s} CH_{3,s} \xrightarrow{H_s} CH_{4,g} \tag{10.8}$$

Instead of reacting with H_s to form CH_4, chain growth can occur by a series of steps such as:

$$CH_{3,s} + CH_{x,s} \rightarrow CH_3CH_{x,s} \tag{10.9}$$

$$CH_3CH_{x,s} + (2-x)H_s \rightarrow CH_3CH_{2,s} \tag{10.10}$$

etc.

Termination and desorption can occur to form either a paraffin or an olefin, e.g.,

$$CH_3C_nH_{2n}CH_x + (3-x)H \rightarrow CH_3C_nH_{2n}CH_3 \tag{10.11}$$

or

$$CH_3C_nH_{2n}CH_2CH_x + (1-x)H \rightarrow CH_3C_nH_{2n}CH=CH_2 \tag{10.12}$$

Olefins appear generally to be the primary product, but some researchers believe that some paraffins are formed as a primary product under some conditions.

Earlier ideas that chain propagation occurs by CO insertion followed by reduction now seem unlikely. However n-alcohols and probably aldehydes are also formed to a lesser degree as primary products, and these may be produced by CO insertion into the alkyl-metal bond upon desorption. Sachtler (1984) has suggested that with iron this insertion step occurs on sites at oxide patches. These would be preferentially formed at high ratios of H_2O-H_2 or CO_2-CO. Another earlier theory was that a species such as M-CHOH was formed as a first step via hydrogenation of chemisorbed CO and that chain growth occurred by condensation of these groups with elimination of water and addition of hydrogen. There is little evidence to support this theory.

A kinetic expression consistent with the carbide theory was developed by Huff and Satterfield (1984) using Langmuir-Hinshelwood kinetics.

$$-R_{H_2 + CO} = \frac{ab\, P_{CO}P_H^2}{P_{H_2O} + bP_{CO}P_{H_2}} \tag{10.13}$$

This expression fits the available data well over a wide range of temperature, pressure, and degree of conversion. Alternative expressions have been developed by others, as reviewed in the aforementioned paper. One common feature of most proposed models is that at conversions of H_2 + CO up to about 60 percent, the expressions reduce to a simple first order in hydrogen:

$$-R_{H_2 + CO} = aP_{H_2} \tag{10.14}$$

Metallic iron as such is not a very active catalyst. Upon exposure to synthesis gas it becomes converted to one or more carbides and its activity increases. Under representative industrial conditions, about 20 to 60 hours or more may be required for a quasi-steady-state activity to be reached. Simultaneously, the iron surface becomes covered with a layer or layers of carbon through which the synthesis gas is transported. However, the catalyst composition can continue to change slowly over a several-hundred-hour period, with a consequent slow change in product composition (Satterfield et al. 1986).

It is evident that the molecular weight of the product molecule is determined by the probability of chain growth relative to that of product desorption. A stepwise mechanism for chain growth was first proposed by Herington in 1946 and has been further developed by many others, notably by R. B. Anderson and coworkers, to allow for such effects as isomer distributions and an explanation for low C_2 product formation. These are briefly reviewed by Satterfield and Huff (1982). More recently, detailed kinetic models have been developed and discussed by Taylor and Wojciechowski (1984) and Schulz et al. (1988).

One relatively simple scheme has been frequently used to analyze observed products solely in terms of carbon-number distribution without concern for isomers or secondary reactions. It is frequently termed the *Schulz-Flory distribution* because in slightly different forms it was derived by Schulz (1935) for the radical polymerization of vinyl monomers and by Flory (1936), using a statistical approach applied to a linear condensation polymerization.

The Schulz expression is

$$W_n = (\ln^2 \alpha) n \alpha^n \qquad (10.15)$$

where W_n is the weight fraction of hydrocarbon containing n carbon atoms and α is the chain-growth probability factor defined as:

$$\alpha = \frac{r_p}{r_p + r_t} \qquad (10.16)$$

where r_p and r_t are the rates of propagation and termination, respectively.

The Flory expression gives the mole fraction, m_n, of molecules in the polymer that contains n structural units as

$$m_n = (1 - \alpha)\alpha^{(n-1)} \qquad (10.17)$$

This has since been shown to apply to any polymerization process, regardless of the mechanism, if the primary step is addition of carbon units one at a time onto the terminus of a growing linear chain and one polymer molecule is produced from each kinetic chain, i.e., termination by coupling is negligible.

If the added weight of each carbon unit is proportional to n, the weight-fraction distribution W_n is

$$W_n = (1 - \alpha)^2 n \alpha^{(n-1)} \qquad (10.18)$$

Flory noted that at $\alpha > 0.5$ this is equivalent to that developed by Schulz.

If oxygenated species are significant in amount, their greater weight per carbon number suggests that the mole fraction, Flory distribution should be the basic relationship for analysis of data.

Eq. (10.17) is conveniently expressed in a logarithmic form:

$$\ln m_n = n \ln (\alpha) + \ln (1 - \alpha/\alpha) \qquad (10.19)$$

If the probability of chain growth and chain termination, and hence α, is independent of chain length, then a plot of $\ln m_n$ versus n should be a straight line. In principle the value of α could be determined from either the slope (as $\ln \alpha$) or the ordinate intercept as $\ln (1 - \alpha)$ at $n = 1$. The slope is generally easier to use and is more reliable.

A straight-line relationship suggested by Eq. (10.19) and a constant value of α up to values of n of approximately 10 is found for iron catalysts under a variety of conditions if all species formed, including oxygenates, are included. Sometimes C_1 (primarily CH_4) deviates, but it may be formed by a different mechanism, so this is not unexpected. The C_2 species, which typically comprise mostly C_2H_4 and C_2H_5OH, are sometimes low, but both of these compounds are highly reactive and they may become incorporated into chains by a secondary reaction under some conditions.

In some studies only hydrocarbon products are reported. The mole ratio of oxygenates to hydrocarbons is often greatest at C_2, decreasing steadily with increasing C number. Some reports of "low C_2" may stem from exclusion of oxygenates from the product. The occurrence of a straight-line relationship when oxygenates are included implies that they, as well as the hydrocarbons, are formed from a common precursor and that the specific type of product formed is determined by the nature of the chain-termination reaction.

On most iron catalysts the data seem to fall on two straight lines breaking at about C_{10}, i.e., the product seems to represent the sum of two Flory distributions with two values of α; α_2 for the higher carbon numbers exceeds α_1, i.e., more higher-molecular-weight material is formed than would be predicted from the molecular weight distribution of the $< C_{10}$ fraction. An example is shown in Fig. 10.4.* The phenomenon is also reported on other types of catalysts, and possible explanations are speculative.

10.2.2 Catalysts

The classical Fischer-Tropsch catalysts are forms of iron or cobalt. More recently ruthenium has received considerable attention in laboratory and pilot plant studies but has not been used commercially. With the iron and cobalt catalysts, by varying promoters, pressure, temperature, H_2/CO ratio and type of reactor, the nature and the average molecular weight of the products can be markedly varied. Cobalt yields a much higher ratio of paraffins to olefins and much less oxygenated species such as alcohols and aldehydes than does iron.

---

*The presentation of data in this form for molar distribution of one or more kinds of products as a function of carbon number is described in the literature as a Flory, Schulz-Flory, or Anderson-Schulz-Flory plot. The three terms are equivalent when referring to a plot of data or an observed distribution. The plot may or may not have mechanistic significance.

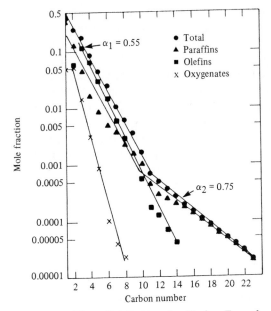

Figure 10.4 Flory distribution for Fischer-Tropsch synthesis products from iron catalyst promoted with MnO: 283°C, 1.24 MPa, $(H_2/CO)_{in}$ = 1.19. (*Satterfield and Stenger 1984. Reprinted with permission from Ind. Eng. Chem., Process Des. Dev. Copyright 1984 by American Chemical Society.*)

Nickel forms predominantly methane. This broad comparison of the behavior of the three elements as catalysts can be rationalized in terms of the general observation that hydrogenation activity increases in the order: Fe < Co < Ni, although the relative effectiveness of these catalysts in adsorbing and dissociating CO also plays a role.

The classical iron catalysts are made either by a precipitation process or a fusion process based on magnetite. The latter forms a more attrition-resistant catalyst, required to minimize catalyst losses in entrained-bed reactors. In either case the catalysts contain a small amount of potassium, which acts as a chemical promoter. The fused catalyst is similar to that used in ammonia synthesis and also contains a structural promoter (alumina) to minimize sintering and loss of catalytic area on reduction. Precipitated iron catalysts may or may not contain a moderate amount of a structural support (usually silica). If silica is present in large amounts, e.g., exceeding perhaps 25 percent of the total, it is difficult to reduce the iron catalysts and performance deteriorates.

Potassium increases catalyst activity over that observed in its absence, up to an optimum amount, and seems to be needed for maintenance of activity over the long term. It also increases average molecular weight of the products and affects secondary reactions.

Potassium is hypothesized to donate electrons to the iron, thereby weakening the C—O bond, strengthening the Fe—C bond, and weakening the Fe—H bond. Consequently the quantity of CO adsorbed increases and that of H_2 decreases. Since C—O bond breaking is postulated to be the rate-limiting step, catalyst activity for all CO-consuming reactions is increased, and the strengthened Fe—C bond increases the probability of the growing chain remaining on the catalyst surface. Hence, product distribution is shifted to compounds of higher carbon number. With the weakened Fe—H bond and less hydrogen adsorption, methane formation drops, less paraffins are formed by secondary hydrogenations, and oxygenate selectivity increases from the enhanced adsorption of CO. The other alkalis act similarly to potassium but less effectively. The alkali may also interact with the silica, lowering the effectiveness of the alkali.

Copper is frequently added to precipitated iron catalysts. Copper allows the reduction temperature to be lowered substantially, reducing sintering and permitting a higher surface area to be obtained. This promoter apparently does not affect the selectivity of the synthesis.

10.2.3 Reaction network

On iron catalysts over a range of conditions of industrial interest, the primary products appear to be α-olefins, and to a much lesser extent, oxygenates, particularly alcohols, plus water. Some investigators report n-paraffins as also being formed as a primary product.

By secondary reactions olefins are hydrogenated to paraffins; α-olefins may be isomerized to β-olefins. Incorporation of olefins into growing chains seems to be minor on iron catalysts at industrial operating conditions. This network is summarized in Fig. 10.5.

The importance of these secondary reactions, relative to each other and to the primary reactions, varies considerably with catalyst com-

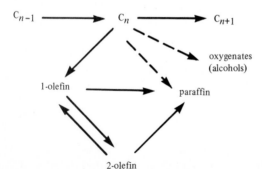

Figure 10.5 The general reaction network for the Fischer-Tropsch synthesis.

position and operating conditions. At temperatures of about 320°C and 2.0 MPa in the entrained-bed reactors at SASOL, 7 to 10 percent aromatics are also found, possibly formed as a primary product. This must involve a considerably different mechanism than the classical Flory-Shultz mechanism. In addition, branched-chain olefin and paraffin selectivity increases.

The extent of secondary reactions is enhanced by higher pressure and especially by very high conversions in a plug-flow-type reactor where the concentration of CO is low. CO is strongly adsorbed onto the catalyst, so much so that it tends to exclude readsorption of olefins and alcohols and hence minimizes their secondary reactions.

10.2.4 The literature

The literature on Fischer-Tropsch synthesis and related matters is vast, encompassing as it does some six decades of activity. The book by Storch et al. (1951) gives much detail about German work through World War II, both the science as well as the technology, and includes early post–World War II work at the U.S. Bureau of Mines. Three detailed and extensive later reviews by Anderson (1956) cover much the same ground, but with more emphasis on catalysts and mechanism and incorporating considerable new information beyond that in the 1951 book. A later book by Anderson (1984) provides an analysis of the literature after the early 1950s from the perspective of a researcher involved at first hand with the subject for decades. Pre–World War II studies and work up to about 1950 are also reviewed by Pichler (1952), a long-time collaborator with Fischer.

With the ten-fold increase in petroleum prices of the 1970s there was a marked upsurge of interest in Fischer-Tropsch synthesis. Dry (1981) focuses on developments from the late 1950s to 1979, with emphasis on the iron catalysts and reactor performance under industrial conditions at SASOL. Other reviews with emphasis on technology and applications include two by Frohning (1980, 1982), a treatment of liquid-phase synthesis by Kölbel and Ralek (1980), and a summary of later work at the U.S. Bureau of Mines by Baird et al. (1980).

Considerations of mechanism have spawned numerous reviews. Those by authors who have been engaged in research in this field for many years include treatments by Ponec (1978, 1982), Bell (1981), Biloen and Sachtler (1981), and Vannice (1976). Other reviews of interest on mechanism include ones by Henrici-Olivé and Olivé (1976), Denny and Whan (1978), Rofer-DePoorter (1981) and Masters (1979). The last one emphasizes insights from related organometallic chemistry. A continuing program of studies of the Fischer-Tropsch synthesis was initiated at the Massachusetts Institute of Technology in 1978 and has been reported on in 32 publications as of 1990. Three recent publications give guidance to much of the earlier work, together with relevant studies by others (Donnelly & Satterfield 1989a, 1989b; Donnelly et al. 1988).

10.3   Water-Gas Shift Reaction

The catalysis of this reaction [Eq. (10.3)] was developed industrially in conjunction with ammonia synthesis, since it provides a way of increasing the yield of hydrogen from synthesis gas and simultaneously decreasing the carbon monoxide content. Carbon oxides are a poison for ammonia-synthesis catalysts and for most metallic hydrogenation catalysts, and must be reduced to a very low level. Since the shift reaction is mildly exothermic to the right, the maximum conversion at equilibrium is attained at the lowest temperatures. Pressure has no significant effect on the equilibrium because there is no volume contraction. The equilibrium constant as a function of temperature is shown in Fig. 10.6 (Bridger & Chinchen 1970, p. 64).

10.3.1   High-temperature shift catalyst

The original catalyst was first used by BASF starting in 1915, and its composition has not been changed much since. The catalyst is basically Fe_3O_4, the stable iron phase under reaction conditions, plus some chromia that acts as a textural promoter to minimize sintering. A typical composition contains about 55 wt % Fe and 6% Cr. The catalyst is supplied with a low sulfur content (for example, <0.07 percent) when the high-temperature converter is to be followed by a low-temperature reactor (see the following) in which the catalyst used is highly sensitive to low concentrations of sulfur compounds. The catalyst is unsupported, usually prepared by a precipitation process, and is available in the form of tablets (6 × 6 mm in size, for example) or rings (OD × ID × h = 10 × 4 × 8 mm, for example).

As prepared, the iron is in the form of Fe_2O_3, which is reduced to Fe_3O_4 (magnetite) before use, usually in situ. The chromium forms an iron-chromium spinel [$Fe(II)Fe(III)_{2-x}Cr_xO_4$]. This exothermic reduction reaction must be carefully controlled, as by the use of a high concentration of steam diluent, to prevent damage to the catalyst. The catalyst is resistant to sulfur compounds, but this is of little concern if the synthesis gas is prepared by steam reforming since an essentially sulfur-free feed is required for this reaction.

The gas composition fed to the water-gas shift reactor may vary considerably, depending on the feedstock and process used to generate the synthesis gas. Typically, after removal of carbon dioxide by scrubbing,

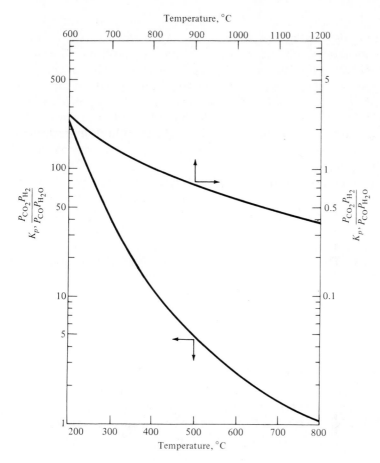

Figure 10.6   Water-gas shift equilibrium. K_p as a function of temperature.
(*Bridger and Chinchen 1970, p. 94*)

a large excess of steam is added to the synthesis gas. The mixture is then passed through an adiabatic converter containing the catalyst. Sufficient steam must be added to prevent formation of an iron-carbide phase that could cause synthesis of hydrocarbons by the Fischer-Tropsch synthesis reaction (Sec. 10.2). Rostrup-Nielsen and Nielsen (1985) give a plot of conditions under which an oxide phase may be expected to convert to a carbide phase. Conditions under which a carbided iron catalyst for Fischer-Tropsch synthesis is converted in part to an oxide are given by Satterfield et al. (1986). Reduction of the Fe_3O_4 to metallic iron could catalyze the formation of carbon from carbon monoxide, and this must also be considered.

An inlet temperature of about 350°C or more must be attained for an adequate reaction rate to be achieved, but the maximum temperature is limited to about 530 to 550°C. The reaction is moderately exothermic and the increase in temperature through the reactor may vary considerably depending on the feed gas composition. The pressure is determined by the requirements in other portions of the process, but may be as high as 3 MPa or more. Higher pressure increases the reaction rate, so a smaller vessel can be used. The superficial contact time is of the order of 3 to 9 s (calculated for wet gas at standard temperature and pressure) but may be 1 s or less in high-pressure operation. Normal catalyst life is several years, but is decreased somewhat at higher pressures.

The book by Bohlbro (1966) gives detailed rate data and rate expressions from studies on the high-temperature catalyst at atmospheric and superatmospheric pressure. An addendum by Mogenson et al. in 1969 [see Bohlbro (1966)] gives further information, especially with respect to industrial procedures such as catalyst reduction, loading, and shutdown. The activated catalyst is pyrophoric. If the catalyst is to be exposed to air and is to be re-reduced and used again, it must be stabilized by surface oxidation with an inert gas containing a low concentration of oxygen. (See also the references at the end of the following section.)

10.3.2 Low-temperature shift catalyst

Considerable carbon monoxide remains in equilibrium (e.g., about 3 mol %, dry basis) at the exit temperature with use of the aforementioned catalyst. In earlier processes the carbon monoxide was removed together with carbon dioxide by scrubbing with a copper liquor (e.g., an aqueous solution of copper ammonium formate). A substantial improvement came about by the development of a low-temperature shift catalyst, first introduced commercially in 1962. With its use the exit gas from the first converter is cooled, usually by quenching with water, which supplies additional steam, and passed into a second converter. Here additional reaction is achieved over a catalyst containing copper, zinc oxide, and alumina—similar to the catalyst used in present-day methanol synthesis (Sec. 10.4.2). Copper metal and zinc oxide are the stable forms under reaction conditions, and the catalyst is active at temperatures as low as 200°C, approximately the lowest that can be used without condensation of steam at typical elevated pressures.

Copper metal is the active species, and one role of the zinc oxide may be to protect the copper from poisoning by adsorbing traces of sulfur compounds and reacting with them. The zinc oxide may also act as a support for the copper. This catalyst is more sensitive to deactivation by thermal sintering than is the high-temperature shift catalyst, since copper has a relatively low melting point. A maximum operating temperature of about 250°C is typical. The temperature rise through the reactor is about 15°C, and the superficial contact time (calculated for wet gas at standard temperature and pressure) is about 1 s.

Representative ICI catalysts have compositions, before reduction, of CuO, 32 to 33 wt %; ZnO 34 to 53 wt %; Al_2O_3 15 to 33 wt %. Under poison-free conditions Al_2O_3-based catalysts apparently have higher activities and greater resistance to deactivation with time on stream than do Cr_2O_3-based catalysts (Lloyd et al. 1989), although some commercial catalysts contain chromia instead of alumina. However, detailed manufacturing methods are important in addition to composition. If poisons are under control, catalyst life is typically 1 to 2 years. On a commercial Cu-ZnO-Al_2O_3 catalyst operated at 1.3 MPa, the reaction becomes diffusion-limited above about 200°C.

The activity and stability to aging may be markedly affected by the method of precipitation of the catalyst, as is also true of the similar catalyst used for methanol synthesis. For maximum activity and stability, the copper crystallites must be as small as possible and separated from one another by the zinc oxide and alumina promoters. These must be even more finely divided than the copper crystallites for maximum effectiveness. In a commercial catalyst the copper crystallites may typically be about 4 nm initially and about 8 nm after 6 months of operation (Young & Clark 1973). The reduction of the copper oxide to metallic copper is highly exothermic and must be carried out carefully, at a temperature not exceeding 220 to 230°C, to avoid sintering. The used catalyst is pyrophoric and is therefore discharged under an inert gas such as nitrogen and then typically doused with water.

The catalyst is poisoned by sulfur and chlorine compounds at concentrations in the range of 1 ppm. However, sulfur compounds react preferentially with the zinc oxide to form zinc sulfide, leaving the copper active. Chlorine causes deactivation of the catalyst by accelerating the sintering of copper, caused by the formation of volatile copper and zinc chlorides. Use of the low-temperature shift catalyst makes it possible to lower the carbon monoxide content in the exit gas to about 0.2 to 0.4 mol %. This is then further reduced to the parts-per-million range by catalytic methanation (Sec. 10.6), a much more satisfactory process than copper liquor scrubbing.

In some applications, carrying out the shift reaction on a gas stream containing concentrations of sulfur compounds that would rapidly poison the aforementioned catalysts may be desirable. In that event a CoMo catalyst, e.g., 4.5 wt % CoO, 15.0 wt % MoO_3, in the sulfided state may be used, on a support stable to water vapor at reaction temperature. In this type of application, various organosulfur compounds may be converted simultaneously to H_2S. This may then be removed together with CO_2 in a subsequent scrubbing operation.

These CoMo catalysts are discussed by Newsome (1980). They are promoted with an alkali, potassium being both effective and inexpensive, and used in the sulfided form. As such they are reported to be comparable in activity to the Cu-ZnO/Al_2O_3 catalysts at, e.g. 260°C. These CoMo catalysts have been used industrially since the early 1970s and are marketed by several catalyst manufacturers, but little information has been published about their performance. They appear to be effective and stable at temperatures in the range of about 450°C to about 200°C. (The lower temperature is limited by the dew point.) These catalysts have a life of the order of 2 years. The CoMo catalysts are several times more active in the sulfided form than in the nonsulfided form, so a minimum ratio of H_2S-H_2O is needed in the gas for maximum activity. In the sulfided form, the CoMo catalyst is reportedly somewhat more active at high temperatures than the conventional iron-chromia catalyst in the fresh form. Srivatsa and Weller (1988) report a study of the water-gas-shift kinetics over a sulfided CoMo/Al_2O_3 catalyst over a pressure range of 0.5 to 2.7 MPa, 250 to 300°C and at gas hourly space velocities (GHSV) of from 4800 to 24,000 hr^{-1}.

For more details on the water-gas shift reaction in general, see Allen (1974), Podolski and Kim (1974) and the later reviews by Lloyd et al. (1989), and that by Newsome (1980). The latter focuses particularly on mechanism and rate expressions on the three kinds of catalysts. Mechanism and kinetics are also treated by Temkin (1979).

10.4   Methanol Synthesis

Methanol is synthesized from carbon monoxide and hydrogen by the reaction:

$$CO + 2H_2 \rightleftharpoons CH_3OH \qquad (10.20)$$

$$-\Delta H_{298} = 91 \text{ kJ/mol}$$

First commercialization was in Germany in about 1923 by BASF, using a ZnO-Cr_2O_3 catalyst developed by a group headed by M. Pier. The early work was closely associated with catalyst studies directed at conversion of carbon monoxide and hydrogen to synthetic fuels (e.g., Fischer-Tropsch synthesis) and with the technology developed for ammonia synthesis. In the synthesis of either ammonia or methanol, specialized and somewhat similar equipment operable at high temperatures and pressures is required. Methanol synthesis is like the oxidation of sulfur dioxide to sulfur trioxide and the water-gas shift reaction, in that the conversion achievable may be greatly limited by thermodynamic equilibrium. Since the reactions are all exothermic, maximum equilibrium conversion is achievable at the lowest temperature.

With methanol and ammonia, the thermodynamic limitation is particularly severe. Reactor design is aimed at operation within a fairly narrow temperature range, set by too low activity at the lower temperatures and a thermodynamic limitation at the higher temperatures. As with ammonia synthesis, high pressures are required in methanol synthesis to achieve reasonable conversions. No by-products are capable of being formed in significant amount in ammonia synthesis, but with a mixture of carbon monoxide and hydrogen a large variety of products are thermodynamically more stable than methanol (Table 10.1). The methanol-synthesis catalyst must therefore be highly selective as well as active.

To produce a relatively pure methanol product directly requires care in catalyst manufacture and procedures to avoid catalyst contamination. Metallic iron or nickel are good methanation catalysts, and thus these metals cannot be allowed to contact the synthesis gas under reaction conditions. Iron can also be transported from one portion of the process to another by the formation of iron carbonyl via the reversible reaction:

$$Fe + 5CO \rightleftharpoons Fe(CO)_5 \qquad (10.21)$$

The reaction is exothermic to the right, and therefore the formation of iron carbonyl is favored at lower temperatures. Iron carbonyl could thus be formed in an upstream heat exchanger and then decompose at a higher temperature in the reactor to deposit metallic iron on the catalyst.

10.4.1 High-pressure process

The catalyst for the original "high-pressure" process was a ZnO-Cr_2O_3 composition in which the active species was zinc oxide. Zinc oxide by itself is an active catalyst initially, but it loses its activity rapidly because of crystal growth. Chromia served primarily as a textural promoter that reduced sintering. In a commercial catalyst all the chromia is in the form of zinc chromite, the remainder of the catalyst being excess ZnO (Kotera et al. 1976). The "zinc chromite" may be a disordered spinel with some interstitial ZnO, but pure zinc chromite spinel is apparently not a very active catalyst.

Even with high-quality commercial ZnO-Cr_2O_3 catalysts, small amounts of methane, higher hydrocarbons, and oxygenated impurities (amounting to, e.g., 2 to 5 wt %) are formed. The development work on these catalysts was reviewed by Natta (1955).

A representative reactor is shown in Fig. 10.7 (Cappelli et al. 1972). The high-pressure catalytic reaction process is now obsolete, but existing high-pressure reactors of this stacked-bed design have been modified for use in the "low-pressure" process described in the following. Similar designs are used for other processes, as in processing of petroleum fractions. Typically there are four or five adiabatic beds in series, between which product gas is cooled indirectly, as by water, or directly by injection of additional synthesis gas, termed *cold-shot cooling* or *quench cooling*. The high-pressure methanol synthesis process was typically operated at about 24 to 30 MPa and 350 to 400°C. The rate of reaction decreases markedly with conversion, so typically the gas leaving the last bed contained only about 3% CH_3OH. The CH_3OH was removed by condensation, and unreacted gases and remaining MeOH were recycled.

10.4.2 Low-pressure process

A more active catalyst than the aforementioned can be made from a combination of copper and zinc together with alumina as a textural promoter. However, these catalysts are readily poisoned by sulfur. The key to their introduction was the growing availability in the 1960s of essentially sulfur-free hydrocarbons, such as natural gas, as feedstocks. Consequently, reaction could be at lower pressure, in the range of about 5 to 10 MPa, and a temperature of about 240 to 260°C. (Above about 270°C deactivation by sintering becomes appreciable.) Capital and operating costs are substantially less by operation at the lower pressure and temperature. Reactor vessels are less costly and, because of the lower pressure, highly efficient large centrifugal compressors driven by steam turbines can be used, instead of reciprocating compressors.

Earlier catalyst compositions used chromia as a promoter, but subsequent studies showed that alumina-based catalysts had better activity and longer-term stability. These catalysts are similar to low-temperature water-gas shift catalysts, but differ in detailed formulation. Formation of by-products in the low-pressure synthesis is less, in part because of the intrinsic properties of the catalyst and in part because of the lower process temperatures that can be used.

Processes based on a Cu/Zn catalyst were introduced by ICI in 1966 and by Lurgi in 1971. These processes are not restricted to any one type of reactor, and the stacked-bed design of the high-pressure process has been used in some cases. However, new reactors are generally either of an ICI or Lurgi design. The ICI reactor utilizes a single bed of

Cool water inlet   Hot water outlet

Electric heater
for the start
up only

1st catalytic layer

Cooling coil

Nonadiabatic
layer

Heat exchanger

Bypass

Gas inlet

Gas outlet

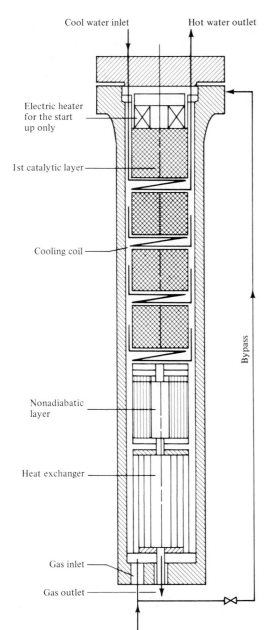

Figure 10.7 Methanol-synthesis reactor, high-pressure process. (*Cappelli et al. 1972. Reprinted with permission from Industrial and Engineering Chemistry, Process Design and Development. Copyright by the American Chemical Society.*)

catalyst and quench cooling, obtained by "lozenge" distributors especially designed to obtain good gas distribution and gas mixing and to permit rapid loading and unloading of catalyst. A schematic diagram of such a reactor is shown in Fig. 10.8.

The Lurgi process utilizes a shell-and-multitube reactor cooled by boiling water at 4 to 4.5 MPa to produce steam that drives the centrifugal compressors and a recirculating compressor. The low-pressure exhaust steam can be used for distillation for methanol purification (Supp 1973, 1981). In the ICI design, steam is generated externally. In the Lurgi design, the temperature variation along the tube reactor can be held to about 10 to 20°C or less depending on tube diameter and other factors.

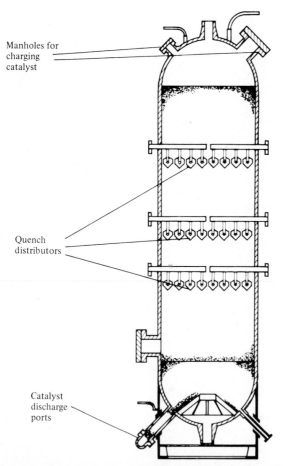

Manholes for charging catalyst

Quench distributors

Catalyst discharge ports

Figure 10.8   ICI internal-quench methanol-synthesis reactor. (*Courtesy of ICI Agricultural Division*)

Figure 10.9 Spherical methanol synthesis reactors. (*Courtesy of M. W. Kellogg Co., Le Blanc and Rovner, Hydrocarbon Process., March 1990*)

A recently constructed plant in southern Chile uses four adiabatic reactors in series with intercoolers between reactors that generate steam (LeBlanc & Rovner 1990). An unusual feature is that the reactors are spherical in shape as shown in the photo in Fig. 10.9 and the isometric view generated by a computer graphic method in Fig. 10.10. The spherical reactors here are reported to weigh about one-half of cylindrical vessels containing the same catalyst volume, which reduces vessel cost and results in savings in foundations and supports. This plant has a capacity of 2500 tons per day, making it probably the world's largest single train methanol synthesis plant. The same type of spherical reactor is used for other processes where an adiabatic reaction is carried out under pressure. Flow is axial so a critical part of the design concerns flow distributors to achieve good gas distribution and complete catalyst utilization.

Industrially, feed gas composition is always adjusted to contain some CO_2 as well as H_2 and CO. The exit stream from the low-pressure process contains 4 to 7 vol % MeOH, which is removed by condensation, and the remaining gas recycled. The recycle ratio is thus high and representative mixed-gas compositions (recycle plus fresh feed) as volume percent are $H_2:CO:CO_2$ = 86–80; 8–10; 6–10. Small amounts of CH_4 or other inert gases may also be present. With

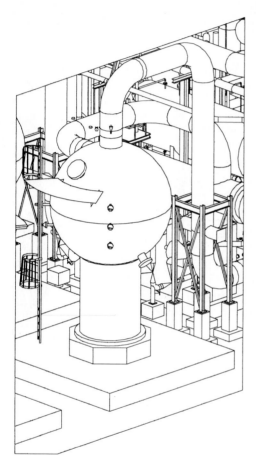

Figure 10.10 Isometric view of spherical reactor area in Fig. 10.9 by computer graphics method. (*Courtesy of M.W. Kellogg Co., Le Blanc and Rovner, Hydrocarbon Process., March 1990*)

synthesis gas from a steam reformer, e.g., design for a not excessively low CH_4 concentration, e.g. 2 to 3 percent, in the reformed gas may be economically advantageous. With synthesis gas from most feedstocks, and especially natural gas, the H_2/CO ratio is higher than the value of 2 called for by stoichiometry. Hence, CO_2 is almost invariably added to the system, e.g., from a nearby ammonia plant or from scrubbed flue gases. Alternately, excess H_2 can be purged, but CO_2 seems to have desirable effects on the catalyst. The additional oxygen from the CO_2 forms water and is removed with the methanol.

A synthesis process developed by Chem Systems and Air Products during the 1980s, with support from the U.S. Department of Energy and the Electric Power Research Institute (EPRI), differs significantly from other present methods. Synthesis gas is passed into a slurry reactor in which catalyst particles are suspended in an inert hydrocarbon liquid, which allows excellent temperature control. The system can handle a wide variety of syngas compositions, but is particularly well-suited for low H_2/CO ratios as are derived from coal. It does not lend itself well to recycle operations and it may be most useful in a "skimming" operation in which unreacted syngas is sent on to another use.

One potential application is in coproduction of power and methanol. The remaining synthesis gas could be burned in a utility boiler and, since it is purified of sulfur compounds, it is a premium fuel. The methanol could be used as turbine fuel during peak power-demand periods. A process development unit of 10 tons per day has been demonstrated. In this process utilizing CO-rich gas (also containing some CO_2), product methanol as condensed is typically 96 to 97 percent pure, water content is about 1 percent and the remainder is mostly higher alcohols. Therefore it could be used directly as fuel.

10.4.3 Kinetics

In spite of the existence of an extensive literature on $Cu/Zn/Al_2O_3$ methanol synthesis catalysts, much remains in dispute concerning the oxidation states of the catalyst components during methanol synthesis, the nature of active sites, and detailed reaction mechanism. Detailed methods of manufacture and reduction procedures are highly important in affecting catalyst activity, selectivity, and life.

The hydrogenation of CO and CO_2 to methanol appears to occur as parallel, independent reactions and probably on different sites. A Langmuir-Hinshelwood rate expression was derived by Graaf et al. (1988) based on this mechanism. It assumes two kinds of adsorption sites, CO and CO_2 adsorbing competitively on one kind, and H_2 and H_2O adsorbing competitively on the second kind. The water-gas shift is assumed to be always in equilibrium.

The chemical state of the catalyst surface depends on the oxidizing characteristics of the vapors in contact with the surface, notably the CO_2 and H_2O content. An optimum CO_2/CO ratio may provide an optimum balance between $Cu°$ and $Cu(I)$ on the catalyst, and the synthesis route via CO_2 gives a higher selectivity to methanol than does the route via CO. The reaction from CO_2 is also more rapid and thus takes place at lower temperature. However, the equilibrium to methanol is less favorable than the synthesis from CO, which militates against use of CO_2 alone with H_2. The reverse water-gas shift also occurs readily on Cu/Zn catalysts to nearly equilibrium. The major impurities industrially are higher alcohols, methyl formate, CH_4, and other hydrocarbons. In the conventional process, the effluent-condensed product is typically about 80% MeOH and 20% H_2O.

The mechanism and kinetics of the reaction probably change substantially through the reactor. In evaluating the literature, distinguishing between studies with CO/H_2, CO_2/H_2, and $CO/CO_2/H_2$ feedstocks is important. With pure CO/H_2 (absence of CO_2, H_2O and O_2), an industrial $CuO/ZnO/Al_2O_3$ catalyst will be overreduced to bulk copper and thus become fairly inactive. However, with industrial synthesis-gas composition conditions ($CO_2/CO > 0.3$), the ICI catalyst contains both metallic and oxidized copper and evidence has shown that, with these gas compositions completely reduced, copper-based catalysts perform well. In fact there is still much disagreement about the role of copper, of copper ion, and of interactions between the two in a working catalyst.

Good catalyst formulations contain finely dispersed copper particles (e.g., 5 to 10 nm). In some cases this is supported on ZnO, which in turn is supported on α alumina. In some ICI formulations microcrystalline copper is supported on microcrystalline $ZnAl_2O_4$, which acts as a textural promoter. Some ZnO is also present.

A great variety of kinetic expressions have been published and will not be reviewed here. For further details see the review of Bart and Sneeden (1987) which has numerous references, a plenary lecture by Andrew (1980), a review by Chinchen et al. (1988) and earlier reviews by Klier (1982) and Kung (1980). See also Bridger and Spencer (1989). Until recent years the major use of methanol has been for conversion to formaldehyde, which in turn is used for thermoset resins, particularly combined with urea, but also with phenol or melamine. Methanol is also used to manufacture acetic acid and a variety of other chemicals. A rapidly growing application is as a transportation fuel, used neat or converted into methyl *tert*-butyl ether (MTBE) (Sec. 7.9), which is blended into gasoline. For fuel applications, "fuel-grade" MeOH is usually satisfactory and the degree of purification required for chemical uses is not necessary. Feedstock cost is a major portion of the cost of producing methanol, so many new plants are being located near sources of low-cost natural gas. MeOH can also be converted into gasoline as by the MTG plant in New Zealand (Sec. 7.7.9).

10.4.4 Higher alcohols

In recent years interest has developed in processes for synthesizing higher alcohols for use as an additive to gasoline (e.g., 2 to 5 wt %) to increase the octane number. By addition of alkali (e.g., 1.7 to 2.5 wt % K_2O) to a $Cu/Zn/Al_2O_3$ catalyst as used for methanol synthesis, considerable quantities of higher alcohols can be synthesized together with methanol. Optimum operation for this purpose involves somewhat higher temperatures and lower H_2-CO feed ratios, but at similar pressures of 5 to 10 MPa. The lower the H_2-CO ratio, the greater the selectivity to higher alcohols.

Typical conditions are 270 to 275°C, and H_2/CO feed ratio of about 1.0. The corresponding product contains about 50 to 60 wt % MeOH, about 5 wt % ketones and esters, and the remainder C_2 to C_7 monohydric alcohols. The quantity of a particular alcohol drops with carbon number in a fashion similar to a Flory distribution with a low α (Sec. 10.2). The ketones and esters are secondary products formed by the reaction of alcohols. By keeping the CO_2 content in the feed gas down to about 1 percent or so, the amount of water in the product, as could be formed by the reverse water-gas shift reaction, can be kept to a very low level, and the resulting liquid product can be added directly to gasoline.

Various other catalysts operating at similar conditions have been reported. IFP has a series of patents on a combination of cobalt and copper with chromia or alumina and containing an alkali and possibly various quantities of other metals. The structure may be copper metal on a cobalt-chromium spinel [see Sheffer and King (1988) and Sheffer et al. (1989)]. The major by-products from these catalysts are hydrocarbons. Reportedly, the selectivity to alcohols is about 60 to 70 percent, and about 50 wt % of the total alcohols are C_2 and higher. This catalyst seems to combine a methanol-synthesis catalyst (copper) with a Fischer-Tropsch synthesis catalyst (cobalt).

Catalysts patented by Dow consist of molybdenum sulfides promoted with potassium on a SiO_2 support. These catalysts are very resistant to residual sulfur in the syngas, but in its absence sulfur is slowly lost from the catalyst, forming traces of thiols and disulfides that may limit the direct use of the product as a gasoline additive without further purification. The ratio of methanol to higher alcohols can be substantially modified by catalyst composition and operating conditions, but considerable quantities of hydrocarbons and CO_2 are also formed, and relatively high pressure and temperature are required (e.g., 100 atm, 300°C).

As of 1990, the Dow process had not been commercialized. The IFP catalysts reportedly have been studied on a pilot-plant scale in Japan. A detailed review by Xu et al. (1987) gives more details on higher-alcohol synthesis. See also a section of the review by Chinchen et al. (1988) on methanol synthesis.

10.5 Ammonia synthesis

The success of ammonia synthesis as a method of nitrogen fixation was a landmark in the development of catalytic processes. Haber developed a method of synthesis under practical conditions, using a catalyst developed by Mittasch, and Bosch developed the high-pressure technology required. The first industrial plant was constructed at Oppau in Germany and put into operation in 1913.

From 1820 to 1900 many futile attempts were made to use platinum and various other substances to catalyze the reaction

$$N_2 + 3H_2 \rightarrow 2NH_3 \tag{10.22}$$

$$-\Delta H_{500°C} = 109 \text{ kJ/mol}$$

Failure was in large part due to the fact that the thermodynamic concepts of equilibrium were still embryonic, and the pressures and temperatures chosen for study were in many cases intrinsically unfavorable for reaction. At the beginning of the twentieth century, problems of gas equilibrium became a major challenge to physical chemists, and the system of nitrogen, hydrogen, and ammonia was a favorite topic. The fixation of atmospheric nitrogen also became a compelling goal from concern that the world would soon exhaust its supplies of nitrates for fertilizer, then coming primarily from Chile.

In Germany, approaching World War I, there was particular concern of limited availability of nitrates required for manufacture of explosives. From 1904 to 1907 the quantitative studies of Ostwald, Nernst, and Haber on the decomposition and formation of ammonia, especially at elevated pressures, led to the first clear understanding of the equilibrium relationships in this system. Figure 10.11 (Jennings & Ward 1989) shows the effect of pressure, temperature, and the presence of 10 percent inert gas, in contrast to a pure stoichiometric mixture, on the equilibrium conversion. Early workers used a variety of catalysts, including platinum foil, osmium, dispersed iron, and electrolytically deposited manganese, but for industrial purposes a rugged and active catalyst needed to be developed.

Mittasch, in the Badische Anilin und Soda Fabrik (BASF), engaged in a search for such a catalyst in which over 8000 compositions were tried. He gradually learned that traces of arsenic, phosphorus, and sulfur were strong catalyst poisons that had to be minimized, and he finally developed a promoted iron catalyst that, with the addition or substitution of other promoters, is the catalyst universally used today. A *singly promoted* catalyst contains alumina, which acts as a textural promoter. A *doubly promoted* catalyst contains K_2O in addition, and a *triply promoted* catalyst also contains CaO. A *quadruply promoted* cat-

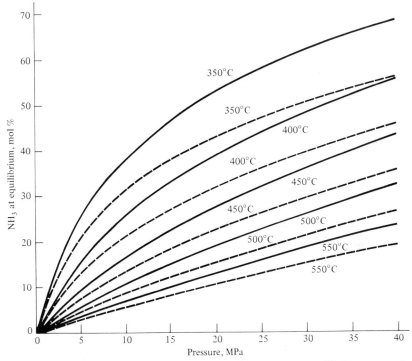

Figure 10.11 Effect of pressure, temperature, and inert gas on equilibrium ammonia concentration. Solid curves, inlet H/N = 3:1; dashed curves, inlet H/N = 3:1 with 7% CH₄ and 3% A. (*Jennings and Ward 1989, p. 384*)

alyst contains Al_2O_3, K_2O, CaO, and MgO. Catalysts used today are of the multiple-promoter type.

Typically, the catalyst is made by fusion of magnetite ore plus promoter precursors into a melt (at 1500°C, for example), followed by cooling, casting, crushing, and sieving. Magnetite, Fe_3O_4, is easier to reduce than Fe_2O_3, and an optimum activity of the ultimate catalyst comes from use of a Fe(II)/Fe(III) ratio approximately equal to that in magnetite. Since finely divided iron is pyrophoric, the catalyst is reduced to the metallic form in the reactor. This must be done at as low a temperature and as low a partial pressure of water vapor (which is formed by reduction) as possible to minimize crystal growth and maximize subsequent activity. This typically requires a few days. To shorten this time a prereduced catalyst is sometimes used. This has been substantially reduced by the catalyst manufacturer and then slightly reoxidized on the surface to make it nonpyrophoric during shipment.

Magnetite, Fe_3O_4, has a spinel structure $Fe(II)[Fe(III)_2O_4]$. During fusion some of the promoters dissolve in the magnetite; e.g., Al(III) replaces Fe(III) and Mg(II) replaces Fe(II). As the oxide is reduced, porosity is developed; dissolved Al_2O_3 and MgO come out of the structure and form a coating of very small crystallites on the iron crystals. These separate the iron crystals and act as a textural promoter. This structure may be seen in electron photomicrographs and is substantiated by comparison of total-area measurements (e.g., by the BET method) compared to iron-area measurements (by chemisorption) on the reduced catalyst. These show, e.g., that although alumina typically amounts to only about 2 wt % of the total mass, it makes up one-third or more of the total surface.

One of the functions of the promoters dissolved in the magnetite structure is to minimize sintering of the iron during reduction, as well as during the subsequent synthesis reaction. K_2O acts essentially as a structural promoter. In the absence of alumina, K_2O does not prevent sintering, and the rate of reaction is, if anything, less than that of iron without any promoter. The mechanism of action of K_2O is still uncertain, but it donates electrons to the iron that can affect the relative adsorptivities of the various species present. The action of CaO is complex. Its major action may be to impart resistance to sintering at elevated temperatures during the synthesis reaction.

A variety of reactions can occur between different promoters, between promoters and impurities in the iron ore, and between these substances and traces of poisons in the feed stream. Since the promoters cover a large percentage of the iron surface in the reduced form of the catalyst, the maximum exposed iron surface per unit weight of catalyst is obtained with a relatively low promoter content. The optimum composition varies with reaction conditions, and the optimum for maximum activity may not be the optimum for long-term stability. Sometimes a reactor may be charged with the more active composition in low-temperature zones, and the more stable composition in the higher-temperature zones. Krabetz and Huberich (1977) discuss promoter effects and interactions in some detail and discuss methods of manufacture.

Five commercial catalysts (Guacci et al. 1977) have chemical compositions within the ranges listed in the second column of Table 10.3. Those of two commercial prereduced catalysts are listed in the third column. The compositions of a large number of catalysts commercially available in 1964 to 1966 are given by Krabetz and Huberich (1977). Some of the minor substances present, such as silica, may be impurities in the magnetite ore or may be added deliberately, and they may have a significant effect. ICI Catalyst 35-4 contains traces of TiO_2, ZrO_2 and V_2O_5 (Jennings & Ward 1989). The activity of all these cat-

TABLE 10.3   Chemical Composition of Industrial Ammonia-
Synthesis Catalysts

	Unreduced types, %	Prereduced types, %
Fe_2O_3	57.5-70.5	1.1-1.7
FeO	33.9-24.2	14.3-14.6
Fe	0-0.54	79.7-81.6
Al_2O_3	2.5-3.1	1.5-2.1
CaO	1.8-3.9	0.1-0.2
SiO_2	0.16-0.70	0.3-0.7
MgO	0.03-0.3	0.3-0.6
K_2O	0.44-0.65	0.1-0.5
Total promoters, %	5.5-7.9	3.7-4.1
Porosity, %	1.8-4.4	40-45

SOURCE: Guacci et al. (1977).

alysts depends, not only on the reduction procedure and the elemental composition, but also to some extent on the particular ore used in manufacture. Details of the mixing, fusion, and cooling process can also be important.

Catalysts are used as crushed granules in different ranges varying from about 2 to 10 mm or larger in size. The ammonia-synthesis reaction is somewhat diffusion-limited on the larger sizes. Smaller particle sizes permit a higher effectiveness factor (Chap. 11), but at the price of higher pressure drop per unit length and hence higher power consumption. The optimum particle size is in the range of 2 mm for use in a radial-flow or horizontal converter, 6 to 10 mm in a conventional axial-flow converter, and as high as 12 to 21 m in other designs. Figure 4.12 shows commercial catalyst of different size ranges. The surface area of these catalysts in the reduced form is typically 10 to 20 m^2/g. Much of this is promoter area, but even the surface area of iron alone, as determined by chemisorption, is not a very good indication of activity because of the complex effects of promoters.

In order to achieve appreciable conversion and a commercially acceptable rate, pressures in the range of 15 to 30 MPa and a minimum temperature of about 430 to 480°C are required. Extensive prepurification of the nitrogen and hydrogen is necessary to minimize poisoning. Water vapor and carbon oxides cause a temporary poisoning that, if the poisons are present in small concentration, can usually be reversed by their removal from the feed stream. However, a recrystallization may occur that lowers the effective area and hence activity of the catalyst. Most sulfur compounds cause severe and irreversible poisoning and must be minimized. In typical commercial operation, a catalyst life of 5 to 8 years may be achieved before activity drops to a level at which the catalyst must be replaced.

10.5.1 Reactors

A variety of ammonia converters have been designed and used. Zardi (1982) gives diagrams of 17 different types, plus four types of methanol synthesis converters. Since the reaction is exothermic and the gas volume decreases on reaction, maximum conversion at equilibrium occurs at high pressure and low temperature. As with methanol synthesis, the temperature profile through the reactor must steer a compromise between inadequate rate if the temperature is too low, and a thermodynamic limitation if the temperature is too high. The maximum catalyst temperature is limited to about 500°C to avoid significant decline in activity with time. The exit gas typically contains about 12 to 14% NH_3, which is condensed before the remaining gas is recycled and added to fresh gas. A very high degree of removal of NH_3 is not justified economically, so the gas mixture fed to the reactor will typically contain in the range of 4% NH_3.

In some of the more widely used designs, the catalyst is held in two or three baskets in series between which cold-shot or quench cooling (a supply of additional synthesis gas at a lower temperature) is provided. Baskets may be stacked above one another in a somewhat similar fashion to the reactor shown in Fig. 10.7 except that cooling is provided by quench gas instead of cooling coils. The exact design is dictated to a large extent by mechanical considerations set by operation at a high pressure and temperature. In general cold synthesis gas is passed between the inside of the pressure vessel and the catalyst containers to prevent decarburization (hydrogen embrittlement) of the pressure vessel that might occur at reaction conditions. An ICI quench converter is similar to that used in the ICI converter for methanol synthesis.

A radial-flow reactor may also be used. Because of the shorter path length through the bed, smaller particle sizes, e.g., 1.5 to 3 mm, may be used without excessive pressure drop. This results in a higher catalyst effectiveness factor and therefore a reduction in the total volume of catalyst required. Figure 10.12 shows a schematic diagram of the design of a Topsøe two-bed radial flow converter, which uses indirect cooling in a heat exchanger for interstage cooling. The accompanying photograph is of a reactor having a capacity of 1500 tons of ammonia per day. The overhead derrick is for installation and removal of the catalyst basket. In the diagram, inlet gas enters at A, passes through the narrow annulus to the bottom, where it is heated by exchange

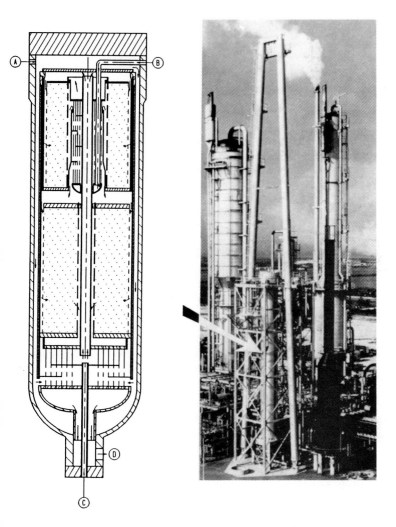

Figure 10.12 Schematic drawing and photograph of a Topsøe radial-flow ammonia-synthesis converter. (*Courtesy of Haldor Topsøe A/S*)

with product gases leaving at D. This gas is then mixed with cold by-pass gas, C, passes upward and flows radially through the first (top) bed from the outside toward the center. The product from this bed is cooled by heat exchange with inlet gas, B, and flows radially through the second, lower bed.

A horizontal converter may also be designed to achieve the same goals. Figure 10.13 shows a photograph of a Kellogg reactor, and Fig. 10.14 a schematic drawing of a unit with three beds of catalyst (Eschenbrenner & Wagner 1972).

Figure 10.13   Photograph of a Kellogg horizontal ammonia converter. (*Courtesy of M. W. Kellogg Co.*)

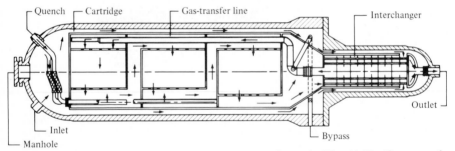

Figure 10.14   Schematic drawing of the converter shown in Fig. 10.13. (*Courtesy of M. W. Kellogg Co.*)

10.5.2   Kinetics

The rate equation almost always used for correlation of data and pre-diction of performance of industrial reactors is based on the formula-tion of Temkin and Pyzhev [see Temkin (1979)]. The original form was derived by assuming that the rate-limiting step is the dissociative chemisorption of nitrogen to form nitrogen atoms. These are assumed to be the main adsorbed species, and their surface concentration is determined by an equilibrium with hydrogen and ammonia in the gas phase. (This is not the equilibrium with the actual concentration of gaseous nitrogen, but instead with the partial pressure of nitrogen that would exist if N_2 were present in thermodynamic equilibrium with the gaseous hydrogen and ammonia present.* The sites were further assumed to have a linear distribution of the heat of adsorption, and of the activation energy for adsorption and desorption of nitrogen. The resulting expression for the rate of reaction is:

$$r = k_1 P_{N_2} \left(\frac{P_{H_2}^3}{P_{NH_3}^2} \right)^\alpha - k_2 \left(\frac{P_{NH_3}^2}{P_{H_2}^3} \right)^\beta \qquad (10.23)$$

The first term is for the rate of formation of ammonia and the second for the rate of decomposition. α and β are both positive, and $\alpha + \beta = 1$. In a detailed review of kinetics of heterogeneous catalytic reactions, Temkin (1979) comments that Eq. (10.23) is unique in chemical kinetics because it holds true for pressures varying from $\frac{1}{4}$ atm to 500 atm—a factor of 2000. No other reaction has been studied over such a wide range of pressure.

The expression has been modified in various ways. Since operation is at high pressure, fugacities are usually substituted for pressures. Other derivations have used different assumptions concerning the energy distribution of the sites and the nature of the principal adsorbed species. The net effect is that, in essence, the form of the Temkin-Pyzhev equation is retained, but α then has a different mechanistic interpretation. The sum of α and β remains 1, but the numerical value of α may vary. Temkin proposed that $\alpha = 0.5$ on all iron catalysts.

In various publications Boudart has commented on the kinetics and mechanism of the synthesis. In a later review (Boudart 1981), he concludes that the likely rate-determining step is dissociative chemisorption of dinitrogen, N_2, on a nonuniform iron surface with N* as the most abundant reaction intermediate, in general accordance with earlier views. This dissociative N_2 chemisorption is followed by reaction with dissociated hydrogen to form adsorbed NH, NH_2 and NH_3 in succession, all in equilibrium. Ertl (1988) has also evaluated evidence for this mechanism. Stoltze and Nørskov (1987) derived a kinetic expression with parameters taken from ultrahigh vacuum conditions for the reactants on single-crystal surfaces and showed that this could describe the observed synthesis kinetics at 375 to 500°C and pressures

---

*This is sometimes termed the *virtual pressure*. In a recent note Ichikawa (1989) gives arguments for its use here and elsewhere.

up to 30 MPa. This is interesting in that rates from surface science measurements could predict rates under industrial conditions.

Careful experimentation with commercial iron catalysts under practical conditions has led various researchers to the conclusion that the best correlation of the experimental data on various individual catalysts was obtained by use of a value of α in the range from 0.4 to 0.75 (Nielsen 1968; Nielsen et al. 1964; Guacci et al. 1977). To expect that α would vary with catalyst composition is not unreasonable, but comparisons of correlations of experimental data using values of α from 0.5 to 0.75 show little or no significant difference (Dyson & Simon 1968; Guacci et al. 1977).

Equation (10.23) clearly cannot be applicable at zero NH_3 concentration. This is generally unimportant for industrial operations, since the feed to the converter contains some NH_3 from recycled gas. In the absence of NH_3, Temkin and coworkers (Temkin 1979) have established that the expression is of the form

$$r = kP_{H_2}^{\alpha}P_{N_2}^{1-\alpha} \tag{10.24}$$

where $\alpha = 0.5$ (Nielsen 1968).

Equation (10.23) is sometimes cast into the functional form:

$$r = k_2\left[K^2 \cdot f_{N_2}\left(\frac{f_{H_2}^3}{f_{NH_3}^2}\right)^{\alpha} - \left(\frac{f_{NH_3}^2}{f_{H_2}^3}\right)^{1-\alpha}\right] \tag{10.25}$$

where K is the equilibrium constant for the reaction $1.5H_2 + 0.5N_2 \rightleftharpoons NH_3$ and k_2 is the reaction rate constant for the *reverse* reaction. (The latter is, of course, proportional to the constant for the forward reaction, k_1). The value of k_2 seems to be independent of pressure if fugacities instead of pressures are used in Eq. (10.25). k_2 can be expressed in the Arrhenius form, $k_2 = Ae^{-E/RT}$, but the value of E depends on the value of α chosen. Nielsen et al. (1964) reported a value of $E = 177$ kJ/mol for their (triply promoted) catalyst, taking $\alpha = 0.64$. Dyson and Simon (1968) recalculated a value of $E = 171$ kJ/mol from the same data with $\alpha = 0.50$. Jennings and Ward (1989) calculate a value of 169 kJ/mol that is compared to the "normally quoted" value of 159 kJ/mol. Guacci et al., in their analysis of the activity of several commercial catalysts, also show how the comparison may vary depending on the value of α chosen and the temperature.

An extensive literature exists on ammonia synthesis, which is not surprising in view of its central importance for the manufacture of fertilizer and explosives and the long-time study devoted to it. The book by Nielsen (1968) gives an extensive treatment of industrial catalysts. Composition, characterization, and detailed results of rate measurements under industrial conditions are presented, with extensive references. In a more recent review (Nielsen 1981), he discusses exploratory and applied research on the synthesis. Much of the earlier understanding of the mechanism of ammonia synthesis is due to P. H. Emmett, who reviewed progress up to 1975 (Emmett 1975).

Surveys of various aspects of the subject may also be found in the book by Vancini (1971), and in earlier reviews by Frankenburg (1955) and Bokhoven et al. (1955). Mittasch (1950) in a personal memoir describes the development of his early concepts of promoter action and multicomponent catalysts, which led to the first practicable catalyst composition. A detailed treatment of ammonia synthesis catalysts, focusing on promoters, poisons, kinetics, and thermodynamics is given by Jennings and Ward (in Twigg, 1989). This appears to be essentially a modest revision of a chapter by Bridger and Snowdon in the first edition of the book. The subject is also reviewed by Ozaki and Aika (1981). A four-part detailed treatise by Slack and James (1974–1977) covers ammonia from an industrial point of view, including the processes for preparation of the synthesis gas, reactor design, and economics. Developments are also reviewed by Shannon (1978). Topham (1985) gives an extensive account of the history of the catalytic synthesis focusing on the details of the work of Haber and Bosch.

10.6 Methanation

The reaction of low concentrations of CO in a mixture with H_2 to form CH_4 was developed as a gas-purification process in the 1950s. Commercial catalysts in essentially all cases are nickel on an alumina or other oxide support. Typical surface areas in the oxide form are 30 to 80 m^2/g. Iron is less active and more subject to carbon deposition but is more resistant to poisons. The gas to be purified typically contains 0.2 to 0.4% CO and a similar amount of CO_2. CO reacts more readily to form CH_4 than does CO_2, but the reaction rate of the latter becomes significant after the CO concentration has been reduced to 200 to 300 ppm. Some CO_2 may also be converted to CO by the reverse of the water-gas shift.

Representative reaction conditions with an inlet composition of 0.5% CO and 0.2% CO_2 are an inlet temperature of 315°C, an exit temperature of 365°C, and exit composition of 5 ppm of total carbon oxides for operation in an adiabatic reactor at 3 MPa (Campbell 1970). With a lower inlet concentration of carbon oxides, the overall adiabatic temperature rise will be less. The inlet temperature is then typically increased slightly to maintain adequate activity in the methanator. Under representative operating conditions the reaction is highly diffusion-limited. Rehmat and Randhava (1970) report that for selective removal of CO with minimum reaction of CO_2, ruthenium is effective. A Raney nickel–type catalyst was almost as effective as ruthenium, but a supported nickel catalyst was much less satisfactory.

Synthetic natural gas (SNG) from synthesis gas was of considerable interest in the 1960s and early 1970s as a shortfall of natural gas supplies was anticipated but did not develop. These syntheses were designed as oil-based processes. Although the economics became less favorable with petroleum price increases in the early 1970s, many plants were still in operation around the world in the mid-1980s. (Pearce et al. 1989). Interest in the United States in the 1970s and into the mid-1980s was in a coal-based process, and a commercial plant was constructed and operated in North Dakota with government subsidy. A variety of SNG processes have been described, and these should be viewed in conjunction with processes for conversion of naphtha to substitute natural gas and "town gas" that contain a lower concentration of CH_4 but may be less expensive to operate.

For SNG manufacture, a supported nickel catalyst is again preferred. With undiluted synthesis gas the reaction is highly exothermic. Temperature control in an adiabatic reactor requires use of a high recycle ratio of partly cooled product gas to fresh feed. Practicable pressures are in the range of 1 to 3 MPa. The ignition temperature is about 200°C under commercial conditions, and this minimum temperature must also be exceeded to avoid formation of nickel carbonyl. The maximum temperature is limited by an excessive rate of inactivation of the catalyst by sintering.

The CO content of the product gas must be less than about 0.1 percent so as not to constitute a health hazard. Taking representative inlet and exit temperatures as 290 and 450°C respectively, the CO in the mixed feed to the reactor, consisting of recycled gas plus fresh feed, cannot exceed about 3 percent for adiabatic operation. Alternately a "tube wall" reactor may be used, in which the catalyst is applied directly to the heat-exchange surface. This allows better temperature control and the ability to avoid or minimize recycling, but a long-lived catalyst that will adhere is required (Haynes et al. 1970) and this is difficult to achieve. With any type of reactor, operation must also be under conditions to avoid carbon deposition (see Sec. 10.1).

Rate expressions have been published by a number of authors. Those of Schoubye (1969) and Van Herwijnen et al. (1973) are for conditions that resemble the dilute concentrations as found in tail-end cleanup in ammonia-synthesis plants. Their reaction conditions were about 90 to 150°C, 0.1 to 1.5 MPa, and up to 20% CO in H_2 (Schoubye), and 170 to 210°C, 0.1 MPa, and less than 2% CO in H_2 (Van Herwijnen). Van Herwijnen used a Girdler G-65 catalyst in particle sizes of 0.03 to 0.4 mm, diluted with quartz, and concluded that diffusion limitations were not significant. Schoubye observed diffusion limitations on particles larger than 0.3 mm. Lee et al. (1970) studied compositions consisting of 2.4 to 10% CO, 2% CO_2, 13 to 34% H_2, and 53 to 82% CH_4, at 0.1 to 6.8 MPa and 275 to 480°C. These conditions are more representative of those for making synthetic methane, but diffusion effects may have been significant.

The rate expressions differ somewhat in form and assume the reaction to be irreversible, which is probably realistic under industrial conditions. Lee's paper includes a summary of the expressions reported by many other investigators. Hausberger et al. (1975) give an approximate empirical procedure used for preliminary design with commercial nickel catalysts, and they compare it to a number of other equations in the literature. An additional complication in using any of these expressions comes from uncertainties about the extent to which direct methanation of CO_2 will occur. That the water-gas shift reaction will be in essential equilibrium under almost all circumstances is probably a good assumption.

A detailed review of catalysts, possible reaction mechanisms, some of the published rate expressions, and industrial considerations is given by Mills and Steffgen (1973). A symposium edited by Seglin (1975) contains papers dealing with kinetics, thermodynamics, catalysts, and reactor considerations. A review by Greyson (1956) covers earlier developments. The review by Pearce et al. (1989) provides a good overall treatment including processes and rate expressions.

References

Allen, D., in A. V. Slack and G. R. James (eds.): *Ammonia*, part 2, Dekker, New York, 1974, p. 3.

Anderson, R. B., in P. H. Emmett (ed.): *Catalysis*, Reinhold, New York, 1956, Vol. 4, p. 1.

Anderson, R. B.: *The Fischer-Tropsch Synthesis*: Academic, New York, 1984.

Andrew, S. P. S.: Plenary Lecture, Post Congress Symposium, 7th International Congress on Catalysis, Osaka, July, 1980. Available as ICI Catalysts Paper 12.

Baird, M. J., R. R. Schehl, W. P. Haynes, and J. T. Cobb: *Ind. Eng. Chem., Prod. Res. Dev.*, **19**, 175 (1980).

Bart, J. C. J., and R. P. A. Sneeden: *Catalysis Today*, **2**, 1 (1987).

Biloen, P., and W. M. H. Sachtler: *Adv. Cat.*, **30**, 165 (1981).

Bell, A.: *Catal. Rev.—Sci. Eng.*, **23**, 203 (1981).

Bohlbro, H.: *An Investigation on the Kinetics of the Conversion of Carbon Monoxide with Water Vapour over Iron Oxide Based Catalysts*, Gjellerup, Copenhagen, 1966. Addendum: E. Mogensen, M. H. Jorgensen and K. Sondergaard: *Industrial Use of Shift Catalysts*, Gjellerup, Copenhagen, 1969.

Bokhoven, C., C. van Heerden, R. Westrik, and P. Zwietering in P. H. Emmett (ed.): *Catalysis*, Vol. 3, Reinhold, 1955, p. 265.

Boudart, M.: *Catal. Rev.—Sci. Eng.*, **23**, 1 (1981).

Bridger, G. W., in *Catalysis*, The Chemical Society, London, 1980, Vol. 3, p. 39.

Bridger, G. W., and G. C. Chinchen: *Catalyst Handbook (ICI)*, Wolfe, London, 1970, chap. 5.

Bridger, G. W., and M. S. Spencer, in M. V. Twigg (ed.): *Catalyst Handbook*, 2nd ed., Wolfe, London, 1989, and CRC Press, Boca Raton, Fla., Chapter 9.

Campbell, J. S.: *Ind. Eng. Chem., Process Des. Dev.*, **9**, 588 (1970).

Cappelli, A., A. Collina, and M. Dente: *Ind. Eng. Chem., Process Des. Dev.*, **11**, 184 (1972).

Carnell, P. J. H., in M. V. Twigg (ed.): *Catalyst Handbook*, 2nd ed., Wolfe, London, 1989, and CRC Press, Boca Raton, Fla., Chapter 4.

Chinchen, G. C., P. J. Denny, J. R. Jennings, M. S. Spencer, and K. C. Waugh: *Appl. Catal.*, **36**, 1 (1988).

Denny, P. J. and D. A. Whan: in *Catalysis*, The Chemical Society, London, 1978, vol. 2, p. 46.

Dent, F. J. and J. W. Cobb: *J. Chem. Soc.*, **2**, 1903 (1929).

Dent, F. J., L. A. Moignard, A. H. Eastwood, W. H. Blackburn, and D. Hebden: *Trans. Inst. Gas Eng.*, 602 (1945).

Dibbern, H. C., P. Olesen, J. R. Rostrup-Nielsen, P. B. Tøttrup, and N. R. Udengaard: *Hydrocarbon Process.*, **65**, 31 (1986).

Donnelly, T. J., and C. N. Satterfield: *Appl. Catal.*, **52**, 93 (1989*a*).

Donnelly, T. J., and C. N. Satterfield: *Appl. Catal.*, **56**, 231 (1989*b*).

Donnelly, T. J., I. C. Yates, and C. N. Satterfield: *Energy & Fuels*, **2**, 734 (1988).

Dry, M. E., in J. R. Anderson and M. Boudart (eds.): *Catalysis: Science and Technology*, Springer, New York, 1981, Vol. 1, Chap. 4, p. 159.

Dyson, D. C. and J. M. Simon: *Ind. Eng. Chem., Fundam.*, **7**, 605 (1968).

Emmett, P. H., in E. Drauglis and R. I. Jaffee (eds.): *The Physical Basis for Heterogeneous Catalysis*, Plenum, New York, 1975, p. 3.

Ertl, G., in T. Inui (ed.): *Successful Design of Catalysts*, Elsevier, Amsterdam, 1988, p. 315.

Eschenbrenner, G. P. and G. A. Wagner, III: *Chem. Eng. Prog.*, January 1972, p. 62.

Flory, P. J.: *J. Amer. Chem. Soc.*, **58**, 1877 (1936).

Frankenburg, W. G., in P. H. Emmett (ed.): *Catalysis*, Vol. 3, Reinhold, New York, 1955, p. 171.

Frohning, C. D., in J. Falbe (ed.): *New Syntheses with Carbon Monoxide*, Springer, New York, 1980, p. 309.

Frohning, C. D., et al., in *Chemical Feedstocks from Coal*, Wiley, 1982, translated from J. Falbe (ed.): *Chemierohstoffe aus Kohle*, Georg Thieme, Stuttgart, 1977, Chap. 8.

Graaf, G. H., E. J. Stamhuis, and A. A. C. M. Beenackers: *Chem. Eng. Sci.*, **43**, 3185 (1988).

Greyson, M., in P. H. Emmett (ed.): *Catalysis*, Reinhold, New York, 1956, vol. 4, p. 473.

Guacci, U., F. Traina, G. Buzzi Ferraris, and R. Barisone: *Ind. Eng. Chem., Process Des. Dev.*, **16**, 166 (1977).

Hausberger, A. L., C. B. Knight, and K. Atwood: *Adv. Chem. Ser. No. 146*, 1975, p. 47.

Haynes, W. P., J. J. Elliott, A. J. Youngblood, and A. J. Forney: *Am. Chem. Soc. Div. Petr. Chem. Prepr.*, **15**(4) A121 (1970).

Henrici-Olivé, G. and S. Olivé: *Angew. Chem., Int. Ed. Engl.*, **15** (3), 136 (1976).

Herington, E. F. G.: *Chem. Ind.*, **65**, 346 (1946).

Huff, G. A., Jr., and C. N. Satterfield: *Ind. Eng. Chem., Process. Des. Dev.*, **23**, 696 (1984).

Ichikawa, S.: *Chem. Eng. Sci.*, **44**, 2754 (1989).

Jennings, J. R., and S. A. Ward, in M. V. Twigg (ed.): *Catalyst Handbook*, 2nd ed., Wolfe, London, 1989, and CRC Press, Boca Raton, Fla., Chapter 8.

Klier, K.: *Adv. Catal.*, **31**, 243 (1982).

Kölbel, H., and M. Ralek: *Catal. Rev.*, **21**, 255 (1980).

Kotera, Y., M. Oba, K. Ogawa, K. Shimomura, and H. Uchida in B. Delmon, P. A. Jacobs, and G. Poncelet (eds.): *Preparation of Catalysts*, Elsevier, Amsterdam, 1976, p. 589.

Krabetz, R., and T. Huberich, in A. V. Slack and G. R. James (eds.): *Ammonia*, part 3, Dekker, New York, 1977, p. 123.

Kung, H. H.: *Catal. Rev.—Sci. Eng.*, **22**, 235 (1980).

LeBlanc, J. R., and J. M. Rovner: *Hydrocarbon Process.*, March 1990, p. 51.

Lee, A. H., H. L. Feldkirchner, and D. G. Tajbl: *Am. Chem. Soc. Div. Pet. Chem., Prepr.*, **15**(4) A93 (1970).

Lloyd, L., D. E. Ridler, and M. V. Twigg, in M. V. Twigg (ed.): *Catalyst Handbook*, 2nd ed., Wolfe, London, 1989, and CRC Press, Boca Raton, Fla., Chapter 6.

Masters, C., *Advances in Organometallic Chemistry*, **17**, 61 (1979).

Mills, G. A., and F. W. Steffgen: *Catal. Rev.*, **8**, 159 (1973).

Mittasch, A.: *Adv. Catal.*, **2**, 82 (1950).

Natta, G., in P. H. Emmett (ed.): *Catalysis*, vol. 3, Reinhold, New York, 1955, p. 349.

Newsome, D. S.: *Catal. Rev.—Sci. Eng.*, **21**, 275 (1980).

Nielsen, A.: *An Investigation on Promoted Iron Catalysts for the Synthesis of Ammonia*, 3rd ed., Gjellerup, Copenhagen, 1968.

Nielsen, A.: *Catal. Rev.—Sci. Eng.*, **23**, 17 (1981).

Nielsen, A., J. Kjaer, and B. Hansen: *J. Catal.*, **3**, 68 (1964).

Ozaki, A., and K. Aika, in J. R. Anderson and M. Boudart (eds.): *Catalysis: Science and Technology*, Vol. 1, Springer, New York, 1981, p. 87.

Pearce, B. B., M. V. Twigg, and C. Woodward, in M. V. Twigg (ed.): *Catalyst Handbook*, 2nd ed., Wolfe, London, 1989, and CRC Press, Boca Raton, Fla., Chapter 7.

Pichler, H.: *Adv. Catal.*, **4**, 271 (1952).

Podolski, W. F., and Y. G. Kim: *Ind. Eng. Chem., Process Des. Dev.*, **13**, 415 (1974).

Ponec, V.: *Catalysis*, Vol. 5, The Chemical Society, London, 1982. Also *Catal. Rev.—Sci. Eng.*, **18**, 151 (1978).

Rehmat, A., and S. S. Randhava: *Ind. Eng. Chem., Prod. Res. Dev.*, **9**, 512 (1970).

Ridler, D. E., and M. V. Twigg in M. V. Twigg (ed.): *Catalyst Handbook*, 2nd ed., Wolfe, London, 1989, and CRC Press, Boca Raton, Fla., Chapter 5.

Rofer-DePoorter, C. K.: *Chem. Reviews*, **81**, 447 (1981).

Ross, J. R. H.: *Catalysis*, The Chemical Society, London, 1983, Vol. 7, p. 1.

Rostrup-Nielsen, J. R.: *Steam Reforming Catalysts*, Danish Technical Press, Copenhagen, 1975.

Rostrup-Nielsen, J. R.: *Chem. Eng. Prog.*, September 1977, p. 87.

Rostrup-Nielsen, J. R., in J. R. Anderson and M. Boudart, (eds.): *Catalysis: Science and Technology*, Springer, New York, Vol. 5, 1984, p. 1.

Rostrup-Nielsen, J. R., and P. E. H. Nielsen, in J. Oudar and H. Wise (eds.): *Deactivation and Poisoning of Catalysts*, Dekker, New York, 1985, p. 259.

Rostrup-Nielsen, J. R., and I. Alstrup in J. W. Ward (ed.): *Catalysis 1987*, Elsevier, Amsterdam, 1988, p. 725.

Rostrup-Nielsen, J. R., and P. B. Tøttrup: paper presented at symposium, *Science of Catalysis and its Application to Industry*, Sindri, India, February 1979.

Sachtler, W. M. H.: *Proceedings, 8th International Congress on Catalysis*, Vol. 1, Verlag Chemie, 1984, p. 151.

Satterfield, C. N., and G. A. Huff, Jr.: *J. Catal.*, **73**, 187 (1982).

Satterfield, C. N., and H. G. Stenger, Jr.: *Ind. Eng. Chem., Process Des. Dev.*, **23**, 26 (1984).

Satterfield, C. N., R. T. Hanlon, S. E. Tung, Z-m Zou, G. C. Papaefthymiou: *Ind. Eng. Chem., Prod. Res. Devel.*, **25**, 401 (1986).

Schoubye, P.: *J. Catal.*, **14**, 238 (1969).

Schulz, G. V.: *Z. Phys. Chem.*, B30, 379 (1935).

Schulz, H., K. Beck, and E. Erich: *Fuel. Proc. Tech.*, **18**, 293 (1988). See also M. J. Phillips and M. Ternan (eds.): *Proceedings, 9th International Congress on Catalysis*, The Chemical Institute of Canada, Ottawa, 1988, p. 829.

Seglin, L. (ed.): *Methanation of Synthesis Gas, Adv. Chem. Ser. No. 146*, 1975.

Shannon, I. R., in *Catalysis*, vol. 2, The Chemical Society (London), 1978, Chap. 2, p. 28.

Sheffer, G. R. and T. S. King: *Appl. Cat.*, **44**, 153 (1988).

Sheffer, G. R, R. A. Jackson, and T. S. King: *J. Catal.*, **116**, 95 (1989).

Slack, A. V., and G. R. James: *Ammonia*, Dekker, New York, 1974–1977, four volumes.

Srivatsa, N. R., and S. W. Weller, in M. J. Phillips and M. Ternan (eds.): *Proceedings, 9th International Congress on Catalysis*, The Chemical Institute of Canada, Ottawa, 1988, p. 1827.

Stoltze, P., and J. K. Nørskov: *J. Vac. Sci. Technol.*, A **5**, 581 (1987).

Storch, H. H., N. Golumbic, and R. B. Anderson: *The Fischer-Tropsch and Related Syntheses*, Wiley, New York, 1951.

Supp, E.: *Chemtech*, July 1973, p. 430.

Supp, E.: *Hydrocarbon Process.*, March 1981, p. 71.

Taylor, P., and B. W. Wojciechowski: *Fuel Process. Tech.*, **8**, 135 (1984).

Temkin, M. I.: *Adv. Catal.*, **28**, 173 (1979).

Topham, S. A., in J. R. Anderson and M. Boudart, (eds.): *Catalysis: Science and Technology*, Vol. 7, Springer, New York, 1985, p. 2.

Twigg, M. V., (ed.): *Catalyst Handbook*, 2nd ed., Wolfe, London, 1989 and CRC Press, Boca Raton, Fla. (The first edition of this book was published in 1970, individual chapters being written by various members of Imperial Chemical Industries. Some of the chapters in the second edition are modestly revised versions of those in the first, but with differently named authors. This makes proper attribution somewhat ambiguous.)

Vancini, C. A.: *Synthesis of Ammonia*, English translation, Macmillan and CRC Press, 1971.

Van Herwijnen, T., H. Van Doesburg, and W. A. De Jong: *J. Catal.*, **28**, 391 (1973).

Van Hook, J. P.: *Catal. Rev.—Sci. Eng.*, **21**, 1 (1980).

Vannice, M. A.: *Catal. Rev.—Sci. Eng.*, **14**, 153 (1976).

Xu, Xiaoding, E. B. M. Doesburg, and J. J. F. Scholten: *Catalysis Today*, **2**, 125 (1987).

Young, P. W., and C. B. Clark: *Chem. Eng. Prog.*, **69** (5), 69 (1973).

Zardi, U.: *Hydrocarbon Process.*, August 1982, p. 129.

11

Experimental Methods

We are concerned here with carrying out studies on catalysts at laboratory or pilot-plant scale. The ways in which this may be done will vary considerably with circumstances, such as scouting new catalysts, determining kinetics, proving a practical catalyst, or studying new feedstocks. Generally, information is needed on activity, selectivity, and catalyst life, but life tests are so expensive that they are generally reserved for the last stages of experimentation. In all these studies it is of the utmost importance that catalysts be evaluated, if at all possible, free of concentration and temperature gradients within and between catalyst pellets in the reactor. This is not easy to do, since porous catalysts are usually desired for high area and therefore high activity per unit of reactor volume and heats of reaction are often substantial. In many cases significant gradients cannot be economically avoided in the industrial reactor, but in research and development to be able to determine the intrinsic behavior of a catalyst as observed in the absence of these gradients is important.

Consider a particle or pellet of solid catalyst in contact with a gas or liquid in which the reactants are present. The solid may be in a fixed bed or may be in motion with respect to the fluid. The latter occurs in a fluidized bed with a gas, or in a stirred vessel of liquid, sometimes termed a *slurry reactor*. The reactants are transferred to the active surface of the catalyst, reaction takes place, and the products are transferred back to the main body of the ambient fluid. If the catalyst is porous, the reactants must diffuse first from the fluid to the outside surface of the pellet and then through minute and irregularly shaped pores to the interior. Chemical potential decreases in the direction of diffusion through the porous structure, so the catalyst surface in the interior of the pellet is in contact with a fluid of lower reactant concentration and higher product concentration than the external or ambient fluid. The internal surface is not as "effective" as it would be if it were all exposed to contact with the external fluid.

Measurements that the experimenter uses for interpretation of data, e.g., measurements of composition and temperature, are almost invariably those of the bulk of the fluid. However, the observed course of the reaction is the sum of the events occurring throughout the catalyst, being determined by the conditions actually existing at each point on the internal surface of the catalyst. When gradients of concentration or temperature are significant, a "falsification of the kinetics" occurs. This is in the sense that the rate and selectivity of the reaction change with measured concentration and temperature in a different manner than they would in the absence of such gradients. In most cases selectivity is affected adversely.

The term *intrinsic kinetics* refers to the behavior of the reaction in the absence of concentration or temperature gradients. The adjective *apparent* or *effective* refers to that which is actually observed. When the difference is significant, the terms *mass- (or heat-) transfer limitation, diffusion limitation*, or *mass- (or heat-) transfer regime* are frequently used, but this phraseology is subject to misinterpretation. Mass- and heat-transfer effects may interact with each other such that effects may be observed when the potential difference between the bulk fluid and the reaction sites amounts to but a few percent of the overall decrease in potential. These gradients *always* exist during reaction. In experimental work the objective is to reduce them to a minimum consistent with other objectives.

Avoiding a significant degree of coupling of physical phenomena with chemical reaction may be difficult, particularly as reactors are scaled up for industrial processing, where high reaction rates are desired. Scientists or engineers engaged in research or development need to be able to conduct studies free of these physical transport limitations if possible in order to interpret their results correctly. They must know how to design such experiments properly, be aware of warning signs to look for in the data, and have some knowledge of what can be done if these effects become significant. Engineers concerned with development, design, and operation of reactors need to be aware of what changes in conversion and selectivity may occur as they change scale or alter operating parameters.

This is a large subject that has received extensive study, and the purpose of this chapter is to introduce the topic. Quantitative methods of analyzing these effects are considered in detail elsewhere (Satterfield 1970), and in numerous texts on chemical reaction engineering. See, e.g., the books by Carberry (1976), Smith (1981), and Froment and Bischoff (1990).

11.1   Commercial Reactors

The ultimate goal is to design and predict the performance of industrial-scale reactors using solid catalysts. This is the task of the chemical reaction engineer, but some understanding of the kinds of reactors most commonly used and of the kinds of information needed for scaleup helps in guiding laboratory work. The basic types are listed in Table 11.1. Table 1.1 (Chap. 1) gives the usual type of reactor used for each of a large number of catalytic reactions. For large-scale processing, especially at elevated pressures and temperatures, reactor mechanical designs may become quite intricate with complex internal methods of heat exchange and mixing for maximum efficiency. We will be concerned here primarily with the case of a gas phase in contact with a solid catalyst held in a fixed-bed reactor.

11.1.1   Adiabatic reactor

The adiabatic reactor is a packed bed of catalyst without internals for transferring heat. The diameter is usually sufficiently great that heat transferred through the outside walls is small relative to that evolved or absorbed by reaction. The fluid moves downward through the reactor in nearly plug flow, and the temperature rise (or drop) for a simple reaction is about in proportion to the percent conversion. Such a reactor may be used for either an exothermic or endothermic reaction. However, most applications involve exothermic reactions, and the following discussion is concerned with this type. An adiabatic reactor is the least expensive kind to build, and usually the first choice if practicable. Reacting gases are fed to the bed at the *ignition temperature*, that at which the rate becomes economically rapid.

A representative design is shown in Fig. 11.1. A set of baffles or perhaps a simple horizontal plate below the opening may be installed to provide more uniform flow of vapors onto the bed. A layer of dense, nonporous, inert material such as alumina or a fused ceramic larger in size than the catalyst particles is usually placed on top of the catalyst, to catch scale and impurities and to assist in flow distribution.

TABLE 11.1   Basic Types of Commercial Catalytic Reactors

Gas-phase reactant	Gas- and liquid-phase reactants
Adiabatic packed bed	Trickle bed; flooded bed
Multitube with heat exchange	—
Fluidized bed	Slurry reactor

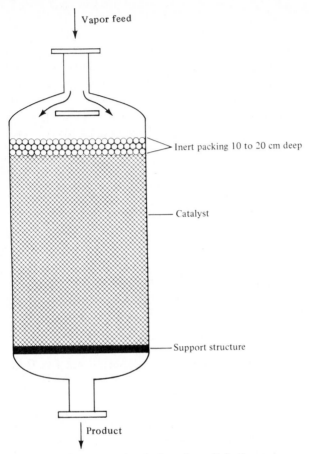

Figure 11.1   Representative design of an adiabatic reactor.

The catalyst is typically supported on a grid, perhaps with screens and/or a layer of inert material between the grid and the catalyst packing. Spent catalyst is usually removed by vacuuming.

In an alternate design, product may be removed at the bottom of the vessel through a collector such as a spider, or through a stack of horizontal plates separated to provide a slotted opening. This is then usually surrounded by inert packing larger than the sizes of the openings. The inert material may be graded in size—coarse to fine in the top of the reactor and fine to coarse in the bottom.

Several beds may be used in series, and often they are all held inside a single shell for mechanical or structural reasons, especially for operation under pressure. Gas from the exit of one bed may be removed, cooled, and fed to a second bed (Fig. 8.7) or cooling coils may be installed in sections between beds. (Fig. 10.7) Cooling coils are seldom embedded within a catalyst bed because this may cause irregular flow through the packing and undesirable temperature gradients. Alternately, reacting gases may be cooled between beds by injection of fresh, cool reactant, *quench gas*, which is mixed with the reaction products to lower the gas temperature before it enters the next bed (Figs. 10.12 and 10.13), or quench gas may be introduced into a single bed of catalyst by specially designed distributors (Fig. 10.8). The use of quench gas is also termed *cold-shot* cooling. With several adiabatic beds in series, the individual beds are often varied in depth, in order to achieve an optimum temperature at the exit of each. This is usually determined by either: (1) the temperature at which the reaction rate drops to too low a level, or (2) the temperature at which side reactions become significant or at which catalyst life may be adversely affected.

To make the temperature change through a reactor sufficiently small that an adiabatic reactor can be used: (1) a portion of the product may be recycled and mixed with fresh feed, (2) an excess of one reactant may be utilized, or (3) an inert gas may be added to the feed. Any of these increases the heat capacity relative to the quantity of heat released. Adiabatic reactors are generally most practical for large-scale, relatively slow reactions not involving large heat effects.

A group of highly exothermic reactions occurs extremely rapidly at high temperature, with reaction times on the order of 0.01 s or less. Examples are NH_3 oxidation to NO, synthesis of HCN from NH_3, CH_4, and air, and conversion of CH_3OH to HCHO on a silver catalyst. The catalyst beds are very thin, frequently 1 cm or less (see Fig. 8.10). The reactions are highly mass-transfer-controlled, so the concentration of reactants and products at the outside catalyst surface is much different from that in the bulk. The catalyst-surface temperature greatly exceeds the bulk-gas temperature, especially at the inlet. Radiative heat transfer from the top and bottom of the bed is usually important and gas is typically fed at nearly ambient temperatures, being brought up to reaction temperature by the hot catalyst. The reactor as a whole is usually nearly adiabatic. These reaction systems are not easily simulated on a small scale in the laboratory, and it is exceedingly difficult to study intrinsic kinetics and reaction mechanisms. These thin beds have a low pressure drop, and, thus, bypassing or channeling can easily arise, causing lower yields. Some minimum bed thickness is needed to avoid this difficulty.

In a *trickle-bed reactor* liquid and gas flow concurrently downward through a packed bed while reaction, essentially adiabatic, takes place. Several beds in series may be utilized with interstage cooling or cold-shot cooling with a gas, analogous to that used in gas-solid adiabatic beds. Alternately, the two phases may flow concurrently upward, with the liquid being the continuous phase, a process termed *flooded flow*. Countercurrent operation is not usually used because, with the catalyst particle sizes of interest, the hydrodynamic flow patterns usually become irregular and unpredictable at gas and liquid flow rates below those usable with parallel flow. The equivalent of the multitube reactor with external heat exchange (see below) does not seem to have been used with trickle-bed reactors. To distribute both gas and liquid uniformly and reliably to several thousand tubes in parallel would require an intricate and expensive design.

The design and operation of trickle-bed reactors is much more complex than that for single-phase flow. Distributor design must permit even distribution of gas and liquid over the bed, at a ratio that does not vary beyond prescribed limits with a change in overall mass flow rate; two-phase flow introduces complex hydrodynamics and variations in contacting efficiency, and these may be exacerbated by volatilization or condensation occurring as reaction proceeds. Trickle-bed reactors have been reviewed (Satterfield 1975) and treated in several texts. See, e.g., Shah (1979), Ramachandran and Chaudhari (1983) and Gianetto and Silveston (1986).

11.1.2 Multitube reactor with heat exchange

If the adiabatic temperature rise is so great that poor selectivity is encountered, unacceptable catalyst deactivation occurs, or the possibility of a runaway reaction exists, a multitube reactor with external cooling is usually the next choice. The reactions here are usually more rapid and more exothermic than those for which adiabatic reactors are suitable. The heat-exchange fluid may be a thermally stable organic substance such as a mixture of diphenyl ethers or of terphenyls, which can be used up to a temperature of about 370 to 430°C ("Dowtherm" or "Therminol"). A molten salt, e.g., a eutectic consisting of 53% KNO_3, 40% $NaNO_2$, and 7% $NaNO_3$, can be used up to about 540°C. At sufficiently low reaction temperatures, water may be boiled to form steam at a pressure set by the desired temperature to be achieved. A representative reactor design is shown in Fig. 8.2.

The tubes are typically 2.5 to 5 cm in diameter and can vary considerably in length, from, e.g., about 1 to 8 m. The smaller the tube diameter, the more closely isothermal operation may be approached, but for a given capacity the number of tubes increases inversely with the square of the internal diameter. Use of tubes much smaller than 2.5 cm would require an unacceptably large number. In a representative design, 7000 to 10,000 tubes 2.5 cm in diameter may be manifolded in parallel in a single vessel. Two or more reactors of such design are typically required for a chemical process to produce a few hundred million pounds per year of product, a typical capacity for a commodity-type chemical. With tubes larger than about 5 cm in diameter, departures from isothermality usually become too great to be acceptable. A closer approach to isothermality can be achieved by diluting the catalyst with inert material; but additional reactor volume is then required, and in practice this may not be economically justified.

With either adiabatic or multitube packed beds, catalyst pellets are typically 1.5 to 6 mm in diameter. Smaller pellets usually cause excessive pressure drop. Larger pellets may lead to diffusion limitations, and if sizes larger than about 6-mm diameter are used, they may be formed as rings, of about equal height and outside diameter, to minimize diffusion problems. In recent years catalysts have become available commercially in an increasing variety of shapes and sizes to meet various desiderata of particular importance for a specific application (Chap. 4).

11.1.3 Fluidized-bed reactor

Here the reacting gas is passed up through a bed of finely divided solid catalyst, which is thus highly agitated and assumes many of the characteristics of a fluid. A particular advantage of this reactor type is the excellent uniformity of temperature. This is achievable throughout the bed because of the motion of the solid and the good heat exchange between solid and gas. The ease of adding and removing solid is an additional advantage. Hence a fluid-bed reactor is of value for a very exothermic reaction that cannot be adequately controlled with a multitube reactor, or when catalyst must be removed and replaced frequently. For a partial oxidation reaction, this kind of reactor also permits a method of readily introducing air and reactant at different locations in the reactor. This avoids formation of an explosive composition that could exist if they were introduced together. A fluid-bed reactor may be less expensive to construct than a multitube reactor of the same capacity, and heat exchange may be simpler than with the adiabatic multibed reactor. However, the hydrodynamics of fluidized beds are complex, scaleup procedures are still relatively empirical, solids-separation equipment must be provided, and the catalyst must be attrition-resistant and not agglomerate.

A mixture of particle sizes, typically in the range of about 20 to 100 μm, is desirable for good fluidization characteristics. At atmospheric or slightly higher pressures, the corresponding maximum linear velocity usable is about 60 cm/s. Much higher velocities cause elutriation of solids from the bed. Cyclone separators are usually installed internally to return the fines to the bed, and these will become overloaded at excessive gas velocities. The minimum bed height to accommodate these and other internal structures, such as heat-exchange surfaces, is typically about 3 m, so using a fluid-bed reactor for reaction times of a few seconds or less is difficult.* A minimum height may also be needed to be able to introduce different feed gases at different locations.

A *transport line reactor* has also been used, in which a solid catalyst and a gas are caused to rise upward concurrently at very high velocities, of the order of 6 m/s. In modern catalytic-cracking processes, this is termed a *riser cracker*.

Fluidized-bed reactors are treated in numerous books; see, e.g., Kunii and Levenspiel (1969), Davidson et al. (1985), and Yates (1983).

11.1.4   Slurry reactor

The reaction of a liquid is often carried out by suspending a solid catalyst in a finely divided form in the liquid. If a gas is to be reacted with the liquid, it may be introduced through a distributor in the bottom of the vessel, which suspends the solid, or it may be dispersed into the liquid by a mechanical agitator. This also acts to keep the solid suspended. The first system is often termed a *bubble-column reactor*, and the second a *slurry reactor*. Elucidation of mass-transfer effects in multiphase reactors such as trickle beds and slurry reactors is an important subject, but is beyond the scope of the present treatment. See, e.g., Satterfield (1975), Shah (1979), Ramachandran and Chaudhari (1983), and Gianetto and Silvestri (1986).

11.1.5   Contact time

To determine the true average residence time of a fluid in a reactor often requires information not readily available. In particular, expansion or contraction of a vapor may occur, caused by a change in number of moles on reaction, or temperature and pressure gradients, or both. The void fraction of a packed or fluidized bed may also be unknown. To sidestep these difficulties, a *contact time* or *superficial contact time*, consisting of the reactor volume (unpacked) divided by the volumetric flow rate, is often quoted. The latter may be calculated at the inlet or reactor conditions, or at standard temperature and pressure (abbreviated STP or NTP) and is usually based on the volume of entering reactant. The reciprocal of this is the *space velocity*, which

---

*Fluid beds are used for various kinds of solids processing, as for combustion, drying, etc., in which case particle sizes may be larger and shorter gas contact times may be utilized. The overall design problem is different.

has units of reciprocal time. In some cases the space velocity is given in terms of the volumetric feed rate of a liquid even though it may be vaporized and mixed with other reactants before entering the catalyst bed. This is termed the *liquid hourly space velocity*, or LHSV. The exact definition used is frequently ambiguous.

11.2   Reaction Regimes

Visualize a porous solid catalyst pellet in contact with a fluid reactant, and consider how the rate of the reaction will change as the temperature is increased. As pointed out by Wicke (1957), three different catalytic reaction regimes may be observed. These are shown diagrammatically in the Arrhenius-type diagram, Fig. 11.2, and in Fig. 11.3. At sufficiently low temperatures, the rate of the reaction is so low that the potential required to provide the diffusion flux is insignificant, and intrinsic kinetics will be observed (regime A).

With increased temperature, the rate of diffusion per unit potential difference (the diffusion coefficient) increases but slowly, whereas the

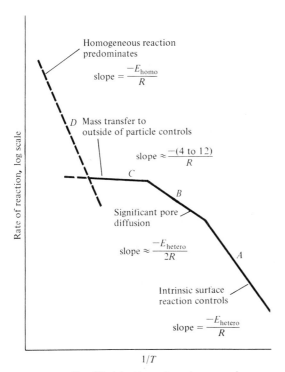

Figure 11.2   Possible kinetic regimes in a gas-phase reaction occurring on a porous solid catalyst.

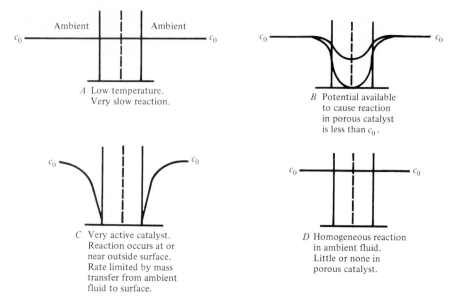

A Low temperature.
Very slow reaction.

B Potential available
to cause reaction
in porous catalyst
is less than c_0.

C Very active catalyst.
Reaction occurs at or
near outside surface.
Rate limited by mass
transfer from ambient
fluid to surface.

D Homogeneous reaction
in ambient fluid.
Little or none in
porous catalyst.

Figure 11.3 Concentration profiles in a porous catalyst under different reaction regimes.

intrinsic rate constant increases exponentially. Thus, an increasing fraction of the total available potential is required for diffusion, leaving less to drive the chemical reaction. A significant concentration gradient of the reactant then develops through the pellet (Fig. 11.3). (Concentration gradients within the catalyst pores usually become significant before those in the ambient fluid.) This second regime, B, in which pore diffusion is significant, is sometimes termed the *internal-diffusion regime*. The apparent activation energy as calculated from an Arrhenius plot will be the arithmetic average of that for the intrinsic reaction and that for diffusion, provided that the reaction is simple, temperature gradients are negligible, and the intrinsic kinetics can be expressed by a power-law relationship. In gas-phase reactions the effect of temperature on diffusion rates is equivalent to an activation energy of the order of only 4 to 12 kJ/mol. This activation energy is small compared with that of most heterogeneous reactions, in which case the observed activation energy will be little more than one-half the intrinsic value. The apparent order of the reaction will shift toward first order; e.g., an intrinsic second-order reaction will appear to be three-halves order. The reasons for this behavior are developed elsewhere (Satterfield 1970).

In complex reactions the selectivity toward an intermediate product will very likely be affected by a change from the intrinsic-kinetics regime to the internal-diffusion regime. The degree of diffusion limitation in the latter is characterized by the *effectiveness factor* η, defined as the ratio of the observed rate of reaction to that which would occur in the absence of diffusion effects within the pores of the catalyst. (Sometimes an effectiveness factor is defined relative to the absence of all diffusion effects, both internal and external.)

In a series-type reaction, e.g., A → B → C, the yield of B falls below that otherwise attainable; but the drop in selectivity to form B occurs at values of η between 1 and about 0.3, i.e., a further decrease in effectiveness factor causes no further decrease in selectivity. At effectiveness factors of η < ~0.3, the maximum yield of B attainable is only about 50 percent of that possible in the absence of diffusional limitations.

For parallel reactions of the type

diffusional limitations do not affect selectivity if both reactions are of the same order. However, if reaction (2) is of a higher order than reaction (1), the ratio B-C increases with decreased effectiveness factor since as the concentration of A drops toward the center of the catalyst pellet, the rate of reaction (2) falls more rapidly than that of reaction (1).

As temperature is further increased, reactant is effectively consumed before it can penetrate very far into the pellet. The concentration difference between the bulk of the fluid and the outside of the catalyst pellet then becomes significant. The internal effectiveness factor continues to drop. In this reaction regime, C, sometimes termed the *external-diffusion regime*, the concentration of reactant at the outside surface of the catalyst pellet approaches zero. The rate-limiting process is one of mass transfer from the ambient fluid and shows the same characteristics as bulk diffusion. The apparent activation energy is then about 4 to 12 kJ/mol for gases, 10 to 20 kJ/mol in liquid hydrocarbons, and 8 to 10 kJ/mol in aqueous systems. In this regime all reactions appear to be first order regardless of their intrinsic kinetics, since mass transfer is a first-order process. All catalysts appear to have the same activity, as determined by the relative rates of bulk diffusion of reactants and products, rather than by the intrinsic characteristics of the reaction.

In regime C the reaction rate is sometimes said to be limited by mass transfer to the catalyst surface, or is sometimes termed a *film-*

diffusion-limited process, but the terminology of a rate-limiting process may be confusing. When two processes occur in series, the two rates must be equal under steady-state conditions. The rate-limiting process is the one that consumes the major portion of the chemical potential available. In regime B, diffusion through the pore structure occurs simultaneously with reaction. Although reactions in this regime are sometimes described loosely as being "limited by pore diffusion," the process is not controlled by a single process as in regime C, since diffusion and reaction occur simultaneously rather than in series. In the external-diffusion regime, if the reaction is highly exothermic, as it usually is, a substantial temperature difference will exist between the outside surface and the bulk fluid, and various instability phenomena may be encountered.

If the same reaction can occur homogeneously as well as catalyzed heterogeneously, the effective activation energy for the homogeneous path is almost invariably greater than that for the heterogeneous route. Since the two competing processes occur in parallel, whichever is faster is the one that will be observed. Homogeneous reaction may predominate over catalytic reaction even at low temperature, depending on the system, but it is shown on the left in Fig. 11.2. This emphasizes that it plays an increasing role at higher temperatures and that the possibility of contributions from homogeneous reaction must be considered in analyzing the results of a seemingly "catalytic" reaction.

The foregoing picture is somewhat simplified. It represents the intrinsic reaction rate by an Arrhenius expression, whereas more complex kinetics are frequently encountered. Indeed, in a few cases, such as the catalytic hydrogenation of ethylene, the intrinsic rate may exhibit a maximum with increase in temperature (Sec. 3.3.3). A decrease in apparent activation energy with increased temperature does not necessarily indicate the onset of the internal-diffusion regime. This behavior may be solely a reflection of the intrinsic kinetics (Chap. 3). The temperature of the gas and solid are taken to be the same, whereas with highly exothermic (or endothermic) reactions significant temperature gradients between the two may occur. With an exothermic reaction, instability effects may develop from the consequences of coupling between temperature and concentration gradients. Nevertheless, the foregoing broad outline describes the transitions from one regime to another as temperature is changed, and has been clearly demonstrated in many experimental studies. (Figure 11.2 represents the separate regimes by intersecting straight lines and omits representation of transition regions.)

The order in which the three catalytic regimes are encountered with increased temperature is as shown in Fig. 11.2, except perhaps in a few highly complex situations. The relative location of the three lines with respect to one another depends on several factors. In the internal-diffusion regime B, the rate, but not the apparent activation energy, is increased by reducing the size of the catalyst particle or by altering the pore structure so as to increase the diffusivity. The line shifts upward, its slope remaining the same. With nonporous solids, regime B is eliminated and transition occurs from intrinsic kinetics directly to the external diffusion regime. Here the rate is a strong function of the linear velocity of the ambient fluid, whereas in the internal regime it is independent of it, bulk concentration being held constant. The relative importance of homogeneous reaction depends on the ratio of bulk-gas volume to catalytic surface, as well as the relative rate constants and the appropriate rate expressions.

There are two general methods of determining whether heat- and mass-transfer gradients are causing significant effects. The most reliable is by experiment, to determine the effects of particle size, temperature, and agitation or fluid velocity. The second is by calculation. The accuracy of the calculation method is limited by the accuracy with which diffusivities and other physical properties can be predicted, by a knowledge of the basic kinetics, and by the complexity of the reaction. The transition temperatures between regimes vary widely with different reactions and different catalysts, as will be seen.

11.2.1 Examples

Some examples of experimental studies to determine the reaction regime are shown in Figs. 11.4 to 11.9. Figure 11.4 is an Arrhenius plot for the gasification of a carbon char in oxygen at 0.1 MPa, over a wide temperature range (Ismail & Walker 1989). The char was a high-purity carbon prepared by carbonizing Saran (copolymer of vinylidene chloride and vinyl chloride) in nitrogen. A 57×100-μm fraction, having a BET area of 808 m^2/g was studied by a thermogravimetric method. The Arrhenius plot shows the three reaction regimes expected from theory and a drop in apparent activation energy from 178 kJ/mol in the intrinsic-kinetic region, to 87 kJ/mol in the pore-diffusion regime, to about 8.4 kJ/mol in the bulk-diffusion regime, values consistent with theory.

Figure 11.5 (Satterfield & Cortez 1970) shows the percent oxidation of dilute hexene in air on passage through a single nonporous platinum gauze, at each of three velocities. The rate increased markedly with increased temperature up to about 380 to 400°C, but it was relatively insensitive to temperature above this point. This suggests that the external-diffusion regime was then encountered. This conclusion was further supported by showing that the observed rates at high tem-

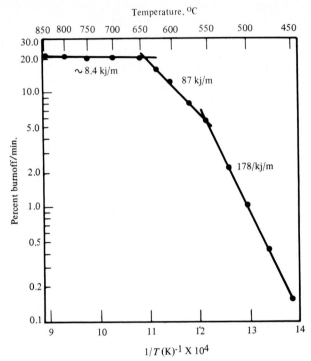

Figure 11.4 Arrhenius plot for gasification of carbon char in 0.1 MPa O_2 between 450–850°C. *(Ismail and Walker 1989. Reprinted with permission from Carbon, copyright 1989, Pergamon Press.)*

peratures agreed closely with those predicted from mass-transfer correlations for a similar geometry but in nonreacting systems. The scatter in the data is not atypical. One seldom encounters a sharp kink in the transition between two regimes, and the use of two straight lines, as here, emphasizes the transition region. In the film-diffusion regime the conversion drops with increased linear velocity since the rate of mass transfer increases with velocity, but to a power less than 1.

Changing mass velocity alone in a packed bed is not a significant test for the external-diffusion regime, since contact time is also changed. Velocity and bed depth must be changed in proportion, in order to keep contact time constant. An example is seen in the results of a study of the water-gas shift reaction on 9.4-mm-diameter iron-oxide pellets as reported by Hulburt and Srini Vasan (1961). The reverse reaction was negligible under these conditions. As shown in Fig. 11.6, the mass velocity had to be increased to a value of 0.034 kg/m^2·s (25 lb/ft^2·h) before bulk mass-transfer resistance was eliminated.

Figure 11.7 shows data on SO_2 oxidation to SO_3 on a commercial

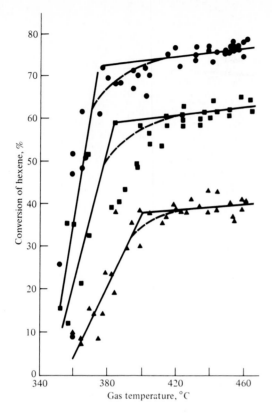

Figure 11.5 Effect of temperature on combustion of hexene: 52-mesh platinum gauze, 0.133% hexene in air. $V_0 = 165$ (●), 250 (■), and 450 (▲) cm^3 (at STP)/s. *(Satterfield and Cortez 1970. Reprinted with permission from Industrial and Engineering Chemistry, Fundamentals. Copyright by the American Chemical Society.)*

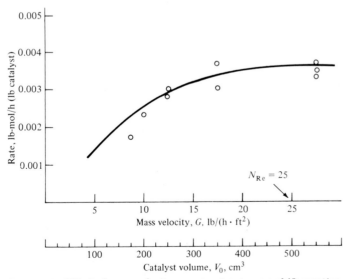

Figure 11.6 Effect of mass velocity on rate of water-gas shift reaction. *(Hulburt and Srini Vasan 1961)*

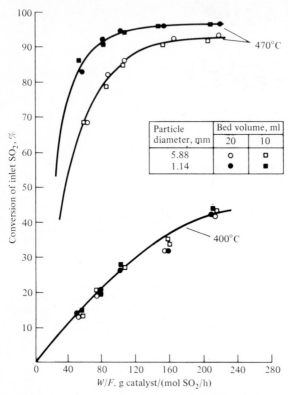

Figure 11.7 Effect of particle size and linear velocity on conversion. Oxidation of SO_2 to SO_3. *(Adapted from Dowden and Bridger 1957. Reprinted with permission from Advances in Catalysis. Copyright by Academic Press.)*

catalyst over a range of linear velocities, using two different bed depths of catalyst and catalyst particle diameters of 5.88 and 1.14 mm. The smaller particles were obtained by crushing the largest size (Dowden & Bridger 1957). These variations make it possible to test for both the pore-diffusion and film-diffusion regimes. (Studies with 2.36-mm particles, not shown, gave essentially identical results to those obtained with 1.14-mm particles.) There is no effect of mass velocity, since the same conversion was obtained with the same value of the ratio of bed depth to flow rate at two different bed depths. Hence, the external-diffusion regime is not encountered. At 400°C the conversion was the same for all particle sizes; hence, internal-diffusion gradients were unimportant here even with the largest particles. At 470°C, however, significant pore-diffusion limitations were encountered with the largest particles. The leveling off of conversion with increased contact time at 470°C utilizing the smaller particles reflects the approach to equilibrium.

Figure 11.8, from the studies of Weisz and Prater (1954) on cracking of cumene, shows an increase in apparent activation energy as particle size was reduced, holding the temperature range constant. This is in agreement with theory for reaction in the internal-diffusion regime for the larger particle sizes, shifting to intrinsic kinetics for the smallest particles.

Figure 11.9 shows data on the decomposition of hydrogen peroxide vapor on: (1) Pyrex glass cleaned with either hydrofluoric or phosphoric acid, (2) on stainless steel, and (3) on platinum, all surfaces being nonporous. With the glass surfaces a marked shift from heterogeneous to homogeneous reaction as the dominating mechanism is seen to occur with increased temperature since the observed rate at the lower temperatures is markedly affected by the method used for cleaning the glass, but at the higher temperatures the observed rate is inde-

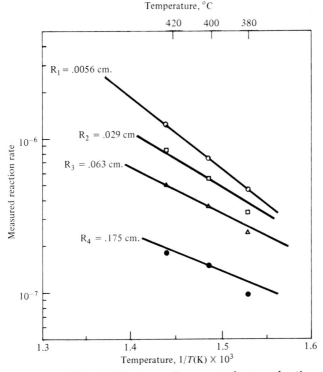

Figure 11.8 Effect of diffusion on the measured rate and activation energy of the cracking of cumene on $SiO_2 \cdot Al_2O_3$ catalyst. ○, $R_1 = 0.0056$ cm; □, $R_2 = 0.029$ cm; △, $R_3 = 0.063$ cm; ●, $R_4 = 0.175$ cm. *(Weisz and Prater 1954. Reprinted with permission from Advances in Catalysis. Copyright by Academic Press.)*

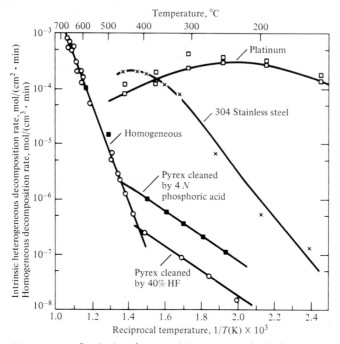

Figure 11.9 Intrinsic decomposition rate of H_2O_2 vapor. *(Satterfield and Yeung 1963. Reprinted with permission from Industrial and Engineering Chemistry, Fundamentals. Copyright by the American Chemical Society.)*

pendent of it. The temperature at which this transition would occur depends on the surface-volume ratio and surface reactivity. For the glass surfaces here, it was about 420 to 460°C. For a more active surface it would be higher. A maximum in the catalyzed rate with increased temperature is observed with stainless steel and especially with platinum. Over a moderate temperature range the seemingly flat curve might, in the absence of other information, be erroneously interpreted as indicating the film-diffusion regime. These results illustrate the hazards of trying to reach conclusions solely from the effect of temperature on apparent activation energy.

Figure 11.10 illustrates the decrease in selectivity observed for a reaction of the type A → B → C as particle size is increased to where the internal-diffusion regime is encountered (Voge & Morgan 1972). The reaction is the dehydrogenation of butene to butadiene in the presence of steam at 620°C on a porous commercial iron-oxide (Shell 205) catalyst. The butadiene may react further to form carbon dioxide and cracked products. In accordance with theory, the selectivity to butadiene achieved was less with the larger particles.

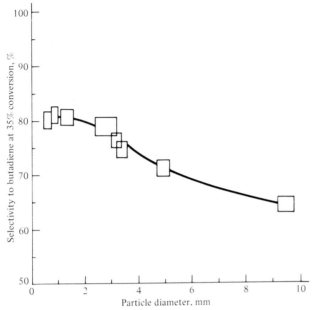

Figure 11.10 Dehydrogenation of butene to butadiene. Selectivity at 35-percent conversion as a function of particle size. *(Voge and Morgan 1972. Reprinted with permission from Industrial and Engineering Chemistry, Process Design and Development. Copyright by the American Chemical Society.)*

A technique suggested by Koros and Nowak (1967) may also be useful, especially for research studies. Pellets are made from a powdered catalyst that is mixed with inert powder of the same size. Measurements are made with pellets made up of two or more ratios of catalyst to inert. If the ratio of the rate constants (or better, turnover number) for the two kinds of pellets is the same as the ratio of amounts of catalyst in the two pellets, diffusional effects are deemed to be negligible. The inert material must be shown to be truly inert; ideally it should be nonporous and have the same deformable characteristics as the catalyst. The diffusional characteristics of the two pellets must be the same; this may be difficult to achieve, but is possibly attainable by pelletizing the two pellets in the same fashion.

Coke deposits occur often in catalytic reactions under reducing conditions, and the distribution of coke through a catalyst pellet is affected by diffusion limitations. This may be readily observed by sectioning catalyst pellets after use. Murakami et al. (1968) studied, both theoretically and experimentally, parallel- and series-type reactions in which the reactant was converted to product or coke. The disproportionation of toluene on an alumina-boria catalyst to form either xylene and benzene, or coke and benzene was chosen as representative of parallel-type kinetics. The dehydrogenation of an alcohol on an alkaline-alumina catalyst to form an aldehyde that then formed coke was taken as representative of a series-type reaction. With the series-type reaction, under a moderate degree of internal-diffusion limitation, coke deposition occurs preferentially in the interior of the pellet. With a high degree of diffusion limitation, the coke deposit appears preferentially at the outside with either type of kinetics. The drawings in Fig. 11.11 illustrate the photographs they published of the cross section of catalyst pellets after the reaction had proceeded for the time interval and at the temperature specified. With the toluene disproportionation reaction there were no diffusion limitations at 400°C but substantial limitations at 530°C. At the higher temperature the toluene essentially all reacted within the outer portion of the pellets (see also Fig. 11.3), so coke appears as an annular ring. With the

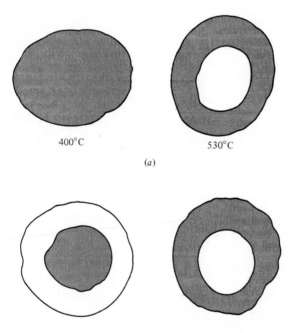

400°C

530°C

(a)

Figure 11.11   Effect of time and nature of reaction on distribution of coke deposits in a catalyst pellet. (a) Cross section of catalyst pellet after disproportionation of toluene for 10 min. (b) Cross section of catalyst pellet after dehydrogenation of n-butyl alcohol. (Murakami et al. 1968. Reprinted with permission from Industrial and Engineering Chemistry, Fundamentals. Copyright by the American Chemical Society.)

series-type reaction, a moderate degree of diffusion limitation was encountered at 400°C, but a more severe degree occurred at 480°C. At 400°C coke appears only in the center of the pellet where the aldehyde concentration has built up to a level that permits significant further reaction to form coke. Under the more strongly diffusion-limiting conditions that occur at higher temperature (480°C), the entire series of reactions goes to completion near the outside pellet surface. In this case coke appears only in an annular ring because no appreciable aldehyde precursor survives to reach the center.

Some additional precautions need to be borne in mind in making experiments of this type. Studying the effect of particle size assumes the particle composition and pore structure to be uniform. The most useful tests usually proceed by crushing a given catalyst to produce two or more smaller particle sizes for study. Studying two or more pellet sizes as made in the laboratory or plant may be misleading since they may have different pore structures. Studying crystals grown to different sizes, as of zeolites, may likewise be misleading since they may have crystal defects to different degrees. If the active catalyst ingredient is concentrated near the outside of a pellet, the effectiveness factor may be essentially unity, whereas it might not be if the active catalyst ingredient were uniformly dispersed. With catalysts having some very fine pores, as with those incorporating zeolites, crushing the catalyst may reveal nothing about possible diffusion limitations in the fine-pore structure when the particle size of the crushed material is still orders of magnitude greater than the pore size.

As conditions are altered to cause a shift from the intrinsic-kinetic region into the internal-diffusion regime, the most sensitive indicator is often a change in reaction selectivity rather than a change in activity. To determine activity requires measurement of both temperature and composition, whereas to determine selectivity requires a knowledge only of composition, which can usually be determined more accurately.

The general topic of heat and mass transfer in heterogeneous catalysis is treated in detail elsewhere (Satterfield 1970; Carberry 1976, 1987, Smith 1981, Froment & Bischoff 1990). The estimation of heat- and mass-transfer properties in packed-bed reactors is reviewed by Kulkarni and Doraiswamy (1980).

11.3   Theoretical Criteria

A number of criteria have been published that make possible the estimate of whether or not a single catalyst particle or packed-bed reactor is being studied under essentially ideal circumstances. These criteria are based on estimated values of pore diffusivity, thermal conductivity, axial dispersion, heat- and mass-transfer coefficients, nature of the kinetics, and other parameters. The accuracy with which such criteria can be applied varies widely from case to case. The most reliable conclusions are usually reached from careful experimentation as discussed in the foregoing rather than from theoretical calculations. This is especially true the more complex the reaction mixture. However, calculations may help to buttress conclusions derived from observations and provide a method of reaching conclusions when experimentation is impractical. Estimation of bulk heat- and mass-transfer coefficients and axial dispersion at the relatively low flow rates characteristically encountered in many laboratory reactors is especially difficult.

Some of the more useful criteria for application to laboratory and pilot-plant-scale studies are summarized in the following. A larger number were discussed by Mears (1971) and by Butt and Weekman (1974). See also discussion in the texts by Carberry (1976), Smith (1981), and Froment and Bischoff (1990). Three kinds of gradients of either concentration or temperature or both, may exist:

   I. Intraparticle (inside catalyst particle)
  II. Interphase (between fluid and particle)
 III. Reactor gradients
     A. Radial gradients
     B. Axial dispersion

These gradients may interact with each other in complex ways. Most of the following criteria assume each can be treated separately, which is usually valid if the criteria indeed are met. To obtain reliable guidance from a criterion that treats two or more kinds of gradients simultaneously usually requires that the values of several parameters be known with a degree of precision that is seldom available.

The degree of departure from ideality is usually expressed as an effectiveness factor, η. This is defined here as the ratio of the actual reaction rate to that which would occur if all of the surface throughout the inside of the catalyst particle were exposed to reactant and product of the same concentration and temperature as that existing in the bulk fluid. For the ideal situation, η approaches unity. Under isothermal conditions, η decreases in value as diffusion limitations become significant, but with a highly exothermic reaction η may exceed unity. This occurs when the catalyst temperature exceeds that of the bulk gas, and the increase in reaction rate by increase in temperature more than outweighs the decrease in rate caused by lower concentration.

These criteria utilize various dimensionless groups of properties, which are summarized in Table 11.2.

TABLE 11.2   Selected Dimensionless Groups

Name	See the following:	Proportional to:
Reynolds number,* $\text{Re} = \dfrac{LG}{\mu}$	Sec. 11.6	$\dfrac{\text{Inertial force}^\dagger}{\text{Viscous force}}$
Prandtl number, $\text{Pr} = \dfrac{c_p \mu}{k_f}$	Secs. 11.6.1, 11.6.2	$\dfrac{\text{Kinematic viscosity}}{\text{Thermal diffusivity}}$
		$\dfrac{\text{Momentum viscosity}^\ddagger}{\text{Thermal diffusivity}}$
Schmidt number, $\text{Sc} = \dfrac{\mu}{\rho D}$	Sec. 11.6	$\dfrac{\text{Kinematic viscosity}}{\text{Molecular diffusivity}}$
Lewis number, $\text{Le} = \dfrac{\text{Pr}}{\text{Sc}}$		$\dfrac{\text{Thermal diffusivity}}{\text{Molecular diffusivity}}$
Biot number, $\text{Bi} = \dfrac{hr_m}{\lambda}$		$\dfrac{\text{Midplane thermal internal resistance}}{\text{Surface film resistance}}$
Nusselt number,* $\text{Nu} = \text{Pe} \cdot \text{St}$ $= \dfrac{hL}{k}$	Sec. 11.6	$\dfrac{\text{Total heat transfer}}{\text{Conductive heat transfer}}$
Sherwood number,* $\text{Sh} = \dfrac{k_c L}{D}$ (Nusselt number for mass transfer)	Sec. 11.6	$\dfrac{\text{Mass diffusivity}}{\text{Molecular diffusivity}}$
Stanton number, $\text{St} = \dfrac{h}{c_p G}$ $= \dfrac{\text{Nu}}{\text{Re} \cdot \text{Pr}}$		$\dfrac{\text{Heat actually transferred}}{\text{Thermal capacity of fluid}}$
Peclet number,*,§ $\text{Pe} = \dfrac{L \bar{u}}{D_a}$	Secs. 11.3.4, 11.6	$\dfrac{\text{Bulk mass transport}}{\text{Diffusive mass transport}}$

*L is a characteristic length, usually taken as d_p for beds of particles.

†Inertial forces tending to disrupt laminar motion are proportional to $\rho V^2 L^2$. Internal (viscous) forces tending to stabilize flow are proportional to $\mu V L$.

‡Kinematic viscosity, μ/ρ, is a diffusivity for momentum or for velocity. If $\text{Pr} = 1$, heat and momentum diffuse through fluid at the same rate.

§In this definition D_a is the effective dispersion coefficient, which may include mixing by turbulence and eddies, as well as molecular diffusivity. In its original definition the term Peclet number was reserved for the case in which D is the molecular diffusivity. Then $\text{Pe} = \text{Re} \cdot \text{Sc}$. When D is a dispersion coefficient, the above dimensionless group is sometimes termed the *Bodenstein number based on particle diameter*, especially in the European literature. A *Peclet number for heat transfer* is usually defined as $\text{Re} \cdot \text{Pr}$.

TABLE 11.2   Selected Dimensionless Groups (Continued)

Name	See the following:	Proportional to:
Damköhler group II,[¶] $$\Phi_s = \frac{r_p^2(-r)}{c_s D_{eff}}$$	Eq. (11.1)	$\dfrac{\text{Chemical reaction rate}}{\text{Molecular diffusion rate}}$
Damköhler group IV, $\Phi_s \lvert\beta\rvert$	Eq. (11.5)	$\dfrac{\text{Heat liberated}}{\text{Conductive heat transfer}}$
Arrhenius group, $\gamma = \dfrac{E}{RT_s}$	Eq. (11.4)	$\dfrac{\text{Activation energy}}{\text{Potential energy of fluid}}$
Heat generation function, or *thermicity,* $$\beta = \frac{c_s(-\Delta H)D_{eff}}{\lambda T_s}$$	Eq. (11.3)	

[¶] This should not be confused with the Thiele modulus, frequently designated by ϕ_s, which is defined differently.

11.3.1   Intraparticle

Isothermal system.   The basic parameter is a form of the Thiele modulus suggested by Wagner in 1943. This consists of four quantities that are known or can be estimated. Symbols are defined in Table 11.11.

$$\Phi_s = \frac{r_p{}^2(-r)}{D_{eff}c_s} \qquad (11.1)$$

The smaller the value of Φ_s, the smaller the concentration gradient through the pellet and the closer the effectiveness factor η approaches unity. Typically, a criterion specifies conditions under which $\eta \geq 0.95$. This is determined by the intrinsic order of the reaction as well as the value of Φ_s. For an irreversible reaction of a single reactant the kinetics of which can be represented by a power-law relationship, $\eta \geq 0.95$ if

$$\Phi_s < 6 \quad \text{zero-order reaction}$$
$$< 1 \quad \text{first-order reaction} \qquad (11.2)$$
$$< 0.3 \quad \text{second-order reaction}$$

If the reaction is strongly inhibited by product adsorption, considerably lower values of Φ_s need be achieved for $\eta \geq 0.95$. A change in volume upon reaction affects the effective diffusivity if the bulk-diffusion regime is encountered inside catalyst pores (see the following). This is usually of secondary importance, and becomes negligible for a dilute reactant. For nonspherical shapes, taking $r_p = 3V_p/S_p$ usually introduces little error. Methods of handling more complex systems, e.g., reversible reactions, and complex kinetics are summarized elsewhere (Satterfield 1970). In a mixture of two or more reactants, Φ_s may be estimated based on the key reactant—the one that diffuses into the porous catalyst least rapidly. For example, in a stoichiometric gas mixture of hydrogen and a reactant A, A is usually the key reactant since hydrogen has a higher diffusivity than any other molecule. In a mixture of A and a great excess of B, where A and B have about the same diffusion coefficient, A will be the key reactant since the concentration gradient for A greatly exceeds that for B.

Nonisothermal systems.   Two new dimensionless groups are now utilized, β and γ.

$$\beta = \frac{c_s(-\Delta H)D_{\text{eff}}}{\lambda T_s} \tag{11.3}$$

ΔH is the enthalpy change on reaction, and λ is the thermal conductivity of the porous catalyst. For an exothermic reaction, β is a positive number and for most reactions is ± 0.1 or less. Even for a highly exothermic reaction, β seldom exceeds 0.2. The value of β is also useful to know since it equals $\Delta T_{\text{max}}/T_s$, the maximum possible temperature difference between the outside pellet surface and the pellet interior, relative to the surface temperature, that occurs under highly diffusion-limited circumstances.

$$\gamma = \frac{E}{RT_s} \tag{11.4}$$

γ is sometimes termed the *Arrhenius group*. E is the intrinsic activation energy, R the gas constant, and T_s the temperature at the outside pellet surface. Values of γ typically will vary in the range between 10 and 40.

The observed rate will deviate from the rate under isothermal conditions by less than 5 percent (Anderson 1963) if

$$\Phi_s|\beta| = \frac{|\Delta H|(-r)r_p^2}{\lambda T_s} < \frac{1}{\gamma} \tag{11.5}$$

This criterion is valid whether or not diffusional limitations exist in the pellet.

If both temperature and concentration gradients occur simultaneously, the criterion for $0.95 < \eta < 1.05$ is

$$\Phi_s < \frac{1}{|n - \gamma\beta|} \tag{11.6}$$

This applies to either endothermic or exothermic reactions, and to power-law kinetics, where n is the order of reaction but does not equal zero. When $|n - \gamma\beta|$ is close to or equals zero (a rather unusual case), this does not apply. If n and $\gamma\beta$ each equal 1.0, the criterion becomes $\Phi_s < 13$ (Peterson 1965).

A criterion for isothermal operation of a catalyst particle was developed by Peterson, by an asymptotic solution for first-order kinetics, as follows:

$$|\gamma\beta| < 0.3 \tag{11.7}$$

11.3.2 Interphase transport

For vapor-phase systems, as temperature differences become important, the temperature difference between the bulk gas and the outside pellet surface is usually much greater than the temperature difference between the pellet surface and the pellet center. On the other hand, concentration differences between the outside pellet surface and the interior normally become severe before the difference between the concentration in bulk gas and that at pellet surface becomes appreciable.

In order for the observed rate not to deviate by more than 5 percent because of a temperature difference between catalyst particle and the bulk fluid (Mears 1971),

$$\frac{(-\Delta H)(-r)r_p}{hT} < 0.15\frac{RT_b}{E} \tag{11.8}$$

Here h is the heat-transfer coefficient and T_b is the bulk temperature of the fluid. If the criterion holds, $T \approx T_b$. The criterion is valid whether or not diffusion limitations exist in the particle. Equation (11.8) is similar in form to Eq. (11.5), with h replacing λ/r_p.

Under *isothermal* conditions, a concentration difference between bulk fluid and outside pellet surface will be insignificant if

$$\frac{(-r)r_p}{c_b k_c} < \frac{0.15}{n} \tag{11.9}$$

Here c_b is the bulk-fluid concentration, and k_c is the mass-transfer coefficient between gas and particle. Mears points out that comparison of Eqs. (11.9) and (11.8) for typical cases demonstrates that temperature gradients become the source of deviations from ideality long before concentration gradients do so.

11.3.3 Reactor gradients

A packed-bed laboratory reactor is usually operated as an integral reactor, i.e., with substantial conversion from entrance to exit. Temperature and concentration may vary from point to point both radially and axially. Hence, analysis of the integrated data obtained from such a system to indicate transport limitations is particularly complex. The most difficult requirement to achieve is isothermality in both the radial and axial directions. If this is attained, the radial concentration gradients (external to catalyst particles) will seldom be significant.

Mears develops the following criterion for the observed reaction rate not to deviate more than 5 percent from the isothermal case, assuming plug flow and assuming that there are no inter- or intraparticle concentration or temperature gradients.

$$\frac{|-\Delta H|(-r)r_R^2}{\lambda T_w} < 0.4\frac{RT_w}{E} \tag{11.10}$$

Here r_R is the reactor radius, λ is the effective thermal conductivity across the bed, and T_w is the wall temperature in degrees kelvin. The expression is similar in form to Eq. (11.5). Strictly the foregoing applies only to the point in the bed at which the highest temperature is reached, which is typically in the region of 20- to 40-percent conversion. An averaged value through the bed will usually be less, so the foregoing criterion must be used cautiously if the reaction rate varies greatly from entrance to exit. The foregoing criterion also assumes that the heat-transfer resistance at the inside wall of the reactor is negligible relative to that through the bed radially. This assumption is valid, e.g., for $r_R/r_p > 50$ to 100, but for small laboratory reactors the right-hand side should be decreased by a factor of about 2, e.g., for $Re < \sim 100$ and $0.05 < r_p/r_R < 0.2$. This makes the criterion twice as stringent. The Reynolds number, Re, characterizes the fluid flow.

The criterion of Eq. (11.10) is very sensitive to reactor radius. This emphasizes the importance of using small-diameter laboratory reactors to obtain isothermality. The catalyst may also be diluted by mixing with inert material of about the same particle size. The rate of reaction, $-r$, in this equation is based on packed reactor volume and includes inert diluent if any. Thus, diluting a catalyst 9:1 with inert material would reduce this term by a factor of 10.

11.3.4 Axial dispersion

Deviations from plug flow may be caused by one or more of several effects. The void fraction of a packed bed next to the wall is higher than in the center. Because of the lower resistance at the wall, the linear velocity next to the wall is greater. This contribution of wall flow to the total flow may be significant for low ratios of r_R/r_p, e.g., 10 or less. The extent to which this may affect reactor performance, however, depends on several other factors such as the value of Re, the bed length, and the conversion. At low Reynolds numbers, molecular diffusion may cause significant axial dispersion. Regardless of the cause, axial dispersion is usually represented by a Peclet number, Pe = $\bar{u}d_p/D_a$, where D_a is the effective axial dispersion and $\bar{u}$ the mean fluid velocity.

Usually axial dispersion is of negligible importance except for very short beds and high conversions at low flow rates. Since this can usually be overcome by lengthening the bed, Mears presents the following criterion for the minimum reactor length necessary to avoid a significant dispersion effect.

$$\frac{L}{d_p} > \frac{20n}{Pe} \ln \frac{c_i}{c_f} \tag{11.11}$$

Here n is the order of the reaction, and c_f/c_i is the fractional conversion. The Peclet number is about 2 for gases at Reynolds numbers above about 2, and if the ratio r_R/r_p is sufficiently great that wall bypassing is not serious. To reduce the latter to a more quantitative statement is difficult, and various suggestions appear in the literature. For Re $\geqslant$ 2, values of r_R/r_p above about 10 seem to suffice. If these conditions do not apply, Pe has a lower value, but to a degree that is difficult to predict. Values of r_R/r_p considerably less than 10 can still be used satisfactorily if the percent conversion sought is not very high.

With the use of larger particles such that r_R/r_p is, say, 2 or 3, a useful diagnostic test is to fill the interstices between the particles with a finer inert material since this will eliminate or minimize wall bypassing. The question of possible wall bypassing often arises with the use of a tubular reactor equipped with a thermocouple well, in which the catalyst is packed in the annulus around the well. Here, a useful diagnostic test may be to remove the thermocouple well for a few runs, or possibly replace it with a single fine-wire thermocouple (but be careful that the thermocouple itself does not have catalytic activity).

Almost all the information on the effect of the Reynolds number on the Peclet number has been obtained from nonreacting, isothermal systems. At low values of Re, convection effects in laboratory reactors may be a far more important source of deviation from plug flow than is generally recognized; e.g., if an exothermic reaction in a downflow reactor is being studied, convection effects may be suspected, especially in a short, squat type of configuration. Prediction of such effects is difficult, but experimentally, if a fairly coarse catalyst is being studied and dispersion by convection is suspected, filling the voids with a finer inert material may be an effective diagnostic procedure. If dispersion by convection is indeed significant, this reduces convection and likely increases conversion. Comparing upflow and downflow configurations may also be useful.

11.4   Effective Diffusivity

To utilize the criteria in Sec. 11.3, determination or estimation of the effective diffusivity of a porous catalyst and the thermal conductivity of a porous catalyst or bed of particles is necessary. Procedures for calculating values to the maximum degree of certainty possible are too extensive to be treated here. Instead, a summary is presented in the following which should permit values to be estimated generally to within an order of magnitude or less, which may suffice for many cases of interest.

An effective diffusivity may be determined by passing two gases past opposite faces of a catalyst pellet and measuring the flux of one gas into the other. This is sometimes termed the *Wicke-Kallenbach experiment*, and data have been published on a large number of catalysts as well as on other porous materials. The effective diffusivity is defined by

$$N = D_{eff} \frac{dc}{dx} \tag{11.12}$$

(See Table 11.11 for nomenclature.) This is *Fick's first law*.

Measurements are made with a pair of inert gases such as hydrogen and nitrogen, or helium and nitrogen, and usually at atmospheric pressure and room temperature. For application to a catalytic reaction it is necessary to be able to extrapolate data to the composition, pressure, and temperature of reaction, or to predict D_{eff} without a diffusion measurement and with only knowledge of certain physical characteristics of the catalyst such as the pore size distribution.

11.4.1   Bulk diffusion

A large amount of data are available on diffusion coefficients in binary gas mixtures, D_{12}, and coefficients not known can be closely estimated from theoretical expressions based on kinetic theory. D_{12} is inversely proportional to pressure up to 20 atm (2 MPa) or more, so values are frequently quoted in the form of the product $D_{12}P$ (where P

is in atmospheres and D_{12} in square centimeters per second). D_{12} increases with temperature, being proportional to T^m, where m is generally between 1.5 and 2. A selection of representative values is given in Table 11.3. For moderately small molecules of the types encountered in most catalytic reactions, $D_{12}P$ is in the vicinity of 0.1 (cm²/s) (atm) at ambient temperature except for pairs with hydrogen, in which the diffusivity is somewhat higher. Methods of estimation and

TABLE 11.3   Diffusion Coefficients for Binary Gas Systems*

Gas pair	T, (K)	$D_{12}P$	Gas pair	T, (K)	$D_{12}P$
Air-ammonia	273	0.198	Ethane-methane	293	0.163
-benzene	298	0.0962	-propane	293	0.0850
-carbon dioxide	273	0.136	Helium-argon	273	0.641
	1000	1.32	-benzene	298	0.384
-chlorine	273	0.124	-ethanol	298	0.494
-diphenyl	491	0.160	-hydrogen	293	1.64
-ethanol	298	0.132			
-iodine	298	0.0834	Hydrogen		
-methanol	298	0.162	-ammonia	298	0.783
-mercury	614	0.473	-benzene	273	0.317
-naphthalene	298	0.0611	-ethanol	340	0.578
-oxygen	273	0.175	-ethylene	298	0.602
-sulfur dioxide	273	0.122	-methane	288	0.694
-toluene	298	0.0844	-nitrogen	293	0.760
-water	298	0.260	-oxygen	273	0.697
	1273	3.253	-propane	300	0.450
Argon-neon	293	0.329	Nitrogen		
			-ammonia	298	0.230
Carbon dioxide-benzene	318	0.0715	-ethylene	298	0.163
-ethanol	273	0.0693	-iodine	273	0.070
-hydrogen	273	0.550	-oxygen	273	0.181
-methane	273	0.153			
-methanol	299	0.105	Oxygen-ammonia	293	0.253
-nitrogen	298	0.167	-benzene	296	0.0939
-propane	298	0.0863	-carbon		
Carbon monoxide			tetrachloride	298	0.071
-ethylene	273	0.151	-ethylene	293	0.182
-hydrogen	273	0.651	Water-hydrogen	307.2	1.020
-nitrogen	288	0.192	-helium	307	0.902
-oxygen	273	0.185	-methane	307.6	0.292
			-ethylene	307.7	0.204
Dichlorodifluoromethane			-nitrogen	307.5	0.256
-ethanol	298	0.0475	-oxygen	352	0.352
-water	298	0.105	-carbon dioxide	307.4	0.198

*Experimental values of $D_{12}P$, where D_{12} is in cm/s and P is in atm.

data on a large number of systems are given by Reid et al. (1987) and Satterfield (1970).

11.4.2   Bulk diffusion in porous catalysts

Pore diffusion may occur by bulk or Knudsen diffusion. If the pores are large and gas relatively dense (or if the pores are filled with liquid), the process is that of *bulk*, or ordinary, *diffusion*. If the pores were an array of cylinders parallel to the diffusion path, the diffusion flux per unit total cross section of the porous solid would be the fraction θ of the flux under similar conditions with no solid present. However, the length of the tortuous diffusion path in real pores is greater than the distance along a straight line in the mean direction of diffusion. Moreover, the channels through which diffusion occurs are of irregular shape and of varying cross section; constructions offer resistances that are not offset by the enlargements. Both of these factors cause the flux to be less than would be possible in a uniform pore of the same length and mean radius. We may thus express a bulk diffusion coefficient per unit cross section of porous mass, $D_{12,\text{eff}}$, as

$$D_{12,\text{eff}} = \frac{D_{12}\theta}{\tau} \qquad (11.13)$$

τ is a tortuosity factor, which is essentially an adjustable parameter that allows for both the varying direction of diffusion and varying pore cross section. For diffusion through a randomly oriented system of cylindrical pores, τ equals 3. Experimental measurements on a variety of commercial catalysts not subjected to excessive sintering conditions yield, in almost all cases, values of τ in the range of 2 to 7. The higher values are generally encountered with materials having lower void fractions. In the absence of other information a value of $\tau = 4$ may be taken for estimation purposes. Values of θ vary from about 0.3 to 0.7. In the absence of other information a value of $\theta = 0.5$ is recommended for estimation purposes.

11.4.3   Knudsen diffusion

If the gas density is low or if the pores are quite small, or both, the molecules collide with the pore wall much more frequently than with each other. This is known as *Knudsen diffusion*. The molecules hitting the wall are momentarily adsorbed and then given off in random directions (diffusively reflected). The gas flux is reduced by the wall "resistance." This causes a delay because of both the diffuse reflection and the finite time the molecule is adsorbed. Knudsen diffusion is not observed in liquids. Kinetic theory provides the following relations for Knudsen diffusion in gases *in a straight cylindrical pore*:

$$N = \frac{D_K}{x_0}(c_1 - c_2) = \frac{D_K}{RT}\frac{(p_1 - p_2)}{x_0} = \frac{2r_e\bar{u}}{3RT}\frac{(p_1 - p_2)}{x_0} \quad (11.14)$$

$$= \frac{2r_e}{3RT}\left(\frac{8RT}{\pi M}\right)^{1/2}\frac{(p_1 - p_2)}{x_0} \quad (11.15)$$

By substitution of Eq. (11.15) into Eq. (11.14),

$$D_K = 9700 r_e \sqrt{\frac{T}{M}} \quad (11.16)$$

In Eq. (11.16) r_e is the pore radius in centimeters, T the temperature in degrees kelvin, and M the molecular weight. The symbols refer to a single component. Since molecular collisions are negligible, flow and diffusion are synonymous, and each component of a mixture behaves as though it alone were present.

The internal geometries of consolidated porous solids are poorly understood, and an empirical factor must be introduced to make the theory useful. The cylindrical pore of radius r_e has a volume-surface ratio of r_e:2. We may logically define the mean pore radius as

$$r_e = \frac{2V_g}{S_g} = \frac{2\theta}{S_g\rho_p} \quad (11.17)$$

where S_g, in square centimeters per gram, is the total surface, and ρ_p, in grams per cubic centimeter, is the pellet density. With this substitution, the Knudsen diffusion coefficient *for a porous solid* becomes

$$D_{K,\text{eff}} = \frac{D_K\theta}{\tau_m} = \frac{8\theta^2}{3\tau_m S_g\rho_p}\sqrt{\frac{2RT}{\pi M}} = 19,400\frac{\theta^2}{\tau_m S_g\rho_p}\sqrt{\frac{T}{M}} \quad (11.18)$$

As in Eq. (11.14), the void fraction θ has been introduced so that the flux N given by $D_{K,\text{eff}}$ will be based on the total cross section of porous solid, not just the pore cross section. As with bulk diffusion, the factor τ_m allows for both the tortuous path and the effect of the varying cross section of individual pores. The subscript m reminds us that τ_m is the value of the tortuosity factor obtained when D_K is calculated from a mean pore radius, defined in Eq. (11.17).

If a significantly broad range of pore sizes exists, the proper average pore radius to use in Eq. (11.16) is given by Eq. (11.19) rather than Eq. (11.17), provided that the flux is completely in the Knudsen range.

$$\bar{r} = \frac{\int\limits_{V_1}^{V_2} r\,dV}{V_2 - V_1} \tag{11.19}$$

dV is the volume of pores having radii between r and $r + dr$.

11.4.4 The transition region

Bulk diffusion occurs when the collisions of molecules with the pore wall are unimportant compared with molecular collisions in the free space of the pore. Knudsen diffusion occurs when this condition is reversed. For a given system at specified conditions of pressure, temperature, and concentration there is a range of pore sizes where both types of collisions are important. This is the *transition region*. However, as pressure is increased, for example, the change from Knudsen to bulk diffusion does not occur suddenly when the mean free path of the gas molecules becomes equal to the pore radius; rather there is a gradual change in the relative contributions from the two mechanisms. Unfortunately the diffusion process in many high-area porous catalysts under reaction conditions is in the transition regime. For equimolar counterdiffusion, which occurs when there is no change in number of moles on reaction,

$$\frac{1}{D_{\text{eff}}} = \frac{1}{D_{K,\text{eff}}} + \frac{1}{D_{12,\text{eff}}} \tag{11.20}$$

In effect two resistances in series exist. The flux is limited by molecules colliding with the wall or with each other or both. Whether Knudsen or ordinary diffusion predominates depends on the ratio D_{12}: D_K and not solely on pore size or pressure. D_{12} varies inversely with pressure and does not depend on pore size; D_K is proportional to pore diameter and independent of pressure. D_K is proportional to $T^{1/2}$; D_{12}, to $T^{3/2 \text{ to } 2}$. In the aforementioned formulation the value of $D_{12,\text{eff}}$ is affected if there is a change in number of moles on reaction since there is then a net molar flux in or out of the catalyst. This is a minor effect if the ratio of molar fluxes is not too great (e.g., within the range of roughly 3 to ⅓), or if much of the gas present does not take part in the reaction. The greater portion of the flux that occurs in the Knudsen and transition region, the less important is this effect on D_{eff}.

Figure 11.12 illustrates the effect of pore size at fixed pressure on the diffusion flux for the binary system hydrogen-nitrogen. The ratio of the fluxes of the two species is inversely proportional to the square root of the ratio of their molecular weights, not only in the Knudsen and transition regime, but also in the bulk regime when the pores are

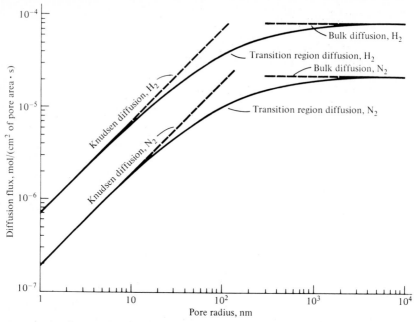

Figure 11.12   Counterdiffusing flux of hydrogen and nitrogen as a function of pore size; atmospheric pressure, $T = 298$ K.

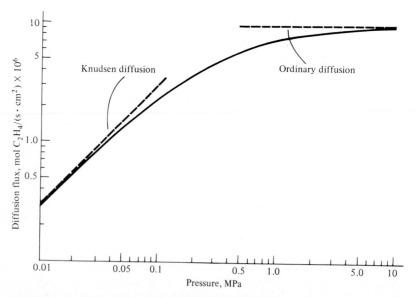

Figure 11.13   Steady-state diffusion flux of ethylene in presence of hydrogen. $T = 298$ K, $\theta = 0.4$, $r_e = 57$ nm, $P = 0.1$ MPa, $D_{12} = 0.602$ cm²/s.

of the order of a micrometer in size. The range of pore sizes for which diffusion will occur in the transition region moves in the direction of smaller pores with increased pressure. Figure 11.13 shows the calculated effect of pressure on the flux through a porous plug in which all pores are taken to be 57 nm in radius. To illustrate the effect of composition, Table 11.4 gives the transition-region limits for some binary gas pairs at 300°C and atmospheric pressure. The transition region is arbitrarily defined as that in which the diffusion flux is 10 percent or more below that predicted by the Knudsen or bulk diffusion equation, whichever is less.

Usually a distribution of pore sizes exists in a catalyst pellet. If this is known, an effective diffusion coefficient through the pellet can be estimated by treating the pore structure as comprising an array of parallel cylindrical pores having the pore size distribution found experimentally. This model is based on one suggested by Johnson and Stewart (1965). The tortuosity factor, termed τ_p here, is taken to be independent of pore size, diffusion mode, or nature of the diffusing species. The flux is integrated across the pore size distribution, and from this an effective diffusivity may be calculated. Mathematically this may be expressed as

$$D_{\text{eff}} = \frac{\rho_p}{\tau_p} \sum_{r=0}^{r=\infty} \frac{\Delta V_g}{(1/D_{1m}) + (1/D_K)} \tag{11.21}$$

where ΔV_g is the incremental pore volume in cubic centimeters per gram. In the transition or Knudsen region, with decreasing pore size the contribution to the flux and hence D_{eff} per unit of incremental pore volume is less. This may be seen from Fig. 11.12. From measurements

TABLE 11.4   Transition Region* for Selected Binary Gas Pairs; 300°C, Atmospheric Pressure

Gas pair	Limiting pore radius, nm	
	Lower	Upper
Hydrogen-carbon monoxide	24.5	2630
Hydrogen-benzene	13.7	1810
Hydrogen-pentadecene	1.9	318
Pentadecene-pentadecane	0.8	53.5
Air-naphthalene	7.6	635

*Diffusion flux 10 percent or more below that predicted for Knudsen or bulk diffusion, whichever is less.

on a large number of commercial catalysts, the tortuosity factor τ_p for this model has been found to be between 3 and 7 in almost all cases, provided that the catalyst has not been excessively sintered. As with bulk diffusion, a value of 4 is recommended for use when no other information is available.

The average pore radius $r_e = 2V_g/S_g = 2\theta/\rho_p S_g$. Taking as representative values $\theta = 0.5$ cm^3 pores per cubic centimeter of pellet and $\rho_p = 2$ g/cm^3, $r_e \approx 1/(2S_g)$. For a catalyst with $S_g = 50$ m^2/g, $r_e = 10$ nm. Thus Fig. 11.12 might imply that for high-area catalysts ($S_g > 50$ m^2/g) the flux would be completely in the Knudsen regime, but this is incorrect. In most industrial catalysts a pore size distribution exists, and the flux at atmospheric pressure in the larger pores may be in the transition or bulk mode.

Calculations of D_{eff} were made for 11 pelleted commercial catalysts of known pore size distribution with $S_g > 40$ m^2/g using Eq. (11.18) and a value of $\tau_m = 4$, and were compared to D_{eff} determined from measurements at ambient temperature and pressure. The experimental and calculated values of D_{eff} are given in Table 11.5, and the nature of the catalysts is described in Table 11.6. For the one very-low-area catalyst (G-58), the flux was predominantly in the bulk regime. For the others, it was in the Knudsen and transition regime. For this group of catalysts, τ_p in the parallel-path model varied between ex-

TABLE 11.5   Effective Diffusivities for Selected Commercial Catalysts and Supports

Designation	Nominal size, mm	Surface area, m^2/g	Total void fraction	$D_{eff} \times 10^3$, cm^2/s[†]	$r_e = 2V_g/S_g$, nm	$D_{eff} \times 10^3$ from Eq. (11.18)
T-126	4.8 × 3.2	197	0.384	29.3	2.9	3.30
T-1258	4.8 × 3.2	302	0.478	33.1	2.36	3.39
T-826	4.8 × 3.2	232	0.389	37.7	2.14	2.45
T-314	4.8 × 3.2	142	0.488	20.0	4.15	6.00
T-310	4.8 × 3.2	154	0.410	16.6	3.43	2.78
G-39	4.8 × 4.8	190	0.354	17.5	2.24	2.32
G-58	4.8 × 4.8	6.4	0.389	87.0	54.3	62.4
T-126	6.3 × 6.3	165	0.527	38.8	4.9	7.66
BASF	5 × 5	87.3	0.500	11.8	4.1	6.05
Harshaw	6.3 × 6.3	44	0.489	13.3	9.1	13.1
Haldor Topsøe	6.3 × 6.3	143	0.433	15.8[‡]	2.58	3.29

[†]Diffusivity of hydrogen through nitrogen, measured at room temperature and atmospheric pressure, average of five sets of samples.

[‡]Diffusivity of helium through nitrogen, multiplied by $\sqrt{4/2}$, average of two sets of samples.

SOURCE: Satterfield and Cadle (1968a).

TABLE 11.6   Catalysts and Supports in Table 11.5 and Fig. 11.14

Catalyst	Description
T-126	Activated γ-alumina
T-1258	Activated γ-alumina
T-826	3% CoO, 10% MoO_3, and 3% NiO on alumina
T-314	About 8–10% Ni and Cr in the form of oxides on an activated alumina
T-310	About 10–12% Ni as the oxide on an activated alumina
G-39	A cobalt-molybdenum catalyst, used for simultaneous hydrodesulfuriza-tion of sulfur compounds and hydrogenation of olefins
G-58	Palladium/alumina catalyst, for selective hydrogenation of acetylene in ethylene
G-52	Approximately 33 wt % Ni on a refractory oxide support, prereduced. Used for oxygen removal from hydrogen and inert gas streams
BASF	A methanol-synthesis catalyst, prereduced
Harshaw	A methanol-synthesis catalyst, prereduced
Haldor Topsøe	A methanol-synthesis catalyst, prereduced

tremes of 2.8 and 7.3. The calculated values from Eq. (11.18) fall below the experimental values by a factor varying from nearly 1 to 10 or more. Thus this expression should not be used even for high-area catalysts except for a very few cases, such as some high-area gelled catalysts, where the pore size distribution is narrow and diffusion is essentially completely in the Knudsen regime.

In the foregoing cases 50 percent or more of the surface area was in pores with $r < 10$ nm, but by the parallel-path model they contributed less than 20 percent of the total flux at most. At higher pressure the dominating regime moves towards bulk diffusion, and the micropore region will contribute to an increasing degree. This emphasizes the importance of knowing the micropore size distribution for applications at substantial pressure. Figure 11.14 gives the helium flux through nitrogen for five commercial catalysts as a function of pressure from 0.1 to 6.5 MPa. The shapes of the curves are as anticipated from theory; the flux increases rapidly with pressure at low temperature and finally approaches a constant value at the highest pressure, where diffusion is almost completely by the bulk mechanism.

Measurements on a group of 17 commercial catalysts at pressures from 0.1 to 6.5 MPa (Satterfield & Cadle 1968a) and on another group of 12 commercial catalysts (Brown et al. 1969) at pressures from 0.1 to 2.0 MPa showed for this wide variety of catalysts that τ_m as calculated from the parallel-path pore model was essentially independent of pressure. Changing the pressure to this extent allows the entire diffusion regime from Knudsen to bulk to be studied, and it leads to the useful

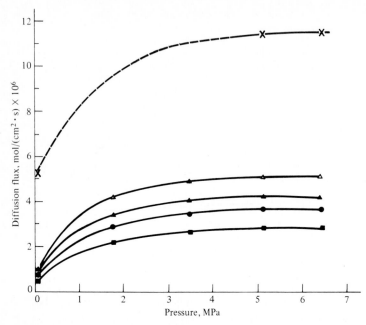

Figure 11.14   Helium flux through nitrogen as a function of pressure. x, G-58, Pd/Al$_2$O$_3$; $\triangle$, G-52, Ni-oxide support; $\blacktriangle$, Haldor-Topsøe ZnO-Cr$_2$O$_3$; $\bullet$, Harshaw ZnO-Cr$_2$O$_3$; $\blacksquare$, BASF ZnO-Cr$_2$O$_3$. *(Satterfield and Cadle 1968b. Reprinted with permission from Industrial and Engineering Chemistry, Fundamentals. Copyright by the American Chemical Society.)*

conclusion that τ may indeed be regarded essentially as a characteristic of the porous structure that is not significantly affected by the diffusion regime.

Catalysts made by a gelling process, such as some silica-alumina and chromia-alumina catalysts, generally have a high area and fine pores with a fairly narrow pore size distribution. Hence, the flux is usually completely in the Knudsen regime. Some representative values of D_{eff} for these types of catalysts are given in Table 11.7. For homogeneous bead catalysts the diffusivity is approximately inversely proportional to surface area. A clay cracking catalyst has a broader pore size distribution, and this can also be produced in a gelled catalyst by incorporation of a finely divided solid material such as α-alumina into it. Such compositions have an effective diffusivity severalfold greater than homogeneous gel structures of the same surface area.

11.4.5   Recommended procedures

In summary, for accurate prediction of D_{eff} the pore size distribution of the catalyst pellet must be known. Application of the parallel-path

TABLE 11.7   Diffusion in Gel-Derived and Related Catalysts

Catalyst	θ	S_g, m^2/g	$D_{eff} \times 10^3$,[*] cm^2/s	Reference
A. Silica-alumina "homogeneous" beads				
1. High-density beads, three samples	0.33–0.37	22–381	17.5–0.6	Weisz and Schwartz (1962)
2. Low-density beads, 35 samples	0.42–0.61	46–450	42–3.0	Weisz and Schwartz (1962)
B. Chromia-alumina and chromia-alumina-molybdena beads, two samples	0.53–0.63	155–162	20–15	Weisz and Schwartz (1962)
C. Silica-magnesia beads, one sample	0.34	442	0.45	Wesiz and Schwartz (1962)
D. Commercial pelleted clay cracking catalysts, in regenerated state after commercial use, two samples	0.26–0.30	65–105	42–49	Weisz and Schwartz (1962)
E. Silica-alumina "homogeneous" beads. Laboratory preparations, three samples		270–400	6–9	Weisz and Goodwin (1963)
F. Commercial molecular-sieve bead catalyst containing 4.5 or 10% zeolite X, 30–40% inert α-alumina, dispersed in silica-alumina matrix, average of 15 particles				Cramer et al. (1967)
1. Fresh catalyst			27–28	
2. After 3 h at 700°C in air			15	
3. Fresh catalyst after 24 h at 650°C in 0.2 MPa of steam		101–121	28–29	
4. After 5 h at 650°C in 0.8 MPa of steam		57–73	36–40	

[*]D_{eff} calculated as diffusion flux of hydrogen through nitrogen at room temperature and atmospheric pressure, divided by concentration gradient (cm^2/s).

model with a τ_m of 4 should predict D_{eff} within a factor of 2 to 4 for most cases. If only information on surface area is available, and one is dealing with a high-area catalyst under conditions where Knudsen diffusion is dominating, a value of D_{eff} calculated from Eq. (11.18) with a value of τ_m = 4 is generally conservative (i.e., the calculated value tends to be lower than the true value). Use of this equation, however, is not recommended in general, since there may be considerable variation in the pore size distribution and, hence, diffusivity among catalysts of approximately the same surface area. If bulk diffusion is clearly the dominating regime, use of Eq. (11.13) with a value of τ = 4 is recommended. Note, however, that if a considerable portion of the diffusion in fact occurs in the transition range, assumption of bulk diffusion will lead to an unrealistically high value of D_{eff}. For more detailed treatment see Satterfield (1970, Chap. 1). Diffusion coefficients in zeolites are very low and are discussed in Chap. 7.

In some cases a catalyst has a bimodal pore size distribution comprising a group of pores in the vicinity of 1 μm in size and another group of the order of 10 nm or less. Application of the foregoing procedures to the larger pores indicates whether diffusion *in and out* of the pellet as a whole is a rate-limiting process, but it is still possible for molecules to become trapped or to diffuse very slowly in the very smallest pores or dead-end pores. Thus some "diffusion-limited" type of behavior can occur even when calculations as outlined in the foregoing indicate that no diffusion limitation occurs in a gross sense through the pellet. Smith (1981) has proposed a "random-pore" or micro-macro pore model that represents the diffusion flux as being the sum of that through macropores, through micropores, and by a series diffusion through both. A comparison of this with the parallel-path model has been published (Satterfield 1970).

Surface diffusion may contribute significantly to the total flux if one or more of the reactants is a vapor not much above its condensation temperature. Then, a physically adsorbed multilayer may form. Under such conditions condensation of reactant (or product) in fine pores may also occur (Chap. 5), possibly significantly blocking diffusion. This may also lead to unusual apparent kinetic behavior as reaction conditions are changed, stemming from hysteresis effects in condensation and evaporation from pores. Surface diffusion may also contribute to the total flux in a few other cases at higher temperatures, encountered primarily with high-area catalysts and possibly at high pressures. Little information is available to indicate how important this mechanism is in general in catalysis.

Multicomponent diffusion in gases, liquids, and solids is treated in a monograph by Cussler (1976). A monograph by Jackson (1977) treats gaseous diffusion in porous media from a fundamental approach, emphasizing the modeling of simultaneous diffusion and reaction in porous catalyst pellets. Aris (1975) has published a detailed and definitive treatment of the mathematical theory of diffusion and reaction in porous and permeable substances.

11.5 Thermal Conductivity of Porous Catalysts

The thermal conductivity of a porous catalyst is of interest here primarily for calculation of the possible temperature gradient through a catalyst pellet during reaction and whether this has a significant effect on the reaction rate. Almost all porous catalysts of practical interest are oxide-type materials or are supported on such. Their thermal conductivity is not greatly affected by porosity or by the extent to which metals are deposited on the support, as will be shown. Relatively little information has been published on the thermal conductivity of porous solids of the types used in catalysis. Reference here is to studies of Sehr (1958), Mischke and Smith (1962), Masamune and Smith (1963a), and Harriott et al. (1975).

Table 11.8 shows thermal conductivities for several porous oxide catalysts as reported by Sehr at a mean temperature of about 90°C in air at atmospheric pressure. Mischke and Smith measured the thermal conductivity of a series of alumina catalyst pellets in the presence of helium or air at pressures from vacuum to atmospheric. The catalysts were prepared by pelletizing alumina powder under different pressures. Masamune and Smith reported similar studies in the presence of air, carbon dioxide, or helium on a series of metal catalysts prepared by compacting microporous silver powder. Representative results from these two studies are presented in Table 11.9, plus data reported by other workers, usually incidental to other studies. θ_{macro} is the fraction of the porous pellet occupied by pores above about 10 or 12 nm in radius. θ_{micro} is the fraction occupied by smaller pores. $(1 - \theta_{macro} - \theta_{micro})$ is the solid fraction present.

Harriott and coworkers measured thermal conductivities by a nonsteady-state method over the temperature range from ambient temperature to about 140°C. Spherical pellets enclosing air in the pores were compacted to various degrees from powders of silica or silica-alumina either as such or after impregnation to deposit nickel.

TABLE 11.8   Thermal Conductivities of Some Porous Catalysts in Air at 90°C, Atmospheric Pressure

Catalyst	$\lambda_{particle}$, W/m·K	λ_{powder}, W/m·K	Density, g/cm³ Particle	Powder
Nickel-tungsten	0.47	0.31	1.83	1.48
Cobalt-molybdenum dehydrogenation catalysts	0.35	0.21	1.63[†]	1.56[†]
	0.24	0.14	1.54[‡]	1.09[‡]
Chromia-alumina reforming catalyst	0.29	0.18	1.4	1.06
Silica-alumina cracking catalyst	0.36	0.18	1.25	0.82
Platinum-alumina reforming catalyst	0.22	0.13	1.15	0.88
Activated carbon	0.27	0.17	0.65	0.52

[†]3.6% CoO and 7.1% MoO_3 on α-alumina, 180 m²/g.
[‡]3.4% CoO and 11.3% MoO_3 on β-alumina, 128 m²/g.
SOURCE: Sehr (1958).

TABLE 11.9 Thermal Conductivities of Selected Porous Materials

Substance	Fluid in pores	Temperature, °C	Pellet Density g/cm³	θ_{macro}	θ_{micro}	λ, (W/m · K) 100 kPa	Vacuum	Reference
Alumina (boehmite) pellets	Air	50	1.12 0.67	0.134 0.450	0.409 0.275	0.22 0.13	0.16 0.07	Mischke and Smith (1962)
Pellets of silver powder	Air	34	2.96 1.35	0.144 0.61	0.574 0.261	0.71 0.17	0.06 0.09	Masamune and Smith (1963a)
Cu on MgO pellets*	Air (?)	25–170	0.7–1.20*	–	–	0.08–0.17	–	Cunningham et al. (1965)
Pt on alumina pellets, 0.05 wt %	Air	–	1.34	0.35	0.15	0.15	–	Miller and Deans (1967)
Pt on alumina pellets	H₂	68	0.57	0.56	0.23	0.26	–	Maymo and Smith (1966)
Bed of stainless steel shot, 71 μm in diameter	Air	42	5.77 (bed density)	0.264	–	0.26	0.02	Masamune and Smith (1963b)
Bed of glass beads 29, 80, 200 or 470 μm in diameter	Air	42	1.50 (bed density)	0.38	–	0.18	0.05	Masamune and Smith (1963b)

*Carbon deposits present to various degrees.

In all cases impregnation was carried out before compacting. The thermal conductivities in Table 11.10 (Harriott et al. 1975) were read from figures and show data points for the two extreme values of θ_{macro} studied. In all cases thermal conductivity decreased with increasing θ_{macro}, as expected. The values range from 0.13 to 0.24 W/m·K.

Except for a pellet of relatively dense silver, the spread of values of thermal conductivity is remarkably small for the wide range of catalysts studied by several investigators. It does not vary greatly with major differences in void fraction and pore size distribution, brought about by varying the pelletizing pressure (void fractions were not reported by Sehr). The study of Harriott shows that the presence of nickel on the support, even in large amounts, has very little effect on the effective conductivity. (The results for nickel impregnated on silica-alumina are slightly high relative to the others, but the reasons for this are unclear.)

The thermal conductivity under vacuum of compacted silver powder is not much different from that of compacted alumina. This emphasizes that this property is dependent primarily on geometrical considerations rather than the thermal conductivity of the solid as such. This is further brought out by a summary published by Masamune and Smith (1963b) of studies of the thermal conductivity of beds of spherical particles of a wide range of metallic and nonmetallic substances (silicon carbide, glass beads, quartz, steel balls, steel shot, lead, glass, and magnesium oxide). The ratio of thermal conductivity of the porous bed of solid under vacuum to that of the nonporous solid itself varied from about 0.05 to 0.001, although the void fractions of the porous beds were all within the range of 0.27 to 0.45. There was no

TABLE 11.10   Thermal Conductivity of Nickel-Impregnated Silica and Silica-Alumina

Composition	Range of θ_{macro}	Range of thermal conductivity, W/m · K
1. Pure silica (particle diameter ∼ 2–3 μm)	0.16–0.5	0.17–0.13
2. Porous silica–25% alumina (particle diameter ∼ 70 μm)	0.12–0.45	0.20–0.13
3. Coprecipitated 62% Ni on silica	0.35–0.43	0.21–0.16
4. 62% Ni impregnated on silica	0.2–0.4	0.21–0.13
5. 5% Ni impregnated on silica	0.16–0.32	0.18–0.16
6. 0.5% Ni impregnated on silica	0.2–0.33	0.17–0.16
7. 0.5% Ni impregnated on silica–25% alumina	0.16–0.33	0.24–0.22

SOURCE: Harriott et al. (1975).

significant correlation between conductivity of the solid and the conductivity of the bed. For sintered copper-tin alloy particles at atmospheric pressure, the ratio varied from about 0.02 to 0.07 at void fractions of 0.33 to 0.4, to about 0.13 at a void fraction of 0.2.

The last two groups of studies in Table 11.9 are representative of the various investigations with beds of spherical particles. For these beds conductivity under vacuum is dependent primarily on the area of contact between particles, and would be expected to be greater for rough than for smooth particle surfaces. As a bed of powder is compacted, the thermal conductivity increases as the contact area between particles is increased. This may also be affected by size, shape, particle size distribution, and any possible subsequent sintering.

Even the most dense porous silver pellet in Table 11.9 exhibited a thermal conductivity that is much less than that of solid silver (which is about 400 W/m · K). However, if porous metals were prepared by a sintering process, as by the usual powder metallurgy methods, one anticipates that the ratio of thermal conductivity of the porous metal to that for pure solid would be substantially greater than that achieved by pressing. This is indicated by the results with copper-tin alloy particles.

Both the solid and fluid phases are continuous in porous catalysts, so the thermal conductivity may be modeled as two conducting paths in parallel, with transfer of heat between the two. The latter contribution is particularly complicated since the pore size distribution of many catalysts is such that, at atmospheric pressure, diffusion is in the transition region between the Knudsen and bulk modes. Here the thermal conductivity of a gas varies significantly with pore size or pressure. The prediction of a model will vary with the geometry postulated for the two paths, but evidently the effective conductivity is determined primarily by that of the phase with the greater thermal conductivity. The greater the differences between the thermal conductivities of the two phases, the greater the divergence between the predictions of different models.

Some feeling for magnitude is helpful at this point. Reaction conditions are usually at atmospheric pressure or higher and at higher temperatures than those at which measurements have been made. The thermal conductivity of a gas is almost independent of pressure when the mean free path is substantially less than the pore size. At room temperature the thermal conductivity of air is about 0.03 W/m · K, that of hydrogen is about 0.18, and that of a wide range of organic vapors, polar and nonpolar, varies from about 0.01 to 0.03. Omitting hydrogen (and helium), these are an order of magnitude less than that of the usual porous catalysts under vacuum. (Thermal conductivities of simple organic liquids are usually 10 to 100 times greater than that of the vapor at the same temperature. Typical values for nonpolar liquids at room temperature are in the range of 0.08 to 0.20 W/m · K and are 2 or 3 times greater than this for highly polar substances.)

Over the temperature range of about 60 to 200°C, the thermal conductivity of a gas typically increases about linearly with temperature and doubles over about a 200°C temperature range. Data in Tables 11.8, 11.9, and 11.10 are for catalyst pores filled with air at atmospheric pressure, with one exception. The thermal conductivity of a liquid or vapor under reaction conditions is usually greater than that of air at room temperature, so the values reported for effective thermal conductivity of porous catalysts in air usually represent the minimum values to be expected during reaction. Temperature gradients calculated by their use would thus represent probable maximum values.

Packed beds.   The few values of thermal conductivity for packed beds given in the foregoing are for fine particles in the presence of stagnant gas. The flow of gas, as in a reactor, increases the effective bed conductivity. The effect is minor for typical laboratory conditions. The radial thermal conductivity is generally expressed by an equation of the form

$$\lambda = A + B \cdot \text{Re} \qquad (11.22)$$

where A is the bed conductivity at zero flow rate, and A and B are empirical constants. Typically it requires a value of Re in the neighborhood of 150 to 200 to double the bed conductivity over the value for stagnant conditions. The Reynolds number in laboratory reactors seldom exceeds about 20.

The thermal conductivity of packed-bed reactors, with considerable attention to data, is reviewed by Schlünder et al. (1978) and treated by Smith (1981) and Froment and Bischoff (1990). Li and Finlayson (1977) evaluated a variety of published data and present recommended correlations. Bed thermal conductivities are not very dependent on the conductivity of the solid particles as such. See also the brief discussion at the end of Sec. 11.9.

In most treatments of thermal conductivity, only contributions from conduction and convection are considered. Little has been published about the contribution of radiative heat transfer relative to the other modes in catalyst beds. The relative contribution of radiation varies with particle size, gas flow rate, and other variables. For representative deep packed beds, radiative heat transfer is probably relatively unimportant up to temperatures in the region of 500°C or more, but since the radiative heat flux is proportional to the fourth power of temperature difference versus first power for conduction and convection, the contribution of radiation can vary greatly over a small temperature change in a critical region. Radiative heat transfer is important with thin hot beds as used in NH_3 oxidation and HCN synthesis in the Andrussow process and probably also in steam reforming.

11.6   Bulk-Mass Transfer

Data on rates of mass transfer between a gas stream and a solid have been obtained by a variety of means, e.g., by observing the rate of volatilization of a low-volatile solid or the rate of evaporation of a liquid from a porous solid. Rates of mass transfer are commonly expressed in terms of a mass-transfer coefficient k_c defined by

$$N = k_c(c_o - c_s) \tag{11.23}$$

where N is the diffusion flux of the constituent in question (mol/s · cm^2), c_s is the concentration at the surface, and c_o is the concentration in the ambient fluid. Alternately, the potential may be expressed in terms of the partial pressure of the diffusing substance, in which case a coefficient k_G may be conveniently defined by

$$N = k_G(p_o - p_s) \tag{11.24}$$

where $k_G = k_c/RT$.

Dimensional considerations suggest representing the mass-transfer coefficient in the form of the Sherwood number, Sh $= k_c d_p/D_{1m}$. This in turn is a function of the Schmidt number, Sc, and the Reynolds number, Re. Alternately, the mass-transfer coefficient may be represented in terms of the group j_D suggested by Chilton and Colburn in 1934 as the basis for an analogy between mass transfer and heat transfer

$$j_D = \frac{\text{Sh}}{\text{Re} \cdot \text{Sc}^{1/3}} = \frac{k_c \rho}{G}\text{Sc}^{2/3} = \frac{k_G P}{G_M}\text{Sc}^{2/3} \tag{11.25}$$

j_D in turn is expressed as a function of Re, which characterizes the flow condition. Much more data are available on heat transfer than on mass transfer, so analogies between the two are useful for checking and extending mass-transfer data.

The Schmidt number and the Reynolds number are defined as

$$\text{Sc} = \frac{\mu}{\rho D_{1m}} \qquad \text{Re} = \frac{d_p G}{\mu} \tag{11.26}$$

Here μ and ρ are the viscosity and density of the fluid, D_{1m} is the molecular diffusion coefficient for the diffusing species in the fluid, and G is the mass velocity of the fluid in grams per second per square centimeter of total or superficial bed cross section normal to mean flow. The Schmidt number for gas mixtures seldom falls outside the range of 0.5 to 3. For dilute aqueous liquids, representative values of Sc are in the range of 400 to 2500; for organic molecules in benzene, a range of 300 to 500 is representative. The length d_p appearing in Re is taken to be the particle diameter in the case of spheres; for cylinders, d_p represents the diameter of a sphere having the same surface.

In laboratory work Re typically ranges from about 10 to 20 down to as low as 0.1 or less. Petrovic and Thodos (1968) present new data and recalculated various earlier studies by Thodos and coworkers to correct previously published data for axial mixing. They recommended the following correlation, for 3 < Re < 2000.

$$\epsilon j_D = \frac{0.357}{Re^{0.359}} \tag{11.27}$$

This is for 1.8 mm < d_p < 9.4 mm.

For lower flow rates and smaller particles, mass-transfer coefficients may be very low, but the situation is confused because of the difficulties of avoiding axial dispersion and end effects in experimental work and the lack of reliable theory for prediction. More data have been reported on heat transfer than on mass transfer, and as a very rough guide the results of several workers may be approximately represented by

$$Sh \approx Nu \approx 0.07 \, Re_p \tag{11.28}$$

For data obtained at 0.1 < Re_p < 10 (Kunii & Suzuki 1967; Cybulski et al. 1975; Wakao & Tanisho 1974). Here Nu = hd_p/k_f, and is the heat-transfer analogy to the Sherwood number, Sh. These and other results agree moderately well with a theory put forward by Nelson and Galloway (1975), although the basis for the theory is debatable.

At these very low flow rates, local mass-transfer coefficients may very likely vary substantially from point to point (Harriott 1974). A low mass-transfer coefficient in one zone of a packed bed is not necessarily compensated for by a higher coefficient elsewhere, so the effect of mass transfer may be more important than would be estimated from an averaged coefficient. Especially with some degree of particle size distribution and hence distribution of voidage, it might be expected that much of the flow would channel around small blocks of fine particles, within which mass transfer is largely by molecular diffusion. Kunii and Suzuki (1967) develop a model for heat and mass transfer between particles and fluid in a packed bed based on this concept. Martin (1978) was able to match the experimental features of data on heat transfer by a model of a packed bed with nonuniform distribution of the void fraction, and consequently nonuniform fluid velocity. Next to the wall the void fraction is much larger than the average, especially at low Reynolds numbers. In Martin's analysis Nu is presented in terms of a Peclet number for heat transfer, defined as $Pe = Re \cdot Pr = c_p \, Gd_p/k_f$.

In summary, qualitative tests to determine whether external mass transfer is a significant resistance by varying, e.g., linear velocity, may give anomalous results at values of Re below about 1 to 10. Also, external mass-transfer coefficients may be so low that external resistance becomes more important than internal resistance. This is the reverse of the usual pattern observed at higher flow rates and with larger particles.

11.6.1   Heat transfer

Heat and mass are transferred between solid and fluid by similar mechanisms, and data on heat transfer in fixed beds are correlated in the same way as data on mass transfer. Thus

$$j_H = \frac{h}{c_p G} Pr^{2/3} \tag{11.29}$$

$$h = \frac{q}{T_s - T_o} \tag{11.30}$$

where

$$Pr = \frac{c_p \mu}{k_f} \tag{11.31}$$

Here h is the heat-transfer coefficient, q is the heat flux (per unit pellet outside surface area), c_p is the heat capacity per unit mass of fluid, Pr is the Prandtl number, T_s is the pellet surface temperature, T_o is the fluid stream temperature, and k_f is the thermal conductivity of the fluid. j_H is approximately equal to j_D, and this forms the basis for estimating mass-transfer coefficients from heat-transfer data.

11.6.2   Temperature difference between solid and fluid

The relationship between the degree of bulk mass-transfer control of a reaction and temperature difference between pellet outside surface and fluid may be easily derived for steady-state conditions. The rate of mass transfer of a reacting species from fluid to solid multiplied by the heat of reaction per mole of diffusing species must equal the rate of heat transfer from solid back to fluid. Hence

$$k_c(c_o - c_s)(-\Delta H) = h(T_s - T_o) \tag{11.32}$$

Substituting the expressions for the Prandtl and Schmidt numbers, and for the j_D and j_H functions,

$$(T_s - T_o) = \frac{j_D}{j_H} \left(\frac{\mathrm{Pr}}{\mathrm{Sc}}\right)^{2/3} \frac{(-\Delta H)}{\rho c_p} (c_o - c_s) \tag{11.33}$$

The extent to which the reaction is bulk mass-transfer-controlled, f, may logically be defined as the ratio $(c_o - c_s)/c_o$, whence Eq. (11.33) becomes

$$(T_s - T_o) = \frac{j_D}{j_H} \left(\frac{\mathrm{Pr}}{\mathrm{Sc}}\right)^{2/3} \left[\frac{(-\Delta H)c_o}{\rho c_p}\right] f \tag{11.34}$$

The temperature difference is seen to be directly proportional to the heat of reaction per mole of diffusing component and to the fractional drop in concentration between bulk fluid and solid. The product $(-\Delta H)c_o$ is the heat that would be released by complete reaction of 1 cm^3 of reactant mixture. The product ρc_p is the volumetric heat capacity of the gas. The quotient $(-\Delta H)c_o/\rho c_p$ represents the temperature rise that would be calculated for complete adiabatic reaction of the fluid mixture.

For many simple gas mixtures, the ratio Pr/Sc is in the vicinity of unity, and j_D/j_H may be taken as 1. For a completely mass-transfer-controlled gas-phase reaction ($f = 1$) corresponding to the foregoing circumstances, the temperature difference between gas phase and solid would thus be approximately equal to the calculated adiabatic temperature rise for complete reaction of the fluid. If fluid properties did not change through the reactor, in theory the solid would be at the same temperature, namely the adiabatic reaction temperature, throughout the bed. In fact such a reaction would probably proceed at high temperature, and radiative heat transfer might be important. A mass-transfer-controlled reaction at the high velocities at which industrial reactors can be operated results in such a short reaction zone that heat transfer by radiation from the bottom and top may result in substantial temperature gradients. For a number of partial oxidation reactions in air the ratio Pr/Sc is actually somewhat less than unity, but the ratio could conceivably exceed unity for some reaction system. In this case it would be possible for the catalyst surface temperature to exceed the adiabatic reaction temperature.

Equation (11.34) emphasizes the fact that, if the heat of reaction is large, mass-transfer limitations may be small, yet heat transfer can still cause significant effects. Consider, e.g., a case in which the calculated adiabatic temperature rise for the reaction is 500°C and the mass-transfer rate at a point in a reactor results in only a 4-percent concentration difference between bulk gas and catalyst, that is,

$f = 0.04$. Taking (j_D/j_H) $(\text{Pr}/\text{Sc})^{2/3}$ as unity, the temperature difference would be 20°C, sufficient to cause a marked increase in the observed rate of reaction over that which would occur if the catalyst were indeed at the bulk-vapor temperature. With sufficiently active catalysts a region of unstable catalyst temperatures exists, as in ammonia oxidation on a platinum gauze (Sec. 8.10). Upon increasing the temperature of the reacting gas, the temperature of the catalyst suddenly jumps to a new, higher level. The situation is analogous to the ignition of a fuel such as carbon in a stream of air.

One of the useful applications of a recirculating differential reactor (Sec. 11.8.4) is to highly exothermic reactions such as the foregoing. An increase in the linear gas velocity through a catalyst bed increases the heat-transfer and mass-transfer coefficients proportionately. If the concentration difference between fluid and outside surface is small to begin with, increased velocity has little effect on surface concentration. Therefore there is little increase in rate of reaction and rate of heat generation. However, increased fluid velocity increases the heat-transfer coefficient and thus reduces the temperature of the catalyst particle closer to that of the fluid.

11.7   Examples of Use of Criteria

Example 11.1: Estimation of D_{eff}.   Estimate D_{eff} for the diffusion of thiophene in hydrogen at 660 K and 30 atm (3 MPa) in a catalyst having a BET surface of 180 m^2/g, a void volume of 40 percent, a pellet density of 1.40 g/cm^3, and exhibiting a narrow pore size distribution. D_{12} is 0.052 cm^2/s. Substituting in Eq. (11.13), we obtain

$$D_{12,\text{eff}} = \frac{D_{12}\theta}{\tau} = \frac{0.052 \times 0.40}{\tau} = \frac{0.0208}{\tau} \text{ cm}^2/\text{s}$$

Substituting in Eq. (11.18), we have

$$D_{K,\text{eff}} = \frac{19400 \times 0.4^2}{\tau_m \times 1,800,000 \times 1.40} \sqrt{\frac{660}{84}} = \frac{0.00344}{\tau_m} \text{ cm}^2/\text{s}$$

In this case $\tau = 2$. Hence $D_{12,\text{eff}} = 0.0104$ and $D_{K,\text{eff}} = 0.00172$ cm^2/s. Knudsen diffusion may be expected to predominate, since $D_{12,\text{eff}}$ is so much larger than $D_{K,\text{eff}}$. Applying Eq. (11.20),

$$\frac{1}{D_{\text{eff}}} = \frac{1}{D_{K,\text{eff}}} + \frac{1}{D_{12,\text{eff}}} = 677$$

$$D_{\text{eff}} = 0.00147 \text{ cm}^2/\text{s}$$

Example 11.2: Use of Φ_s.   Archibald et al. (1952) studied the rate of catalytic cracking of a West Texas gas oil at 550 and 630°C and atmospheric pressure by passing the vaporized feed through a packed bed containing a silica-alumina cracking catalyst of each of several sizes ranging from 8 to 14 mesh to 35 to 48 mesh (See Table 5.2). They report that at 630°C the apparent catalyst activity was inversely proportional to catalyst particle size. This implies that the catalyst is operating at a relatively low effectiveness factor and Φ_s should be considerably greater than unity. We can check this by suitable calculations based on their run on 8- to 14-mesh catalyst. The average particle radius may be taken as 0.088 cm.

They report 50-percent conversion at a liquid hourly space velocity (LHSV) of 60 cm^3 of liquid per cubic centimeter of reactor volume per hour. The liquid density is 0.869, and its average molecular weight is 255. The effective density of the packed bed was about 0.7 g catalyst per cubic centimeter of reactor volume. The molecular weight of the products was about 70.

Pore-structure characteristics for a commercial homogeneous silica-alumina are as follows: average pore radius = 2.8 nm, catalyst particle density ρ_p = 0.95, θ = 0.46, S_g = 338 m^2/g. Take τ = 4. From Eq. (11.18),

$$D_{\text{eff}} = 19,400 \frac{\theta^2}{\tau S_g \rho_p} \sqrt{\frac{T}{M}}$$

$$= \frac{(19,400)(0.46)^2}{(4)(338 \times 10^4)(0.95)} \sqrt{\frac{903}{255}} = 6.0 \times 10^{-4} \text{ cm}^2/\text{s}$$

The rate of reaction is 50 percent of the rate of feed,

$$-r = \frac{(60)(0.869)}{255} \left(\frac{1}{3600}\right) \left(\frac{1}{0.7}\right) (0.95)(0.5)$$

$$= 3.86 \times 10^{-5} \text{ mol/s·cm}^3 \text{ pellet volume}$$

For the average concentration of reactant outside the pellets, an arithmetic average of inlet and exit concentrations is sufficiently precise for this example. This corresponds to conditions at 25-percent conversion.

Each mole of gas oil produces 255/70 = 3.64 moles of products. Per 100 moles entering, at 25-percent conversion there remain 75 moles of gas oil and (25)(3.64) = 91 moles of products, for a total of 166 moles.

The average reactant concentration is therefore

$$\frac{1}{22,400} \left(\frac{273}{903}\right) \left(\frac{75}{166}\right) = 0.61 \times 10^{-5} \text{ mol/cm}^3$$

The average catalyst particle radius is 0.088 cm; whence, from Eq. (11.1),

$$\Phi_s = \frac{(0.088)^2}{6 \times 10^{-4}} (3.86 \times 10^{-5}) \times \frac{1}{0.61 \times 10^{-5}} = 81$$

Regardless of the kinetics, this reaction is highly diffusion-limited.

Example 11.3: Use of Φ_s. Weisz (1957) reports measurements of the rate of burnoff in air at atmospheric pressure of carbonaceous deposits formed on a silica-alumina cracking catalyst. Oxygen consumption rates are reported for two particle sizes, 0.20-cm beads and 0.01-cm powder, at temperatures of 460°C and higher. At 460°C, the rate per unit mass of catalyst was the same for both particle sizes, demonstrating that the effectiveness factor for the 0.20-cm beads at 460°C was nearly unity. Significant differences between the rates on the two particle sizes began to appear at a temperature of about 475°C. The corresponding rate of oxygen consumption was about 4×10^{-7} mol/s · cm³. The diffusivity of catalyst samples, using hydrogen and nitrogen on opposing faces, was measured and found to be 6.2×10^{-3} cm²/s for hydrogen at 20°C. Temperature gradients within the pellet are unimportant in this reaction. Compare the rate of reaction at the temperature at which diffusion begins to be appreciable with that expected from the critical value of Φ_s.

Carbon combustion is about first order in oxygen, and, in the presence of excess air, inhibition by products is probably negligible. The critical value of the parameter Φ_s will be about 1.0. Diffusion is assumed to be by the Knudsen mode. Eq. (11.18) is used to convert to applicable conditions.

$$D_{\text{eff}} = 6.2 \times 10^{-3} \sqrt{\frac{748}{293} \times \frac{2}{32}} = 2.48 \times 10^{-3} \text{ cm}^2/\text{s}$$

$$c_s = \frac{0.21}{22,400} \times \frac{273}{748} = 3.42 \times 10^{-6} \text{ mol/cm}^3$$

Calculate the value of the maximum reaction rate in the 0.20-cm particles above which diffusion will become appreciable. From Eqs. (11.1) and (11.2),

$$\frac{r_p^2(-r)}{D_{\text{eff}}c_s} = \Phi_s = 1$$

$$\frac{(0.20)^2}{2.48 \times 10^{-3}} \times \frac{1}{(3.42 \times 10^{-6})} \times (-r) = 1$$

$$-r \approx 2.12 \times 10^{-7} \text{ mol/s} \cdot \text{cm}^3$$

This compares closely with the value of about 4×10^{-7} found experimentally.

Example 11.4: Nonisothermality.   Consider the data on catalytic cracking of gas oil on a silica-alumina catalyst as analyzed in Example 11.2, in which isothermality was assumed. Test the validity of this assumption by use of the criterion of Eq. (11.5).

The endothermic heat of reaction varies with degree of reaction because of secondary processes, but the maximum is about 167 kJ/mol. Assume the thermal conductivity of silica-alumina to be that given by Sehr (Table 11.8), namely 0.36 W/m · K. The effective diffusivity was estimated in the earlier example to be about 6.0×10^{-4} cm²/s. Consider conditions at the entrance to the bed, with a reaction temperature of 630°C:

$$\beta = \frac{c_s(-\Delta H)D_{\text{eff}}}{\lambda T_s} = \frac{\left(\frac{1}{22,400} \times \frac{273}{903}\right)(-167 \times 10^3)(8.0 \times 10^{-4}) \times 10^2}{(0.36)(903)}$$

$$= -0.00055$$

Since $\beta = \Delta T_{max}/T_s$, the maximum temperature difference that could exist between particle surface and interior is about 0.5°C, and this will occur only under highly diffusion-limiting conditions.

The maximum activation energy for this reaction is about 167 kJ/mol. Hence, using Eq. (11.4), $\gamma = 167{,}000/(8.32)(903) = 22$. Applying the criterion of Eq. (11.5),

$$\Phi_s|\beta| < \frac{1}{\gamma}$$

From Example 11.2,
$$\Phi_s = 81$$

$$(81)(0.00055) < 1/22$$

$$0.04 < 0.05$$

The criterion is just barely met.

Example 11.5 Nonisothermality. Consider the dehydrogenation of cyclohexane over a platinum-alumina reforming catalyst at 2.5 MPa and 450°C. A large excess of hydrogen is used to prevent carbon formation on the catalyst, so a 4:1 hydrogen-hydrocarbon ratio will be considered. Prater (1958) gives the following data:

$$\Delta H \text{ of reaction} = + 220 \text{ kJ/mol}$$

$$D_{eff} = 16 \times 10^{-3} \text{ cm/s}^2 \text{ for cyclohexane}$$
$$\text{(assume this is completely Knudsen diffusion)}$$

$$\text{Thermal conductivity} = 0.22 \text{ W/m} \cdot \text{K}$$

At 450°C, the reaction is effectively irreversible. The value of β using Eq. (11.3) is

$$\frac{\left(\dfrac{1}{22{,}400} \times \dfrac{273}{723} \times \dfrac{2.5}{0.5}\right)(-220 \times 10^3)(16 \times 10^{-3}) \times 10^2}{(0.22)(723)} = -0.18$$

The reaction is highly endothermic. Recall that $\beta = \Delta T_{max}/T_s$. Hence, under highly diffusion-limiting cases, the temperature in the center of a catalyst pellet could be as much as $(0.18)(450 + 273) = 130°C$ below that at the outside surface.

11.8 Experimental Laboratory Reactors

A variety of reactors may be utilized at the laboratory or pilot-plant scale depending on the particular purpose at hand. A gaseous reaction catalyzed by a solid is the most common, and fast, highly exothermic reactions are some of the most difficult to study effectively. In the following we consider four types of reactors that are representative of those that may be utilized in a research and development program leading to the final design of a fixed-bed, adiabatic or multitubular, reactor involving an exothermic reaction.

11.8.1 A scouting laboratory reactor

The purpose of this reactor is to provide a means of characterizing intrinsic catalyst activity with a minimum of interference from extraneous effects caused by concentration and temperature gradients. This is to ensure that a promising catalyst composition is not overlooked because it is tested under conditions such that the data are falsified by these extraneous effects.

This reactor is typically a U tube or straight tube about 6 mm in inside diameter, held at nearly constant temperature in a fluidized sand bath or tube furnace. In the latter case a straight reactor tube may be inserted in a metal block to minimize temperature gradients. The block in turn is held in the furnace. A fluidized sand bath generally gives a more uniform temperature along the reactor wall than does a tube furnace, but it may be more time-consuming to replace catalyst samples, which is of importance if this is to be done frequently. The narrow reactor diameter maximizes the degree of approach to isothermality. Thermocouples may be embedded into the outside portion of the reactor wall, or, with a fluidized sand bath, the temperature of the bath may usually be taken as a close approximation of the wall temperature. This requires, however, that the bath be well fluidized and that the thermocouple be placed close to the reactor tube. A straight-tube reactor should always be arranged vertically rather than horizontally to avoid bypassing that could occur with settling of catalyst. Downflow is generally preferred in order to avoid blowing catalyst out of the reactor. Sometimes a thermowell is inserted axially within a straight-tube reactor, but in that case the possibility of significant bypassing should be considered.

The quantity of catalyst required is small, of the order of a few cubic centimeters, so a large number of catalyst preparations can be rapidly screened, the temperature and gas composition being varied in a systematic way. For an exposition of good experimental design, see Box et al. (1978). Since small quantities of reactants are utilized, this scale of operation is desirable for studies with model compounds that may be expensive. Catalyst particles should in general not be finer than about 400 μm, in order to avoid excessive pressure drop and bed plugging, and not coarser than about 2 mm, in order to minimize the possibility of diffusion limitations and significant bypassing. Particles as small as 100 to 200 μm may be satisfactory if a narrow size distribution is used and the Reynolds number is not so low (Re $< \sim 1$) that poor heat and mass transfer occur.

If the particles dust, break up readily, agglomerate, or are too fine, they may be spread out on a coarse inert support (e.g., 20- to 40-mesh quartz) that acts to keep the bed open. In any case as narrow a particle size distribution as possible is preferable to minimize packing and channelling. Increasing gas flow gradually in bringing the reactor on stream is especially desirable with fine powders because this minimizes the possibility of forming an impenetrable plug. Studies should also be made with the reactor emptied of catalyst in order to determine if the reactor wall contributes significant catalytic activity or if homogeneous reaction is important.

Observing a drop in performance from acceptable to unacceptable levels after a period of as long as 50 to 100 h is not unusual, especially with an amorphous catalyst. Catalysts that survive this long usually have reached a relatively stable structure and exhibit only slow further change, except for that caused by poisoning, fouling, etc.

If an inert diluent is used, a nonporous substance such as glass, quartz, or α-alumina is preferred. Blank runs should be made to ensure that the diluent is truly inert, not only to the primary reactant but also to intermediates that may be formed. Thus intermediates as well as reactants should be tested. High-area substances, such as silica gel, that are inert by themselves can nevertheless sometimes significantly affect performance. By adsorbing impurities or coke precursors, they can cause performance to be altered over that observed in their absence.

With the aforementioned precautions, the reactor should operate in essentially plug flow and essentially isothermally, particularly if a fluidized sand bath is used. If there is reason to suspect significant departure from these ideal conditions, measurements may be made in two reactors varying in diameter by 50 percent or more and with two or more particle sizes. Liquids are typically fed with a syringe pump and then vaporized. Gases and vapors are typically fed with mass flow controllers. Product samples are usually analyzed by gas chromatography, supplemented when required by off-line gas chromatography/ mass spectrometry or in some cases by on-line mass spectrometry. The pressure drop across the reactor should be monitored to indicate incipient catalyst fouling or breakup. Small-scale laboratory reactors have some less obvious disadvantages, especially when a wide range of products is produced, as in the Fischer-Tropsch synthesis. Operating for many hours may be necessary to collect a truly representative sample of products, and to achieve a satisfactory material balance. Metering of very small flow rates may offer difficulties, and the handling of very small samples may introduce uncertainties. The question of possible wall effects should also always be borne in mind.

Studies are sometimes done with a *micropulse* reactor, which utilizes a small quantity of catalyst held in a fixed bed at specified temperature. An inert gas (e.g., helium) or one of the reactants (e.g., hydrogen) is fed continuously through the bed. From time to time a short pulse of another reactant is injected into the feed stream, e.g., by use of a hypodermic needle through a rubber septum. The exit gas may be run directly into a gas chromatograph or other system for on-line analysis. Such apparatus is simple to set up and use and avoids the necessity for precise metering and feed pumps for a liquid reactant. Hypodermic injection is practicable to pressures up to about 1 MPa.

Such apparatus is useful in oxidation catalysis for revealing the change in catalyst activity and selectivity as its oxidation state changes, as on successive pulsing of a reactant without intermediate reoxidation of the catalyst. The effects of poisoning on catalyst behavior may also be readily studied. This experimental procedure should, however, be regarded as secondary. The catalyst is not at equilibrium with the gas, and adsorption-desorption effects may be much different than in a steady-state reactor. Kinetic data are sometimes reported from micropulse reactor studies, but the nonsteady-state nature of the process introduces uncertainties. Reliable rate data are almost impossible to obtain because the instantaneous concentrations are unknown. This type of reactor is reviewed by Choudhary and Doraiswamy (1971).

11.8.2   A catalyst-optimization reactor

The best catalyst candidates from the screening reactor above must now be prepared and tested in a form that would be satisfactory commercially, e.g., as pellets or extrudates of sufficient size that an acceptably low pressure drop can be obtained in the final reactor. Considerable experimentation with carriers, binders, and methods of preparation may be required at this stage. The reactor will now necessarily be of larger diameter, probably about the same as that expected to be ultimately used commercially if a multitube reactor is chosen. This typically would be about 2.5 cm in diameter. Generally, the laboratory unit will be from 30 to 100 cm long; it will be heated in a tube furnace or with electrical windings and have a thermocouple well (e.g., about 3-mm outside diameter) down the center to obtain axial temperature profiles. This larger scale of operation is frequently also needed to test the reliability of the foregoing small-scale studies.

The question of concentration and temperature gradients within catalyst pellets and between the pellet outside surface and bulk fluid should again be reexamined both experimentally and theoretically. It may well develop that marked temperature gradients cannot be avoided commercially, and suitable mathematical simulation becomes appropriate at this point to indicate the optimum in tube diameter, flow rates, and other variables (Sec. 11.9). In order to avoid effectiveness factors much below unity and, consequently, poorer selectivity, consideration of other catalyst formulations may be desirable at this point. These may have a more open pore structure, larger pores, or a bimodal pore structure. The possibility of decreasing particle size somewhat or the use of rings or other catalyst shapes instead of pellets should also be examined.

If the reaction is ultimately to be run at approximately atmospheric pressure, the laboratory reactor is almost invariably operated at atmospheric pressure. However, the commercial reactor is usually operated at a pressure sufficient to overcome the pressure drop through downstream processing equipment. The reactor pressure is then typically in the neighborhood of from 200 kPa to as much as 400 kPa. This may affect the kinetics, but, possibly more importantly, the heat-transfer problem may become more difficult. With a first-order reaction, an increase in pressure of from 100 to 400 kPa quadruples the reaction rate and hence the rate of heat release, but it has only a small effect on the heat-transfer coefficient. Hence, temperature gradients are exacerbated. A reactor of the type considered allows the exploration of this possibility. Reactor pressure drop considerations are considered briefly in the introduction to Chap. 4.

If pellets as large as, say, 6 mm in diameter are being studied in a 25-mm-diameter tube with a thermowell, only about two pellets can be positioned side by side in the annulus, so some bypassing may occur. However, for a specified contact time the linear flow rate here will be considerably greater than in the laboratory reactor. With a correspondingly higher Reynolds number (e.g., 10 to 100) axial dispersion may be much less important (see Sec. 11.3.4).

The possibility of a fluidized-bed reactor may arise at this point, and scouting work might be done with a bed of 2.5- to 5-cm diameter. Wall effects may be significant in small-diameter, fluidized-bed reactors. The performance of a laboratory reactor of this size may be somewhat better than that achievable in a plant-scale reactor, because gas-solid contacting usually becomes worse in larger vessels and at higher superficial velocities.

11.8.3 The prototype reactor

If a multitube reactor appears to be that desired for the ultimate commercial reactor, a full-scale experiment on a jacketed and packed tube of the final proposed size is generally required. This is to prove out the activity and selectivity that can be expected to be obtained in the full-scale reactor. Although expensive, this stage of experimentation may be needed for several possible reasons, including the following:

1. The much higher linear flow rates and possibly different tube diameter than that used in the catalyst-optimization reactor may

lead to somewhat different temperature profiles along the tube, with consequent effect on performance. Although these can be estimated from a reactor model, correlations of the thermal conductivity of packed beds may be insufficiently accurate. In particular, relatively large particles may be used for low pressure drop, resulting in a tube diameter-particle diameter ratio having values possibly in the range of 3 to 6. There is no inherent reason why this needs to be avoided, but the effective bed thermal conductivity for these systems can be predicted much less accurately than for more conventional cases in which a continuum model applies.

2. The pressure drop through the reactor may significantly affect either the kinetics or the economics. This needs to be established.

3. The major heat-transfer resistance is inside the packed tube. Typically, it is divided approximately equally between resistance at the inside wall and that through the bed. The actual temperature profile along the tube, which is determined in part by the reactant flow rate and characteristics of the heat-transfer medium, should be established. These should be similar to that achievable in the commercial reactor.

4. Reproducibility of pressure drop through the tube may be poor on repacking, especially at low tube diameter-particle diameter ratios. This needs to be checked. The heat-transfer coefficient at the interior wall varies with particle shape, and small changes in catalyst size and shape can significantly affect the manner of packing.

In the design of the commercial reactor several new problems require attention. These include means of securing even flow of coolant around tubes and even distribution of gas into all tubes. The resistance to flow must be the same through each tube in order to avoid different residence times in different parallel tubes, which could reduce overall performance. The pressure drop is often measured across each tube under standardized conditions after it is substantially loaded, and the amount of catalyst present is adjusted if necessary so that no packed tube deviates beyond a specified degree from the average.

11.8.4 Gradientless reactors

For careful kinetic studies work may be performed with a *differential reactor*, one in which the gas and solid composition, pressure, and temperature are essentially uniform throughout the reactor. This may sometimes be achieved in a packed-bed reactor of the type described in Sec. 11.8.1, but often flow rates are so low that possible heat- and mass-transfer gradients raise doubts about the validity of the results obtained. The term *differential reactor* means a reactor in which the conversion is limited to not more than a few percent. It does *not* mean a particular piece of apparatus. A laboratory fixed-bed reactor may possibly be operated in a differential mode, but to do so over a very wide range of operating conditions is different.

A variety of gradientless reactors have been designed and studied, and a considerable amount of performance information and results of specific studies have been reported. In each case a small amount of catalyst is used, and the relative velocity of the fluid with respect to the solid is increased over that achieved in an ordinary laboratory fixed-bed reactor. This improves the heat- and mass-transfer characteristics external to catalyst particles. Two representative designs are shown in Figs. 11.15 and 11.16. In the Carberry (Notre Dame) reactor, pellets are held in mesh baskets and revolved. In the Berty reactor, the pellets are stationary and fluid is recirculated. In the latter a magnetic coupling is used to avoid sealing and contaminant problems.

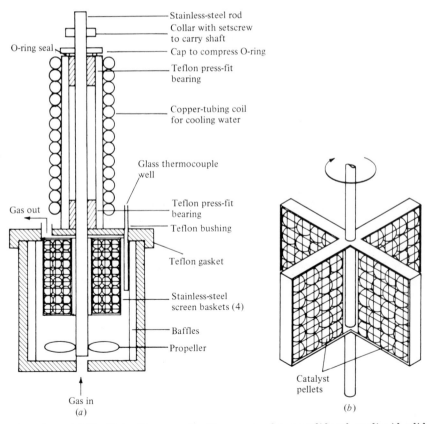

Figure 11.15   (a) The Notre Dame gradientless reactor for gas-solid and gas-liquid-solid studies. (b) The catalyst disposition. *(Carberry 1976, p. 406.)*

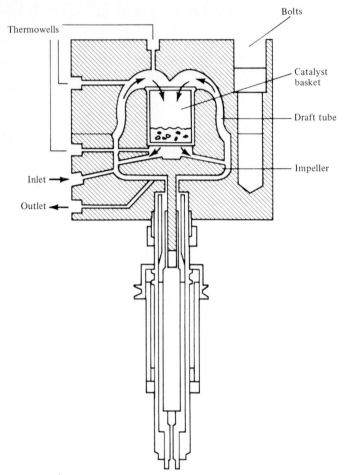

Figure 11.16   Berty gradientless reactor.

This particular design can be used at high pressure and has a low gas volume to minimize homogeneous reaction. The flow rate through the bed is calculated by measuring the pressure drop through the bed.

The particular advantages of these reactors are:

1. They provide a means of obtaining differential kinetic data for a simple reaction over a range of experimental conditions often not achievable by other reactors. The fresh feed rate can be varied over a wide range to simulate local conditions from the entrance to the exit of an integral reactor.

2. Commercial reactors are much longer than laboratory reactors. Hence, for a given contact time, the linear velocity in the commercial reactor will be much greater than in a conventional laboratory

unit. If bulk heat- and mass-transfer limitations exist industrially, the gradientless reactor provides a means of simulating commercial conditions in the laboratory.

3. In a packed-bed reactor a poison is often adsorbed preferentially on the upstream portions of the bed. A band of poisoned catalyst moves downward with time, increasing in depth in a chromatographic effect while the remainder of the bed remains active. The results may thus be difficult to interpret. Gradientless reactors are an effective means of studying poisoning since a thin bed of material can be used without concern for bypassing. The role of certain intermediate products, which may be formed and then disappear before the gas leaves the reactor, can be studied by deliberate addition.

4. The composition of a catalyst depends on the environment, e.g., the value of x in a metal-oxide catalyst MO_x. The relative amounts of reactants, intermediates, and products adsorbed on the catalyst are also affected. This in turn can affect activity and selectivity. In a packed-bed reactor under steady-state conditions, the catalyst assumes a steady-state composition both in the bulk and on the surface. This, however, may vary substantially from inlet to exit. In a fluid-bed reactor the solid moves in a complex pattern with respect to the gas and in many cases is not in equilibrium with it. Consequently, adsorption-desorption processes will occur in a different manner than in a fixed-bed reactor, and this may conceivably be a reason for different behavior of a catalyst in a fixed-bed and a fluid-bed reactor mode. One way of sorting out such effects is with a recirculating reactor. Here the catalyst composition will be in equilibrium with the particular gas composition present.

Some precautions to consider in the use of gradientless reactors are:

1. The ratio of void volume to packed-bed volume is much higher in a recirculating reactor than in a conventional packed bed. Data from a recirculating reactor may be misleading if homogeneous reactions are significant or if heterohomogeneous processes occur. Sometimes reactive intermediates are formed, as in some catalytic partial oxidation reactions, and their fate depends on whether they react homogeneously or catalytically. The possibility of reaction on the wall of the reactor or on mechanical bearings, etc., should be considered.

2. Some ranges of temperature and pressure achievable in packed-bed reactors may not be obtainable in a recirculating reactor.

3. The possibility of contamination from sealing mechanisms should be considered.

4. The gas composition is assumed to be uniform, but this needs to be checked, e.g., by pulse tracer experiments. Operating conditions must be established that provide an adequate recycle rate relative to feed rate in the internal recirculation reactor. In the revolving basket reactor, design must ensure that bypassing of feed gas to the exit does not occur. Also, the bulk mass-transfer characteristics vary substantially between pellets close to the axis and those far from the center.

For some kinds of reactions it is necessary to minimize mixing of a feed with a product that may in turn cause formation of an undesired by-product, e.g., in the case of $A \rightarrow B \rightarrow C \xrightarrow{\Delta} D$, where C is desired but D is undesired. A specific example is the conversion of methanol to gasoline in the Mobil MTG process (Sec. 7.7.9). Here plug-flow type behavior or at least minimum axial dispersion is required. A gradientless reactor, which is inherently a CSTR (continuous stirred tank reactor), may give a falsely low indication of the selectivity otherwise obtainable.

For development of a commercial process, a recirculating reactor can reveal important information, but a reactor configuration of the type to be used industrially must be constructed and operated as an integral reactor to prove out the reaction. Various types of laboratory recirculation reactors are reviewed by Doraiswamy and Tajbl (1974) and by Carberry (1969). Livbjerg and Villadsen (1971) describe an internal recirculating reactor for studying the SO_2 oxidation and give references to previous apparatus of this type. The operating characteristics of the Berty reactor are described by Berty (1974). He generally recommends a lower pressure limit of about 300 kPa in order to maintain good recirculation rates, but a set of conditions for suitable operation at lower pressures has been published by Kuchcinski and Squires (1976). Gradientless reactors in general are discussed by Bernard et al. (1972) and Bennett et al. (1972). The various types of laboratory reactors are also critically compared and contrasted by Weekman (1974) and Sunderland (1976). A review by Christoffel (1982) focuses on some of the more theoretical aspects. A review by Pratt (1987) discusses a wide variety of laboratory reactors, with more emphasis on experimental considerations.

11.9   Reactor Modeling: An Example

During the course of laboratory experimentation a point arises at which a tentative design of a commercial reactor is needed to estimate performance and costs. For a multitube reactor, typical variables are tube diameter, contact time (tube length), and wall temperature. For a highly exothermic reaction, holding the reaction temperature substantially constant without the use of tubes of impracticably small diameter is impossible. A hot zone, at a temperature considerably above that of the tube wall and the coolant, appears at some distance down from the inlet. An optimum design aims at keeping the temperature here within bounds to maximize selectivity and minimize catalyst aging, and at the same time using tubes of as large diameter as feasible to lower costs. With a reliable kinetic expression in hand and information on physical and transport properties, the reactor performance can be modeled by computer simulation and the effects of changing variables can be quickly ascertained.

The following illustrates such reactor modeling for a reaction of industrial importance, the partial oxidation of o-xylene in air to phthalic anhydride. This in turn may be further oxidized to carbon monoxide and carbon dioxide. Some o-xylene may also be directly oxidized to these by-products without the intermediate formation of phthalic anhydride. These steps are shown in Fig. 11.17.

This reaction was modeled using the kinetic data and other information published by Froment (1967) for a vanadium oxide type of catalyst. The inlet mole fraction of xylene is taken as 0.93 percent. Since a large excess of air is used, each of the three reactions may be expressed as pseudo-first order. The heat of reaction (1) is 1285 kJ/mol; that of reaction (3) is 4564 kJ/mol. The activation energies for the reactions are $E_1 = 113$ kJ/mol, $E_2 = 131$ kJ/mol, and $E_3 = 120$ kJ/mol. A minimum temperature is needed to achieve an economic rate of reaction, but increased temperature evidently increases the undesired reactions relative to the desired ones. Reaction (3) releases much more heat than reaction (1), so an increased temperature, which increases reaction (2) relative to reaction (1), also increases the heat load and therefore the heat-transfer problem. In a reaction of this type, achieving nearly complete consumption of reactant is often desirable if this can be achieved at acceptable selectivity. This avoids the cost of recovery and recycle of reactant.

For the case here, the superficial mass velocity is held constant at

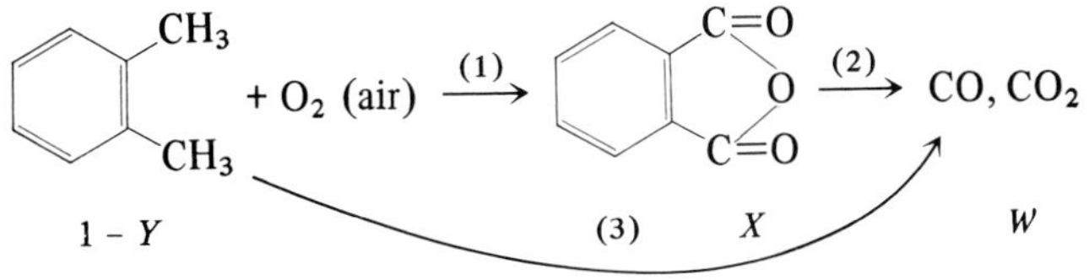

Figure 11.17 Reaction rate model for partial oxidation of o-xylene to phthalic anyhdride.

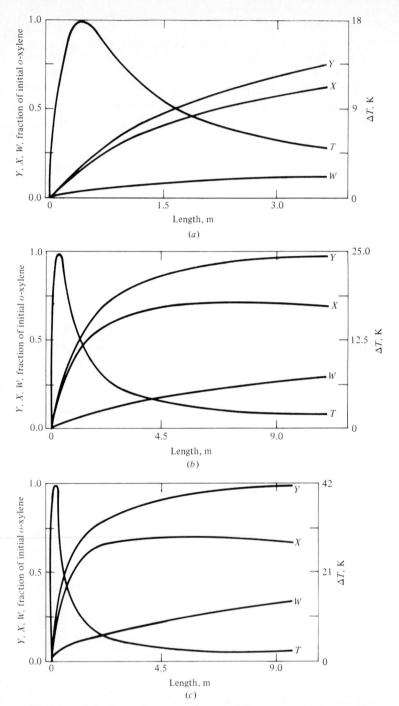

Figure 11.18 Reactor simulation (see text for definitions of X, Y, and W). (a) $d_t = 0.025$ m, wall $T = 625$ K. (b) $d_t = 0.025$ m, wall $T = 630$ K. (c) $d_t = 0.025$ m, wall $T = 635$ K.

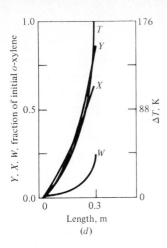

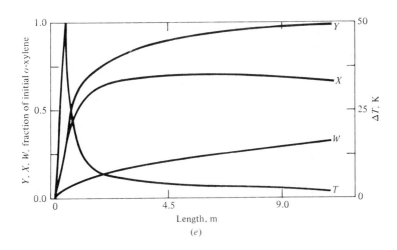

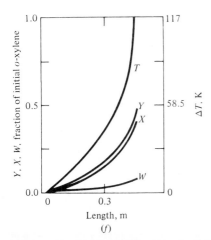

Figure 11.18 *(Continued)* Reactor simulation (see text for definitions of X, Y, and W). (d) $d_t = 0.025$ m, wall $T = 637$ K. (e) $d_t = 0.030$ m, wall $T = 630$ K. (f) $d_t = 0.035$ m, wall $T = 630$ K.

$4684 \text{ kg/m}^2 \cdot \text{h}$, and the consequences of changing the effect of wall temperature, taken to be the same as the inlet temperature, and the tube diameter are explored. The heat-transfer resistance is all lumped at the wall; that is, at any distance downstream the bed temperature is taken to be uniform radially, but it is higher than the wall. The heat-transfer coefficient is taken to be $96.2 \text{ W/m}^2 \cdot \text{s} \cdot \text{K}$.

Representative results of the simulation are given in Figs. 11.18a through 11.18f which show plots of Y, the fractional conversion of o-xylene to any type of product; X, the fraction of the feed that is converted to phthalic anhydride; and W, the fraction of the feed that is converted to by-products (left vertical axis). $X + W = Y$. Also shown is the temperature rise, in degrees kelvin, above the wall (equals inlet) temperature (right vertical axis), scaled relative to the maximum temperature reached in each case.

A variety of comparisons can be made from these and additional computations. Figures 11.18a, b, c, and d show the effects of holding the tube diameter constant and systematically increasing wall temperature. The maximum temperature of the·hot zone increases with wall temperature. An instability is reached in the neighborhood of 635 to 637 K at which a slight increase in temperature causes a marked increase in bed temperature. It was assumed here that if the bed temperature exceeded the wall temperature by 200 K this would be unacceptable, and the computer program was terminated at this point. Figures 11.18b, e, and f show the effects of holding wall temperature constant and increasing tube diameter. Again, the hot-zone temperature is increased, and between a tube diameter of 0.030 and 0.035 m the hot zone reaches an unacceptable level. An operating region of *parametric sensitivity* clearly exists, and this will need to be explored carefully by more detailed simulation [see, e.g., Froment and Bischoff (1990)]. These calculations also illustrate why only a fairly narrow range of tube diameters are practicable for highly exothermic reactions.

This particular example is treated in more detail by Froment and Bischoff. The reaction in fact is more complex than the foregoing scheme suggests, as discussed in Sec. 8.6.2. Any simulation can be only as good as the data used, which emphasizes the importance of studies in a prototype reactor (see Sec. 11.8.3) before the final design is established.

Reactor modeling may be done for several purposes, with correspondingly different levels of attention to various aspects of the simulation. For a first approximation a set of a priori assumptions may be made as in the foregoing considerably simplified illustration. Modeling may also be used for scaleup purposes or for interpretation of the performance of a commercial unit. Here it was assumed that gradients of concentration and temperature occur only axially and that plug flow exists. (In fact axial dispersion is usually of little consequence except for very thin beds or unless nearly complete conversion is sought in a deep bed.) This is sometimes termed the basic one-dimensional model. Resistance to flow of heat and mass is taken to occur only at the interface between inside tube wall and packing.

If the reaction has a strong heat effect, a two-dimensional pseudo-homogeneous model may be necessary in which transport of heat is divided into two contributions, an effective thermal conductivity at the wall and an effective bed thermal conductivity. In both of these models no gradients within catalyst particles or between gas and catalyst are considered. For many cases these factors must be introduced. Pressure drop may also be significant. As the catalyst deactivates, reactor temperature is usually increased to keep product yield constant, and simulation of change in reactor performance with time is of concern.

The detailed behavior of the reactor system at the hot spot can assume overriding importance. The possibility of a runaway reaction may be associated with a highly exothermic secondary reaction about which little is known. In a partial oxidation reaction this might be the increased formation of CO and CO_2. In a hydrogenation reaction this might be an increasing degree of hydrocracking. Even in an adiabatic packed-bed reactor localized hot spots may develop from variations in activity of individual catalyst particles, perhaps exacerbated by uneven deactivation rates or uneven flows caused by deposits. Maldistribution of gas and liquid in a trickle-bed reactor can likewise cause substantial variations in temperature both radially and axially.

Reactor modelling is of major concern in chemical reactor engineering and various texts may be consulted for more detailed treatment, e.g. Carberry (1976), Smith (1981), and Froment and Bischoff (1990). Eigenberger and Ruppel (1986) discuss, with examples, problems of mathematical modeling of industrial fixed-bed reactors.

TABLE 11.11   Nomenclature for Chap. 11*

Symbol	Definition
c	Concentration (mol/cm^3); c_o or c_b for concentration in the bulk-gas phase; c_s for concentration at outside particle surface; c_g for local gas-phase concentration; dc/dx for concentration gradient
c_p	Heat capacity (kJ/kg·K)
d	Diameter of pore (cm)
d_p	Diameter of particle (cm)
D	Coefficient of molecular diffusion (molecular diffusivity) (cm^2/s). D_a for effective dispersion, as in Pe.
D_{12}	Diffusion coefficient for bulk diffusion of species 1 in a mixture of species 1 and 2 (cm^2/s); D_{1m} for diffusion of species 1 in a multicomponent mixture.
D_K	Knudsen diffusion coefficient for a straight cylindrical pore (cm^2/s)

TABLE 11.11   Nomenclature for Chap. 11* (Continued)

Symbol	Definition
D_{eff}	Effective diffusion coefficient for a porous solid, based on *total* cross section normal to direction of diffusion; equal to ratio of flux to concentration gradient, $$\frac{\text{mol/s·cm}^2 \text{of solid}}{(\text{mol/cm}^3 \text{ fluid}) (1/\text{cm of solid})} = \frac{\text{cm}^3 \text{ fluid}}{\text{cm solid · s}} = \frac{\text{cm}^2}{\text{s}}$$
$D_{12,\text{eff}}$	Effective diffusion coefficient for a porous solid under conditions of bulk or ordinary diffusion, based on *total* cross section of porous solid normal to direction of diffusion (cm^2/s); $D_{12,\text{ eff}} = D_{12}\theta/\tau$
$D_{K1,\text{ eff}}$	Effective Knudsen diffusion coefficient for species 1 in a porous solid (cm^2/s); $D_{K1,\text{ eff}} = D_{K1}\theta/\tau$
E	Activation energy for reaction (kJ/mol)
G	Mass velocity of fluid (g/s · cm^3 of total or superficial bed cross section normal to mean flow); G_M for molal velocity, $= G/M$
h	Heat-transfer coefficient (W/m^2 · K)
ΔH	Enthalpy change on reaction (kJ/mol)
j_D	$(k_c\rho/G)$ Sc$^{2/3} = (k_g P/G_M)$ Sc$^{2/3}$
j_H	$\dfrac{h}{c_p G}$ Pr$^{2/3}$
k	Reaction rate constant; k_s for intrinsic first-order reaction rate constant for surface reaction (cm/s)
k_c	Mass-transfer coefficient (cm/s)
k_f	Thermal conductivity of fluid, (J · m/s · m^2 · K) = (W/m · K)
k_G	Mass-transfer coefficient (mol/s · cm^2 · atm); $k_G = k_c/RT$
L	Length (cm). In dimensionless groups (Table 11.2) L is a characteristic length, usually taken as d_p for packed beds of particles.
M	Molecular weight
n	Order of reaction
N	Diffusion flux (mol/s · cm^2)
P	Total pressure (in atm in Chap. 11), p for partial pressure
r	Reaction rate. As used in Chap. 11, r is the *observed* rate of reaction (mol/s · cm^3 of catalyst pellet).
r_e	Equivalent radius of pore (cm); $= 2V_g/S_g$
r_m	Distance from midpoint to surface (cm)
r_p	Radius of particle (cm)
r_R	Radius of cylindrical reactor (cm)
R	Gas constant; $= 8.314$ kJ/mol · K or 82.057 cm^3 · atm/mol · K
S_g	Total surface area per unit mass of porous solid (cm^2/g or m^2/g) (as measured, for example, by the BET method)
S_p	Outside area of particle (cm^2)
S_v	Total area of catalyst per unit volume of catalyst pellet (cm^2/cm^3) $= \rho_p S_g$
T	Temperature (degrees kelvin or centigrade); T_s at outside surface of particles; T_o or T_b for bulk-gas phase; T_w at the reactor wall
u	Fluid velocity (cm/s)
V_c	Catalyst particle volume (cm^3)
V_g	Pore volume per unit mass of catalyst (cm^3/g); $V_g = \theta/\rho_p = (1/\rho_p) - (1/\rho_t)$
V_p	Volume of particle (cm^3)
x_0	path length for diffusion (cm)
Greek	
β	Heat generation function $= c_s(-\Delta H)D_{\text{eff}}/\lambda T_s$
γ	Exponent in Arrhenius reaction rate expression $= E/RT_s$
ϵ	Void fraction in packed bed
η	Effectiveness factor; equals ratio of actual rate of reaction in a porous catalyst to that which would occur if the pellet interior were all exposed to reactants at the same concentration and temperature as that existing at the outside surface of the pellet
θ	Porosity (void fraction) of catalyst (fraction of gross volume of catalyst pellet that is pore space) $= V_g\rho_p$ (cm^3 pores/cm^3 pellet)
λ	Thermal conductivity of packed bed, of a porous structure, or of a solid, watts/(m^2 of total cross section) (K$^\circ$/m) = W/m · K
μ	Viscosity (N · s/m^2)

TABLE 11.11   Nomenclature for Chap. 11* (Continued)

Symbol	Definition
ρ	Density of fluid (g/cm^3)
ρ_p	Particle density (g/cm^3 of particle volume); ρ_t for true density of solid material in porous catalyst (g/cm^3); $\rho_p = \rho_t(1 - \theta)$
τ	Tortuosity factor, an empirical factor to correct for "tortuosity" and for nonuniformity of pore cross section; $\tau = D\theta/D_{\text{eff}}$; τ_m for tortuosity factor obtained assuming completely Knudsen diffusion and a mean pore radius defined by Eq. (11.17) to calculate D_K; τ_p for tortuosity factor calculated by parallel-path pore model, Eq. (11.21).

*Some symbols used only once are defined at point of use and are not included in this list.

References

Anderson, J. B.: *Chem. Eng. Sci.*, **18**, 147 (1963).

Archibald, R. C., N. C. May, and B. S. Greensfelder: *Ind. Eng. Chem.*, **44**, 1811 (1952).

Aris, R.: *The Mathematical Theory of Diffusion and Reaction in Permeable Catalysts*, Clarendon Press, Oxford, 1975, 2 vols.

Bennett, C. O., M. B. Cutlip, and C. C. Yang: *Chem. Eng. Sci.*, **27**, 2255 (1972).

Bernard, J. R., B. L. Villemin, and S. J. Teichner: *Can. J. Chem. Eng.*, **50**, 431 (1972).

Berty, J. M.: *Chem. Eng. Prog.*, **70**(5), 78 (1974). *Catal. Rev.-Sci. Eng.*, **20**, 75 (1979).

Box, G. E. P., W. G. Hunter, and J. S. Hunter: *Statistics for Experimenters: An Introduction to Design, Data Analysis and Model Building*, Wiley, New York: 1978.

Brown, L. F., H. W. Haynes, and W. H. Manogue: *J. Catal.*, **14**, 220 (1969).

Butt, J. B. and V. W. Weekman, Jr.: *AIChE Symp. Ser.*, **70**(143) 27 (1974).

Carberry, J. J.: *Catal. Rev.*, **3**, 61 (1969).

Carberry, J. J.: *Chemical and Catalytic Reaction Engineering*, McGraw-Hill, New York: 1976.

Carberry, J. J., in J. R. Anderson and M. Boudart (eds.): *Catalysis: Science and Technology*, vol. 8, Springer, New York, 1987, p. 131.

Chilton, T. H., and A. P. Colburn: *Ind. Eng. Chem.*, **26**, 1183 (1934).

Choudhary, V. R., and L. K. Doraiswamy: *Ind. Eng. Chem., Prod. Res. Dev.*, **10**, 219 (1971).

Christoffel, E. G.: *Catal. Rev.-Sci. Eng.*, **24**, 159 (1982).

Cramer, R. H., A. F. Houser, and K. I. Jagel: U.S. Patent 3,312,615 (Apr. 4, 1967) (to Mobil).

Cunningham, R. A., J. J. Carberry, and J. M. Smith: *AIChE J.*, **11**, 636 (1965).

Cussler, E. L., *Multicomponent Diffusion*, Elsevier, Amsterdam, 1976.

Cybulski, A., M. J. Van Dalen, J. W. Verkerk, and P. J. Van Den Berg: *Chem. Eng. Sci.*, **30**, 1015 (1975).

Davidson, J. F., R. Clift, and D. Harrison (eds.): *Fluidization*, 2nd ed., Academic, New York, 1985.

Doraiswamy, L. K. and D. G. Tajbl: *Catal. Rev.—Sci. Eng.*, **10**, 177 (1974).

Dowden, D. A. and G. W. Bridger: *Adv. Catal.*, **9**, 669 (1957).

Eigenberger, G. and W. Ruppel: *Ger. Chem. Eng.*, **9**, 74 (1986).

Froment, G.: *Ind. Eng. Chem.*, **59**(2), 23 (1967).

Froment, G. F., and K. B. Bischoff: *Chemical Reactor Analysis and Design*, 2nd ed., Wiley, New York, 1990.

Gianetto, A., and P. L. Silveston: *Multiphase Chemical Reactors: Theory, Design, Scale-Up*, Hemisphere, New York, 1986.

Harriott, P.: *Chem. Eng. Sci.*, **29**, 1309 (1974).

Harriott, P.: *Chem. Eng. J.*, **10**, 65 (1975). [See also P. Harriott and R. Hughes: *Chem. Eng. J.*, **10**, 73 (1975).]

Hulburt, H. H., and C. D. Srini Vasan: *AIChE J.*, **7**, 143 (1961).

Ismail, I. M. K., and P. L. Walker, Jr.: *Carbon*, **27**, 549 (1989).

Jackson, R.: *Transport in Porous Catalysts*, Elsevier, Amsterdam, 1977.

Johnson, M. F. L., and W. E. Stewart: *J. Catal.*, **4**, 248 (1965).

Koros, R. M., and E. J. Nowak: *Chem. Eng. Sci.*, **22**, 470 (1967).
Kuchcinski, G. R., and R. G. Squires: *J. Catal.*, **41**, 486 (1976).
Kulkarni, B. D., and L. K. Doraiswamy: *Catal. Rev.—Sci. Eng.*, **22**, 431 (1980).
Kunii, D., and O. Levenspiel: *Fluidization Engineering*, Wiley, 1969.
Kunii, D., and M. Suzuki: *Int. J. Heat Mass Transfer*, **10**, 845 (1967).
Li, C-H., and B. A. Finlayson: *Chem. Eng. Sci.*, **32**, 1055 (1977).
Livbjerg, H., and J. Villadsen: *Chem. Eng. Sci.*, **26**, 1495 (1971).
Martin, H.: *Chem. Eng. Sci.*, **33**, 913 (1978).
Masamune, S., and J. M. Smith: *J. Chem. Eng. Data.*, **8**, 54 (1963a).
Masamune, S., and J. M. Smith: *Ind. Eng. Chem., Fund.*, **2**, 137 (1963b).
Maymo, J. A., and J. M. Smith: *AIChE J.*, **12**, 845 (1966).
Mears, D.: *Ind. Eng. Chem., Process Des. Dev.*, **10**, 541 (1971).
Miller, F. W., and H. A. Deans: *AIChE J.*, **13**, 45 (1967).
Mischke, R. A., and J. M. Smith: *Ind. Eng. Chem., Fund.*, **1**, 288 (1962).
Murakami, Y., T. Kobayashi, T. Hattori, and M. Masuda: *Ind. Eng. Chem., Fund.*, **7**, 599 (1968).
Nelson, P. A., and T. R. Galloway: *Chem. Eng. Sci.*, **30**, 1 (1975).
Peterson, E. E.: *Chemical Reaction Analysis*, Prentice-Hall, 1965.
Petrovic, L. J., and G. Thodos: *Ind. Eng. Chem., Fund.*, **7**, 274 (1968).
Prater, C. D.: *Chem. Eng. Sci.*, **8**, 284 (1958).
Pratt, K. C., in J. R. Anderson and M. Boudart (eds.): *Catalysis: Science and Technology*, Vol. 8, Springer, Amsterdam, 1987, p. 173.
Ramachandran, P. A., and R. V. Chaudhari: *Three-Phase Catalytic Reactors*, Gordon & Breach, London, 1983.
Reid, R. C., J. M. Prausnitz, and B. E. Poling: *The Properties of Gases and Liquids*, 4th ed., McGraw-Hill, New York, 1987.
Satterfield, C. N.: *AIChE J.*, **21**, 209 (1975).
Satterfield, C. N.: *Mass Transfer in Heterogeneous Catalysis*, M.I.T. Press, Cambridge, Mass., 1970. Reprint edition 1981, Krieger, Melbourne, Florida.
Satterfield, C. N., and P. J. Cadle: *Ind. Eng. Chem., Process Des. Dev.*, **7**, 256 (1968a).
Satterfield, C. N., and P. J. Cadle: *Ind. Eng. Chem., Fund.*, **7**, 202 (1968b).
Satterfield, C. N., and D. H. Cortez: *Ind. Eng. Chem., Fund.*, **9**, 613 (1970).
Satterfield, C. N., and R. S. C. Yeung: *Ind. Eng. Chem., Fund.*, **2**, 257 (1963).
Schlünder, E. U., D. Luss, and V. W. Weekman, Jr. (eds.): *Chemical Reaction Engineering Reviews—Houston*, ACS Symposium Series #72, 1978, p. 110.
Sehr, R. A.: *Chem. Eng. Sci.*, **9**, 145 (1958).
Shah, Y. T.: *Gas-Liquid-Solid Reactor Design*, McGraw-Hill, New York, 1979.
Smith, J. M.: *Chemical Engineering Kinetics*, 3rd ed., McGraw-Hill, New York, 1981.
Sunderland, P.: *Trans. Inst. Chem. Eng.*, **54**, 135 (1976).
Voge, H. H., and C. Z. Morgan: *Ind. Eng. Chem., Process Des. Dev.*, **11**, 454 (1972).
Wagner, C.: *Z. Phys. Chem.*, **A193**, 1 (1943).
Wakao, N., and S. Tanisho: *Chem. Eng. Sci.*, **29**, 1991 (1974).
Weekman, V. W., Jr.: *AIChE J.*, **20**, 833 (1974).
Weisz, P. B.: *Z. Phys. Chem. Neue Folge*, **11**, 1 (1957).
Weisz, P. B., and R. D. Goodman: *J. Catal.*, **2**, 397 (1963).
Weisz, P. B., and C. D. Prater: *Adv. Catal.*, **6**, 144 (1954).
Weisz, P. B., and A. B. Schwartz: *J. Catal.*, **1**, 399 (1962).
Wicke, E.: *Chem.-Ing.-Tech.*, **29**, 305 (1957).
Yates, J. G.: *Fundamentals of Fluidized-Bed Chemical Processes*, Butterworths, London, 1983.

Index

ABOUT THE AUTHOR

Charles N. Satterfield is a professor of chemical engineering at the Massachusetts Institute of Technology. He has published over one hundred and fifty technical articles, many of them on the subject of heterogeneous catalysis. He has also written and coauthored several books on the subject. He received the Wilhelm Award by the American Institute of Chemical Engineers in 1980 for "distinguished and continuing contributions to chemical reaction engineering" and was identified as one of the "twenty top chemical engineering scientists" in the world by the Science Studies Unit of the University of Leiden in 1987. He holds a B.S. in Chemistry from Harvard University, and M.S. and Sc.D. degrees in Chemical Engineering from the Massachusetts Institute of Technology.